Research, Development
and
Technological Innovation

Research, Development, and Technological Innovation

AN INTRODUCTION

By

JAMES R. BRIGHT

Professor of Business Administration
Graduate School of Business Administration
Harvard University

RICHARD D. IRWIN, INC.

1964 · HOMEWOOD, ILLINOIS

First Printing, August, 1964
Second Printing, January, 1968

Library of Congress Catalog Card No. 64–11711

PRINTED IN THE UNITED STATES OF AMERICA

PREFACE

WHEN MY study of thirteen highly automatic factories was published in 1958, the occasion prompted a review of their condition.[1] I was startled to find that every one of these plants, which had been the last word in technological progress in 1955, was now surpassed. These (and other automation concepts studied in 1954–55) represented expenditures of almost a quarter of a billion dollars. In three years the production advances bought by this enormous investment had been overtaken. While all but one plant was still a "good" production system, *none* of them was any longer the lowest cost producer. None of them would have been duplicated by their managements as proper "1958" designs. Technological change had invalidated a large amount of their technique and equipment.

This personal incident was concurrent with other strong signals of technological change. In 1957, Sputnik shocked and excited the world. The airframe industry, which in 1957 was the largest employer of manufacturing labor, lost hundreds of thousands of jobs to the missile industry by 1960. It also lost its profitable existence. Government expenditures for "R & D" while dubiously classified, were unquestionably on an exponentially rising curve that reflected a growing technological effort. From $3 or $4 billion annually, projections indicated $9, $10, $12 billion and more within a few years. And this was larger than all but a few of our existing industries.

A look at industry confirmed that technological ferment was burgeoning. The growth of the computer exceeded all but the wildest expectations. The numerically controlled machine tool was far more useful than most of us had believed. Aluminum was invading the tin can market; prestressed concrete was replacing the steel girder in many applications. Fiberglas was revolutionizing small-boat construction. The jet transport was changing concepts of distance for business and pleasure travel.

And Custer's last stand was barely seventy-five years ago—one lifetime old!

Although a learned, imaginative man of the eighteenth century—say Benjamin Franklin or Lavoisier—could probably have grasped quickly the essential technology underlying the steam locomotive and the electric motor of the 1930's, we can suspect that he would have been lost in an explanation of the transistor, television, the atom bomb, the computer, penicillin, and the numerically controlled machine tool in the 1950's.

It seemed to me that the business problem was sharply outlined: The

---

[1] James R. Bright, *Automation and Management* (Boston: Division of Research, Harvard Business School, 1958).

rate of technological change was accelerating. The impact of technological advances was in many cases extremely severe and disrupting. At the same time, it offered major opportunities. Was conventional business school training adequate for this environment? I believed that it was not. One thing we needed, I thought, was an explicit study on the topic of technological change. Through the kindness and vision of Dean Stanley Teele, I was given the opportunity for exploration of the desirability and feasibility of formal training in this area. How should business education respond to this need?

WHY NOT EDUCATION FOR RESEARCH MANAGEMENT?

An apparently logical answer is a course in research management. This was my initial assumption when I began the exploration in 1959. However, as I studied the problem and discussed the educational need with accomplished scientists—engineers like Dr. Simon Ramo, and businessmen like James La Pierre, Executive Vice President of General Electric's aviation and military products activities—it became clear that research management was a secondary educational target. The greatest need was not better management of research work. Of course, better research management would help, for better management helps any field. But the real need lay in general management's understanding of and response to technological change. The major gap in business education was the one between top management and directors of research, and between them and technological progress in the outside world.

Technology is probably the most powerful force in today's business environment. What do we know about its generation, implementation and diffusion? Should not managers *study* this force? The primary educational need, therefore, was to create *a sound understanding of technological innovation and its problems for all managers*. This education was necessary for managers in production, financial, marketing, and technical areas, but it was especially vital for key policy makers, who must direct the efforts of their organizations.

The goal of this book (and our new course in technological innovation at Harvard Business School) is to provide this basic background for all students of management. Ideally, this course should be followed by one in research management, and then a third course in the management of product development, prototype manufacture, and pilot plant operations. Conceptually, we should move from a general understanding of technology and business, to the management of the search for new concepts, through the translation of laboratory findings into viable production operations. This book is directed at the first of these three course goals. While "research management" is the most understandable and perhaps most appealing course idea to business educators, I am certain that it is not the most important need in business education. We must understand technological change as a major factor in the business environment.

Although Harvard Business School is traditionally case-oriented, this book includes readings and exercises as sources of knowledge, which then can be applied to the case problems that are included. Otherwise, the student lacks vocabulary and facts, and simply proceeds from a void of ignorance studded with misunderstanding and popular mythology about technological innovation (e.g., that industry should devote itself heavily to basic research in order to stay competitive, or that the "breakthrough" technological concepts are largely originated by the industrial laboratories of great corporations).

The material in this book is divided into five sections, which are described in the Introduction on page 1. I believe that there are many ways to use this material, and offer these tentative opinions.

SUGGESTIONS ON ADAPTING THIS TEXT TO DIFFERENT COURSES

A Course on Technological Innovation for Business and Engineering

Sections I, II, III, and V provide the framework for a basic understanding of technological change as an essential element of the manager's training. The course can be shortened by omitting some of the cases in Section II, or extended by adding appropriate cases and readings in technological innovation from other sources. However, such studies should be added, I believe, *only* after the student has completed Section I, the first eight items in Section III, and the first two in Section V.

A Research Management Course

Many schools feel the need for a course on the management of research and development activities. As I stressed earlier, such a course should *follow* this introductory course (or be intermingled with its latter stages). It is foolish to commence study of research management without a proper understanding of technological innovation. Before we look inward on the job of the director of research, we must look outward on the environment in which he works and contributes. Therefore, I urge students interested in research management first to study Sections I, III, and V, and to intersperse between Sections III, and V such cases from Section II and their own supplementary sources as seem useful.

If one desires to stress the human relations problems in the laboratory, the files of the Intercollegiate Case Clearing House contain a few items.[2] Several books for further study are listed in the Bibliography, page 773. Here and there, casebooks contain R & D problems which can be added to this nucleus to fill out a research management course.

As a Supplement to a Production Management Course

Technological innovation has its roots in production more than any other business school fields. Here, too, the impact is prompt.

---

[2] Located at Soldiers Field, Boston 63, Massachusetts.

Section IV provides automation cases as a supplement to existing production courses. Through these seven cases the production student will gain a good understanding of problems of adapting radically new technology to the production system. The last two items in Section II, which deal with choosing a product and a production technique in a highly volatile field, can be added to this focus. The Union Oil cases in Section II also have major production implications. Section I, III, and the first two items in Section V provide basic background. Then the student should tackle the Photon series as well as the Thermal Dynamics series (in Section II). Here, he can follow the developing production problems as innovation proceeds from idea to reality.

As a Supplement to a Marketing Course

Marketing courses directed toward advanced technological products should insist upon preliminary study of Section I. Then, by adding the following items, a nucleus for a marketing course focused on advanced technology will be available: From Section II, the Photon and Thermal Dynamics series, and the Clark Equipment Company and Herman Kurt cases, are excellent practical problems in innovation. Be sure not to overlook the Load Glide case from Section III and the Oceanographic and Adcole cases. Marketing managers from major firms have expressed appreciation of the note on "Appraising the Potential Significance of Radical Technological Advances." I consider the study of Martin Barrett, Parsons & Akron, Modern Packaging Machinery, and the paper by Ansoff to be very useful for marketing students. For background on long-range product planning, add Section V.

As a Supplement to Business Policy Courses

Many students of business policy do not understand the process of technological innovation and have fuzzy, incorrect notions of what research and development involve. Frankly, I find that this also is true of many managers in industry who have not worked with highly technical products in technologically fast-moving industries. The shortcoming is not lack of intelligence or interest, but simply that they have had neither organized study nor opportunity to learn by experience. The reaction of managers and several directors of research from major firms to some of the "policy" materials in this book has been most gratifying. They confirm that any business policy course should first assure that its students understand the process and problems of technological innovation; that students do not say "basic research" when they mean "product development"; that they do not call for "scientists" when they need "engineers"; and that they have some reasonable concept of the time and resources needed for innovation. Critical study of Section I, or at least the first five items in Section I, will go far toward providing this understanding.

The Photon series in Section II provides a study of policy around an innovation. There are strong policy tones in the Clark and Thermal Dynamics cases. The first two items in Section III, as well as the note on "Potential Significance," also are excellent for policy considerations. All of Section V is pointed toward long-range planning. The second item by Professor Quinn, and the exercises on the "Plane Makers under Stress," are essentially policy questions.

Engineering School and Liberal Arts Courses

I have talked to many very sensitive and imaginative instructors in technical and liberal arts schools. Just what their programs should do in this field, I would not presume to say, but it is striking that I am repeatedly asked to address liberal arts and engineering audiences on the very theme of Section I in this book. Reactions of instructors and administrators from such leading schools as the Massachusetts Institute of Technology, the Carnegie Institute of Technology, the University of Illinois, and the University of California at Los Angeles suggest that engineers should have some explicit study of technology, its appraisal, its impact, and its management. Section I, section V, and elements of Section III will provide a nucleus for such a course.

In the liberal arts school the economist, the sociologist, the historian, and the labor relations teacher will find, I believe, that this book provides useful materials for the interaction of their special fields with technological advances.

A Caution

I hope that student and instructor will forgive my obvious enthusiasm for this material. Once again, I suggest that it is not so much that we offer brand-new concepts to management students. The usefulness of this approach lies in the specific focus on technology as a force in the environment.

No pretense is made that this book completely covers the field. Establishing research budgets and selecting directors of research are, for example, two subjects on which I have been unable to clear case materials. Indeed, the whole area is frustrating to the case writer because timely materials are too sensitive for many firms to release.

Other students will notice that I have not included anything from the extensive literature on the mathematics of decision making in research. After some experimentation in my classes and exploration with a number of leading research men and scientists, it seemed that relatively little material of value to management had yet emerged. I reluctantly passed by this material. My conclusion is not intended to disparage this effort, but only to point out that "research on research" largely is still "in the laboratory." In another five years the story should be different.

I also regret the lack of material on patents, confidential disclosure, and the security of technological work. Admittedly, we barely touch on creativity and on organization for technological advances. Another edition will see this rectified.

As the teacher will recognize, the publishing issue has been whether to wait several more years for a better coverage of the field, or to provide this material as a starting point on which others also can build. Discussion with my colleagues, the administration at Harvard Business School, and fellow teachers in the field led me to conclude that a publishing start, even though incomplete, would be a worthwhile contribution. Requests for our teaching materials from industry, as well as colleges, cemented this decision. As this book goes to press new cases on patents, industrial security, and other missing topics are being completed in mimeograph form. I shall be glad to supply current listings of new materials to those who request it.

I hope that readers will accept this beginning effort with a kindly tolerance. I shall welcome all their suggestions for future improvements.

JAMES R. BRIGHT

HARVARD UNIVERSITY
   July, 1964

ACKNOWLEDGMENTS

PROFESSOR Franklin E. Folts urged me, in 1958, to pursue this field in hopes of helping to bridge the educational gap between technology and management. I am grateful for his steady encouragement and implied confidence. Dean Stanley F. Teele generously provided time and funds for me to explore the possibility of effective teaching on technology and management. Subsequently, Associate Deans Russell Hassler and, later, George Lombard, helped me to translate my field research into a seminar, and then into a formal course in the second year MBA program at the Harvard Business School. Dean George P. Baker kindly enabled me to develop this textbook, which cuts across so many fields, and which proposes to look at old problems from a new position.

Throughout the course development program of the past four years I have had the assistance of many colleagues. I am particularly grateful to Professors Bertrand Fox, Edward Bursk, Paul Lawrence, Howard Raiffa, Renato Tagiuri, Raymond Bauer, Ralph Hidy, Richard Dooley, and Richard Rosenbloom for contributing ideas and moral support.

Professors from other institutions have been of great help and encouragement. I especially appreciate the suggestions and reactions of Brian Quinn of Dartmouth's Amos Tuck School, Edwin Mansfield of the University of Pennsylvania's Wharton School, and Louis Strasbourg, from the School of Business Administration at UCLA. Many professors from other schools have encouraged me by their interest and use of these case materials.

Outside the schools, a number of highly capable managers and scientists have given me guidance and understanding on the direction and substance of the course. High on the list are Dr. Edwin Land, Polaroid Corporation; Dr. Simon Ramo, Thompson-Ramo-Woolridge; Dr. Mel Hurni, General Electric Company; David B. Smith, Vice-President, (then) Philco Corporation; James La Pierre, Executive Vice-President of General Electric; Dr. James Hackett, Vice-President of Research, Owens-Illinois; and Mr. John Rockett, founder of the unique Product Development Corporation. Although I cannot identify all the 60 or 70 people who attended a seminar session on this course concept at Massachusetts Institute of Technology in 1963, I appreciated that splendid opportunity to test the teaching concepts. Professor Don Marquis provided this occasion.

Singlehanded, I could not have created this coverage of the field in less than many years. I thank the individuals who allowed me to adapt their materials to my purpose. Their names and contributions, in order of appearance in the book, are:

DAVID NOVICK, "What Do We Mean by 'Research and Development'?" Extracts from *Hearings* on "Administered Prices," Part 18, U.S. Senate, 86th Congress, Washington, D.C.

R. E. GIBSON, Director Applied Research Laboratory, Johns Hopkins University, "A Systems Approach to Research Management." Condensed from *Research Management*, Vol. 5, p. 215 (1962), p. 423 (1962), and Vol. 6, p. 15 (1963) by permission of the author and the Industrial Research Institute.

R. J. McCRORY, Mechanical Engineering Department, Battelle Memorial Institute, "The Design Method—A Scientific Approach to Valid Design." Presented before the Design Engineering Conference of the American Society of Mechanical Engineers, May, 1963. Reproduced in condensed form by permission of the author and the ASME.

EDITORS, *American Economic Review*. "The Process of Technological Innovation" by W. R. MACLAURIN. Reprinted from *American Economic Review*, Vol. XL, No. 1 (March, 1950).

S. COLUM GILFILLAN, "The Social Principles of Invention." Reproduced from *The Sociology of Invention*, pp. 5–13 (Chicago: Follett Publishing Company, 1935), now out of print. Corrections made 1960 at request of author. Reproduced by permission of author.

S. COLUM GILFILLAN, "The Prediction of Technical Change." Condensed from *The Prediction of Technical Change*, in *The Review of Economics and Statistics*, pp. 368–85, Vol. 34, No. 4 (November, 1952), (Cambridge: Harvard University Press, Copyright, 1952). Reproduced by permission of the editors.

DR. ELTING E. MORISON, Massachusetts Institute of Technology, Department of Economics and Social Science, "A Case Study of Innovation." Publications in Social Science, Series 3, No. 10.

E. I. GREEN, Vice President, Bell Telephone Laboratories, "Creative Thinking in Scientific Work." Condensed from *Electrical Engineering*, Vol. 73 (June, 1954), by permission of the author and the publisher.

PROFESSOR WILLARD F. MUELLER, "Origins of DuPont's Major Innovations, 1920–1950." Reproduced from *The Origins of the Basic Inventions Underlying DuPont's Major Product and Process Innovation, 1920 to 1959*, a paper submitted to the Conference on the Economic and Social Factors Determining the Rate and Direction of Inventive Activity May 12–14, 1960 (New York: The National Bureau of Economic Research). Reproduced by permission of the author, the National Bureau of Economic Research, and Princeton University Press.

H. I. ANSOFF, Vice-President and General Manager, Information Technology Division Lockheed Electronics Company, "Evaluation of Applied Research in a Business Firm."* Reproduced by permission of the author and the Division of Research, Harvard Business School.

M. P. O'BRIEN, Dean Emeritus, College of Engineering, University of California, Berkeley, "Technological Planning and Misplanning."* Reproduced by permission of the author and the Division of Research, Harvard Business School.

JAMES BRIAN QUINN, PROFESSOR, Amos Tuck School of Business Administration, Dartmouth College, "Top Management Guides for Research Planning."* Re-

* These papers were contributions to a seminar that was held at the Harvard Business School in September, 1961. They appear in the proceedings: *Technological Planning on the Corporate Level*, James R. Bright (ed). (Boston: Division of Research, Harvard Business School, 1961).

produced by permission of the author and the Division of Research, Harvard Business School.

JOSEPH L. FISHER, President, Resources for the Future, Inc., "Natural Resources Projections and Their Contribution to Technological Planning."* Reproduced by permission of the author and the Division of Research, Harvard Business School.

EDITORS, *Fortune;* "The Plane Makers under Stress" by CHARLES J. V. MURPHY. Reprinted from the June and July, 1960, issues of *Fortune* magazine by special permission; © 1960 Time, Inc.

Unless listed here, all the cases were prepared by myself or under my immediate direction. Otherwise, I am indebted to the following colleagues at the Harvard Business School for their permission to use the items they prepared for other courses:

PROFESSOR PAUL CHERINGTON, "Riverlake Belt Conveyor Lines, Inc. (A)."

PROFESSOR CHARLES D. ORTH, "Dallas Chemical Corporation," and "El Paso Electronics Corporation." These cases were made possible by a grant from the Industrial Research Institute which was extended to provide case material for the first seminar on the Management of Industrial Research. They were prepared by James W. Stratton under the direction of Charles D. Orth.

ARNOLD C. COOPER (now Assistant Professor at Purdue) and PROFESSOR W. ARNOLD HOSMER, "Thermal Dynamics Corporation (A), (B), (C), (D)," and "Adcole Corporation (B)." These cases were originally prepared by Arnold C. Cooper under the direction of Professor W. Arnold Hosmer as part of the materials gathered during the preparation of his Doctoral Dissertation.

PROFESSOR W. ARNOLD HOSMER, "Oceanographic Instrumentation." This case was prepared by A. Jenkins, III under the direction of Professor Arnold Hosmer.

PROFESSOR RICHARD F. VANCIL, "Modern Packaging Machinery Corporation."

PROFESSOR RICHARD S. ROSENBLOOM, "Ampex Corporation (A)."

In my own case work, I appreciated the help of research assistants Ronald Jablonski on "Union Oil (A) and (B)" and Mark Candee on "Photon (A) and (B)." In the classroom I have stressed that the best test of understanding and growth of competence is to tackle a current management problem in real life. Therefore, students are encouraged to follow the firms that we have studied in previous cases, and with that background, to analyze new and current technological-managerial issues. These term reports have been of such quality that, with suitable direction, some teaching cases have resulted. I am delighted to acknowledge these fine student contributions:

"Photon, Inc. (C), (D), (E)." Prepared by Eugene B. Mosier and Richard A. Wedemeyer.

"Sarepta Paper Company (A), (B)." Prepared by S. Page Williamson.

"Electronic Associates, Inc." and "Technical Note on Microelectronics (Mid–1963)." Prepared by Curtis P. McLaughlin, a doctoral candidate. Portions of the material originally were prepared by M.B.A. candidates Paul E. Huber, Richard M. Pell, Edward C. V. Winn, and Gerard Wolin.

The MBA students who have taken this course have been a great help to me. Their backgrounds often brought advanced technical training (and sometimes years of responsible research and development experience) to the class. They have enriched the course by their contributions, and aided my understanding of the teaching needs. Some of the term reports they have written for this course are of professional quality, and deserve publication. Several have received wide attention from industry and the Department of Defense.

No book would come into being without a patient, loyal secretary. My thanks go to Mrs. Patricia Allen for bearing with me, and carrying out the tedious, painstaking details.

For permission to use their cases, I express my thanks to the President and Fellows of Harvard College.

Obviously, this book is a pioneering effort at a new concept—a general, managerial understanding of technological innovation. Its shortcomings are mine alone.

JAMES RIESER BRIGHT

HARVARD UNIVERSITY
July, 1964

TABLE OF CONTENTS

SECTION III. FINDING AND EVALUATING SIGNIFICANT TECHNOLOGICAL OPPORTUNITIES

THE MANAGER of tomorrow will need increased ability to deal with radical technological change, both as a businessman and as a citizen. Not only is technological change the most powerful factor influencing the success and decline of many firms and some industries, but major government decisions on national and international levels are predicated upon technological advances. Business must respond to and help to guide national choices of technological directions and support. This will be true in the foreseeable future. Business schools, therefore, must train men to be effective managers in an environment in which violent technological change and severe interactions with social, economic, and political factors are major elements of many business decisions.

Technical schools, too, should give attention to this area. The scientist and engineer play deterministic and, often, managerial roles in the *process of technological innovation.* They should be sensitive to the interplay between business, society, and technological change so as to increase their effectiveness. Hopefully, they will help management to improve the wisdom and efficiency with which their advances are introduced.

Liberal arts colleges have a similar responsibility to develop in their students an understanding of the most powerful factor in current society. As materials in this book will demonstrate, courses around "science" are not enough. A unique chronological process involving science, technology, economics, entrepreneurship, and management is the medium that translates scientific knowledge into the physical realities that are changing society. This *process of technological innovation* is the heart of the basic understanding which the competent manager, the effective technologist, the sound government official, and the educated member of society should have in the world of tomorrow.

Of course, technological change is nothing new. It certainly reshaped the world through the Industrial Revolution, and it has continued as a major force in business and society ever since. However, there are at least five reasons why technological innovation deserves more attention today:

1. Many technological advances are *order-of-magnitude increases.* Thus, their effects and/or their inputs are significantly greater than in the past simply because of the scale of the increase in performance. The missile and the nuclear warhead wiped out the defense value of oceans, distance, and time in about five years, due to the magnitude of the increase in speed (say, 10 to 20 times) and in power (say, 1,000 times and more)

1

over previous techniques. The computer surpassed man's computation speed by 200 times with Mark I and 100,000 times with ENIAC in 1946.

2. *Far greater man-hours, power, facilities, and funds must be applied* to bring about many of these technological advances. Many enterprises require a massive commitment of resources to research and development work. R & D is literally a major item in the national budget. Substantial financial, manpower, educational, and economic resources are being devoted to creating technological advances.

3. For the individual firm, *profits, employment, and even continued existence* will depend, in many cases, upon the ability of management to respond effectively to technological opportunity and threat. In addition to technological advances in a given product, there is growing technological competition across traditional industry lines. The automobile as a replacement of the horse is an historical joke; but the effect of the motor truck and the airplane on the railroad is a serious national problem.

Many more such interindustry struggles are shaping up: Aluminum is taking part of the tin can market, a field held exclusively by the steel industry until 1957. And now plastics, paper, and composite materials are after this same container market. We can expect similar struggles between paper and textiles, between atomic energy and fossil fuels, between transportation systems and high-voltage power lines (as means of moving energy), and between many other materials, products, and services.

Television destroyed the traditional form of the motion-picture industry in less than ten years. How long will it be before some form of home audio-visual record invades the domain of live TV and of books? As this is written, electric home heating is just beginning to challenge traditional hot-air and hot-water domestic heating systems. Businessmen will have to learn to identify and respond rapidly and effectively to developments like these, which wipe out existing ways of doing things, and which create great demands within a few years.

4. *New social structures and organizations* are required by some advances. Consider that the space program has created new communities and required new forms of international co-operation for testing, monitoring, and operating. Business will follow military and government uses of such technical advances. New business organizations will have to be created, of which the Communications Satellite Corporation is a current example.

5. Out of these technological advances come *major social changes* such as labor displacement, unemployment, decline and growth of communities, expanded employment, new skill and training needs, new educational needs, and assorted social problems and opportunities on a scale not previously encountered. These are coming with a frequency and speed that compound the difficulties of adjustment, of supply and demand.

THE FOCUS OF THIS BOOK

How shall business education respond to this need? A logical reaction may be that conventional courses already deal with problems of technological change. This is true. I hope that I shall not be too unfair in suggesting that this is part of the difficulty. Traditional business courses do not usually provide an adequate background for tackling problems of *radical technological advances* as distinct from routine product improvement. As simple but important examples:

The vital distinction between *research* and *development* may not be carefully established. The significantly different mechanics and activities of research, of development, of product engineering, and their related objectives and needs are not taught. Thus, student efforts on the staffing of R & D departments and the setting of research goals and distribution of research and development budgets are poorly understood and poorly done. How can a business policy student consider wisely the direction and amount of a corporate research effort when he does not know what research is? How can he make sound timing decisions on technological innovations when he has no perspective on typical time requirements? How can he deal with long-range planning when he is ill informed on technological planning—one of the prime determinants of future conditions?

Of course, technical change goes on all the time through routine product refinement, production engineering, and other technical modifications of services, products, and tools. Here, conventional courses do a fine job. But such advances generally represent fractional improvements over present practice. The impact is minor, and the social and business consequences are therefore relatively easy to identify, if not to master. However, when we turn to order-of-magnitude advances (i.e., tenfold or better), or concepts which mankind has not previously encountered, we add new elements of uncertainty to business decisions. Often the essence of the business problem is the correct technological decision, or the proper interpretation or prediction of technological progress. That is why this book focuses on *radical* technological advances (meaning situational problems meeting the three criteria below). We shall concentrate on decision making in those business situations:

1. Involving a high degree of technological uncertainty;
2. Where the technology is relatively certain but the advance is so great that the introduction, impact, and consequences are significantly uncertain;
3. Where the technological dimension interacts with other environmental factors of business to produce extreme changes requiring special consideration.

The specific educational topics in the following cases and readings are directed to help the student:

1. *Understand the process* of technological innovation as it springs from scientific research or invention and proceeds from theory, experiment, or speculation to economic reality.
2. *Identify and deal with managerial problems* as they appear in this sequence. Emphasis will be on those problems relatively unique to technological change (such as evaluating technical competition, establishing research policy, estimating the significance of radical technological developments, changing managerial problems as innovation proceeds).
3. Understand the broad economic, industrial, and social *parameters that encourage or inhibit technological changes,* including nontechnological factors, such as the changing raw-materials base and population growth.
4. Develop skill in *encouraging and guiding technological progress* in the enterprise, and in reacting wisely to such progress external to the firm.
5. *Encourage creativity*, imagination, and receptiveness with respect to technological innovations.
6. Establish receptivity to science and technology as elements of public policy; and *sensitivity to the social consequences* of technological progress.

It is not intended that a course based on this text should duplicate or extensively overlap existing courses. The student and instructor should regard this book as a flexible vehicle which they will supplement to give their course the desired emphasis in view of their special interests and resources, the supplementary materials that are available, and the topics that are already adequately taught in other courses. The discussion in the Preface suggests such allocations for materials in this book. This book is designed around five concepts:

Section I. The Process of Technological Innovation

The student studies the major directions of technological change, the process of technological innovation, and the associated special managerial considerations. He learns the research sequence, the design sequence, the innovation sequence, and the interaction of new knowledge and new needs on the cycle of technology. *Research, development, design, exploratory research, applied research, invention,* and similar terms are given accurate meanings. He gains an understanding of the role of the scientist, the inventor, the engineer, and the entrepreneur.

The social environment of invention and innovation are examined for "principles" that can guide management. The student learns to consider resistance to technological innovation as a phenomenon that must be expected, and which can be softened (or used defensively) by employing certain mediums.

The concept of creativity in individuals and organizations is also raised.

Section II. Case Studies in Technological Innovation

Seventeen cases provide situations in which management must deal with the assessment and implementation of radical technological advances, or with problems in some portions of their innovation process. Topics include funding decisions, research decisions, choosing directions of technical support, the management of R & D activities, market-engineering analyses of proposed innovations, and a few human relations aspects of the management of technical personnel.

Three sequences of cases from single companies demonstrate the change of problems as the innovation passes through different phases to maturity. They also develop the interaction of concurrent industrial and political events on the economic merits of the technological concepts. At least three cases lead toward research policy issues and the area of research strategy. Both large and small firms are represented.

Section III. Finding and Evaluating New Technological Concepts

Here the student concentrates on one of the basic and most troublesome business problems: How do we get new technological concepts, and how can we evaluate them imaginatively and soundly? Five different approaches to evaluation are examined. The sources of important technological concepts in a major corporation are studied.

Finally, the student examines a new technological frontier (oceanography) to relate that field to a specific company's capabilities. A case on top management's appraisal of a radical, highly uncertain concept is included.

Section IV. Using Advanced Technology—Automation and Related Subjects

Not all management's concern is with the *generation* of technological advances. A major need is *to employ effectively the technological advances offered by others.* This section of the text enables those who want to stress automation to have a substantial nucleus of course work. Cases cover the automation of a finishing line, the operating consequences of highly automatic production systems, manufacturing problems with exceedingly critical specifications and precision assembly, and the introduction of computer control of a processing line.

A most important case is Imperial Oil, which involves top management appraisal of the firm's major operations research study.

Section V. Technological Planning

The purpose of this section is to develop understanding of technological planning as it relates to research policy and to corporate long-range planning. The student also deals with long-range changes in population, social trends, natural resource positions, and other technological progress, as they affect a firm, an industry, and a present technological competence. Exercises serve the viewpoint of top management, as well as that of directors of research and corporate planners.

Two final exercises open up the possibilities of technological forecasting, a primitive area and controversial notion. I hope that this brief exposure will inspire others to advance this concept, which may some day be a highly useful managerial tool.

Throughout these materials, I have interspersed many brief extracts and quotations. No significance is intended in their order. They offer controversial ideas and supplementary material. Some are substantive and thought-provoking; other are just plain fun, having, perhaps, a bit of truth underlying the humor.

SECTION I

The Process of Technological Innovation

Preliminary Design of an Experimental World-Circling Spaceship

Although the crystal ball is cloudy, two things seem clear—

1. A satellite vehicle with appropriate instrumentation can be expected to be one of the most potent scientific tools of the Twentieth Century.
2. The achievement of a satellite craft by the United States would inflame the imagination of mankind, and would probably produce repercussions in the world comparable to the explosion of the atomic bomb. . . .

Since mastery of the elements is a reliable index of material progress, the nation which first makes significant achievements in space travel will be acknowledged as the world leader in both military and scientific techniques. To visualize the impact on the world, one can imagine the consternation and admiration that would be felt here if the U.S. were to discover suddenly, that some other nation had already put up a successful satellite.

. . . In making the decision as to whether or not to undertake construction of such a craft now, it is not inappropriate to view our present situation as similar to that in airplanes prior to the flight of the Wright brothers. We can see no more clearly now all of the utility and implications of spaceships than the Wright brothers could see flights of B-29's bombing Japan and air transports circling the globe.

FROM: *Preliminary Design of an Experimental World-Circling Spaceship*, Project RAND Engineering Report to the Army Air Force, Santa Monica, May, 1946. Cited in *Technology and Culture*, Fall, 1963.

OPPORTUNITY AND THREAT IN TECHNOLOGICAL CHANGE

PERHAPS THE most striking characteristic of our world is man's growing ability to master his physical environment. While the technological changes that bring about these advances may be no different in concept than they have been throughout history, their total impact seems to be more pronounced because of the degree of advance, the rapid-fire frequency of introduction, the size of the resources needed to bring them about, the rate of diffusion, and interaction with political, economic, and military events. Furthermore, these technical changes are often more significant in combination than as individual advances, to which the guided missile and nuclear bomb are unhappy testimony. Technological change, I believe, is the most powerful factor in the business environment today, and its power seems to be growing. Automation may be the public whipping boy, but automation is only one of the directions of technological change.

Technological change is impressive not only for its variety but also for its "chain reaction" of effects on industry and society. Consider such examples as the following:

By 1963 the missile reduced aircraft manufacturing employment by more than one third of the number so employed in the mid-1950's. It created literally thousands of new suppliers around advanced technical specialties. It shifted the location of employment, upgraded the manufacturing skills required, changed the educational background needed by engineers and designers, and required different plant facilities, processes, and new service activities. It demanded new power sources, new fuels, new materials, control systems, and test instrumentation. A basic and applied research activity has resulted, which is in itself larger than most traditional industries. Meanwhile, missile development is indirectly reducing many activities required to support the traditional form, quantity, and operation of military aircraft.

Television, which became a household item in less than ten years, almost destroyed the traditional form of the motion-picture industry, made serious inroads on popular magazine publications, and has established itself as a powerful vehicle and competitor for advertising dollars. As an educational tool, we have scarcely touched its possibilities.

The computer, the most powerful mechanization concept since the

10

advent of electric power, has built a major new industry with myriads of special components and many suppliers of associated input-output devices since the first commercial installation in 1952. Computer growth is expanding beyond the prediction of even the most enthusiastic spokesman of ten years ago. Who would have predicted sales of four thousand computers a year! Computer application is having effects so far-reaching and profound that we can only dimly outline some of the consequences. Each week, new applications are revealed—patent law, medical research, programming of Broadway plays, operation of steel mills, oil refineries, railroads, tax collection, and even the design of a system to beat the house odds in blackjack gambling games!

The space program is hardly understandable in terms of dollars, but is better measured as percentages of the national income. These expenditures are for goals that are hard to justify in traditional terms. This effort is also creating new fields of study, new research needs, new hardware, materials, controls, energy, and life-support requirements. New organizations are required, and even new communities such as Cape Kennedy and the Houston Manned Flight Space Center have resulted. Now we see that new forms of international co-operation for testing, monitoring, and operation must emerge.

And on a more mundane scale, but equally violent, is the war between materials: e.g. aluminum invaded the tin can market in 1957. By 1960, it had taken virtually 100 per cent of the frozen citrus juice container market. In 1963, aluminum made further heavy inroads into steel's eight-billion-unit annual beer can market.

Need for Awareness

Unquestionably, our era of dynamic business change is based on technological progress and technological competition. In this mercurial environment, traditional products, materials, skills, and production facilities are made obsolete in a few years and, in some cases, a few months. At the same time, new findings of science and achievements of technology offer opportunities equally great. The calls for new technological advances seem endless. Thousands of businesses are going to rise or fall on the ability of their managers to respond effectively. How can managements understand this environment, and how can they meet it wisely? These new opportunities do not present themselves nicely at the doors of obsolete businesses, nor do potential disrupting innovations announce their birth with trumpets.

There is no certain way to success and security in this technological ferment, but leaders and planners of all types—industrial, military, political, and social—must become more skillful in dealing with technological change.

I believe that the first requirement for the businessman is a keen sensitivity, awareness, and receptivity to technological change as a major environmental force which he can employ, and to which he must respond. In many businesses, it will be far and away the most important force for management to consider.

Seven Trends

As an initial effort toward understanding, seven important technological trends are given. Each is outlined in chart form, Exhibits 1–7, with

Exhibit 1

INCREASED TRANSPORTATION CAPABILITY

Areas of Advance	*Some Typical Means*	*Some Results*
Mastery of greater distances in less time and/or cost	Jet transports, helicopters, ground effects machines "Piggy-back" rail transport, container ships and trains Pipe lines Supertankers, hydrofoil boats Passenger conveyors Missiles and rockets	World-wide commercial and pleasure travel of up to three thousand miles in eight hours Overnight freight service nationally and to most international centers Specialized transportation systems for high-volume items or dense traffic patterns Specialized handling devices linked to these transport systems
Movement and operations in new mediums: 1. Space 2. Underseas 3. Arctic areas	Aerospace vehicles Submarines, bathyscapes, and aqua lungs Arctic housing, utilities, trackless trains Life support systems in space, the Arctic, and under water	Warfare in new mediums, with associated attack, defense, surveillance, and communications devices Development of new support devices Acquisition of scientific knowledge Beginnings of new commercial operations (e.g., communications satellites, weather stations)

listings of the major areas of advance, typical means of advance, and a few significant results.

These charts are obviously incomplete, dated, and only suggestive. However, I believe they identify the major directions of technological change. By extrapolation, inference, cross reference, and combination, we can see some of the business consequences and opportunities that lie ahead, and to which wise management will be alert.

Social Phenomena Influencing Technology Progress

Technology does not exist in an independent world. There are powerful factors that encourage technological change and that influence its

Exhibit 2

INCREASED MASTERY OF ENERGY

Areas of Advance	Some Typical Means	Some Results
Far greater magnitudes and intensities of power available	H-bombs, nuclear reactors and nuclear dynamite, chemical fuels for rockets	Major change in methods of warfare, national defense, strategy and tactics, and international politics New scientific knowledge New power-plant fuels Thousands of new technical needs Possibilities for major alteration of geographic features
Energy handled in more minute quantities and controlled with increased precision	Semiconductors, lasers, microelectronics	Thousands of new components, products, and processes New instrumentation Many new demands for scientific and technical knowledge Reduction in size of many devices Production processes based on high-energy forming, spark erosion, electrodeposition and polishing, ultrasonics, and so on
Power generated and transformed by new sources and devices	Nuclear reactors, fuel cells, solar cells, magnetohydrodynamics, thermoionics, jet engines	Continuing pressure for advances in fuels, materials, and controls Need for scientific knowledge and technical development
Significant advances in energy storage	Atomic fuel, fuel cells, nickel-cadmium batteries, pumped-hydro power, and tidal power	Increased portability Longer operation between refuelings Lower power costs
New techniques for large-scale transportation of energy and fuels	Extra-high voltage transmission lines; liquid propane gas ships; oil, gas, and coal pipe lines; unit trains; and cross-country conveyor belts	Cheaper movement of many fuels Transportation of energy and fuels feasible over greater distances Specialized construction and transportation equipment

direction, degree of advance, timing, and rate of diffusion. If we are to anticipate and respond wisely to this progress, it is not enough to consider technology and its underlying sciences alone. We must consider major factors influencing technological progress. At least four important social phenomena can be identified:

The Rising Population in the United States and the World. Before World War II the United States had about 130 million people. Now we

Exhibit 3

INCREASED ABILITY TO EXTEND AND CONTROL THE LIFE
OF ANIMATE AND INANIMATE THINGS

Areas of Advance	*Some Typical Means*	*Some Results*
Alteration of living things: Longer life Toleration of extreme climatic conditions Control of growth, with respect to proportions and timing; and maximization of most valuable portions Greater resistance to disease and accident Elimination of undesirable life	Selective breeding Development of hybrids and special strains Special feeding and fertilizing Protective treatment by antibiotics and chemicals Environmental control of temperature and moisture	More economic value per unit Usefulness maintained for longer times and over a wider range of conditions Production possible in new regions Demand for special treatments and equipment
Longer life for perishable foods and other organic products and items	Packaging methods Protective environments, such as freezing, dehydration, and irradiation	Shelf life increased Seasonality effects and limitations reduced
Reduced deterioration in physical goods	More durable materials Treatments to inhibit insect infestation, corrosion, wear, fungi, and other factors Better construction and design	Less maintenance Longer life Fewer parts
Prolongation and regulation of human life	Drugs to fight diseases and germs (e.g., antibiotics, antimalaria drugs) Drugs to regulate mental and physical responses (e.g., tranquilizers, birth control pills) Transplanting of human organs Mechanical substitutes for human organs New surgical techniques	Lower death rate and greater life expectancy Vast increase of knowledge and skill required of medical men Increased complexity and cost of medical facilities and care Less time lost through illness Heavy research outlay for * producers of medical drugs and devices

have about 183 million. By 1980, some projections suggest 230 million, with upward of 330 million by A.D. 2000. If these numbers materialize and anything approximating present living standards is maintained, transportation systems, road networks, living space, and recreational facilities must be substantially increased (and probably altered in form). Air and water pollution, medical care, education facilities, and probably many other facets of our society will require major technological help.

Exhibit 4

INCREASED ABILITY TO ALTER THE CHARACTERISTICS
OF MATERIALS

Areas of Advance	*Some Typical Means*	*Some Results*
New properties for old materials	Chemical and metallurgical knowledge applied to alter properties of materials	Improvement of properties such as strength, weight, heat resistance, and corrosion resistance
Synthetic materials	Better control of purity, additives, and processes. New production processes	End users require different production processes and work-force skills. New product design opportunities
Combinations of materials to provide unique characteristics	Typical examples: aluminum engine blocks, paper and plastic replacement of textile cloth. Synthetic fibers, rubber, oil, and food. Fiberglas, prestressed concrete, ceramic-metallic compounds, laminated wood beams, and panels of aluminum-plastic honeycomb construction	Lower cost for many materials and/or end products. New and specialized production facilities for producer and fabricator. Highly selective materials specifications

A Rising Standard of Living throughout the World. The affluent society is no longer peculiar to the United States. Collectively, Europe is becoming a substantial producer and consumer of all types of goods. Japan is well known for her progress. Russia and possibly China also are raising their living standards. And we in the United States are moving toward the two-car, summer home, multi-TV set, multirecreation family. This means a growing consumption of raw materials and energy per capita throughout the world. As we use more marginal materials and imports, these materials costs will rise. Meanwhile, technology will lower the cost of competitive materials. Somewhere before the turn of the century, many raw materials will be in a cost struggle against synthetics.

The problem well may be accelerated as many of the overseas raw-material-supplying countries express their new-found nationalism in ways that discourage sales, at least low-cost sales, to the United States. Technology will respond to this supply-and-demand picture.

Role of the Government in Technological Support and Direction. With the TFX fight in the headlines as this is written, it is dramatically clear that much technological progress will be controlled by government decisions. And this applies not only to the Department of Defense, but to the Department of Agriculture, the Federal Communications Commission, the Interstate Commerce Commission, the National Aeronautics and

Exhibit 5

EXTENSION OF MAN'S SENSORY CAPABILITIES

Areas of Advance	*Some Typical Means*	*Some Results*
Vision	Radar Electron microscope Television, wired and wireless Radio astronomy	Transportation and war operations under previously limiting conditions of darkness, fog, rain, and so on; ability to "see" roughly two hundred miles New knowledge of materials, biology, diseases New mode of education, news, entertainment Extension of knowledge of the universe
Hearing	Microphone pickup and amplification techniques, magnetic tape recording	High-fidelity radio and phonograph equipment Sound detection for war and police use
Touch	Instrumentation and control combinations which identify minute or distant conditions and provide for human response to alter them	Power-assisted machinery such as power steering, power brakes, aircraft controls Remote control of pipe lines Radio-control drone aircraft, industrial cranes, and special vehicles
Power of discrimination—visual, olfactory, aural, and so on	Instrumentation to detect minute quantities and dimensions Measurement and amplification techniques	Precise measurement, leading to new scientific knowledge, to delicate control, to safety devices
Memory (preservation of visual and aural impressions)	Great advances in photographic sensitivity and accuracy of reduction Duplication techniques (e.g., xerography) Instant preservation and recall of vision and sound through video tape, magnetic sound tape, polaroid photography	New capability for recording and studying information for science, war, technology, sociology, business New entertainment devices New capability for acquiring, storing, and retrieving information

Space Administration, the Atomic Energy Commission, and dozens of other agencies. For the government not only buys technology; it also sets rules that determine the economics of different technological solutions. This customer, the United States government, has unique characteristics, some of which are listed here:

1. The government is the largest customer for many products and firms.
2. It is the most demanding in terms of desires, complexity, degree of advance, and frequency of change.
3. Performance considerations outweigh cost in many cases.

Exhibit 6

GROWING MECHANIZATION OF PHYSICAL ACTIVITIES

Areas of Advance	*Some Typical Means*	*Some Results*
Production: Direct labor tasks Work feeding Materials handling Assembly Testing and inspection Packaging	Power hand tools, numerically controlled tools Vibratory feeders Lift trucks, cranes, conveyors Assembly machines Electronic, electrical, pneumatic, and other inspection devices Automatic packaging machinery	Larger machine content and investment Change in work-force skills (usually) Reduction in labor per unit of output Increased maintenance (usually) Greater capacity Less flexibility (usually) Faster response to demands on production system
Distribution: Shipping and receiving Warehousing Carrier loading	Lift trucks, cranes, conveyors, automatic palletizers, automated material movement and control systems based on conveyors and retrievers Pneumatic bulk loading	Better customer service Improved quality Less scrap and waste Less inventory and work in process
Communications and control: Movement of papers, blueprints, mail Recording and assembly of data	Air-tube carriers, facsimile transmitters, wired TV, vertical selective conveyors, two-way radio, dictating and transcribing equipment, teletypewriters and telescribers	
Extractive industries and construction: Earth moving Mining Lumbering Agriculture	Heavy-duty cross-country conveyors, one-hundred-ton power shovels, spread of special purpose vehicles such as tractor shovels, load carriers, straddle carriers, bulldozers, and so on	

4. The buyer-seller relationship is more cumbersome in many instances, less flexible, and less amenable to sudden developments (usually); there is less adherence to conventional industrial procedures, standards, and relationships.

5. Massive resources are available; and failure to perform does not seem to discourage future relationships, as it would in industry.

6. There is frequent and periodic replacement of key policy makers.

7. Directions of technological progress sometimes are altered abruptly, often for side effects that may have little bearing on the technological merits. Typical external influences are:

Exhibit 7

GROWING MECHANIZATION OF INTELLECTUAL PROCESSES

Areas of Advance	Some Typical Means	Some Results
Direction of long, intricate machinery actions	Feedback control of process equipment Punched-card control of bulk-materials batching Numerically controlled machine tools Punched-tape control of typewriters and so on	Increased accuracy, reduced setup time, improved uniformity, reduction in operator training, need for programmers Increase in equipment utilization Increased cost per unit of equipment
Information processing	Computers and business machinery to acquire, sort, manipulate, interpret, store, and display selected data Mechanical reproduction of selected data, forms, checks, and so on	Reduction of clerical labor Increased speed in preparing papers of all types Improved accuracy Speed in summarizing business conditions Better information for management Faster response to management decisions
Problem solving	Computer solutions of complex scientific, engineering, and business calculations Computer simulation of business and military problems Operations research problem analysis by computers	Solution of problems otherwise unfeasible Exploration of complex problems Decision-making assistance on major business and military policies and strategies Ability to test effect of tentative solutions to problems

a) Political struggles between areas of the country, political parties, internal bureaus, industry lobbies, and government agencies.
b) Military organization and military developments.
c) International political developments.
d) Sensitivity to popular impressions and agitation through public media.

It follows that no alert management can afford to ignore government decisions influencing technical progress.

Changing Forms of Ownership and Finance. Some major technological developments will occur only as new forms of financing and sponsorship emerge. Four developments especially affect some projects:

1. The growing acceptance of leasing and rental.
2. The assembly of large capital groupings (private and private-governmental combinations) for major projects.
3. The spread of state sponsorship and operation in competition with private sponsorship.
4. International combinations of resources for major projects (e.g., the St. Lawrence Seaway and the British-French supersonic transport plane).

QUESTIONS

1. Consider the trends above as they may affect the future of:
   a) International Harvester
   b) United Airlines
   c) Dan River Cotton Mills
   d) Westinghouse Electric Corporation
   e) Detroit Edison (electric power utility)
   f) Bethlehem Steel Company
   g) Electric Storage Battery Corporation
   h) The United States State Department
   i) The United States Army, Navy, and Air Force
   j) Newport News Shipbuilding Corporation
   k) General Foods
   l) A large state university system
   m) Cincinnati Milling Machine Company
   n) McGraw-Hill Book Company, Inc. (publisher of technical books for industry and colleges)
   o) Harvard Medical School and its associated complex of hospitals
   p) The Federal Bureau of Investigation
   Suggestion: A study of an annual report is a good starting point.

2. What is the likely trend in new-product development time? Cost? Frequency? What are the marketing implications?

3. What may happen to the technical concepts and the real cost of:
   a) Automobiles?
   b) Electric power?
   c) Harvesting of fruit?
   d) Operation of an industrial research facility?
   e) Cans, bottles, tubes, and similar household containers?

4. How should a firm organize to deal with the technological future? Indeed, is any special effort indicated?

5. Assuming that management is concerned about the broad sweep of technology, what should it observe and study?
   Suggestion: Choose a specific firm.

6. What duties should be assigned to the research and development department in the study of the firm's technological environment?

7. Describe the general effects of continued technological progress on each of the basic business functional areas:
   a) Production
   b) Marketing
   c) Finance
   d) Control
   e) Human relations
   f) Policy

   What training or understanding seems desirable for the top corporate officer in each of these areas in future years?

The Superior Advantages of Railways and Steam Carriages over Canal Navigation

Albany, 11th March 1812

I had before heard your very ingenious propositions as to the railway communication. I fear, however, in mature reflection, that they will be liable to serious objections, and ultimately more expensive than a canal. They must be double, so as to prevent the danger of two such heavy bodies meeting. The walls on which they are placed must at least be four feet below the surface, and three above, and must be clamped with iron, and even then would hardly sustain so heavy a weight as you propose moving at the rate of four miles an hour on wheels. As to wood, it would not last a week; they must be covered with iron, and that, too, very thick and strong. The means of stopping these heavy carriages without a great shock, and of preventing them from running upon each other (for there would be many on the road at once) would be very difficult. In case of accidental stops, or the necessary stops to take wood and water, etc. many accidents would happen. The carriage of condensed water would be very troublesome. Upon the whole, I fear the expense would be much greater than that of canals, without being so convenient.

ROBERT B. LIVINGSTONE
(Steamboat Pioneer)

FROM: John Stevens, *Documents Tending to Prove the Superior Advantages of Railways and Steam Carriages over Canal Navigation* (New York, 1812).

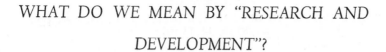

WHAT DO WE MEAN BY "RESEARCH AND DEVELOPMENT"?

Introduction[1]

The statement and testimony that appear on the following pages represent an attempt to identify and classify the various types of activities and functions that are included in the general term "research and development."

The witness, David Novick, is head of the Cost Analysis Department of the RAND Corporation. He was invited to testify before the Antitrust and Monopoly Subcommittee of the Senate Judiciary Committee during the hearings on administered prices in the drug industry.

STATEMENT OF DAVID NOVICK

As evidence that we are doing more "research and development," we point, with some pride, to the Defense Department's budget calling for $3.9 billion for research and development in fiscal 1961 as compared with $650 million identifiable for military research and development in fiscal year 1950. Similarly, we say that business has expanded its R & D effort from less than $200 million in 1930 to $1 billion a few years ago, and current reports indicate that business expenditures may total close to $7 billion this year.

But what do we mean when we say the Defense Department is spending $3.9 billion for research and development, or that industry is spending $7 billion? Are we really increasing our research effort, or are we merely reclassifying traditional outlays in terms of the now fashionable "research and development" effort? How are the dollars actually being spent?

In trying to come up with some answers, I classified research and development into four steps, each being based on the degree of certainty of pay-off and the promise for the future which each activity provided. The classifications I used are shown in Exhibit 1.

Using this four-step breakdown of the research and development process, I then attempted to distribute the reported $10-billion expenditure in 1959, with the results shown in the following table:

Promise	Guessed Distribution
Step I. "Brave new world"	$ 100,000,000
Step II. Possible use of new discovery	300,000,000
Step III. Application of new knowledge	2,600,000,000
Step IV. Improved application	7,000,000,000

[1] Extracts from *Hearings on Administered Prices*, Part 18, U.S. Senate, 86th Congress (Washington, D.C.: U.S. Government Printing Office, April, 1960). Novick has presented papers on this same theme before many societies and in the Spring, 1960, issue of the *California Management Review*.

Exhibit 1

RESEARCH AND DEVELOPMENT: STEPS, ACTIVITIES, AND PROMISES FOR
THE FUTURE

Activity	*Promise*
Step I. Basic research, experimental research, basic development.	Understanding of universe and organization of knowledge about it to: *a)* Permit major changes in ways of looking at phenomena and activities; *b)* Create new devices and methods for accomplishing scientific objectives; and *c)* Identify phenomena and activities which permit revolutionary changes in existing products, methods, and approaches. Its promise is great but not identified as to specific purposes, and the possibility of fulfillment is highly uncertain.
Step II. Applied research, advanced development, basic evaluation, basic testing.	Singling out or identifying specific potentials or applications with a view to developing devices or methods for utilizing the new general knowledge obtained in step I. Scientific application or usefulness is identified, but the economy, efficiency, and acceptability of the proposals remain uncertain. Promise is for great new things.
Step III. Product development, product testing, product evaluation, pilot production.	Specific devices or methods appear as likely solutions but must be brought reasonably close to final application to determine effectiveness, economy, and acceptability. Doability has been established, and major advances are promised.
Step IV. Product application, application research, applied testing, applied evaluation.	New uses and applications or modifications of existing uses or applications are sought for existing methods, products, or components; may result in substantial benefits to users or producers. Some success is reasonably assured, since it is evolutionary rather than revolutionary.

From this, you can see, I do not think that a significant part of the effort called "research and development" is going into the "brave new world" type of activities which we normally imply when we say "research and development." As I said in my paper, I agree with Cornelia and Bergen Evans, who, in their *Dictionary of Contemporary America Usage*, gave as one of their definitions of research:

Research has become very popular in the United States since the outbreak of World War II. As Henry D. Smyth has observed, the idea that the object of research is new knowledge does not seem to be widely understood and "a schoolboy looking up a word in the dictionary is now said to be doing research." Indeed it has been debased even further. Research is frequently used to describe reading by those to whom reading, apparently, is a recherche activity and for many a graduate student it is a euphemism for wholesale plagiarism. The word needs a rest or at least less promiscuous handling.

The Evanses probably intended to include "development" in their definition of "research" when that word is used as in the familiar "research and development" phrase.

And both the scientists and the administrators of research programs seemingly agree with this view.

. . . .

In another presentation at . . . Dr. Merle A. Tuve said: ". . . all of us [scientists] have contributed to a more or less purposeful confusion in our use of the words 'basic research.' We have lumped under 'research and development' so many huge technological activities in the national budget, and correspondingly in corporation budgets and elsewhere that the figures have become practically meaningless."[2]

These and many other statements indicate clearly, I think, the need to do a better job of identification of the various kinds of research and development, test and evaluation, and to project the kinds of changes that each of these activities promises for the future. The identification is needed by both government and industry as a tool to help make management decisions as to where and how resources should be allocated.

However, the undertaking is an ambitious one which I approach with humility, recognizing that the results are not likely to be completely satisfactory to anyone. All that can be said with certainty is that the present situation is both confused and confusing.

Before turning to the application of my identification system to the history of penicillin, let me review with you some of the logic used in determining my measurements.

One reason the step I, or "brave new world," outlay is small is that the type of activity is normally low in its resource demands. Only occasionally, as in the Project "M" linear accelerator at Stanford, do expenditures reach the multimillion-dollar level. For the most part, this research involves one or a few highly qualified individuals, the equipment is paper and pencil, or blackboard and chalk, and relatively small laboratories. It is only when use or application is involved that expenditures jump sharply.

Probably most important in establishing the low level of activity in step 1 is the fact that we in the United States have been more interested in application or experimentation than in pure research. Most of our science has been imported, chiefly from Europe, either as principles or as scientists who developed their ideas in this country. The bulge in our scientific discoveries in the last twenty-five years is probably more the result of European scientists coming to this country to escape fascism, communism, and Naziism than any real expansion in our indigenous capability. Einstein, Fermi, Von Neuman, and Teller are a few of the scientists whose U.S. contributions are transplants from Europe. There is no assurance that we have yet developed the essential "climate" for basic research in this country.

Another reason for the low expenditures in step I is the small number of people capable of or interested in this kind of activity. Recently, there has been a marked increase in emphasis on education in mathematics, engineering, and science, and larger numbers of students are being encouraged to enter and

[2] *Symposium on Basic Research* (sponsored by the National Academy of Sciences, the American Association for the Advancement of Science, and the Alfred P. Sloan Foundation, May 14–15, 1959, Publication No. 56 (Washington, D.C.: American Association for the Advancement of Science, 1959).

are entering these fields. Whether the rate of activity at the basic research level can be made directly proportional to the numbers turned out in these fields of education remains to be seen. Great ideas are few and far between. Speeding up the process may or may not be susceptible to the numbers treatment.

Step II is three times step I, according to my guess. It is still small for the same reasons that apply in step I. Some increase occurs because, in general, more people are available for and capable of this type of work, and more elaborate and methods can be used. More people become available as the nature and kind of guidance and direction are now more easily established. The equipment, in many cases, is still simple compared to that used in steps III and IV. However, it is likely to be more complex and in larger quantity, and more costly than that used in step I. Illustrative of this was the estimate, in 1940, that $100,000 would be required to attempt the first nuclear chain reaction. Very little had been spent in the basic projections. Billions were required for step III in nuclear fission.

The relationship between steps II and III in the atomic development program is representative of the general military interaction. In the atomic case, and in many modern weapon developments, the size of the resource demands for product development, testing, and evaluation becomes spectacular because of the time concentration. When time pressures are not so great as in national security, expenditures in step III are smaller. The build-up is more gradual. Over the years involved in a leisurely approach, many of the problems in one development are solved as part of other research.

Most research expenditures are in step IV, for a wide variety of reasons. First and most important is industry's willingness to make the investment, since the changes now sought are small-order variations in proven methods, devices, and approaches with reasonable assurance of success.

Second, because so much is already known about the undertaking, very large numbers of people are available for and interested in this kind of work. Third, in most activities, whether production, management, or marketing involving equipment, cosmetics, or social services, making improvements and changes of this kind is the essence of day-to-day business or professional activity.

Because the pay-offs are reasonably assured, it is easy to understand why it should comprise the great bulk of the effort. Perhaps equally important, unless there is a large output in steps I and II, additional research and development can only seek the relatively small improvements which in my concept characterize step IV.

Against this background, I shall now turn to the history of penicillin to illustrate how my classification may be applied to that history.

Probably the first question which must be answered is a determination of the relationship between the scientific story of the mold discovered by Sir Alexander Fleming to the application work or attempts to discover the uses to which the phenomena observed in the laboratory could be put.

The word "application," as I have used it, does not include commercial application, since I am assuming that the first interest also of the scientists is understanding rather than a salable product.

This distinction between pure and industrial research was best described by Charles Kettering. He pointed out that in the university, only two factors were involved in true scientific research: (1) matter and (2) energy. In industry, he said, research involved four factors: (1) matter, (2) energy, (3) economics, and (4) psychology.

As he put it, "industry research must partake as much of economic horse sense as science."[3]

I think this statement of Kettering's explains much of the confusion about the many varieties and kinds of research. It can be applied directly to the story of penicillin.

In my opinion, the early work of Fleming, Raistrick, and his co-workers, Thom and the others, was undertaken primarily as part of a search for an understanding of the phenomena of mold. Their work on conditions for extracting this substance was aimed chiefly at an examination of both its biochemical and its biological properties.

Obviously, they were pleased when they found practical results of their efforts. However, as scientists, their real interest was a better understanding of the phenomena first observing by Fleming.

Probably the best evidence of the difference between the purely scientific effort and the later commercial effort is the statement which Florey and Chain submitted to the natural science division of the Rockefeller Foundation in November, 1939. The academic interest in the study was even more strongly stated in the two-volume book *Antibiotics,* by Florey, Chain, Heatley, Jennings, Sanders, and Abraham.

Although in the application the possible practical results were brought forward, the research was conceived of as an academic study with possibilities of wide theoretical interest, both chemical and biological. Statements have appeared from time to time that the work on penicillin was started as an attempt to contribute to the treatment of septic wounds in World War II. This is quite erroneous as the work was planned well before the outbreak of war, and in any case there was then no idea that pencillin could play the important part which it has done in the treatment of war injuries.[4]

Thus the efforts from Fleming's discovery in 1929 until 1940 seem to fall within the categories I would call step I and step II of the research and development process. In other words, the work of Fleming provided an observation which promised a better understanding of a part of the universe. The promise was great but not yet identified as to specific purpose. The possibility of fulfillment was highly uncertain. This might truly be described as step I.

This work was picked up by other groups both in England and in the United States. Now the effort was to discover some of the possible scientific uses of Fleming's observation.

Subsequently, when laboratory experiments gave "grounds for the hope that penicillin would have some systematic chemotherapeutic properties," Florey described the situation, saying:

The difficulties in raising the scale of laboratory production were formidable, and the decision had to be taken whether it would be more profitable to struggle on with the methods already in use, which gave only a tiny yield per liter of culture fluid, until enough had been made for trial in man, or whether to hold up production while a search was made into possible means of increasing the yield. The former policy was

---

[3] T. A. Boyd, *Professional Amateur: The Biography of Charles Franklin Kettering* (New York: E. P. Dutton & Co., Inc., 1957).

[4] Federal Trade Commission, *Economic Report on Antibiotics Manufacture* (Washington, D.C.: U.S. Government Printing Office, June, 1958), p. 308.

adopted, rightly as it seems now, for once the chemotherapeutic effectiveness of penicillin in man had been demonstrated the impulse to further work became sufficient to make the provision of facilities for the subsequent large scale investigations by industrial and other research bodies a matter of high priority. However, at the same time as laboratory large scale brewing was being carried out, attempts were made at Oxford to increase the yield by changing the composition of the medium and by selecting high yielding strains. Among those tested were single spore isolates from the strain already in use and from cultures obtained toward the end of 1940 from Fleming. These investigations gave no useful results at the time, though more extended work on similar lines which was done later in America was highly successful.[5]

Widespread interest in this mold started with the publication by Florey and his co-workers of their paper, "Penicillin as a Chemotherapeutic Agent," which appeared in the *Lancet* of August 24, 1940, followed by a 1941 report by Abraham, Chain, Fletcher, Florey, Gardner, Heatley, and Jennings. Subsequently, the Committee on Medical Research of the U.S. Office of Scientific Research and Development and the General Penicillin Committee in Great Britain figured prominently in the picture.

These committees took the program from the research laboratories and transferred it into full-scale production, development, tests, and evaluation—step III—activity conducted by commercial firms in Britain, the United States, and Canada. Among the first companies to attack the problem seriously were Merck & Co., Inc., E. R. Squibb & Sons, and Charles Pfizer & Co., Inc.

With the belief of both the British and the U.S. committees that the promise for new products was great, we are ready for step III, with the commercial interests anxious to tackle the many problems seriously.

On October 20, 1941, Thom wrote from Beltsville, informing Richards [of the Committee on Medical Research] of what had been learned on the trip. At least six commercial companies, including manufacturers of fine and medicinal chemicals as well as pharmaceutical houses, were reported by Thom to have manifested varying degrees of interest in the production of penicillin by fermentation. The word from Peoria was particularly encouraging: "Moyer has been able to increase the experimental yield of penicillin to three times what Heatley could produce by his methods." The members of the staff who had been working on penicillin were interested; and while they realized that the regional laboratory was not equipped for large-scale production of penicillin, they believed that the laboratory could contribute to the research work necessary, if support were provided for such a program as was outlined in their recommendations. This program included:

1. Further experiments to increase the yield from Fleming's organism.
2. Improvement and standardization of the assay method to determine yield and effectiveness.
3. Search of a large number of organisms for one capable of producing a satisfactory yield.
4. Further study of the "drum" method of fermentation is very desirable.[6]

---

[5] *Ibid.*, p. 311.
[6] *Ibid.*, p. 322.

Subsequently, very substantial work was done in steps III and IV. The job was now to provide better methods of processing, stabilized products, to conduct clinical tests to determine both the safety of the products and their limitations, and ultimately to find new and improved products and methods of synthesizing penicillin or its therapeutic equivalent.

The British scientist A. L. Bachrach of Glazo Laboratories, Ltd., summarized briefly the four historic stages between the discovery of penicillin and the year 1955, when the article was written. Slightly paraphrasing his language, these stages are: first, the work of Fleming on its biological properties and the initial studies by Raistrick and his colleagues of its chemistry, and the means to purify it; second, the brilliant and arduous work of Florey and his colleagues at Oxford, which not only made it desirable to produce penicillin on a large scale, but also gave many valuable pointers to the means of doing it; next, a period of building up the new antibiotic industry, under wartime conditions, on the basis of surface culture, aided by the use of corn steep liquor and various other devices for raising titres; and the last phase, in which we still are, that due to the use of surface growing strains, and their continued upgrading, in deep fermenters.[7]

I do not have any specific statistics which could measure, in terms of dollars or resources, the effort applied to each of the four phases in the development of penicillin in the long period from 1928 to 1945. However, I do think that some index of that relationship may be obtained from the fact that the first Rockefeller grant to Dr. Florey was for $5,000 for a year's support in 1940 and a second grant of $5,000 was made in 1941.

Grants of this size would seem to indicate that only very small resources were expended for the first two stages in penicillin development.

I have no doubt that the subsequent work, in what I call step III, ran many times the amounts spent in either step I or step II before doability had been established.

I am equally sure that even the larger amounts spent on actually getting a useful product (step III) are only a fraction of what has been spent since that time in step IV, the subsequent development for improving, packaging, and marketing the product.

There is, however, as I pointed out earlier, nothing particularly unusual about this expenditure pattern. Outlay is usually small in step I, or the "brave new world," because the demand for resources is small and work in this area is, to a large extent, dependent on the quality of the researcher.

Step II is still small, although the cost may run several times step I, according to my guess. This increase is caused generally because more people are available and capable of work in this area, and more elaborate equipment and methods can be used.

Step III is the point when size of resource can go up markedly, particularly in military development. The cost goes up sharply because of time pressures. Of course, when time pressures are not so great as in national security, expenditures are smaller. The build-up is more gradual. Over the years involved in a leisurely approach, many of the problems in one development are solved as part of other research effort.

Most research expenditures are in step IV, for a variety of reasons. There is at that point a reasonable assurance of success, since the changes sought are small-order variations in proven methods, devices, and approaches. Because a substantial body of information is available, very large numbers of people can

---

[7] *Ibid.*, p. 354.

be employed at this point. Finally, making changes and improvements of this kind is the essence of day-to-day business or professional activity.

The small improvements which characterize step IV, and the long cycle which started in 1928 with Fleming's discovery and ended in 1945 with the availability of commercially produced penicillin, may both be by-products of the failure to provide more adequate support at steps I and II.

SENATOR HART: . . . I sense from your explanation that some of the increase in our money spent for research is really just changing the accountant's designation of moneys which traditionally have been spent. In light of that, and the change in the value of the dollar, do you believe that we are spending more, and, if so, about how much more, doing the really basic part I and II research now than we were ten years ago?

MR. NOVICK: Dr. Tuve made some very interesting remarks about that at the symposium last May. One of his major complaints was what he called the "big wheel" and "big deal" aspect of modern scientific work. I don't know that I can quote him accurately, but essentially what he said is that one man doing a research job is a relatively inexpensive enterprise.

It is now difficult to get support for that kind of thing. You have to have a big project to interest the administrators. This means that it is not easy to get support for what one might do for $25,000. So we blow it up into something like $250,000, or more probably $2.5 million, and then we can get somebody interested in it. At this juncture the scientist who had the idea ceases to be a scientist and instead becomes an administrator. Instead of being a scientist, he is a big wheeler and dealer.

As a consequence, it was implicit in Tuve's statement that we are getting a lot less for $250,000 or 2.5 million than we could have gotten for $25,000 ten years ago. Now that, plus the other kinds of adjustments that are involved in the data, makes the kind of estimate you want very, very difficult. In addition, the data are inadequate.

I did not know this statistical picture was as fragmentary and inadequate as it turned out to be when I started this research.

Data were not the problem I started out to study. I turned to it on discovering that the statistics are rather meaningless. To illustrate the data problem, let me quote from the McGraw-Hill series an article by Dexter Keezer and his colleagues:

All forecasts of R & D expenditures must be given in terms of data that are admittedly shaky both as to cover and definition.

Then he goes on:

The best set of estimates for R & D expenditures running back to the year 1945 is this one, because it is as we know [that is, the McGraw-Hill series] the only set of such estimates.

This question of "how much" has never really been studied. To the extent that it has been examined, it is done with "best guesses," and this means that when you are done, you don't really know much more than you did when you started.

. . . .

SENATOR HRUSKA: To find out what their relative expenditures are in the four steps which you outline?

MR. NOVICK: Actually, Dr. Hutcheson of Westinghouse Electric made the best statement I know of. In fact, it was his statement that set me off on this tangent. In announcing his $185-million Westinghouse research budget for 1959, he pointed out that to measure research spending as a percentage of something is meaningless unless the objectives are well defined and the figures broken down in these categories.[8]

Three and a half million dollars for blue-sky research not connected in any way with current products.

SENATOR HRUSKA: Was that step I? Is that the brave new world he is looking for?

MR. NOVICK: That's right; in fact, even in that, it is not clear that he is looking for a brave new world. He is looking for a new world, and how much of this is really basic research on which there is no assurance of pay-off and how much of it is research in which there has been an inkling that there may be a pay-off is not clear. But in his own classification, he would at best put $20 million of that into what I could call steps I and II, about $30 million into step III, and $135 million, or 80 per cent, as he termed it, "development to customers' orders for customer-tailored equipment," and that is pretty much my step IV.

SENATOR HRUSKA: That related to a single company. Do you know of any effort made to apply these principles in this classification to an entire industry?

MR. NOVICK: Well, you have the statistics which are put out by the National Science Foundation and others. The first report of this kind was done by Dr. Bush's committee, then Dr. Steelman's committee, and we now get out two series, the McGraw-Hill one and a National Science Foundation series.

SENATOR HRUSKA: And to what do they apply?

MR. NOVICK: They try to break things into basic research, applied research, development, and so forth.

SENATOR HRUSKA: For what activity?

MR. NOVICK: Well, the statistics are fragmentary. For example, you can get classifications by industry in terms of food and kindred products, chemical and allied products, and so forth. For example, the total R & D for 1953, which is the only year for which I could find this kind of a breakdown, the principal industries doing R & D were electrical equipment, which is essentially electronics, and aircraft and parts, which is primarily the munitions industry. Basic research for electrical industries was $19 million; for aircraft and parts, $18 million.

In other words, in these two cases, less than 3 per cent of the reported R & D was going into basic research, and these two industries represented over half of the industrial R & D reported. When you get these numbers and look at them twice, they are awfully hard to take. For example, one of the industries doing the largest amount of basic research was food and kindred products. Now, it

---

[8] As reported by Mr. Novick in *What Do We Mean by Research and Development?* P-1779 (Santa Monica: RAND Corp., August, 1959), Dr. Hutcheson defined his company's proposed research program as:

$3.5 million, or 1.9 per cent . . . . Blue-sky research not connected in any way with current products but promising for the long-range future

$6 million, or 3.2 per cent . . . . Long-range major development programs aimed at identifying characteristics of products we believe we shall be making five to ten years from now

$12 million, or 6.4 per cent . . . . Search for new knowledge we know we need, based on past research

$30 million, or 9.6 per cent . . . . Standard product development to update and improve existing products

$133.5 million, or 78.9 per cent . . . . . . Development to customers' orders for customer-tailored equipment

is conceivable that they do a lot of basic research, but would they be the outstanding leaders in this area? And then you find that in another report, several years later, somebody apparently has called this to their attention, and their basic research drops way down. In fact, someone has suggested that the first measure of basic research meant stuff that did not come out of the oven up to standard.

SENATOR HRUSKA: Has any effort been made to apply this to the pharmaceutical industry?

MR. NOVICK: You have the chemical and allied products group where the drug industry would be. Their total R & D for the year 1953 was reported at $361 million, of which $38 million was basic research, or 10 per cent basic research.

. . . .

All I am suggesting, Senator, is that since this is such an important question, someone should undertake to get the guidelines organized a little bit better, so that we just don't point to 60 times as many dollars and say this represents 60 times more activity of the same kind.

COMMENTARY ON THE NATURE OF RESEARCH RESULTS BY J. R. B.

Novick includes in "step I activities" basic research and experimental research, and then demonstrates common misuse of the word "research." If the goal of *basic* research is "understanding of the universe and organization of knowledge about it," what will the immediate tangible output of research work be? By definition, it will be knowledge, which is physically embodied in papers, tabular data, illustrations, and, possibly, in samples or sets of classified physical objects. The result of *basic* research is, therefore, not hardware, or even working models. It is simply knowledge. The extent to which businessmen should indulge in basic research, including the hiring of scientists capable of such work, is a moot point. (See the arguments of Dr. M. J. O'Brien in Section V, and note the reactions of his audience, which included about 125 corporate vice presidents and research directors.)

A related question of importance is how to measure the amount of basic research performed and its effectiveness. In a study for the United States Navy, personnel of Arthur D. Little, Inc., concluded that the best measurement of research output was papers. They begged off on the measurement of quality, impact, or importance, and dealt solely with numbers of publications. Dr. Derek Price, a noted historian of science at Yale, has similarly used numbers of papers, numbers of scientific journals, and numbers of abstracts to measure scientific activity and its results.

A fruitful idea for analyzing the output of researchers has been advanced by Dr. Ben Lipetz, an independent research management consultant at Carlisle, Massachusetts. He accepts the idea that the tangible output of research will be papers. But he holds that there are six elements or types of conclusions that can be identified in such papers:

Description..........................Statements of things seen
Definition..........................Of phenomena observed
Explanation..........................Of phenomena (to some extent)
Theory or Hypothesis..................Formulation of possible laws, rules, cause and effect, relationships, methods of analysis
Prediction..........................Opinion as to probable results, directions, effects
Statements of Manipulative Technique....Guidance and explanation for others on methods of doing the same or further research

Dr. Lipetz holds that these types of results can be identified and counted in research papers, and that a crude measure of efficiency or achievement of a laboratory or an individual is thus obtained. He makes no claim to evaluate the originality or the commercial, social, or scientific value of these elements when identified.

QUESTIONS

1. Define *research; development*. What is *invention? Discovery?*
2. What is the difference between *basic, applied, experimental,* and *pure research?*
3. Distinguish between *product design, product development, product engineering,* and *manufacturing engineering.*
4. What corporate strategy is implied by Dr. Hutcheson's research-funding program?
5. What criteria should govern the total amount of a firm's research and development budget? Of the distribution of this fund?
6. What kind of technical education and training, personality traits, and interests would you consider desirable in men hired for each of the activities you defined in questions 1, 2 and 3?
7. What characteristics are needed in a director of research in an industrial firm? A director of engineering?
8. How should management judge the effectiveness of its R & D department? Its R & D director?

Creativity in the Sciences

There are, of course, gifted individuals who seem to require little interaction with the rest of the world; perhaps there is little that can be done to accelerate or decelerate their output. Most of us, however, are responsive to the environment, and group stimulus seems to be one of the best means of enhancing creativity. . . . There are several components which I believe to be essential. First, there is a slight feeling of discontent, of not being completely accepted. This leads to a banding together of individuals to create a micro-environment. Those within the group can get satisfactions and a meeting of the need for human fellowship from within this tiny intellectual island. It is then possible to adopt the attitude that the value system of the rest of the world does not really count, that a common interest in advancing an area of science is the most important and the only tenable activity in which the individual can engage. Thus, the group provides motivation. Moreover, if a member temporarily loses his élan, he can soon regain it, for at all times there are some present who are brimming with infective enthusiasm.

Unfortunately, bringing a group together only occasionally produces this favorable mutual stimulus. Sometimes the necessary external spurs are missing. Often the composition of the group is not right. It should consist of people whose educational background and temperament are somewhat different. To be effective there must be, within the island, at least one enthusiast who resonates to new ideas. There must also be a person of good judgment who is capable of recognizing what new leads are apt to prove valuable, and who is capable of quietly disposing of those which are trivial, unsound, or sterile. It is also usually desirable that the group contain a compromiser or peacemaker, for in a closely knit, tight environment tensions and rivalries can spring up. Indeed, the greatest hazard in group activity is internal dissension. When adrenalin begins to flow, creativity goes out the window. A person engaged in a serious personal clash of wills invariably gives first priority in his thinking to the matter at issue.

One of the other hazards to creativity, for both the group and the individual is success. Some individuals possess sufficient deepseated motivation to be able to cope with good fortune, but all too often this is not the case. I have seen few "fat cats" who were truly creative. When a group is successful and attains recognition, some of the ties that bind it disappear, and suppressed rivalries tend to assert themselves. One of my concerns about our national creative vigor is that scientists are too well liked, get too much recognition. As a result there is a tendence toward complacency, and scientists are no longer as critical of each other or as intolerant of shoddy work as they once were.

Dr. Philip H. Abelson
Editor, *Science*

FROM: "Creativity in the Sciences," *Science*, Vol. 140, No. 3573 (June 21, 1963), p. 1271.

A SYSTEMS APPROACH TO RESEARCH MANAGEMENT[1]

By R. E. *Gibson*

Director, Applied Research Laboratory, Johns Hopkins University

DISCUSSION OF research management frequently flounders in a morass of arguments between those who claim that management has no place in research and those who claim that unless research is well managed it is ineffective. In order to avoid this type of argument, I should like to

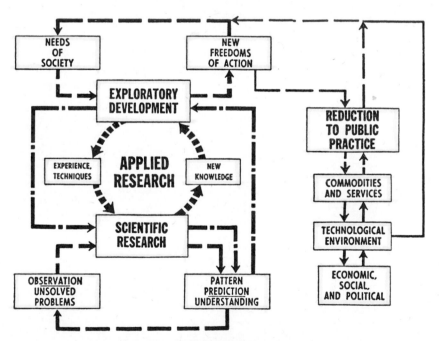

Figure 1. Technology block diagram

comment on the place and scope of management in research operations, using the block diagram of technology shown in Figure 1 as a frame of reference. . . .

---

[1] Condensed from *Research Management*, Vol. V (1962), pp. 215–423; and Vol. VI (1963), p. 15, by permission of the author and the Industrial Research Institute.

Scientific Research

Near the bottom of Figure 1, we see a block labeled "scientific research," which is still a very individual activity. It is motivated by curiosity or an uneasy feeling that a discrepancy exists between preconceived ideas and our observations of natural phenomena. Its objective is understanding, or the fitting of new and strange observations into patterns of established fact. In this type of research the role of management is one of complete restraint and noninterference. A decision is made to invest some money in an individual and his assistants in the hope that their talents, intuition, and skill will lead them to the discovery of new and significant knowledge and the broadening of the basis of our understanding of nature. Thereafter, they are best left alone.

Exploratory Development

A second activity shown in Figure 1 is called "exploratory development" and is the field that used to be the territory of the inventor. Its incentives are the realization that limitations to human activity can be broken down by the application of knowledge and ingenuity to produce new devices, commodities, or services that give us new freedoms of action. The invention of the steam engine, Daimler's invention of a high-speed internal-combustion engine, the Wright brothers' demonstration at Kittyhawk, Goddard's liquid-fuel rockets in 1926—all were events that made available to man new freedoms of action which he has exploited with far-reaching social consequences. In this area the role of management is a tenuous one and depends primarily on the number of people involved in a given exploratory enterprise. Indeed, in both of the activities that I have mentioned—scientific research and exploratory development—it seems that management, in the classical sense of the word, can play a role only in getting the expeditions started. When, like a band of explorers [researchers] penetrate into the unknown, they are on their own, and decisions for action must be taken in the light of the new and strange situations that arise. As the size of the band increases, the need for management goes up, but it is emphasized that the important decisions must be made by those closest to the front line.

Applied Research and Development

In the middle of the diagram is an area entitled "applied research," which bridges the gap between scientific research and exploratory development. Its functions are to provide the exploratory developer with accurate and systematized knowledge and understanding from scientific research, and to carry the unsolved problems uncovered in the course of a development back to the laboratories for solution and understanding. This is the area in which the large research and development laboratories of government, industry, and nonprofit corporations now operate. It is an area where time scales are important, where the product interacts closely with the environment described in the next paragraph. It is the area to which I shall refer when I speak of management of research and development in this paper.

Reduction to Public Practice

New freedoms of action become effective in society only after they are reduced to public practice, and this entails the investment of large sums of money and manpower, an investment which must be amortized by the returns brought in by products. Here, of course, is a place where management, business acumen, and an intimate knowledge of the technological, economic, social, and political environment are of paramount importance. Since the operation of an applied research organization involves expenditures of considerable sums of money and the investment of intellectual and practical talents of a number of scientists and engineers, it becomes important that those responsible for the management of this work also understand intimately the interactions of its products or potential products with the technological, political, economic, and social world, and the processes whereby new freedoms of action are reduced to public practice. This knowledge is fundamental to the initiation of research and development programs likely to obtain "profitable" results at the right time. I think, therefore, that we can safely assume that the subject before us is not irrelevant and that management of the right kind has a very important part to play in the realization of the maximum potential inherent in an applied research organization.

The function of research management is to operate effectively the system referred to as applied research in Figure 1. . . .

Before doing so, however, it might be wise to say a word or two about "management."

. . . .

There is no doubt at all that the modern "management" school is making extremely important contributions by attacking objectively the complicated problems that arise when human beings co-operate in a system. It is questioning the dogmas, studying and systematizing the methods of successful practitioners, and evolving new techniques and broadening our basis of understanding. However, along with very sound results, there has grown up and been widely sold a mythology that gives the impression that "professional management" can be substituted for leadership, glib *expertise* for hard-earned experience, and academic formulas for common sense. Discrimination is of the essence in management.

This paper may be regarded as a delineation of my own definition of "management" as applied to an R & D organization or program. What I have in mind is really "leadership" or "generalship," where the prime object of the exercise is to advance technology by means of an organization and the secondary objective is to operate the organization smoothly.

SYSTEMATIC DISCUSSION OF THE COMPONENTS OF MODERN TECHNOLOGY—THEIR INTERACTIONS AND FEEDBACKS

Scientific Research

Figure 2 gives a simplified picture of scientific research in block diagram form. The first block in this system is labeled "experimental research." Its inputs are human industry, intelligent questions, existing knowledge, accurate observation of phenomena, imagination, and skill—all motivated by curiosity to understand exactly what is going on, through the establishment of valid facts determined by controlled experiments. I

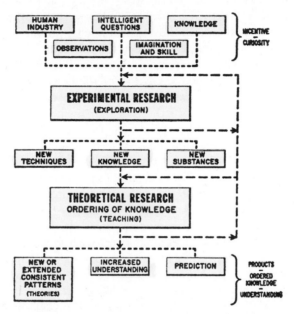

Figure 2.   Some feedbacks in scientific research

cannot dwell here on the immense amount of hard work and ingenuity that must be expended to establish one fact, to be sure that it can be reproduced exactly by any competent observer and that it can be expressed unambiguously in quantitative terms. The outputs of this box are new knowledge, new techniques, new substances.

The second block, of equal or even greater importance than the first, is labeled "theoretical research or the ordering of knowledge." The input to this block is new and old knowledge, and the function of this block is to arrange the new facts and the old knowledge in consistent and satisfying patterns which we call theories. Its outputs are new or extended consistent patterns of knowledge—increased understanding that comes when the new and strange are logically related to the old and familiar and the power of predicting new facts by extrapolation from well-established theories. In other words, the primary function of this block is to reduce the myriad facts emerging from experimental research to systematic and manageable form.

Figure 2 brings out several important feedbacks. The first is the "interplay of experimental theory and experimental practice," to quote Claude Bernard; the second is the feedback from the output to the input of the experimental research box; and the third is the feedback from the output of theoretical research not only to its own input but also to the input of the experimental box. These are discussed in more detail in the following paragraphs.[2]

1. From observation and careful study of phenomena or events, facts are obtained which may then be fitted together in an experimental pattern, i.e., a working hypothesis. If the facts fit well into the hypothesis, the latter immediately suggests new subjects for observation or new experiments from which come new facts, and so the activity in the circuit builds up, and with it *confidence in the validity of the facts and the consistency of the theory*. On the other hand, if the facts do not fit into a recognized pattern, one must first make a further study of their validity to insure that they have not been vitiated by some error (and errors may arise in very subtle ways). At the same time, it may be necessary to re-examine the pattern or theory and, if necessary, modify it to accommodate the new facts. The process is a cyclic one, and only when the *facts and the experimental theory fit together* can we be content with either. The product of this circuit is a satisfying pattern or general theory which enables us to understand the phenomena or events in the field of study, which comprehends all the facts, links them with facts from other fields, and enables us to predict verifiable new phenomena or events. The outputs of this circuit are the major theories or patterns which accommodate large bodies of facts such as the laws of thermodynamics, the laws of motion, the theory of relativity, the quantum theory, Maxwell's electromagnetic equations, the Mendelian laws.

2. In order to extend and integrate the patterns and to assay their consistency over wide ranges of facts, it has been found necessary to seek facts in every region susceptible to precise observation. The new substances, instruments, and techniques—we may even include concepts—discovered and developed in the course of one series of researches may be used to explore other new regions for more facts. The build-up in the circuit due to this positive feedback has been most spectacular; indeed, the history of natural philosophy is marked by milestones, each indicating the

---

[2] Earlier in the original paper, Dr. Gibson defined negative feedback as occurring when the increase in the output of the system tends to cut down input and thus achieve equilibrium. Positive feedback, he said, occurs when an increase in output acts to increase the input, thus leading to exponential growth of output.—J. R. B.

discovery of a new device or technique which opened up to human experience regions that were hitherto inaccessible. These devices were means to an end, but the end would never have been achieved without the means. Telescopes, microscopes, X rays, radioactivity, alpha particles, neutrons, cyclotrons, chemical analysis, electronics, high-speed computing machines—all have been means of opening up new continents for valid experiences. The positive feedback from its output to its input gives experimental research an ever-expanding potential to break down existing barriers to its own advances.

3. The arrow from the output of theoretical research to the input of the whole system also indicates a positive feedback, the autocatalytic effect of *understanding*. A satisfactory theory or pattern of facts broadens and deepens understanding, pointing the way to new fruitful fields where facts of significance, interest, and potential for application are likely to be discovered. In short, it permits the asking of more *intelligent* questions. It helps research men to make more intelligently the most important decision of all, namely, the choice of problems in which to invest years of their lives. With the aid of new instruments, techniques, and methods, both experimental and theoretical, these decisions may be implemented, and the investigators may pursue their researches into new and more complex fields with increasing facility and confidence.

The effects of these feedbacks on the growth of scientific knowledge and understanding have been really extraordinary. It is very difficult to get a quantitative expression of the size and extent of scientific knowledge at any one time, but all indices that have been examined indicate that scientific knowledge doubles every 10 or 15 years and has done so steadily since 1700.[3]

There are regions of interest in science where it is not possible to make precise observations or accumulate facts under completely controlled conditions. In such cases the system works in a deductive mode through the feedback from "satisfying patterns" to observation. In cosmogony or petrogenesis, for example, it is not practical to build up a theory of the origin of the universe or of rocks from reproducible facts obtained from direct observation of the processes concerned. However, starting from a comprehensive pattern of facts from physics and chemistry and certain assumptions, it is possible to draw a theoretical picture of the origin of the universe or rocks in *sufficient* detail that certain critical consequences which are susceptible to observation may be deduced. Facts extracted from observations may then be compared with those deducted from theory. The history of the sciences I have mentioned shows clearly that as our satisfying patterns grow in depth and breadth, the deductions drawn lead to more and more pertinent and refined observations, and our

---

[3] D. J. Price, *Discovery*, Vol. XVII (1956), p. 240.

confidence in them grows accordingly. This circuit has found wide application in attacks on complicated problems or those dealing with past or future events. Its power depends on the existence of broadly based, established patterns of facts, a condition which is sometimes not fully appreciated in attempts to apply "scientific methods" in new or complicated fields such as the social sciences.

There is one interesting philosophical implication of the role of positive feedbacks in scientific research. When positive feedback exists, we may say that the output is coherent with the input and the subject *grows*. When, however, the outputs of either block are erroneous (facts being contaminated with error or theories with fallacy), they will be out of phase with the input when fed back; in other words, the outputs and inputs are incoherent in this case. Positive feedback may become negative. We might suggest, therefore, that the criterion of truth can be related to the coherence of the outputs and inputs of these blocks.

Truth leads to rapid growth of knowledge; error leads to stagnation. Examples of incoherence of output and input are not hard to find in the history of science. For example, Lord Kelvin's theory of the cooling of the earth caused a temporary but significant stagnation in the science of geophysics, which started again on a rapid growth only after the growing knowledge of radioactivity corrected the error in Kelvin's theory. The struggles of the kinetic theory to explain quantitatively the properties of gases in pre-quantum-theory days is another striking example.

It is also interesting to notice two rather important differences between science and art. Positive feedbacks are strong in science, and their effects are of greatest significance. In art the feedbacks are quite weak—one masterpiece seldom paves the way for a greater one. The absence of strong, positive feedbacks has resulted in the arts growing much less steadily than the sciences. A second difference is to be found in the communications, which must be exact and quantitative in science; they need not be so in art.

I cannot leave the subject of scientific research without emphasizing the extreme importance of ordering our knowledge into patterns that make it interesting and manageable. "Order is remembered—chaos is forgotten." Since knowledge grows only in the minds of people, we must recognize the key role of the teacher in ordering new knowledge and experience into interesting and stimulating patterns that excite the interest of the student to assimilate this knowledge in his mind. The teachers who inspire students and write textbooks systematizing the knowledge in a given field play just as important a role in the advancement of science as do those who discover new knowledge by experimental research. However, it is the present-day fashion to underrate the former, and the road to academic promotion is paved with reprints, without too much regard to their quality. The quality of our scientific education reflects this distressing imbalance.

EXPLORATORY DEVELOPMENT

In the words of Howard Wilcox: "By exploratory development we mean the practice of investigating, creating, and designing new techniques and devices which promise to break through limitations hitherto set by nature on man's freedom of choice and action." Although the techniques and methods employed in exploratory development are often similar to those employed in scientific research, and there has always been a close connection and interchange of results between the two, their objectives are quite different. Scientific research seeks new and uncontaminated knowledge from which to make patterns of facts and ideas that lead to a deeper understanding of man and his environment. The exploratory developer, sensing the need for a new freedom of choice and action, uses all the knowledge he can glean from any source whatever, and exerts his ingenuity to put it together to give a new device, commodity, technique, or service that supplies this need. In the field of photography the close relation between scientific research and exploratory development is well seen. Actually, photography has always been an exploratory development. It has used scientific knowledge wherever available, but the exploratory development of new processes and techniques has so outrun the scientific understanding that C. E. K. Mees once remarked: "Photography has done more for science than science has for photography."

The general nature of exploratory development is illustrated by the block diagram in Figure 3. Its inputs are human industry, existing knowledge and understanding, existing arts, imagination, and skill; its outputs are new devices and techniques that are capable of giving us new possibilities for action.

It is through this system that human knowledge, imagination, ingenuity, and skill contribute to the material progress of mankind. Exploratory developments such as the domestication of animals, the invention of the sail, the steam engine, and the high-speed internal-combustion engine have literally changed the ecological patterns of the world and determined the course of civilization. The correlation between the availability of wind-driven ships as by far the best means of hauling heavy loads over long distances and the rise of centers of populations adjacent to rivers and sea coasts is ample evidence of this. Exploratory development is a much older activity than scientific research; it goes back to and perhaps even marks the dawn of civilization. For thousands of years, it remained the field of the lone inventor or the master artist and his apprentices. The old inventors used whatever knowledge they could find—some of it sound, but most of it unsound. Hence, invention was a haphazard game with chances of success rather slim, so that when successful and profitable results were obtained, the techniques and processes were held in tight secrecy. Positive feedbacks were severely limited or nonexistent. The

Edisonian method of invention emerged during the last century. It was based on empirical knowledge systematically obtained by the combined trial and error of a team of workers. It was successful in its day, but the growth of scientific knowledge has brought about its obsolescence. Modern exploratory development now relies heavily on systematic knowledge and understanding, the product of scientific research; and the

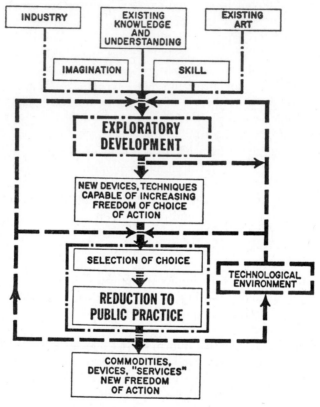

Figure 3.   Feedbacks in exploratory development

applied research organization I have described in connection with Figure 1 provides its inputs. The arrow on the dashed lines in Figure 3 indicate important feedbacks that now exist in exploratory development—all are positive; and our new devices, techniques, and freedoms of choice and action are increasing exponentially.

REDUCTION TO PUBLIC PRACTICE

In the over-all realm of technology the function of the research scientist is to seek and understand new human experiences; that of the exploratory developer is to apply established experience to create new devices and techniques which widen our freedom of choice and action in all fields of human endeavor. However, the selection of courses of action to be taken from the variety of choices available is not made by the scientist or the inventor but by the entrepreneurs of the business, financial, military, and political world. The introduction of a new commodity or service into use by the public at large (reduction to public practice) is an undertaking that requires capital and facilities, and in the past has been motivated either by a known demand or by the probability that a demand for a product or a service may be created when it is attractively presented to the public.

Thus, when the potentialities of a new development are demonstrated, a decision to choose it as the basis for a course of action must be taken in the light of the investment in money, manpower, and skill that must be made to prepare it for public use. Its promised performance must be realized with safety, reliability, and ease of operation when it is placed in the hands of the using public. In the absence of other compelling circumstances, its cost must be within the means of potential users and must, of course, be favorable when compared with competing items designed to do the same job. All these attributes must be engineered into the commodity before it can be said to be *reduced to public practice.* Even then, the economic atmosphere must be such that the demand for the commodity will be large enough to justify the investment in it. The same applies to the introduction of a new service or technique; for example, a new drug or surgical operation must be tested under all conceivable conditions, the results evaluated carefully, and necessary precautions defined. The techniques and methods must be reduced to a routine that can be safely followed by any qualified practitioner. What I have said applies to automobiles, hair dryers, washing machines, and television sets, as well as to the practice of medicine, surgery, and agriculture, or even the operation machine tools.

An important factor in determining the reduction to public practice of new knowledge or developments is the "technological environment" prevailing at the time. By technological environment, I mean the products of former developments that have been reduced to public practice. This comprises the sum total of all the know-how, skills, techniques, tools, materials, and appurtenances that are items of commerce, readily available for producing a new device or perfecting a service, so that it can be presented to the using public in simple, reliable, and economical form. For example, if we wish to make a modern loud-speaker cabinet, the technological environment that affects us is the kind of wood we have available, the hand or power tools we have, the screws, the glue, the paint that we can obtain. If we had to cut down a tree, dress it with an adze, drill it with red-hot irons and chisels, and hold the pieces together with wooden pegs, the job would be much slower and more difficult than it is when we have plenty of plywood and a well-stocked modern basement fortified by a good neighborhood hardware store. Indeed, it might be so difficult that we should find it impossible.

The interactions between the new development and the technological environment give rise to a system of feedback loops as shown in Figures 1, 3, and 4. A new development enriches the technological environment not only by itself but also by the demands it makes for auxiliary materials, tools, techniques, and so forth. On the other hand, the resources of the prevailing technological environment have a great effect on the speed at

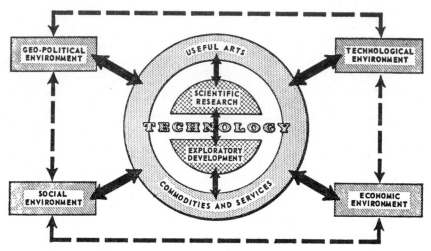

Figure 4.   Technology and its environment

which a development is reduced to public practice—a lack of such resources may even prevent the exploitation of a development. It was many years after Newcomen first demonstrated the feasibility of a steam engine that artisans were able to bore a cylinder more than eight inches in diameter, round enough to accommodate a tight-fitting piston. The introduction of the steam engine into public practice was delayed for a long time. Indeed, one can say without exaggeration that the interactions with the technological environment have played a dominant role in determining the direction of technological progress. The technological environment is only one of the external elements that influence the course of technology. Figure 4 shows diagrammatically other environments that influence the direction of technological growth.

The economic environment plays an important role in determining the reduction to public practice of a potential commodity or service. Indeed, in countries encouraging and practicing free enterprise, the operation of the economic feedback loops has played the most important part in determining the direction of technological progress except in time of emergency. The "reduction to public practice" of a new development has depended strongly on its ability to fulfill a need for which people not only *wanted* to pay but for which they *could* pay. The result has been intense efforts to reduce prices without apparent loss of performance, to stimulate wants by advertising and ability to pay by extension of credit. These factors have had a strong influence on the course technology has taken. On the other hand, a healthy technology has raised its economic environment to a point where standards of living are high and the ability to assimilate more technological developments is correspondingly great.

Recently, another feedback has become apparent or, rather, has spread its sphere of influence. I refer to the geopolitical or national prestige feedback. This has existed for centuries in the military sphere, where nations whose technology could support development and production of advanced weapons rose to positions of eminence. However, in nonmilitary fields the economic loop was the determining factor. The competition in space rendered acute by the successful launching of Sputnik I in October, 1957, has extended the national prestige value of technological developments beyond the purely military sphere, and the geopolitical feedback loop is becoming important in stimulating technological advances. The question of how long the political feedback will be a dominating factor in a free enterprise society is a very interesting one, but somewhat beyond the scope of this paper. It is my opinion, however, that its effects are more likely to grow than to diminish during the next decade.

It will be seen that the successful conduct of modern research and development activities requires that those responsible for planning and execution broaden their thinking to include the whole system shown diagrammatically in Figure 4. We cannot think of technology without considering its interactions with the environment of which the four main elements are shown in this diagram. The size and cost of R & D programs and the short time scale between new ideas and new commodities and services demand that the interactions with environment be taken into account even before the initiation of a substantial program.

Probably the most difficult set of problems in the management of research and development is not immediately apparent in an idealized diagram such as Figure 4. I refer to those arising from all the noise in the communication links. The signals in the lines to technology from its environments and back again are always buried deep in a background of noise coming from the caprices and conflicts that envelop human beings. The detection of the true meaning of these signals is an art that the research director must learn.

Through scientific research, experience is being accumulated and understood at a rapidly accelerating rate, thereby furnishing an ever-growing wealth of organized knowledge for new exploratory developments. Through these exploratory developments, natural limitations to freedom of action are being broken down at an even more rapid rate. The problem is shifting from one of removing limitations to freedom of action, to one of choosing wisely from the plethora of choices presented to us.

The technological environment is becoming increasingly richer; consequently, the technological problems associated with the reduction of a development to public practice are becoming easier. The time between the completion of a radically new development and its reduction to public practice is shortening to a few years. Over 100 years elapsed between the first demonstration of Newcomen's engine and the first commercial railroad train. It was 50 years after Faraday first demonstrated a generator of electrical energy that the first electrical generating station supplying power to the public was opened by Edison. It was only 20 or 25 years after Daimler's invention of a lightweight gasoline engine that the automobile became a reasonably reliable and widely used means of transportation. Within 18 years after Goddard's 200-pound-thrust liquid-fuel rocket performed successfully for the first time, the German V–2, with a thrust of 50,000 pounds, was being produced in large quantities. Less than three years after the Chicago atomic pile first went critical, large-scale atomic piles were operating to produce plutonium, and the first bomb had exploded. Within 10 years, practical atomic fuel power plants were operating; and within 15 years, atomic-powered submarines were in commission, and large-scale atomic plants were providing the public with electric power. Science, technology, and their environments now form an integrated system in which causes in any one part of the system lead rapidly to effects in another. The manager of research must now regard this whole system as his province. Even this is not enough, for technology must now be regarded as a game played in a world arena.

Migration of Technology

Although a technology may be developed and flourish in one particular country, it actually knows no national boundaries. There is a worldwide recognition that technology offers high standards of living and is actually necessary to support the tide of urbanization which is sweeping inexorably over all the world. It is an established fact that any nation which has the will to develop itself technologically can do so, and an increasing number of nations throughout the world are becoming convinced that their only hope for escaping poverty lies in modern technology.

We must, therefore, expect that the rate of growth of world-wide technology will by no means diminish in the future, and that we shall be faced with increasing competition in fields of technology and industry where we have held the leading position.

Indeed, two very old and fundamental limitations to the migration of technology are being removed, namely, the limitations imposed by supplies of energy and trained manpower. The effects of the removal of these limitations will be felt more and more strongly in the next decade. With the development of atomic energy and of solar energy, the ready availability of fossil fuels need no longer be the dominant factor in the location of industries. The rapid advances in the field of automatic control, the automatic operation and control of industrial processes, are removing the requirements for large numbers of highly skilled workers as a critical factor controlling the technological expansion of a society. Very shortly, a handful of highly trained technicians will be able to supply a large population with industrial products. Recognition of the ease with which technology migrates throughout the world and of the fact that many of our own developments may be more easily used advantageously by others than by ourselves, with no disruption of vested interests, raises matters of grave concern to those charged with the planning of technological efforts at all levels.

Our vulnerability to the threats of international competition demands more than merely holding a Maginot line of our present industrial might. It requires a dynamic and farsighted policy to explore new capabilities and objectives in which we can excel for a reasonable length of time. Such a policy calls for an increased national investment in scientific research and education, in exploratory development to find new freedoms of action and potential capabilities, and for wise policy planning on the part of the entrepreneurs in the industrial, political, and military world to see new objectives in new capabilities and reduce them to practice at the proper time.

Objectives and Functions of Management of Research and Development

On the basis of the above discussion of scientific research and exploratory development as components of technology and of the relation of technology to society as a whole, it is possible to deduce some of the fundamental functions associated with the management of R & D organizations, for these organizations themselves are systems with communications, feedbacks, coherence and incoherence of inputs and outputs, and constraints imposed upon them from external organizations in the economic, political, and social world. We have seen that the internal feedbacks in technology are responsible for its exponential growth; the same is true of R & D organizations. We have seen that the external feedbacks existing between technology and its environments are responsible for the *direction* of its growth; the same is true of an R & D organization. Thus an intimate knowledge of these feedbacks and their implications is an essential part of the equipment of the management of an R & D organization.

Expanding growth is a characteristic of technology and all its components. It seems highly probable that the capacity for expanding growth and change must also be an important characteristic of an R & D organization if it is to remain dynamic and successful. This growth, however, need not be reflected in terms of commonly accepted criteria such as number of staff, floor space, volume of sales, profits, etc.; indeed, these may not measure growth but merely inflation. Real growth is measured by the slope of the output curve; and significant outputs of lasting value are (1) hardware—exploratory developments that find a permanent place in the useful arts and in public practice, (2) patents, (3) publications in scientific literature, and (4) men of experience and judgment. These outputs are not arranged in order of importance. Their quality and quantity may or may not depend on the size of the organization, but they do depend on its vitality and on the functioning of important positive feedbacks associated with internal and external links.

In the first place, a network of communication channels to carry clear, certain, and timely information must be established. This requires a common basis of understanding throughout an organization, not only among groups trained in the same discipline but also among groups and individuals trained in diverse disciplines. An important function of management is to promote this common basis of understanding and a common set of values throughout the organization. Without it, the channels shown in Figure 1 are not effective. Vertical channels are essential for spreading a sound knowledge of the objectives throughout the organization and for insuring that new ideas generated at any level receive prompt attention at the top. Effective horizontal communications are the best assurance of avoiding the negative effects of duplication and enhancing the positive effects of exchanging knowledge and critical discussion. A positive feedback arises from the fact that a basis of mutual understanding promotes better internal communications, and better communications broaden the common basis of understanding.

A second feedback that repays attention is that existing between the outputs and the inputs of a group in an organization. This will be positive if the output of the group is of such a quality that it is coherent with the inputs. If, however, the quality and timeliness of the output of a group drop through causes such as sloppy thinking, shoddy workmanship, poor planning, or tardy communications, this feedback ceases and even becomes negative. In most research and development activities, timeliness and clarity of communications are extremely important; the delays in communicating results may well destroy the positive nature of the feedbacks.

It is generally agreed that one of the most baffling problems in the management of research and development is the establishment of criteria for evaluating the productivity of a group or organization. It is suggested that the feedbacks from output to input of the group constitute a focal spot for such an evaluation. If these are highly positive, the group cannot fail to be productive; if they are low or negative, remedial measures are imperative.

The *external* links involving interactions with the technological, economic, social, and political environments are the channels through which the raw material for policy making flows into an organization. They provide the basis for estimating the compatibility of the products of R & D with the potential and demands of the environment, and of assessing the probability that a development will not only be excellent technically but that it can be reduced to public practice with "profitable" results, using the term in its broadest sense. Because of lead times and "noise," these environmental interactions present particularly difficult problems to the management of R & D organizations, who not only must know the present state of environments but must be able to forecast future economic, social, and geopolitical demands years before they become acutely obvious.

These problems are difficult and important enough to warrant the full-time attention of a staff group specializing in a study of environmental interactions and operations analysis or other methods of assessing the relative potential values of different developments. Such staff groups are absolutely essential if the implications of the complex environmental interactions are to be reduced to understandable form.

Probably the chief function of the research manager is to insure that the organization over which he presides and all its members make the most effective use of time, as measured in years rather than hours. Time is the commodity in shortest supply and is a basis on which all compete on equal terms. The effective use of time not only requires skillful planning; it also requires a scrutiny of all activities in an organization to insure that they contribute positive feedbacks. If they do not, their usefulness is in question. For example, a reporting system should be such that each stage contributes a real feedback to the previous one, as well as a significant communication forward. This feedback should always clarify or add to the ideas of the person writing the report as well as those of the reader.

THE OPERATION AND MANAGEMENT OF RESEARCH AND DEVELOPMENT ORGANIZATIONS

. . . .

This section deals with a number of ideas which have been shown by practical experience to be important in the operation of a research and development laboratory. They also have direct application to the management of R & D programs, such as those of the Department of Defense, where the efforts of many people are needed to carry out a program directed toward a given objective. We shall attempt to suggest a number of general principles, using as the framework of our discussion the following topics: (1) the nucleus, (2) objectives, (3) delegation, (4) leadership, (5) enthusiasm, (6) disseminated competence, (7) accomplishments, (8) positive feedbacks, and (9) negative factors and feedbacks. These headings may seem somewhat unorthodox, but I hope to show in the next few paragraphs that they do comprise principles essential to the operation of a productive organization or the conduct of a co-operative program.

The Nucleus

The idea expressed under this heading is brought out very clearly by the following quotation taken from a speech by Lee DuBridge: "And whenever you find a highly successful group I suggest you seek the causes for its success not in the organization chart, not in the budget book, not by counting uniforms or rank, but by finding a man or a small group of men who have created the spirit of the place and who know how to preserve that spirit. . . ."[4]

It is this small group that I have termed the nucleus of an R & D organization. I must emphasize that an important characteristic of the men who compose this group is the fact that they are competent in science and/or engineering and that they have personally made creative contributions to the subject that they profess. In other words, this group must be composed of men who have learned at first hand the spirit and standards of scientific research, and know from direct experience the many detailed labors of mind and hand that underlie an advance in science or a contribution to the state of an art. In order that this nucleus may exert its influence to the full in the operation of the organization, it is important that its members occupy a place of recognized authority in the structure, not subservient to any administrative authority, for example. The nucleus must set the tone of the whole organization and be in a position where it can inspire imaginative thinking, skillful action, and high standards from the whole staff, and at the same time convey to everyone from top to bottom the confidence that these qualities will not only be appreciated but will also lead to advancement. In short, the "top management" of a productive R & D laboratory must be composed of productive R & D men.

Objectives

The only reason for the existence of a research and development laboratory is the attainment of certain well-chosen and useful technical objectives. The setting of these objectives is one of the prime functions of the nucleus. Once these objectives are set, the whole operation of the laboratory must be focused around achieving them with timeliness, imagination, and high standards of perfection. When it is remembered that the efforts of many people and expenditures mounting into millions of dollars may go into the attainment of these objectives, it will be seen

---

[4] "Science Serving the Nation," an address given by Lee DuBridge on the occasion of the opening of the Applied Physics Laboratory in Howard County, Maryland, October 16, 1954.

that the initial choice is a decision which requires the very best thought the organization can give. Such a decision must be based on a sound knowledge of all technical and operational factors involved, brought to as sharp a focus as possible by operations analysis, assessment, and technical synthesis. These are the staff activities that establish the direct and feedback links with the environment and formulate the implications of the information flowing in them. Not only must the objectives be well formulated; they must also be understood by all levels of the organization, or rather, all levels of the organization must understand where their work fits into the attainment of the organization's objectives. This is often dismissed under the heading of "a problem in communications," but I would suggest that it involves much broader considerations, which are introduced in the next three paragraphs.

Delegation

The problem of delegating responsibility and authority throughout a research and development laboratory is one of the greatest importance, and its successful solution fulfills a variety of desirable purposes. By delegation, I mean the assignment of *complete* responsibility for specific portions of the laboratory's program to individuals (supervisors) supported by groups of assistants, and the subsequent assignment of specific projects by these supervisors to their subordinates. It is essential that these individuals be made to feel that they are responsible for their portion of the program being carried out imaginatively, thoroughly, on time, and in consonance with the organization's over-all objectives. To do so, the individual must inform himself thoroughly as to what the objectives are and utilize to the fullest extent his scientific knowledge in planning work for his subordinates. Furthermore, adequate delegation of responsibility calls for delegation of corresponding authority to get the job done in an integrated way. Excessive detailed reviews from higher authority weaken an individual's initiative and feeling of responsibility for the quality of work done by him and his group. He must, however, understand that he is accountable for the end result and for making the most effective use of the time of his people and himself.

Leadership

Delegation of responsibility for identifiable projects to individuals inevitably results in their developing effective qualities of leadership with competence reinforced by confidence, and decisiveness tempered by responsibility. They must learn to be leaders or quit. Indeed, unless delegation does grow leaders, it is not really successful. Like an effective army or naval task force, an R & D laboratory depends on the initiative, competence, and leadership of many subordinate commanders to tackle the numerous problems encountered in a complex development. Most of these leaders must be trained, and the environment for such training is one in which the embryo leader, placed in a situation *within his capacity*, stands or falls by his own efforts.

Enthusiasm

A wholehearted policy of delegation of responsibility and authority brings in its wake enthusiasm and disseminated competence. Enthusiasm is the most precious ingredient of any research and development organization. When people feel enthusiastic about their objectives, their work, and the details of their daily problems, their productivity goes up almost without limit, and the quality and imaginativeness of their output far transcends that of a group of high-caliber but bored investigators. Enthusiasm for the job at hand has been the characteristic of individual scientists and inventive engineers from time immemorial. If this quality gets crushed by the wheels of a large organization, mediocrity soon sets in; indeed, the organization is soon moribund. It is emphasized that enthusiasm is a product of a generalship which not only calls for initiative from the subordinate leaders but also gives them a feeling of responsibility for their own mistakes and of satisfaction in the recognition of their own achievements. It is also a by-product of an important feedback loop generated by free and full exchange of information and critical discussion among investigators.

Disseminated Competence

It goes without saying that the strength of any organization lies in the strength of the individuals who compose it. Enthusiasm for the objectives and the work of the laboratory inspires the individuals to become more proficient in their jobs, to learn more, to fill gaps in their education, and to sharpen the skills they are called upon to use. Through administrative devices, opportunities may be gven to members of the staff of an organization to extend their education and to improve their skills; but without enthusiasm for what they are doing, individuals will not make the best of these opportunities. The proper delegation of responsibility and authority can lead to enthusiasm and disseminated competence throughout the whole staff. It brings with it a desire on the part of the individual members to ask and know what are the objectives of the laboratory, to seek out more clearly the part they have to play in achieving these objectives, and to make themselves better fitted to play this part. The growth of an organization does not necessarily call for expansion in size. Through enthusiasm, widespread competence, and industry, a small organization can often do more than a large one. Growth of the individuals and their output is the essential factor in the healthy growth of an organization.

Accomplishments

A research and development laboratory exists to find new knowledge, to extend understanding, and to provide mankind with new freedoms of action. It feeds on success, but the positive feedback of success is effective only if it permeates the consciousness of all individuals who compose the organization. Not only must they feel a corporate pride in the achievements of the laboratory as a whole, but each individual must feel that his part in these accomplishments is recognized by the management and the technical world. The creation of an atmosphere in which this recognition is effectively promulgated presents a problem of greater magnitude than is often realized. It involves the internal recognition of the contributions of each individual by the management and by his colleagues, as well as the reputations of the organization and its members in the larger world of technology. This recognition must, in the last analysis, be based on first-hand knowledge and sophisticated appreciation.

Positive Feedbacks

There is a direct link from one to the next of the subjects discussed under the foregoing seven headings. There are also many important positive feedback links. For instance, spectacular accomplishments feed back to reinforce enthusiasm and disseminated competence as well as the choice of new objectives. Spectacular accomplishments depend to a large extent on well-chosen initial objectives, but the established ability of an organization to accomplish outstanding results catalyzes wise and adventurous choices of new and fertile objectives. Positive feedback in this area alone brings about the growth of a successful organization. If, for any artificial reason, the growth of a successful organization is curtailed, this feedback will produce intolerable tensions. Another feedback of importance extends from disseminated competence back to the nucleus. Through processes of delegation, leadership development, inspiration of enthusiasm, and establishment of disseminated competence, there is a feedback which assures the existence and the strengthening of the nucleus itself.

Negative Factors

Like any healthy organism, a research and development organization must be able to eliminate the toxic products which invariably follow its life and growth. Under the heading of negative factors, I should like to outline some by-products of the operation of an organization which can easily reduce its effectiveness.

1. The first is definitely the cancerous (wild) growth of administrative practices. All administrative practices arise from the necessity of people working together in an organization. Their principal purpose is to facilitate the operation of the organization in such a way that its objectives are attained effectively and expeditiously in spite of the frailties of its human components. However, when these practices begin to absorb energies that should be devoted toward attaining the objectives of the organization, the time has come for drastic pruning or elimination. Unless special attention

is paid to this problem, superfluous practices increase almost imperceptibly, but with deadening results.

2. A second negative factor arises from outworn technical practices and structures. A particular structure and set of practices may serve excellently for the achievement of one technical objective and be quite unsuited to another. Unless the organization can change its technical practices and habits and is alert to the necessity for such changes, this negative factor will slow up its output and diminish its enthusiasm. It is merely a matter of new wine and old bottles, but emphasizes the necessity of flexibility and capacity for change in a technical organization.

3. A third negative factor arises from the indiscriminate application of so-called "accepted management doctrine" to research and development organizations. It is my opinion that the same good management principles may be applied to any organization, R & D being no exception, if proper judgment is used. However, it is not at all clear that many accepted management dogmas really work in old-line organizations or, indeed, in any organization. In fact, management is an art which is not yet well understood and must therefore be regarded as a matter for investigation, the agreement between theory and practice being subjected to constant and close scrutiny. In an R & D laboratory the technical work must be carried on in an atmosphere where criticism is free and untrammeled, where objective criteria for the validity of facts or theories prevail, and where the loop involving experimental theory and experimental practice must be closed before one can be satisfied that the results are sound. It is impossible to exclude the management theory and practice of such an organization from such scrutiny, and hence the inconsistencies in accepted management doctrines are likely to become more obvious in an R & D organization than in one that is devoted solely to production of a standard item of commerce. Insistence of the acceptance of management dogmas without regard for their consistency or common sense can undermine seriously the confidence of the staff in the management.

4. It is a common observation that many newly established laboratories start out with all the positive qualities I have mentioned, that the quality and quantity of their outputs are initially of the highest but, after the lapse of years, drop down to routine, mediocre, or worse. It is also held in many circles that a research institution especially needs a continuous throughput of investigators, usually graduate students, to preserve its freshness and creativity. The examples of successful universities are cited as confirmation of this view, and I think that it is sound where applicable. However, a research and development laboratory in industry or government can effect a continuous renewal of its technical staff only to a very limited extent. Opportunities for a career and advancement with stability of employment are essential to its well-being. A complete turnover of the associate staff every few years is out of the question and perhaps not essential to its vitality.

It seems to me that many laboratories suffer from "fatigue of objectives," which reflects on the staff and its output. Instead of relying on change of staff for vitality, an R & D organization can achieve freshness by modifying its objectives, terminating some even when they are still far removed from the stage of diminishing returns. Then the staff may take up the challenge of new problems that move them into new regions of science and engineering.

The problems posed by fatigue of objectives and its avoidance are complicated and difficult to solve, but this negative factor is probably the most far-reaching of all that tend to slow up the productivity of any R & D organization—including universities and especially government laboratories. The symptoms are easily recognizable. Long devotion to a specialized field induces in the staff an excessive concern over the protection of their intellectual investment. An attitude of intense conservatism is built up, which manifests itself in a tendency to show why new ideas will not work or to stifle enthusiasm with the remark that such and such an idea was tried years ago without success. Individuals lose their self-confidence to embark on new programs. Excessive attention is paid to details, and there is a tendency to drift into regions of low return.

DIVERSITY OF TALENTS[5]

I have advocated the establishment of a common basis of understanding in teams of scientists and engineers; I must also emphasize the necessity for diversity of talents, training, and attributes of mind in those working co-operatively toward a complex technical objective. I should like to say a word or two about the significance of mental attributes. If we take a cross section of productive research workers, perhaps by studying the authors of articles in the better journals, we find represented at least six kinds of mind: (1) the Promethean or creative, (2) the critical and analytical, (3) the cumulative and inductive, (4) the cumulative and descriptive, (5) the meticulous, and (6) the routine industrious. It is evident that more than one of these attributes is found in any given individual, although one will generally predominate.

1. The creative mind tries to inject something new into anything it does; it may provide the flash of genius that shows up a new continent of knowledge or gives rise to a new all-embracing theory: it may throw new light on old tough problems; it may just invent an easier and better way of doing an old job. It is a mind that transmutes ideas from one field of experience to another.
2. The critical and analytical mind takes nothing for granted but examines closely all statements presented to it, probing deeply into their consequences for consistency and rigor. It is the questioning mind so needed for

[5] The following paragraphs are taken from an article by the author in *Armed Forces Chemical Journal*, Vol. VII (1953), p. 26.

clarification of complex situations and for establishing the validity of experience.

3. The cumulative-inductive mind ranges in the literature and in experiment, collecting facts and attempting to put them in order. It is a type of mind which has contributed largely to physical chemistry.

4. The cumulative and descriptive mind is that of the trained and keen observer who remembers what he sees and describes it clearly for others to read. It is the mind which has laid the foundations of the complex sciences of astronomy, geology, and natural history. It is always evident on the frontiers of knowledge and is the stock in trade of the effective teacher.

5. The meticulous mind is concerned about the correctness of all details in observation, procedure, and processes. It is concerned with the search for accuracy and precision.

6. Finally, we have the routine industrious mind that follows through relentlessly, especially where many experiments are needed to establish one fact and where repetitive processes are of the essence.

History has shown that all these mental attributes have important roles to play in the sound and steady growth of all branches of science and engineering, and we should be guilty of intellectual snobbery if we discounted any one of them. The meticulous worker who spends years establishing the real facts in a complex phenomenon or perfecting a technique, or the routine industrious man who explores an area thoroughly by a long series of measurements, provides means and materials for the inductive thinker and the creative artist, materials they might not be able to get for themselves. The critical mind keeps thought and observation on the track, saving costly detours along false trails, paying particular attention to the coherence of the inputs and outputs. Each has his place, and the secret of the efficient use of manpower either on a laboratory scale or on a nationwide basis lies in assigning to each mind a job suited to its attributes and carrying with full recognition of contributions to a worth-while objective.

I suggest that problems in the distribution and employment of manpower may be approached more realistically on the basis of the mental attributes of scientists and engineers (similar to those I have enumerated), rather than on the basis of their professional training alone. Examples of men successfully transferring their activities from one discipline to another are common, but I believe that if creative minds are set to work on routine problems, or if routine industrious minds are given problems that depend on creative ability even in the field of their own training, frustration of men, mediocrity of product, and a general waste of time are the results.

QUESTIONS

1. Re-examine the definitions you developed for the Novick paper.
2. What is "exploratory development"?

3. Examine Exhibit 1 and, by a dotted line, circumscribe the areas of activities that should be assigned to a corporate R & D department. Now, modify the enclosure to include marketing and production responsibilities. What problems and procedures are suggested?

4. Describe the process of scientific research.

5. What is involved in "reduction to public practice"?

6. Review your criteria for the selection of a director of research of a corporate laboratory.

7. What can top management do to minimize the negative factors identified by Dr. Gibson?

8. Discuss the six types of mental attributes with regard to their usefulness in (a) research and (b) development work in industry.

9. How would you identify the above attributes in individuals being interviewed for research and development jobs?

Synthesis of Concepts in the Design Method

Unfortunately, the lines of communication between information-producing researchers and designers remain nebulous. The justifiable complaint is often heard that the researcher and the designer do not care to, or are not able to, speak the same language. To bridge this gap, the designer must take the initiative and approach the researcher, because it is the designer who is directly responsible for utilizing advanced technology.

If the designer is to be in a position to take this initiative and to become aware of broad ranges of capabilities, many companies realize that they must support extensive research laboratories and programs. Although the designer must avail himself of literature sources, the sharpest impact on his vision comes from his exchanges with research people. Industrial researchers are in a position to develop new art which is most pertinent to the company's field of interest. They are also able to keep up with developments contributed by other research workers. The need for this flow of information has been recognized by many of the most progress-oriented companies who have located their research laboratories and advanced design departments in communities of like organizations.

It must be recognized that state of the art, wherever generated or however communicated, has the singular ultimate purpose of supporting the design function. The extent to which the designer taps into this resource will largely determine the value of his design concepts.

FROM: R. J. McCrory, W. H. Wilkinson, and D. W. Frink, "Synthesis of Concepts in the Design Method," Battelle Memorial Institute. Presented before the Design Engineering Conference of the American Society of Mechanical Engineers, May, 1963.

THE DESIGN METHOD—A SCIENTIFIC APPROACH TO VALID DESIGN[1]

By R. J. McCrory

Mechanical Engineering Department, Battelle Memorial Institute

DESIGN IS regarded as the process of selectively applying the total spectrum of science and technology to the attainment of an end result which serves a valuable purpose. It is the segment of engineering which devises and develops new things, in contrast to other segments which emphasize the solving of problems or the generation of engineering information. The responsibility of the design engineer is to use the maximum powers of creativity, judgment, technical perception, economic awareness, and analytical logic to devise uniquely useful systems, devices, and processes. His function is usually not to originate the basic scientific building blocks, but rather to utilize them so that the result is a useful creation.

The designer could be considered somewhat similar to the artist. The artist does not create new colors and forms. He combines colors and forms into new creations; and the results are, at times, masterpieces.

But imposed upon technological design is a crucial requirement which has no counterpart in classic art. Design must adhere to a plan which has objectives involving cost, performance, effort for attainment, probability of success, and even aesthetics. The fact that design must traverse a closely evaluated path, starting from a well-considered if not urgent need statement to a functioning achievement, requires that it follow a methodology. By methodology is not meant the tricks of the trade such as drafting competence, or analytical ability, or for that matter a flair for "brainstorming." Methodology in design is considered rather as being the framework for the design process within which a sequence of action steps can be based and from which check points to evaluate progress can be established.

The design process being guided by and evaluated in terms of a method is comparable to the scientific community's use of the "scientific method." Although many scientists discount the conscious use of the scientific method, reflection upon scientific progress shows that it is

---

[1] Presented before the Design Engineering Conference of the American Society of Mechanical Engineers, May, 1963. Reproduced in condensed form by permission of the author and the ASME.

applied and that scientific "laws" have been accepted or rejected very much in accordance with the criteria demanded by the scientific method.

REVIEW OF SCIENTIFIC METHOD[2]

•   •   •   •   •   •   •

This idealized version of the scientific method is usually not categorically and sequentially used by scientists. There are many simultaneous activities going on which involve doubling back to check and revise and jumping ahead in anticipation of results in order to originate new hypotheses. Nevertheless, the scientific method is so inherent in guiding and evaluating scientific progress that it relentlessly imposes itself, regardless of short-term abandonment.

STRUCTURE OF THE DESIGN METHOD

The design process follows a methodology similar to that of the scientific method, although the design method has not been so carefully defined nor has it been historically so well established. Nevertheless, the design method is as inherent to the design process as the scientific method

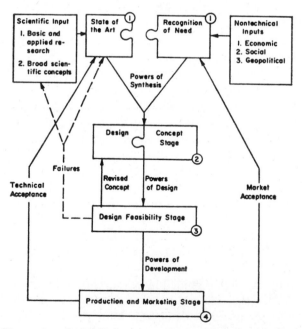

Figure 1.   Graphical representation of design method

_____

[2] Refer to R. E. Gibson, "A Systems Approach to Research Management," p. 34, which is approximately similar to, but more detailed than, the omitted description of the scientific method.

is to scientific exploration. Designers will do well to recognize its structure so that the design method can be used consciously to clarify some of the costly "mysteries" of design.

The design method, graphically described in Figure 1, parallels the scientific method. Each is a closed loop, with experiences gained during the execution and completion of the process providing the basis for subsequent applications of the method. Both the scientific method and the design method have stages, defined plateaus which can be used to identify when a recognizable degree of attainment has been reached. The comparable stages of the two methods are given in Table 1.

Table 1

Stage	Scientific Method	Design Method
1	Existing knowledge	State of the art/recognition of need
2	Hypothesis	Design concept
3	Confirmation	Design feasibility
4	Proof	Production and marketing
1	Existing knowledge	State of the art/recognition of need

To progress from one stage to the next, each method requires that certain intellectual powers be brought to bear. For the two methods, Table 2 gives the comparable steps that are involved.

Table 2

Steps between Stages	Scientific Method	Design Method
1–2	Powers of reflective observation	Powers of synthesis
2–3	Powers of logic	Powers of design
3–4	Powers of experiment	Powers of development
4–1	Powers of communication	Powers of acceptance

The design method is compounded by multiple interconnecting steps and auxiliary stages. But these are ancillary to the basic methodology and can vary, depending upon individual situations.

State of the Art and Recognition of Need

The starting point of the design method is more comprehensive than that of the scientific method. Unlike fundamental scientific research, design is motivated by need rather than by curiosity. Therefore, in addition to requiring knowledge of the state of the technical art, the design method requires recognition of a need which warrants an investment of effort and funds.

Recognition of need can be considered the marketing input to the design method. In the case of industry, this input involves the analysis of market needs in the light of corporate objectives. Military and space programs are planned to meet needs identified through broad studies of our over-all security posture and anticipation of future move-countermove situations.

But whether government or industrial needs are being considered, the designer must realize that much of the input required to define the need is not technical, but rather socio-economic-geopolitical. Therefore the designer must appreciate those key nontechnical factors which are significant in defining whether the results of his design work will fulfill a basic social, economic, or security need. With this appreciation, the designer is better qualified to extrapolate current requirements and creatively anticipate tomorrow's needs.

Given a need-oriented assignment, the designer can encounter a series point of vulnerability; he must realize that the purpose of the design effort is to produce something which is truly useful. The purpose is not, as he might prefer, to provide a result which is technically self-gratifying and elegant, but from which the pay-off can only be a technical paper to his peers. Because designers are required to satisfy profit or security motives, the definition of need is critical to the design method, and each suceeding stage must be planned and judged on the basis of the need.

Along with the recognition and definition of the need, the design method requires an appraisal of the pertinent state of the art. State of the art includes materials capabilities, phenomena understanding, and previous design experience. As important as previous experience is, if designers are unduly dependent upon experience, design progress can be reduced to a series of small improvements. The design method requires that the designer tap into the total spectrum of technology with the objective of obtaining the greatest design advance consistent with the state of the art, wherever the art may exist. Experience which exists in technical or product fields foreign to that of the designer can often suggest the most advantageous design approaches.

But perhaps even more significant to design advances is the input which can be obtained from basic and applied research. As materials are devised and phenomena quantified, new raw inputs to the design method are made available. New scientific concepts such as nuclear heat sources and semiconductors open up vast areas for design exploitation. The design method therefore necessitates keeping open a direct link between the resources of scientific research and the state of the art available to the designer. The degree to which the designer can intercept the latest scientific information can determine the extent to which he can make significant design advances.

The Design Concept

A design concept is created when, through the designer's powers of synthesis, a recognized need and technical capability as represented by the state of the art are matched. When the designer can arrange technical art into useful combinations which form a system satisfying a need, he has a design concept.

Matching can originate from either the need or the art. Given a defined need, the designer can search the art for the inputs which can be synthesized to satisfy the need. Conversely, there are many concepts which are originated largely on the basis of known art, and the concept stage is attained by finding a need which can be fulfilled. The latter approach to design conception is the principal justification for the massive engineering research being conducted in energy conversion, materials, and other generic fields of technology.

If an idea does not satisfy a need, a design concept as defined by the design method does not exist, regardless of how clever or novel the idea might be. Nor does a concept exist when a design which would satisfy a need requires a capability beyond the state of the art. The principal advantage to be derived is a feedback to the research laboratories.

The designer fulfills his synthesis function by an orderly procedure.[3] He first analyzes the need in considerable depth, perhaps allowing the need analysis to suggest a design concept. He then spatially visualizes systems which are advantageous combinations. Or he might utilize a further technique which is not so broadly recognized. This is to explore analytically the area of design interest, manipulating generalized mathematical expressions with the hope that unique design approaches will be derived which would not be apparent from only spatial analysis.

Attainment of the design concept stage of the design method means that a design approach has been derived having the potential of satisfying the need as well as the potential of being attained without violating the state of the art. Many ideas may be rejected by the designer before he arrives at one which qualifies as a design concept. On the other hand, he may finally have available more than one design concept showing attractive potential. At the design concept stage, the concept need not be described completely. Rather, it may be expressed in terms of functional requirements or "black boxes." The key criterion is that, in the judgment of the designer, the concept has sufficient potential to justify further effort in designing the individual elements of the system.

Design Feasibility

The design concept stage having been attained, the next step of the design method is to establish design feasibility. Feasibility is established by determining whether all of the necessary functions of the system can be worked out and whether, when the design is in detail form, it still is attractive in terms of the need and the probability of successful attainment. To go from the design concept stage to the feasibility stage of the design

---

[3] R. J. McCrory, W. H. Wilkinson, and D. W. Frink, "Synthesis of Concepts in the Design Method," a paper presented at the ASME Design Engineering Conference, New York, May, 1963.

method means to convert the design, as described in its functional form, to specific elements. The steps[4] which may be used in this conversion process include:

1. Definition of the concept in terms of its optimum combination of functions.
2. Expression of detail design requirements in terms of functional and/or performance specifications.
3. Design of specific elements to meet specifications (to be done in accordance with design method, using specifications as need statement).
4. Trade-off analysis comparing design alternatives and, if required, revision of specifications.
5. Critical experimentation to test specific questionable aspects of the design concept.
6. Operation of experimental prototype to confirm adequate funtioning of total system or subsystems.

Frequently, the design concept fails to reach the stage of feasibility because the technical problems cannot be solved successfully or because the concept does not fulfill its apparent potential of being attractive in terms of the need. The probability of this happening should be reduced if designers knowledgeably go through the prior steps of the design method. When failure does occur, it is necessary to return to the concept stage and revise the concept in the light of the intervening experience. However, if failure is complete, the most that can be salvaged is the failure experience which can be interjected into the state of the art as a guide to subsequent design programs.

PRODUCTION AND MARKETING

When the designer is convinced that a feasible design is in hand, he is ready to move on to the next stage in the design method. This is the attainment of a design which can be produced successfully and marketed. The process by which a feasible design is converted into a production design is broadly termed development. In actual practice, development tasks are extremely demanding in terms of engineering skills and usually involve the major expenditure of funds and time in the entire design process.

Within the framework of the design method, the development step is still very much a design function.[5] The designer remains responsible for perfecting the design in terms of performance, reliability, and cost. Although specialists in value analysis, tooling, field testing, and marketing may more prominently enter the picture, they cannot recover success if

---

[4] H. A. Cress and E. S. Cheaney, "Determining Design Feasibility," a paper presented at the ASME Design Engineering Conference, New York, May, 1963.

[5] R. J. McCrory, "The Science of Design," a paper presented at the Second Conference on Engineering Design Education, Los Angeles, September, 1962.

the requirements of the earlier stages of the design method were not validly satisfied. Presuming skillful engineering and marketing, the development steps, although costly, are not highly risky. The mistakes which lead to disastrous failures are more likely to occur at the stages when decisions regarding need, concept selection, and feasibility are made.

The loop of the design method closes when the design is judged a technical and marketing success. This experience in market acceptance extends the understanding of need and invariably leads to the identification of new areas of need. The technical successes and failures expand and temper the state of technical art and are inserted into other design programs.

VARIANCES TO THE IDEALIZED DESIGN METHOD

The design method is presented in the foregoing as an idealized representation of the design process. If individual design programs were discrete entities, the design method as described here in skeletal form would be accurate. In actual fact, design programs seem to blend into one another to the extent that a complete progression of the design method is difficult to recognize. As actually practiced, design progress involves a pattern of superimposed programs, each subject to the requirements of the design method. This pattern may include:

1. Design programs in which the outcome is the selection of a means of approaching a broad national or industry need. This type of program is being applied to the transportation problems of the East Coast Megalopolis. The application of the design method here will involve over-all systems concepts whose feasibility will be established by computer analysis rather than by operation of prototype hardware. The outcome will be the need statements for other design programs.
2. Numerous design programs which originate from the same need recognition. Some will be parallel programs conducted by different design groups searching for the same end result. Theoretically, application of the design method should result in the same outcome for each program. But the personalities and backgrounds of the individual design groups are so important to the functioning of the design method that results which are different in both approach and quality are inevitable.
3. New programs which are initiated before an original design program is completed which have as their objectives the improvement upon the results of the first program. The demands of progress often cannot wait for the sequential completions of related design programs.
4. Auxiliary programs on subsystems and components which are part of an original over-all program. The concept having most potential may require an element which is identified as beyond the state of the design art. But the attractiveness of the concept warrants the risk of initiating a separate design program to expand the state of the art. While establishing feasibility, the designing of individual functional members becomes a number of subprograms calling for use of the design method.

.   .   .   .

APPLICABILITY OF DESIGN METHOD

The design method as outlined is not to be considered as restricted to large programs having comprehensive objectives. It has been and is being used on programs having objectives as varied as hair dryers, hydraulic systems, large radio antennas, and advanced nuclear reactor systems.

Varying degrees of management may be required, depending upon the nature of the individual programs. For vast systems programs the design method can be administered through formalized procedures. For smaller programs the designer himself may monitor the execution of the program to conform to the requirements of the design method. Here the attitude and comprehension of the individual designer are critical to the adoption of the design method.

Whether the design method is applied to a design program which is large or small, its basic purpose is the same. The design method is to serve as a disciplining influence in providing a framework upon which design progress can be planned and design pertinence evaluated. In order to proceed in accordance with the design method, the following conditions must be satisfied sequentially:

1. There must be a well-understood starting point for the design in terms of:
    a) A thorough awareness of the supporting technology.
    b) A clear definition of the objective. These considerations are so important that considerable technical and marketing research can be justified to attain the required levels of understanding.
2. The concept must be the result of a searching synthesis based upon (1). Many potential concepts should be obtained and scanned for preliminary determination of general feasibility and attractiveness. The design method requires searching for the best obtainable concept rather than accepting the first evolved, and it should be a restraint against premature selection.
3. Feasibility must be established in terms of whether:
    a) The concept retains its pertinence to the need.
    b) All facets of the concept have been considered and are acceptable.
    c) The remaining steps are realistically gauged.

The feasibility stage must be approached coldly to avoid overoptimism in presuming feasibility and to insure realistic estimating of the effort required to reach the next stage of production and marketing success.

In addition to being a controlling influence upon the design process, the design method also serves as a communications medium. Management often does not understand the steps through which a design program must pass between its inception and its completion. Consequently, miscalculations can result which cause either the continued support of unpromising programs or the premature cancellation of some which are promising. A typical example of misunderstanding is the false assumption that a prototype which only shows feasibility is a production model. The design method can provide a "universal language" understandable to both the designer and his management. Identification of program status as being at or between stages of the design method can provide the communications link to permit management to conduct surveillance and planning realistically, with fewer problems of semantics.

Conclusion

The purpose of this discussion is to identify and describe a methodology which should be inherent in all design programs but which is seldom recognized and consciously utilized. The failures resulting from attempts to avoid or short-cut the stages of the design process can be reduced if the controls and guidelines of the design method are knowingly used. In practice, the design process as exemplified by the design method is often badly distorted, especially in the critical early stages. Need is seldom adequately defined, and the socioeconomic factors are often miscalculated. The route by which the designer may tap the state of the technical art is long and hazardous, and eagerness to accept and invest heavily in initial ideas sometimes causes designers to overlook the importance of the concept synthesis steps. In many programs the feasibility stage is by-passed.

The idealized design method presented here should be adapted to the peculiar requirements of each design task. Then it should be used as the disciplining influence and communicating tool which is needed to make design a more profitable and satisfying endeavor.

QUESTIONS

1. Compare Gibson's "systems approach" in research to McCrory's "design method."
2. At what points in the design method (if any) should top management supply inputs? Controls?
3. What should be the inputs of marketing to the design method? Of production? Who should take the initiative and responsibility for supplying these inputs?
4. Analyze a current or historical case study in research and development by graphical reconstruction of Gibson's and McCrory's schematic charts. Have phases of these systems been slighted or overlabored in the instance you have chosen? How could the end goal have been achieved more effectively?
   Suggestions: In addition to your own field studies in current industry projects, the bibliography in this book lists some useful sources.

What Made the Manhattan Project Successful?

Looking back, I think I can see five main factors that made the Manhattan Project a successful operation:

First, we had a clearly defined, unmistakable, specific objective. Although at first there was considerable doubt about what it was. Consequently the people in responsible positions were able to tailor their every action to its accomplishment.

Second, each part of the project had a specific task. These tasks were carefully allocated and supervised so that the sum of their parts would result in the accomplishment of our over-all mission. This system of compartmentalization had two principal advantages. The most obvious of these was that it simplified the maintenance of security. But over and above that, it required every member of the project to attend strictly to his own business. The result was an operation whose efficiency was without precedent.

Third, there was positive, clear-cut, unquestioned direction of the project at all levels. Authority was invariably delegated with responsibility, and this delegation was absolute and without reservation. Only in this way could the many apparently autonomous organizations working on the many apparently independent tasks be pulled together to achieve our final objective.

Fourth, the project made a maximum use of already existing agencies, facilities and services—governmental, industrial and academic. Since our objective was finite, we did not design our organization to operate in perpetuity. Consequently, our people were able to devote themselves exclusively to the task at hand, and had no reason to engage in independent empire-building.

Fifth, and finally, we had the full backing of our government, combined with the nearly infinite potential of American science, engineering and industry, and an almost unlimited supply of people endowed with ingenuity and determination.

Leslie R. Groves, Lt. Gen.

U.S. Army, Retired

from: *Now It Can Be Told—The Story of the Manhattan Project* (New York: Harper & Bros., 1962).

THE PROCESS OF TECHNOLOGICAL INNOVATION:
THE LAUNCHING OF A NEW SCIENTIFIC INDUSTRY[1]

By W. Rupert Maclaurin[2]

ECONOMISTS OWE a major debt to Professor Schumpeter for understanding intuitively the critical significance of innovations in economic development. Yet, until quite recently, we have neglected to explore his provocative suggestions.[3] There are encouraging signs that this is changing. For example, Dr. Arthur Cole at Harvard has dedicated himself to unravel the role of the entrepreneur in economic history. Under his stimulus, there is now a considerable group of people actively interested in entrepreneurship.

I want to attempt here to add to the small but growing body of published material on innovation and entrepreneurship by discussing the process of innovation in the launching of a modern industry—radio.[4]

The economist, making empirical studies of industrial change, is faced at the outset with the difficult problem of whether to confine his analysis

---

[1] Reproduced by permission of the American Economic Association from *American Economic Review*, March, 1950.

This article was originally presented as a paper before the Research Center in Entrepreneurial History at Harvard under Dr. Arthur Cole and Professor Joseph Schumpeter. Some of the historical material has since been published in a book entitled *Invention and Innovation in the Radio Industry* (New York: Macmillan Co., 1949), designed for radio engineers and the radio trade, and reproduced here by permission.

As Professor Schumpeter has recently died, I should like to pay tribute to the encouragement he gave to professional workers in very diverse fields. In my own case, since my days as a student at the Harvard Business School, he consistently pressed me to push forward with my investigations of the process of innovation. And in the case of this paper, he strongly urged me to make it available to economists generally. It was his hope, and mine, that it would serve to stimulate the exploration of an area he believed of critical significance.

[2] The author was Professor of Economics at Massachusetts Institute of Technology.

[3] See, in particular, *The Theory of Economic Development* (Cambridge: Harvard University Press, 1934); *Business Cycles* (New York: McGraw-Hill Book Co., Inc., 1939); and *Capitalism, Socialism and Democracy* (New York: Harper & Bros., 1942). An exception to this lack of exploration was Professor Taussig's *Inventors and Money Makers* (New York: Macmillan Co., 1915), and Taussig and Joslyn's *American Business Leaders* (New York: Macmillan Co., 1932).

[4] This and companion studies of the glass, lighting, and paper industries were made possible by a grant from the Rockefeller Foundation to explore "the economics of technological change."

to measurable data. There is much that the statistician can do to explain the characteristics of economic development in modern industry. But there are many important questions that he cannot tackle at all. I have gained courage from my distinguished mathematics colleague, Dr. Norbert Wiener, who feels strongly that social scientists should ask the questions they think of most significance—not be too much worried about measurement, and *do the best they can* with the information available.

The particular study reported here is an historical account of how the process of innovation took place when the radio industry was launched. Radio is an industry in which scientists and engineers have forced the pace of technological innovation. As a consequence, there have been radical shifts in the product and its applications about every ten years since 1900.[5] I believe that such industries will increasingly become the norm and that we can expect existing products to be rendered obsolete almost continuously for many years to come. There is growing evidence that we are now living in a second industrial revolution, in which calculations based on assumptions of economic stability will be almost valueless.

Much of the traditional apparatus of economic analysis has been concerned with entrepreneurial decisions on costs and prices of existing products. Economists have apparently not yet come to recognize the full impact of science and engineering in making such decisions of secondary significance in the life of a firm. I do not mean that the cost-price problems of established products are not important. But in situations where rapid advances in technology are taking place, the life of the firm is often dependent on concentrating its most creative talents on the successful introduction of *new products*. Insufficient attention has been directed to the critical importance of the innovating entrepreneur and the factors which influence his major decisions. We have been too much concerned with local tactics and not enough with over-all strategy.

The major problem, in fact, for any company which wishes to prosper where scientific progress dictates the pace of change is to *be in* on the new developments or to *get in* at the proper time. For industries where products or processes are likely to be rendered obsolete in ten years or even less, a useful theory of economic development will have to be based on the dynamics of technological advance.

In analyzing an industry, therefore, I think it important to ask the following questions: (1) Are major advances occurring in the sciences underlying the industry? (2) Is engineering art in close touch with and contributing to these advances? (3) Is the economic organization of the industry conducive to innovation? (4) Is capital freely available for radical new developments? (5) Do the entrepreneurs possess the requisite skills for successful innovation?

---

[5] Involving successively ship-to-shore service, wireless telephony, short-wave communications, entertainment broadcasting, portable radios, FM, and television.

I should like to try out these questions on the radio industry, and to center the analysis on the period from 1890 to 1912, when commercial wireless first came into being and had its early growth.

THE UNDERLYING SCIENCES AND THE BIRTH OF THE RADIO INDUSTRY

The radio industry was a direct outgrowth of a revolution in the science of physics and its applications to the study of electricity. In the first half of the nineteenth century a succession of brilliant physicists in various countries opened up a whole new conception of the nature of electricity, which had been puzzling man for centuries.

Radio communication was only one small aspect of this total field, but it sprang directly from the work of the scientists. Progress with "the wireless" was at first exceedingly slow, for two main reasons. First, there were other more important and more obvious aspects of electricity to be examined, leading to such applications as the dynamo, the electric motor, the electric lamp, the telegraph, and the telephone. Secondly, there were comparatively few individuals devoted to the advancement of engineering art. New ideas and suggestions frequently lay unexplored for several decades. Thus, it was fifty years after the original suggestion that radio waves might exist before the first wireless company was launched.

In 1846, Michael Faraday, at the Royal Institution in London, delivered a lecture called "Thoughts on Ray Vibrations," in which he suggested somewhat vaguely that electromagnetic waves might be propagated in space. In 1864, James Clerk Maxwell, a brilliant mathematical physicist at King's College, London, building on such hypotheses and the laws of Ampère, published his famous *Dynamical Theory of the Electro-Magnetic Field*.

Maxwell was a theoretical physicist and not an experimentalist. Twenty-two years after his formulation of the theory of electromagnetic induction, and forty years after Faraday's original suggestion that ether waves existed, Professor Heinrich Hertz in Germany proved their existence by experiment.[6]

Hertz designed a spark-gap oscillator which would generate wireless waves, a metallic mirror for reflecting them, and a loop type of antenna for detection. By such means, he was able to send and receive signals from one end of his laboratory to the other without an interconnecting wire.

Following Hertz, scientists in various countries turned their attention to wireless communication. None of these early pioneers were consciously thinking about commercial developments. Rather, they were exploring a

---

[6] Hertz was acquainted with the work of Faraday and Maxwell, but he was also influenced by the parallel continental explorations in electricity of Ampère, Gauss, Weber, von Helmholtz, and others.

new phenomenon of nature because it was not yet fully understood.

The other key scientific discovery on which modern radio is based is the thermionic vacuum tube. Thermionic emission of electrons was explored originally as a separate problem of physics, with no thought of its ultimate value for the detection of electromagnetic waves. This research came to a climax with the work at the University of Cambridge of J. J. Thomson, and especially of his pupil, O. W. Richardson, who finally worked out the theory of thermionic emission of electrons from hot filaments. It was on top of this scientific work that De Forest introduced his three-electrode vacuum tube as a wireless detector.

Without the pioneer work of the university physicist, the practical development of radio communications would have been impossible. Marconi himself did not have the background in experimental physics which would have led him to make the discoveries of Hertz. His main scientific contribution was in improving the laboratory-type apparatus of his predecessors and making it perform much more consistently.

THE RELATIONSHIP BETWEEN FUNDAMENTAL SCIENCE AND ENGINEERING ART

The growth of the engineering profession has made a radical difference in the speed with which new scientific discoveries are translated into commercial practice. The principal emphasis during the nineteenth century, both in this country and abroad, was in training a limited group of *scientists* rather than a large number of professional *engineers*. Germany was an exception to this rule and was the first country to pioneer in engineering education. The American engineering school began to expand rapidly after the Civil War; but until the twentieth century, our schools were inadequately financed and considerably less scientific than their German counterparts.

The principal contributors to electrical invention in the United States in the 1870's and 1880's were men like Thomas A. Edison and Alexander Graham Bell, who were largely self-taught. By 1900, however, electrical engineering departments had been established in a considerable number of universities, and streams of young men were beginning to flow into industry who combined some basic training in science with an intense interest in practical applications. This meant that several of the leading electrical concerns were acquiring a sufficient supply of trained engineers to be capable of shortening the time lag between the scientific discovery of wireless and its commercial applications.

THE ORGANIZATION OF THE ELECTRICAL INDUSTRIES IN 1900 AND THEIR CONTRIBUTIONS TO WIRELESS

By the 1890's, rapid scientific progress was being made toward understanding the propagation and detection of electromagnetic waves. Referring to this work, the British physicist William Crookes wrote in 1892:

> Here is unfolded to us a new and astonishing world, one which is hard to conceive should contain no possibilities of transmitting and receiving intelligence.
>
> Rays of light will not pierce through a wall, nor as we know only too well, through a London fog. But the electrical vibrations of a yard or more in wavelength . . . will easily pierce such mediums, which to them will be transparent. Here, then, is revealed the bewildering possibility of telegraphy without wires, posts, cables or any of our present costly appliances.
>
> This is no mere dream of a visionary philosopher. All the requisites needed to bring it within grasp of daily life are well within the possibilities of discovery, and are so reasonable and so clearly in the path of researches which are now being actively prosecuted in every capital of Europe that we may any day expect to hear that they have emerged from the realms of speculation to those of sober fact.[7]

If Crookes's predictions were to come true, they would have a profound effect on the telegraph, cable, and telephone industries and on electrical manufacturing. Yet the established companies in electrical communications failed to envisage this new field.

What were the leading American companies doing at the turn of the century, when Marconi launched his first wireless company; and why did they not, in fact, take part in this new development? In 1900, Western Union, Postal Telegraph, and the American Telephone and Telegraph Company were all flourishing enterprises in electrical communications; and General Electric, Western Electric, and Westinghouse were important producers of electrical equipment. From the standpoint of economic organization, these related industries were in a favorable position to exploit a new method of communication. There was a sufficient "degree of monopoly" to support research and new projects, and yet enough competition to provide a stimulus to innovation.

The Telegraph and Cable Industry

The most powerful of all the electrical companies was Western Union. The telegraph industry had experienced a spectacular rise since the Morse company was founded in 1845. In 1902, Western Union, operating over one million miles of telegraph lines and two international cables, reported gross revenues of $29 million. Postal, though considerably smaller, had 266,000 miles of telegraph lines; and its affiliate, Commercial Cable, owned four cables with gross earnings of $10 million.

The telegraph industry, however, had failed to visualize the potential importance of the telephone and, by 1900, was beginning to feel the competition of this alternative method of communication which it could have controlled.

The managements of both Western Union and Postal were apparently

---

[7] William Crookes, "Some Possibilities in Electricity," *London Fortnightly Review*, Vol. LI (February, 1892), p. 173.

more interested in buying up competitors and making protective agreements than in the fundamental development of communications. Western Union had been willing to withdraw from the telephone field in 1879 in exchange for Bell's promise to keep out of the telegraph business. And in the case of radio, it was not until the new industry was thoroughly established that the telegraph companies gave serious consideration to its potentialities. Neither Western Union nor Postal employed many trained engineers in 1900; they had no plans for the development of a separate research department to keep them abreast of scientific advances.[8] As a one-time Postal Telegraph executive of this period expressed it: "We were *telegraph* men, and we did not think about alternative methods of communication."[9]

The Telephone Industry

The American Bell Telephone Company was probably the most research-minded concern in the communications industry and the best equipped to appreciate "the new and astonishing world" that William Crookes saw unfolding. Alexander Graham Bell had started an experimental workshop in Boston in 1876; and when he ceased working actively on the telephone, the laboratory was continued as a center for research and the development of patents. Trained men were also added in other divisions; and by 1901, there were 125 engineers and technicians employed in the various technical departments of the telephone system.[10]

However, wire telephony was in such an early and vigorous growth period that it kept this talent fully occupied. The basic Bell patents had expired in 1893 and 1894, and a number of small concerns had begun to expand into new regions not yet reached by the Bell system. Although the American Telephone Company continued to control the most densely populated and lucrative sections of the country, it was facing vigorous competition from the independents.[11] At the close of the year 1902, there were 1,317,000 Bell-owned stations and 1,054,000 independently owned stations. The telephone company was primarily concerned with acquiring undisputed national supremacy; its scientific energies were absorbed in developing central switchboards and increasing the distances that might be covered by its long-lines division.

The Electrical Manufacturing Industry

Just as Western Union, Postal Telegraph, and the American Bell Telephone Company were the principal concerns in the communications

---

[8] Interview with E. J. Nally, November, 1946. Western Union did not establish its first real "laboratory" until 1916.

[9] Nally interview. Nally later became General Manager of American Marconi.

[10] Federal Communications Commission, *Proposed Report: Telephone Investigation*, 74th Congress, pursuant to Public Resolution No. 8 (Washington, D.C.: U.S. Government Printing Office, 1938), p. 206.

[11] No less than 508 new independent telephone systems were established in the year 1900.

industry, so also a few firms produced the major portion of electrical apparatus. Although the electrification of the household had only just begun, the electrical equipment industry had a volume of sales of nearly $100 million in 1900.

The largest and most powerful concern was General Electric, formed in 1892 as a merger of the Thomson-Houston and Edison companies. The focus of research attention at GE was on alternating and direct currents,[12] motors, dynamos, and lamps. There was so much to be accomplished in these fields in which the companies had a substantial stake that no consideration was given to radio and electronics. This was to come later when a broad research program had been established.

And even today, in the best industrial research laboratories, like that of GE, it is not possible to cover all aspects of knowledge relevant to the company's interests; new approaches are often neglected for want of a sponsor, either in the laboratory or among the operating executives.

.   .   .   .

For these various reasons, the *established* electrical companies played no part in the early developmental phases of the American radio industry. This advance was to come from new concerns and new capital.[13]

It should be said in passing that a policy of waiting for new developments to prove themselves is frequently justified. Proper timing is of crucial importance in the exploitation of a new invention. Thus, General Electric's Owen D. Young, who was responsible for the formation of the Radio Corporation of America in 1919, declared: "Fifteen years is about the average period of probation, and during that time the inventor, the promoter and investor, who see a great future for the invention, generally lose their shirts. Public demand even for a great invention is always slow in developing. That is why the wise capitalist keeps out of exploiting new inventions."[14]

As we shall see, of the early exploiters of wireless, De Forest and Fessenden did "lose their shirts," and Marconi came very close to doing so.

THE AVAILABILITY OF SPECULATIVE CAPITAL FOR NEW VENTURES

What role did venture capital play in launching the radio industry in this country? The three most important early American concerns were the American Marconi Company, the National Electric Signaling Company (NESCO), and De Forest Wireless Telegraphy Company. The

---

[12] Steinmetz, for example, formulated a mathematical system for solving problems of alternating current distribution.

[13] Cf. Schumpeter: "It is not the owner of stage coaches who builds railways."

[14] G. Archer, *History of Radio to 1926* (New York: American Historical Co., 1938), p. 94.

American Marconi Company was financed by investment bankers in England and the United States; its stock was largely privately subscribed and held in substantial blocks. NESCO, financed entirely by two wealthy Pittsburgh capitalists, conducted the first experiments made by any commercial company on the wireless telephone. The De Forest Wireless Telegraph Company, which was sold by high-pressure salesmanship as an out-and-out speculation, later went into receivership; but its principal inventor, Lee de Forest, made one of the most revolutionary inventions of the last fifty years—the three-element vacuum tube. Very few of our modern developments in electronics would have been possible without De Forest's historic discovery of the tremendous increase in sensitivity that can be obtained by introducing a third element between the cathode an the anode of a vacuum tube.

These three companies, therefore, were financed with different types of capital: American Marconi with investment money, NESCO with long-term speculative money of wealthy individuals, and De Forest's company with "get rich quick" money from many small investors. The Marconi investment ultimately proved very profitable, NESCO broke even, and De Forest failed. But the fact that all types of capital were readily available for financing new ventures contributed materially to advancing radio technology.

Not only inventive talent and venture capital were needed for the success of these new scientific enterprises. The most important ingredient was entrepreneurial skill. The nature of this skill and its relation to invention need special elaboration.

THE QUALITY OF ENTREPRENEURIAL LEADERSHIP

Marconi

Guglielmo Marconi was not a highly trained scientist. Educated in Italy primarily by tutors, Marconi early developed an absorbing interest in physics and chemistry. When he was 20 (1894), he read for the first time in an Italian electrical journal of the work and experiments of Hertz.[15] Marconi's imagination was stirred by the possibility of making wireless communication a practical reality. Two large rooms at the top of his parents' villa were set aside for experiments, and there young Marconi worked almost constantly on perfecting home-made radio equipment. By the beginning of 1896, Marconi was receiving Morse code messages over a distance of nearly two miles. There was no outstanding originality in this work, which had been anticipated by many scientists, but it was very competent and thorough.

As Marconi's family had wealth, there was no practical necessity for

---

[15] B. L. Jacot and D. M. B. Collier, *Marconi, Master of Space* (London: Hutchinson, 1935), p. 24.

him to earn a living. He was swept into wireless experimentation with an irresistible inner compulsion; and his persistence, to the exclusion of almost all other interests, was perhaps the principal reason for his phenomenal success. There was also a certain *narrowness* about Marconi which seems to be characteristic of many successful entrepreneurs. His career bears out a conclusion of Benjamin Franklin: "I have always thought that a man of tolerable abilities may work great changes, and accomplish great affairs among mankind, if he first forms a good plan, and, cutting off all amusements or other employments that would divert his attention, makes the execution of that same plan his sole study and business."

Marconi was also greatly aided by his family connections. His mother was of the Irish aristocracy and moved in the "best circles" in England. The family concluded that Guglielmo would have a better chance to commercialize his inventions there than in Italy. A visit was arranged in 1896, and the young inventor (then 22) was introduced to government officials and capitalists who might be interested in the radio field. Among these officials was William Preece,[16] engineer-in-chief of the British Post Office. He took a keen interest in Marconi, and planned a demonstration for the Post-Office engineers. Marconi, who had been steadily improving the workmanship of every part of his equipment, showed that messages could be sent up to eight miles. This success and the interest displayed by Preece led to the formation of the British Marconi company in 1897.

Two years later an American subsidiary was launched. From then until the formation of the Radio Corporation of America in 1919, the Marconi companies were the dominant concerns in British and American wireless.

The original capital of the British Marconi company (£100,000) was subscribed largely by wealthy individuals who wanted a speculative investment in the new wireless venture. The company had a distinguished directorate; and considering the fact that Marconi himself was only 23 at the time, the terms were exceptionally favorable. Marconi obtained £15,000 in cash and 60 per cent of the original stock in exchange for almost all of his patent rights.[17]

The technical obstacles to the commercial transmission of wireless messages proved much more difficult than Marconi anticipated. Immediately after his company was formed, Marconi began experimenting with long-distance communications. He decided to erect an experimental station in England and one in Newfoundland, 1,700 miles away. His receiving station was on a high bluff beside the ocean. On the twelfth of December, 1901, he flew a kite with wires connecting it to the receiving station, and

---

[16] Preece himself was an inventor of distinction who had worked on inductive wireless telegraphy.

[17] He reserved to himself his patents in Italy and her dependencies. Marconi testimony, *Marconi Wireless Telegraph Company of America* v. *De Forest Radio Telephone and Telegraph Company*, USDC, SDNY, in Equity 8211.

was able to hear faintly a signal of the Morse telegraphic letter *S* transmitted from England.[18]

Despite this initial success and the excellent backing that Marconi received, the Marconi enterprises were to go through a very trying period. The company soon began to feel the opposition of the vested interests in the cable and the telegraph lines. Marconi's apparatus was far from perfected; for long distances, communication by cable remained much more reliable.

Development of Ship Communications. Marconi soon realized that his company would not survive if it relied primarily on international communications. A more promising field for exploitation seemed to be communication with ships. This proved to be a very significant move and illustrates the principle that *the most profitable outlet for an innovation is frequently not the one which is explored first.*

Marconi's plans for marine wireless were ambitious. He hoped to control the basic patents in the art, and to equip ships of all nations with wireless apparatus. He hoped also to erect shore stations at key points around the world, through which all ship messages would be sent. In the pursuit of these objectives, Marconi was determined to obtain a monopolistic position. Although he succeeded, his aggressive tactics created great antagonism. And yet, if one reviews carefully this period and the nature of the opposition, it seems probable that his aggressiveness was an essential element in his success.[19]

Despite Marconi's strenuous campaign to control ship-to-shore communications, his companies remained in financial difficulties until about 1910. Wireless was still regarded as a luxury for most ships, and the volume of traffic was scarcely sufficient to yield a return on the capital involved. The sinking of the *Republic* in 1909 and the *Titanic* in 1912 brought dramatic attention to the practical importance of wireless for safety of life at sea.[20] From 1910 to 1912, laws were passed in the United States, England, and other maritime countries requiring all ships above a certain size to carry wireless.

This legislation gave a substantial boost to radio. The position of the Marconi company was also materially strengthened by the fact that its principal American rival—United Wireless (originally a De Forest company)—went into bankruptcy in 1912, and its assets were acquired by Marconi. United Wireless had been found guilty of infringing the Mar-

---

[18] R. N. Vyvyan, *Wireless over Thirty Years* (London: Routledge, 1933), p. 29.

[19] Cf. Aldous Huxley's statement that "as a matter of historical fact, scientific progressiveness has never been divorced from aggressiveness." *Ends and Means* (New York: Harper & Bros., 1937), p. 23.

[20] The *Carpathia*, which responded to the *Titanic's* SOS signal and rescued 700 survivors, was 58 miles away and did not reach the scene for several hours. Later, it was discovered that a "dead ship"—a freighter without wireless—had passed within 25 miles at the time the *Titanic* sank, and that the *California* was less than 20 miles away but her wireless operator had retired for the night.

coni "four sevens" patent and the Lodge tuning patent.[21] American Marconi thus gained control of the 400 ship installations and 17 land stations belonging to its competitor. This gave it almost "all the coast stations of importance on the Atlantic and Pacific coasts, besides practically the whole of the American Mercantile Marine at present fitted with wireless installation."[22] The result was that the company carried on about 90 per cent of the American ship-to-shore business between 1912 and the outbreak of war in 1917.[23] And from 1912 on, the company enjoyed increasing prosperity (see Table I).

Table I

MARCONI WIRELESS TELEGRAPH COMPANY OF AMERICA
Income and Expenses, 1903–18

Year Ended	Organization Expenses and Deficit Account	Net Income after Taxes	Depreciation after Reserves	Net Profit
Jan. 31, 1903........	$ 35,468	Deficit	......	......
Jan. 31, 1904........	85,183	Deficit	......	......
Jan. 31, 1905........	168,843	Deficit	......	......
Jan. 31, 1906........	257,475	Deficit	......	......
Jan. 31, 1907........	384,804	Deficit	......	......
Jan. 31, 1908........	422,422	Deficit	......	......
Jan. 31, 1909........	448,803	Deficit	......	......
Jan. 31, 1910........	445,102*	$ 16,637	$ 12,936	$ 3,701
Jan. 31, 1911........	......	9,405	11,126	1,721 (def.)
Jan. 31, 1912........	......	26,499	11,261	15,238
Jan. 31, 1913........	......	242,235	30,989	211,246
Dec. 31, 1913†......	......	211,484	33,233	178,251
Dec. 31, 1914.......	......	271,889	122,011	149,877
Dec. 31, 1915.......	......	288,995	111,678	177,317
Dec. 31, 1916.......	......	336,041	76,152	259,889
Dec. 31, 1917.......	......	780,592	162,820	617,773
Dec. 31, 1918.......	......	897,325	286,516	711,842‡

* The cumulative deficit was written off in 1911 and 1912.
† For eleven months.
‡ Includes $101,033 described as "other income."
SOURCE: *Annual Reports*, Marconi Wireless Telegraph Company of America.

Marconi's contributions to the commercialization of wireless made him more important as an innovator than as an inventor. Yet the Marconi company acquired, in wireless patents, a dominant position which far exceeded that of any of its rivals. Marconi applied for patents on everything he did, and he was the first worker in the field whose interest was in *practical* wireless telegraphy. His principal patents were on improved

[21] See *Annual Report* of the American Marconi company for the year ended January 21, 1912, pp. 4–5.

[22] *Annual Report*, 1913, p. 5.

[23] Testimony of Vice President Nally in 1918 before the Committee on Merchant Marine and Fisheries in the House hearings held on Hr 13159 for government control of radio.

types of vertical antennas, on the improved "coherer," on the magnetic detector, and on methods of selective tuning. The coherer illustrates the way Marconi was able to obtain a strong position without doing the fundamental work. Professor Edouard Branly patented the coherer but did not conceive of its use for wireless.[24] Professor Oliver Lodge used it first for radio reception but did not feel that he had made an invention and did not apply for a patent. Marconi improved the coherer and was able to get the basic patents for its use in wireless.

Sir Ambrose Fleming, long a close associate of Marconi, probably had Marconi in mind when he wrote:

> Invention consists in overcoming the practical difficulties of the new advance, not merely talking or writing about the new thing, but in *doing it*, and doing it so that those who come after have had real obstacles cleared out of their way, and have a process or appliance at their disposal which was not there before the inventor entered the field. In most cases, however, the removal of the obstacles which block the way is not entirely the work of one person. The fort is captured only after a series of attacks, each conducted under a different leader. In these cases the inventor who breaks down the last obstruction or leads the final assault is more particularly associated in the public mind with the victory than are his predecessors.[25]

Marconi's principal weakness was that he emphasized the perfecting of existing methods instead of reaching out for radically new discoveries in wireless. Although this may occur in any research organization, there is more danger of it where the director takes a restricted scientific view of the functions of his company. Marconi's intense drive for the rapid commercialization of wireless produced a number of blind spots, the most serious of which was his failure to visualize continuous-wave operation in transatlantic working, and in turn the significance of radio *telephony*. No one, of course, foresaw the development of the radiobroadcasting industry. But there were many of Marconi's contemporary inventors who believed in the wireless telephone. Marconi thought that the Morse code was adequate for communication with ships and for transoceanic messages and saw no clear need for voice transmission. Since his approach was pragmatic, he was not interested in the scientific investigation of a field whose commercial possibilities seemed remote. This was unfortunate, both for the Marconi company and for the advancement of the art. The early experimentation with the radio telephone was left almost entirely to Marconi's American rivals, Lee de Forest and Reginald Fessenden, neither of whom had at his disposal the managerial skill of the Marconi enterprises. In fact, the most difficult ingredient to supply in the new industry proved to be *effective management*.

---

[24] Professor Oliver Lodge first conceived of using the Branly coherer as a wireless detector and is credited with giving it the name "coherer." O. E. Dunlap, *Radio's 100 Men of Science* (New York: Harper & Bros., 1944), p. 76.

[25] Ambrose Fleming, *Principles of Electric Wave Telegraphy* (London: Longmans, Green, 1906).

Reginald Fessenden

Professor Reginald Fessenden of the University of Pittsburgh was the first important American inventor to experiment with wireless. In December, 1900, Fessenden gave a demonstration for the United States Weather Bureau in which he tried to transmit *speech* by electromagnetic waves, using two masts 50 feet high and one mile apart. He used spark apparatus, which was not satisfactory for voice transmission; but the Weather Bureau was so interested that work on a larger scale was planned and some of it completed. However, Fessenden had a choleric personality; his relations with the Bureau soon became so strained that he resigned—the final break precipitated by a quarrel over patent rights.

Fessenden then succeeded in interesting two Pittsburgh capitalists—Hay Walker, Jr., and Thomas R. Given—in forming the National Electric Signaling Company to support his work on wireless telegraphy and telephony. It was now clear to the inventor that speech transmission would require a train of continuous waves, on which the voice currents could be superimposed, rather than the spark apparatus used hitherto.

Nikola Tesla, a Yugoslav physicist, had first conceived the idea of transmitting continuous waves and had pioneered in high-frequency alternators in the 1890's, but he was not successful in his radio experiments. Fessenden, taking up where Tesla left off, was more persistent. He was convinced that eventually he could design apparatus capable of carrying telephone conversations between America and Europe. His first high-frequency alternator was built to his specifications by Steinmetz of the General Electric Company in 1903. This was a 10,000-cycle machine and did not prove sufficiently powerful to transmit over long distances. Thereafter, Fessenden pressed for apparatus of higher and higher power.

It was to take years before an alternator capable of regular voice broadcasts across the Atlantic was developed by Alexanderson of the General Electric Company. In the end, however, the continuous-wave methods were to triumph over the spark.[26] But many of the leading engineers in the industry, especially those associated with the Marconi enterprises, remained skeptical until they actually saw the demonstrations of the Alexanderson equipment.

Fessenden was much more effective as an inventor than as an innovator. The National Electric Signaling Company never proved successful as a business venture. Launched as an inventor's laboratory, neither manufacturing nor commercial communications were contemplated. Fessenden was to be given an opportunity to experiment with wireless and to make

---

[26] There were also parallel developments of high-frequency alternators by the Germans. Powerful Goldschmidt alternators for transatlantic communication were installed at Sayville, Long Island, in 1912 and at Tuckerton, New Jersey, in 1914. On the West Coast the Federal Telegraph of California began installing a series of high-power Poulsen arcs in 1911. The Poulsen arc had been invented in Denmark in 1903.

inventions which it was hoped would be sufficiently basic and sweeping so that the Fessenden system could be sold at a substantial profit to a wireless operating company.

The establishment of an inventor's laboratory, with relatively broad scientific objectives and somewhat remote commercial prospects, was not a rare occurrence at this time. It was the era of the individual inventor, and wealthy businessmen in the United States were surprisingly willing to finance talent even when the inventors showed very little business judgment. The imagination of the business community had been stirred by the potentialities of an age of electricity. The courts were generous in their interpretation of patent rights, and the rewards for backing an Edison or a Graham Bell had proved spectacular. A high percentage of these scientific ventures were failures. Yet this did not discourage capitalists from underwriting new inventors, nor investors from buying stocks in wildcat promotions.

The backers of Fessenden—Walker and Given—were men of substantial means who believed that wireless was on the verge of a great development and that an investment in a laboratory and experimental stations would prove highly profitable.

On December 11, 1906, Fessenden gave a demonstration of radio telephony from Brant Rock to Plymouth, Massachusetts—a distance of eleven miles. Following these tests, Walker and Given tried hard to sell out to some existing firm. American Telephone and Telegraph, Western Union, and Postal were approached. The telephone executives showed considerable interest, and an engineering investigation was ordered. The original report was favorable and optimistic. Chief Engineer Hayes, in transmitting it to President Fish, concluded: "I feel that there is such a reasonable probability of wireless telegraphy and telephony being of commercial value to our company that I would advise taking steps to associate ourselves with Mr. Fessenden if some satisfactory arrangement can be made."[27]

But in 1907 a change of banking control of the Bell Telephone Company from Boston to the Morgan-Baker banking interests of New York[28] led to the replacement of President Fish by Theodore N. Vail. The study of the Fessenden wireless matter was continued now under the new regime with much greater skepticism, and the final decision was negative.

In the succeeding years the relations between Fessenden and his backers steadily deteriorated. Fessenden was an exceedingly difficult person. And from what evidence is available, neither Walker nor Given possessed a great amount of tact or managerial skill. Quarrels were continuous, and

---

[27] Memorandum of April 2, 1907 (files of telephone company).

[28] Memorandum of October 28, 1947, sent to the author by Lloyd Espenschied of the Bell Telephone Laboratories. A large block of convertible bonds had been issued in the fall of 1906, a sizable portion of which proved to be not readily marketable and were taken at a discount by the Morgan-Baker banking interests.

finally an open break occurred. The Pittsburgh capitalists came to feel that Fessenden was no longer working for their interests. As they had put in all the money, they notified Fessenden in January, 1911, of his dismissal. Fessenden then brought suit for breach of contract, won his case in the lower court, and was awarded damages of $400,000. To conserve assets pending an appeal, receivers were appointed for NESCO in 1912.

Walker and Given had overrated the commercial potentialities of Fessenden's inventions, failing to recognize that there were many alternative methods of perfecting radio communications. They also made the common mistake of underestimating the time required to develop a new industry to the point of mass production. No one was willing to pay large sums for patents as long as the manufacture of radio apparatus remained primarily a specialized engineering job in which very few standard units were produced. Not until after the first World War could the Fessenden system be sold for a price at all commensurate with research and development expenses.

The experiences of Walker, Given, and Fessenden illustrate the difficulties inherent in launching a scientific enterprise when the men who put up the money do not understand technical problems and when, as is so frequently the case, the key inventor has a troublesome personality.

Lee de Forest

Lee de Forest, the most prominent of the American radio inventors, is primarily distinguished for the three-element vacuum tube or triode. Dr. Rabi, who recently won the Nobel Prize in physics, has described the triode as "so outstanding in its consequences that it almost ranks with the greatest inventions of all time."[29] De Forest was one of the first Americans to write a Ph.D. thesis on wireless telegraphy.[30] On graduation in 1899, he got a job with the Western Electric Company in Chicago, where he devoted all his spare energy and most of his "company time" to developing wireless apparatus of his own:

March 18, 1900. Experiments on my new wireless "Responder," as I then called it, began to occupy more and more of my time. My work on telephone tests and devices was never brilliant, to speak charitably, for my thoughts were ever elsewhere. Dean became progressively more impatient with my work, but was too considerate to fire me, although he saw little of merit or promise in the experiments I was wrapped up in. Certainly he saw no possibility that the great Western Electric Company would ever become interested in Wireless Communication! One day he exclaimed: "Look here, de Forest. You'll never make a telephone engineer. As far as I am concerned you can go to hell, in your own way. Do as you damn please!" With typical recklessness I took

---

[29] I. I. Rabi, "The Physicist Returns from the War," *Atlantic Monthly*, October, 1945, p. 109.

[30] "The Reflection of Short Hertzian Waves from the Ends of Parallel Wires," Yale University, 1899. Georgette Carneal, *A Conquerer of Space* (New York: Horace Liveright, 1930), p. 83.

him at his word, turned to my little corner where I had my spark gap and responder parts, and thereafter spent eight hours a day at my own delectable tests, totally oblivious to the telephone work going on about me and for which I was supposed to be paid.

September 3, 1900. I am starting in a new job with poor pay. But I am on the right track and feel that it is destined to make me independent.

Nights I worked with partner Smythe in my room, on the Responder. Without much delay I got a job as assistant editor on the staff of the *Western Electrician*. Salary was $10 a week. Every night not spent in the library was devoted to experimenting with the electrolytic anticoherer. Smythe was comparatively rich, earning $30 a week. Naturally, our budget for experimental work was very limited. . . .

October 28, 1900. I have begun to hazard my job with the *Western Electrician* by working half-time in the laboratory of Armour Institute, teaching two nights weekly at Lewis Institute. I am risking mediocricy [*sic*] and weak contentment for a chance of great success. . . . Soon the experiments became so engrossing that it was impracticable for me to continue to work even half time for the *Western Electrician*. So once more I crossed the Rubicon, burned my bridges, and with only the amount of $5 paid by Lewis Institute per week, and an equal amount advanced by Smythe, determined to continue my life as an inventor. . . .' "[31]

De Forest's first chance to demonstrate his wireless apparatus came in 1901 with an offer from the Publishers' Press Association, which was willing to pay him $800 if he could successfully report the International Yacht Races. The trial was a failure.

De Forest had been able to borrow $1,000 to manufacture his equipment for the races; and later that year, through the sale of stock to the public, he got an opportunity to set up a laboratory of his own. He proved a prolific inventor. Between 1902 and 1906, he took out thirty-four patents on all phases of wireless telegraphy, including loop antennas, receiver tuning, generators, and antenna de-icers.[32]

His major search was for a detector which would not infringe the Marconi or Fessenden patents. In 1900, he had noticed that the gas light in the laboratory dimmed while his spark equipment was operating, and that it returned to full strength when the apparatus stopped.[33] This suggested that a gas flame might be used to detect wireless signals (later the dimming of the flame was shown to have been caused by sound waves from the spark gap). De Forest, therefore, tried to make a detector consisting of a bulb filled with gas and containing two electrodes intended to be heated by a dynamo. This gas detector was later described by the courts as "utterly useless."[34]

---

[31] Excerpts from unpublished diary of Lee de Forest, George Clark Collection.

[32] Carneal, *op. cit.*, p. 165.

[33] This experience illustrates the oft-remarked role of chance observation in the process of invention. But as Pasteur declared: "Le hasard ne favorise que les esprits preparés."

[34] Decision of the District Court, *Marconi Wireless Telegraph Company of America* v. *De Forest Radio Telephone and Telegraph Company, op. cit.*, September 20, 1916.

However, it led to the invention that was to revolutionize the radio art.[35] Continuing to experiment with gas-filled and partially evacuated two-element tubes, De Forest placed a third electrode, called a grid, between the incandescent electrode (the cathode) and the cold electrode (the anode). He then attached a battery and, by changing the voltage on the grid, was able to control the flow of current across the space between the hot and cold electrodes.

De Forest himself did not fully understand the principles of the triode. Despite his doctoral training, he was more an inventor than a scientist. He did not attempt to relate his experiments to the general literature of physics, and thus overlooked clues which might have assisted him in making a more reliable electronic device. His triodes were not uniform in performance and proved less satisfactory than other competing devices, such as the electrolytic, magnetic, and crystal detectors.[36]

Between 1907 and 1912, De Forest made few scientific experiments with the triode. He turned his attention primarily to wireless telephony, giving his first demonstration in the spring of 1907 between a Lackawanna ferry and the Hoboken and Manhattan terminals. Shortly thereafter the Navy installed De Forest sets on a number of ships; and in the tests that followed, communication over twenty miles was achieved. But De Forest's company was inadequately financed, and the volume of radio sales was not large enough to sustain an effective program of development. When his laboratory was destroyed by fire in 1908, he took a year to re-equip it. Finally, in 1911, in order to earn a living, De Forest went to California to work for the Federal Telegraph Company, hoping still that some miracle would lift his firm from the economic doldrums. This never happened.

De Forest, as an inventor, lacked the persistence to carry any one project through to a completely successful conclusion. Like many highly creative individuals, he had far more ideas than he was capable of handling. And his restless mind was always seeking new fields to explore, in an apparently "irresistible urge to invent."[37]

He would sweep down on a problem with a hungry rush and his imagination had an astonishing faculty for leaping difficulties. If the quarry snagged or proved elusive, however, he had to hop to something else. When necessity did compel him to work at something without respite, his nerves rebelled. "The jumpies" de Forest called these attacks.[38]

---

[35] U.S. Patent No. 879,532 was applied for January 29, 1907, and issued February 18, 1908. Lubell reports that it took De Forest three weeks to raise the $15 necessary for the patent application. Samuel Lubell, "Magnificent Failure," *Saturday Evening Post*, January 24, 1942, p. 36.

[36] While inherently superior to other detectors, De Forest's triodes needed such frequent adjustment that commercial users found them too bothersome.

[37] See Taussig, *Inventors and Money Makers*, pp. 23–24. "The instinct of contrivance in man unlike the corresponding instinct in animals, is not directed to one specific end. . . . It is directed to all sorts of contrivances no longer restricted to those immediately serviceable. . . . There seems to develop an erratic streak."

[38] Lubell, *op cit.*

De Forest, like his American rival Fessenden, had little of the entre-preneurial ability displayed by Marconi. De Forest's high inventive skill enabled him to launch a large number of companies, but none of these survived long. He seemed incapable of building on solid foundations an enterprise in which stable customer relations were cultivated.

Thus, although De Forest was perhaps the most imaginative inventor in the history of the radio industry, and had the opportunity to create a great radio enterprise, he failed entirely to do so. His career, when compared with Marconi's, illustrates the fact that an inventor, to achieve commercial success, must associate himself with men of exceptional business judgment.

CONCLUSIONS

The Role of Fundamental Science in the Process of Innovation

In analyzing an industry from the standpoint of technical progress, I suggested earlier that it was important to assess the status of the underlying sciences and to determine whether they were undergoing a major advance. The key role that can be played by a few outstanding scientists exploring new lines of basic inquiry with imagination and freedom from routine could not have been demonstrated more clearly than in the pioneering work of Maxwell, Hertz, J. J. Thomson, and others in laying the foundations of the modern radio industry.

And in the United States today, where our genius has lain more in applied research and engineering development, it is of critical significance to the process of innovation that we encourage a flourishing spirit of basic scientific inquiry.[39] Despite all the support that is now being given to science, there is real danger that research funds will be channeled pri-marily into applications in which prompt results can be expected. Original investigation into unexplored territory flourishes only in an environment where special efforts have been made to foster it.

Engineering Art and Fundamental Science

Science and the practical arts have advanced most rapidly when there has been a combination of diverse talents at work on a particular problem, the theorist positing the basic concepts, the experimentalist testing reality with the use of these tools, and the inventor converting the results to practical achievement for the use of mankind.

Nineteenth-century industrialism encouraged the universities in Europe to undertake fundamental scientific inquiry.[40] And by 1900, there was a

---

[39] For an elaboration of this point, see V. Bush, *Science: The Endless Frontier* (Washington, D.C.: U.S. Government Printing Office, 1945); and the author's "Fed-eral Support for Scientific Research," *Harvard Business Review*, Spring, 1947, pp. 385–396.

[40] Maxwell's chair at Cambridge, for example, and the Cavendish Laboratories over which he presided were founded in response to a demand from industrial leaders that the teaching of science be modernized.

sufficient number of trained engineers interested in direct applications to translate the findings of the scientists into a vital new industry. It was not, however, the engineers in the well-established electrical concerns who seized the opportunity afforded by this new field. Instead, young men like Marconi, De Forest, and Fessenden undertook the major risks of pioneering.

I hope that I have succeeded in recapturing the spirit of optimistic and zestful inquiry which characterized the activities of these men. I have tried also to show how they built on the foundations laid by the scientists. But if one were to criticize these inventor-engineers, it would be that they did not keep in *close enough touch with science.* De Forest did not really understand the principle of the triode, which prevented him from making it into an effective commercial device. And Marconi's major blind spot was his failure to visualize radio communications as an advancing art in which Morse code spark telegraphy would inevitably be replaced by continuous-wave voice transmission.

The Relation of the Structure of the Industry to Innovation

During the first decade of the twentieth century the leading concerns in the electrical industry had achieved a sufficient degree of monopoly to be financially capable of expanding into a new area.

A monopolistic position can affect entrepreneurs in different ways. In most instances, I think, American business leaders have been conscious of the "perennial gale of competition." The response frequently has been to get in on new developments through vigorous support of research and engineering. For example, the General Electric Company established a laboratory for fundamental research as early as 1901 and under the leadership of Willis R. Whitney built up a remarkable team of scientists. And at a later stage, both General Electric and the telephone company made a whole series of exceedingly important contributions to radio science and art. Yet in the early 1900's the managements of these two forward-looking concerns concluded, as a matter of business judgment, that the time was not ripe for vigorous exploration of wireless telegraphy.

Western Union and Postal Telegraph, by contrast, took a different view. They chose to protect their established field by agreements rather than the support of research. The danger of this practice, when the underlying sciences are undergoing a revolutionary change, is that the well-protected field will eventually become of minor significance. And this, in fact, happened both to the telegraph and to the cable.

The telegraph and cable companies did their best to prevent Marconi from getting a franchise in Newfoundland. Somewhat later, Austen Chamberlain, as Postmaster-General of Great Britain, saw the Marconi company primarily as a potential competitor of the government-controlled telegraph industry and adamantly refused to connect the Marconi overseas service with the Post-Office telegraph lines. But the opposition was overcome with time, and no one could prevent Marconi from developing ship-to-shore communication, which was a new and hitherto unexploited field.

The attitude of monopolists toward new developments remains ambivalent today. There are many companies which behave as Schumpeter suggested when he wrote: "The first thing a modern concern does as soon as it feels that it can afford it is to establish a research department, every member of which knows that his bread and butter depend on his success in devising improvements."[41]

But the joker here is the word "modern." There are monopolistic enterprises, particularly among the older industries, whose research organization (if it exists) is largely window dressing and where there is, in fact, no genuine interest in radically new products.

I do not personally believe that it is possible to predict how monopolists will behave toward a new development except in the light of the institutional background of the company and the personal characteristics of its principal executives. Frequently, I suspect, the reaction depends more on the personalities of the key entrepreneurs than on the formal organization of the industry. This was borne out, for example, by the different attitude of President Fish and President Vail of the telephone company toward the wireless telephone.[42] And it should also be stressed that even under President Fish, it was not Western Electric[43] which backed De Forest nor the Bell Telephone Company which financed Fessenden's early experiments. This support came from new concerns and new capital.

The Relation of Venture Capital and New Companies to Innovation

There were almost no barriers to speculative investment in the period under review. In fact, with De Forest, it was remarkable how readily he succeeded in getting a series of individuals to back him in enterprise after enterprise which ended in failure. The inventor of the early 1900's, if he had almost any kind of an idea and was a good salesman, could raise money for a new venture. Of the seeds sown in this fashion, there was a high percentage of bankruptcies but a few spectacular successes. This ready flow of funds was important, for new companies were of critical significance in the early history of radio.

And what of today? Is it still important to have new firms arise to take risks in unexplored areas?

Since the turn of the century, our well-established industries have made great strides in their capacity to contribute to the advancement of science. The modern industrial research laboratory has made it possible for the

---

[41] Schumpeter, *Capitalism, Socialism and Democracy*, p. 96.

[42] Vail was put into office by the New York bankers because he was considered to have "sounder" business judgement than Fish and he was much less interested in "visionary" new developments. Nonetheless, basic telephone research developed vigorously and effectively under Vail's leadership.

[43] A subsidiary of the American Bell Telephone Company since 1881.

large concern to move much more freely into new fields. Yet I think it will be unfortunate if the translation of scientific advances into new products and new industries is left entirely to the great corporations. Any large, well-established institution almost inevitably tends to become somewhat bureaucratic. It develops fields of special interest; and no matter how hard it tries to be receptive to new ideas, the radical notion and the new risk-taking approach are not always exploited. We can expect our great industrial corporations to take substantial risks and to be very forward-looking in many areas. But some of the less obvious developments which are off the beaten track and which are in the highly speculative stage where their potentialities cannot be visualized are still likely to be neglected.

In the days when American Marconi and NESCO were launched, many wealthy individuals were willing and able to put capital into new ventures; with tremendous increases in taxation the number of such individuals has dwindled rapidly. At the same time the large corporation is in a much more dominant position to restrict entry into its field. This suggests that special efforts must be made to insure a flow of capital into new enterprises.[44]

The Role of Entrepreneurial Leadership in Innovation

Our review of early radio history has also served to stress the importance of specialized entrepreneurial skills in the successful launching of new ventures. The principal characteristics required were perhaps visionary boldness, "narrowness," aggressiveness, persistence, business judgment, salesmanship, the capacity to pick able associates, the delegation of authority, and the ability to inspire loyalty in a working organization. This is an unusual collection of skills for any one man to possess—which presumably explains why there are not more innovating entrepreneurs. De Forest and Fessenden were highly imaginative inventors, but their lack of other skills led to their failure as innovators.

No case has come to my attention in the history of the radio industry in which very high inventive talent and the capacity for successful innovation were combined in one man. There have been such cases, of course, in other industries (e.g., Thomas Edison);[45] but it is apparently a rare phenomenon. Successful invention seems normally to require intensive application to the problem which is being tackled, to the temporary exclusion of all other considerations; it is an egocentric activity which, for those gripped by it, is all-absorbing. De Forest and Fessenden were such men. When De Forest was working on a new invention, everything else was forgotten. He burned with an intense flame, and his success seems to have been a product of brilliant imagination and intense application. The

---

[44] The recent establishment of the American Research and Development Corporation is an important forward step in this direction.

[45] Though Edison was more successful as an inventor than as an innovator.

pace was so energy-consuming that he could not maintain it for long. And during his periods of creative productivity the commercial aspects of his enterprises were completely neglected. Moreover, De Forest had far more ideas than he was capable of handling. And both he and Fessenden were gamblers, willing to risk everything on their particular interest of the moment.

Marconi, in contrast, succeeded because he was much shrewder (and incidentally less creative), of a more equable temperament, and capable of delegating the formulation of commercial policy to skillful business associates. He did not, however, learn for some years how to select his associates and to delegate authority, and his enterprises nearly ended in failure during the learning process.

But while all three of the inventor-entrepreneurs whom we studied lacked some of the important qualities of entrepreneurial leadership, they all possessed a capacity for visualizing important new scientific developments. I believe that the careers of such men are particularly worthy of study because we have entered an era in which radical innovations are likely to be much more intimately connected than in the past with advances in the frontiers of knowledge. The challenge of the second industrial revolution in which we are now living is to make certain that in every industry there is the maximum possible encouragement to explore new lines of endeavor with imagination and freedom.

Although we have come a long way since Marconi's time toward more "informed entrepreneurship,"[46] there has yet to emerge a class of "scientific entrepreneurs" who are attempting to apply the latest advances in the physical and social sciences to the solution of their problems. This will be difficult because some of the success of an inventor-entrepreneur like Marconi was due to his "narrowness." And yet this limited vision inhibited him from appreciating the critical importance of the wireless telephone—which was perhaps his major error.

I should expect that the scientific entrepreneur of the future will be recognized and rewarded for his capacity to "be in on new developments" *at the proper time*. The handling of innovations will be regarded as his major task, and he will require a specialized staff to keep him informed on the underlying forces affecting the various aspects of his enterprise. The determination of cost-price relationships on existing products will be delegated primarily to subordinates. And if he is to make use of economic analysis, new tools must be forged for his basic needs.

QUESTIONS

1. Identify the significant phases in the evolution of radio from speculation into widespread commercial adoption. In each phase:
   a) What is the time span?

---

[46] I have borrowed this term from Arthur Cole.

b) What kind of people were required to carry on the innovation?

c) What financial resources were required?

d) What parallel technological efforts encouraged or inhibited the activity?

e) What nontechnical factors were significant to the progress of the innovation.

2. Do any principles, hypotheses, or observations of possible usefulness to management emerge from Maclaurin's study?

3. Contrast the personal characteristics of Marconi, Fessenden, and De Forest. How can the corporation work successfully with such men?

4. Does the nature of this evolutionary process suggest an explanation for the difficulties firms often encounter in transferring laboratory results into commercially successful enterprises?

On Change

Time is a sort of river of passing events, and strong is its current; no sooner is a thing brought to sight than it is swept by and another takes its place, and this too will be swept away.

Meditations of Marcus Aurelius

THE SOCIAL PRINCIPLES OF INVENTION[1]

By S. Colum Gilfillan

The Nature of Invention

1. (*a*) What is called an important invention is a perpetual *accretion* of little details, (*b*) probably having neither beginning, completion, nor definable limits, (*c*) though it is hazily and somewhat arbitrarily defined by a word or phrase in the English language, and by our standardizing habits in thought and industry, as well as in language. (*d*) An invention is an *evolution*, rather than a series of creations, and much resembles a *biologic* process.

2. (*a*) An invention is essentially a *complex* of most diverse elements— a design for a physical object, a process of working with it, the needed elements of science, if any; the constituent materials, a method for building it, the raw materials used in working it, such as fuel, accumulated capital such as factories and docks, with which it must be used, its crew with their skills, ideas, and shortcomings, its financial backing and management, its purpose and use in conjunction with other sides of civilization, and its popular evaluation. Most of these parts in turn have their separately variable elements. (*b*) A change in any one of the elements of the complex will alter, stimulate, depress, or quite inhibit the whole.

3. (*a*) Invention is a *new combination* from the "prior art," i.e., ideas previously known from all the above categories, (*b*) having varying number, ripeness, and recency.

4. Invention need not be based on *prior science*. It often precedes and evokes the apposite science.

5. Invention would become much easier with advancing civilization, were "invention" not defined by language usage, which sets the modern standard higher. Hence, some "important inventions" of early times would be too simple and easy to be called inventions if made today.

Changes Evoking Invention

6. (*a*) The achievements of the inventor himself, and of his compeers, are a major cause of changes in the milieu out of which is compounded the inventional complex described in principle 2. "Invention

---

[1] Reproduced from S. Colum Gilfillan, *The Sociology of Invention* (Chicago: Follett Publishing Co., 1935; now out of print), pp. 5–13. Corrections made in 1960 at request of author. Reproduced by permission of author.

is [one] mother of necessity." (*b*) Some other chief *change causing invention* are growths of wealth, education, population, industrialism, and commercial organization.

7. (*a*) The more *recent changes* in this milieu, commonly evidenced by a notable change in the price of something, or being a scientific discovery, or falling to hand of an adaptable invention, have two special significances: (1) Though weak, they may serve as "triggers"; and (2) they attract attention, stimulating inventive adjustment. (*b*) One or more recent changes may be identified as the triggers or the active causes of almost any invention.

The Rate of Growth and Life Cycle of an Invention

8. Inventions normally progress but slowly in the period before they become practical propositions.

9. (*a*) The rate of *increase* in the *use* of an invention probably tends to decline continuously from the start of practical success, and with time enough will become a growing rate of decrease in use. (*b*) The decline of the invention is largely a *semantic* rather than real phenomenon, due to the fluid, Protean realities of technology outgrowing the definition of our invention.

10. (*a*) An invention which saves anything tends to *reduce its own importance* and insofar discourages further invention in the same line. (*b*) If, as usually, it is one out of a chain of steps toward a final production, it encourages that production and stimulates invention for each other step toward it. (*c*) Whether an economical invention will ultimately diminish or increase its own importance depends upon the size of its share in producing the final consumption good, and on the flexibility of demand for that good. (*d*) An invention which saves nothing, but gives a new or improved product, is bound to increase its own field.

11. *Inventions persist.* (*a*) In the modern world, they rarely pass totally out of use, still less out of memory. (*b*) Hence, technology is cumulative, and the idea fund for further new combinations continually increases.

12. But inventions are *rarely rejuvenated*. Once the progress of one has ceased, it is rarely resumed in like nature.

13. The perfecting of a type of object mechanically is evidenced by its attainment of *beauty*.

14. Inventions having each their own trend, and their understandable causation, they can be and have been successfully *predicted* even centuries ahead.

Factors Fostering, Retarding, and Locating Invention

15. *Use promotes improvement.* The rate of progress on an invention tends to vary with the absolute rate at which that device is being

turned out in practice. But there are so many other factors affecting the invention's progress that the action of this principle is often negated.

16. (*a*) Hence, invention in each line centers in a few regions which most abundantly produce that line, these being responsible for about all the progress in it, the rest looking to the *fountain lands*, and rarely doing more than borrow and adapt their inventions to local needs. (*b*) Invention is localized by best *climate*, more than perhaps any other mental activity of man.

17. Invention is helped by all *specializations* of labor (Spencerian integration resulting in a piling-up of one kind of work at one point), whether between (*a*) regions, (*b*) firms, or (*c*) workmen, since these all enable a more intensive, full use of the capital required to devise, build, and operate an invention, especially one that would increase output. Further, (*a*) and (*b*) encourage very helpful fourth and fifth forms of specialization, (*d*) the coming of the professional inventor and (*e*) the laboratory which splits up, specializes the diverse inventors and their assistants.

18. *Leading Organizations.* (*a*) There is a tendency from the last three principles for the firms or government bureaus upon whom the largest amount of a certain production has become centralized to make the most inventions thereon, since they can exploit the invention most intensively and with least obstruction from the patent system, and they most need such inventions as are adaptations to a greater scale of production than heretofore reached. (*b*) *Governments* have played a large part in invention since the dawn of civilization, and their share has been increasing since the late nineteenth century.

19. But the *standardization* which tends to accompany wide organization obstructs inventions which would require changing the standard form.

20. (*a*) More *durable* capital construction contains one trait especially hostile to revolutionary invention, since most novelties require the discarding of equipment, both what is directly redesigned and that which must interact with it, like trains and tracks. (*b*) Acquired specialized knowledge, workmen's skill, and commercial good will are durable forms of capital that similarly oppose upsetting inventions.

21. A *rapid expansion* of population and industry, as in America hitherto, is *favorable* to invention since it facilitates adding new equipment without scrapping old.

22. A larger *population* and/or industry also stimulate invention, in that they increase the absolute weight of need for an invention, and the number of potential finders, while the necessary cost to find it remains the same.

Principles of Chance

23. (*a*) The inventors are led by perceptions of the possibility and need of making easily enough some recombinations of elements of the "prior art" and milieu. (*b*) Invention by *accident* is very *rare* in marine history, and usually requires that the need for the invention be already felt by an inventive observer of the accident.

24. *Inevitability*. With the progress of the craft of invention, apparently a device can no longer remain unfound when the time for it is ripe, i.e., when the needed factors indicated in Principles 2, 6, and 7 are present.

25. Hence, approximately simultaneous *duplicate invention* repeatedly occurs, and would occur still oftener if not forestalled by news that the invention is already made.

Inventors and Other Classes, and Tendencies in the Craft

26. There is no indication that any individual's genius has been necessary to any invention that has had any importance. To the historian and social scientist the progress of invention appears *impersonal*.

27. (*a*) Yet invention can only come at the hand of some sort of *inventors*, and its directions, frequency, and efficiency are determined wholly through deliberate actions by these men, in some proportion to their absolute numbers; assistance; intelligence; moral traits; strength of motives for inventing; time free for it; mental, instrumental, library, and general equipment; and funds and organization for it. (*b*) By Darwinian principles the *races* must be unequal in inventive and every other kind of ability. By historical observation, most races have never produced a demonstrable and good invention, and therefore should be judged probably short on inventive ability, until proof to the contrary is forthcoming.

28. Perception of the need and the way to meet it depends first upon any individuals of a numerous inventive class, but *indirectly* upon the suggestions tossed up by a wider intelligent and technologically minded class, more indirectly upon the whole population's thoughts, *ultimately* upon the physical environment and the general social and racial heritage, which determine the mental level and slant of each class and country.

29. The inventors are checked by a variable brake of *conservatism in the patrons* of invention, whether enterprisers or consumers. The more restricted, select, specialized, and intelligent is this patron class, the less will be its conservatism and the faster progress.

30. The popular notions of great inventors are essentially mythology; and that man is preferred as the *titular inventor* who belongs to one's own or a related country, and who first achieved commercial success with the device.

31. The craft of invention reveals the following *trends:* (*a*) from the empiric toward the theoretical; (*b*) from the unconscious inventor through the amateur to the professional one; (*c*) from the evolutionary toward the discrete or broken, epochal; but (*d*) from the accidental toward the deliberate and sure; and (*e*) from the individual source to the organized inventing group. (*f*) A consequence of these trends (and others) is a prodigious rise in the efficiency and rate of invention.

32. The inventions which revolutionize a device or industry are commonly made by men *outsiders* to it, yet informed regarding it; the far greater and more valuable mass of perfecting inventions are made made by *insiders.*

33. The inventors are in partnership usually with *enterprisers* or government *officials,* whose courage, intelligence, and means are commonly of importance comparable with that of the inventors themselves.

Effects of Invention

34. *Equivalent Invention.* Perceived needs are met by various *unlike,* as well as by duplicate solutions, so that any great invention is simultaneously paralleled by other, often utterly dissimilar means for reaching the same end at the same time, e.g., reaching California by clipper, steamer, pony express, railroad, and telegraph. Inventions may be seen as arriving in groups of several for one function.

35. Hence, *no* single *invention* ever *revolutionizes civilization,* nor brings, simply through having been invented, any important changes in the life of the mass of men.

36. An invention coming *before its time* remains undeveloped and practically useless.

37. The *desirability* and acceptance of inventions are matters of their meeting the felt needs of certain individuals, and not of society; so an invention may flourish and be practically imposed on all, through competition, though it only decreases the general wealth or welfare.

38. (*a*) Inventions may save labor, land, capital, lives, or may not save anything, but add science to destruction, or bring a private profit, or a new enjoyment or convenience for the public. (*b*) Between *labor-,* *land-* and *capital-saving* inventions the discrimination of effects is complicated, but as a rule the factor chiefly economized loses in relative share of the distribution of the national income, while usually all ultimately gain in their absolute shares.

Two of these principles, the thirteenth and the thirtieth, we have extensively discussed in *Inventing the Ship,* respectively in connection with the beauty of the sailship, and the Fulton and Ericsson myths. . . .

QUESTIONS

1. Consider each "principle" of invention. If correct, what significance has it for management? For the United States Secretary of Defense?
2. Does any principle appear to be erroneous in the light of today's technology and environment?
3. Can you suggest other principles of invention or technological innovation which are useful hypotheses for management?

The Successful Pioneer

The successful pioneer in a new area of technology has confounded the skeptics who said that the idea would not work, or that it was of no value, or that it had been tried before unsuccessfully, and so forth; also, he has resisted the suggestions of supporters who urged delay to permit improvement. He has been forced by the obstacles inherent in such work to defend his chosen course of action—his compromise between performance, cost, and time—to defend it so consistently and vigorously that he comes to regard it as the best possible result, rather than as a practical compromise, and consequently probably subject to improvement. . . . This phenomenon is accentuated in the case of the pioneers in a new field, but it is found to some degree among the ex-leaders of more prosaic development projects after they move on to other assignments. The objectives they sought were so novel and so difficult that they are often not receptive to suggestions for improvement or for development of a new concept which will supplant their own work.

> M. P. O'Brien, Dean Emeritus
> College of Engineering
> University of California

from: "Technological Planning & Misplanning," *Technological Planning on the Corporate Level* (Boston; Harvard Business School, 1961).

A CASE STUDY OF INNOVATION[1]

By Elting E. Morison

IN THE early days of the last war, when armaments of all kinds were in short supply, the British, I am told, made use of a venerable field piece that had come down to them from previous generations. The honorable past of this light artillery stretched back, in fact, to the Boer War. In the days of uncertainty after the fall of France, these guns, hitched to trucks, served as useful mobile units in the coast defense. But it was felt that the rapidity of fire could be increased. A time-motion expert was therefore called in to suggest ways to simplify the firing procedures. He watched one of the gun crews of five men at practice in the field for some time. Puzzled by certain aspects of the procedures, he took some slow-motion pictures of the soldiers performing the loading, aiming, and firing routines.

When he ran these pictures over once or twice, he noticed something that appeared odd to him. A moment before the firing, two members of the gun crew ceased all activity and came to attention for a three-second interval, extending throughout the discharge of the gun. He summoned an old colonel of artillery, showed him the pictures, and pointed out this strange behavior. What, he asked the colonel, did it mean? The colonel, too, was puzzled. He asked to see the pictures again. "Ah," he said, when the performance was over, "I have it. They are holding the horses."

This story, true or not—and I am told it is true—suggests nicely the pain with which the human being accommodates himself to changing conditions. The tendency is apparently involuntary and immediate to protect oneself against the shock of change by continuing in the presence of altered situations the familiar habits, however incongruous, of the past.

Yet, if human beings are attached to the known, to the realm of things as they are, they also, regrettably for their peace of mind, are incessantly attracted to the unknown and to things as they might be. As Ecclesiastes glumly pointed out, men persist in disordering their settled ways and beliefs by seeking out many inventions.

The point is obvious. Change has always been a constant in human

---

[1] Reproduced by permission of *Engineering and Science Monthly*, April, 1950, and the author, who is a Professor of History at Massachusetts Institute of Technology.

affairs; today, indeed, it is one of the determining characteristics of our civilization. In our relatively shapeless social organization the shifts from station to station are fast and easy. More important for our immediate purpose, America is fundamentally an industrial society in a time of tremendous technological development. We are thus constantly presented with new devices or new forms of power that, in their refinement and extension, continually bombard the fixed structure of our habits of mind and behavior. Under such conditions, our salvation, or at least our peace of mind, appears to depend upon how successfully we can in the future become what has been called in an excellent phrase a completely "adaptive society."

It is interesting, in view of all this, that so little investigation, relatively, has been made of the process of change and human responses to it. Recently, psychologists, sociologists, and cultural anthropologists have addressed themselves to the subject with suggestive results. But we are still far from a full understanding of the process, and still farther from knowing how we can set about simplifying and assisting an individual's or a group's accommodation to new machines or new ideas.

With these things in mind, I thought it might be interesting and perhaps useful to examine historically a changing situation within a society; to see if from this examination we can discover how the new machines or ideas that introduced the changing situation developed; to see who introduces them, who resists them, what points of friction or tension in the social structure are produced by the innovation, and perhaps why they are produced and what, if anything, may be done about it. For this case study the introduction of continuous-aim firing in the United States Navy has been selected. The system, first devised by an English officer in 1898, was introduced into our Navy in the years 1900–1902.

I have chosen to study this episode for two reasons. First, a navy is not unlike a society that has been placed under laboratory conditions. Its dimensions are severely limited; it is beautifully ordered and articulated; it is relatively isolated from random influences. For these reasons the impact of change can be clearly discerned, the resulting dislocations in the structure easily discovered and marked out. In the second place, the development of continuous-aim firing rests upon mechanical devices. It therefore presents for study a concrete, durable situation. It is not like many other innovating reagents—a Manichean heresy, or Marxism, or the views of Sigmund Freud—that can be shoved and hauled out of shape by contending forces or conflicting prejudices. At all times, we know exactly what continuous-aim firing really is. It will be well now to describe, as briefly as possible, *what* it is.

The governing fact in gunfire at sea is that the gun is mounted on an unstable platform—a rolling ship. This constant motion obviously complicates the problem of holding a steady aim. Before 1898, this problem was solved in the following elementary fashion. A gun pointer estimated the range of the target—ordinarily about 2,800 yards. He then raised the gun barrel to give the gun the elevation to carry the shell to the target at the estimated range. This was accomplished by turning a small wheel on the gun mount that operated the elevating gears. With the gun thus fixed for range, the gun pointer peered through open sights, not unlike those on a small rifle, and waited until the roll of the ship brought the sights on the target. He then pressed the firing button that discharged the gun. There were, by 1898, on some naval guns, telescope sights which naturally enlarged the image of the target for the gun pointer. But these sights were rarely used by gun pointers. They were lashed securely to the gun barrel and, recoiling with the barrel, jammed back against the unwary pointer's eye. Therefore, when used at all, they were used only to take an initial sight for purposes of estimating the range before the gun was fired.

Notice, now, two things about the process. First of all, the rapidity of fire was controlled by the rolling period of the ship. Pointers had to wait for the one moment in the roll when the sights were brought on the target. Notice also this: There is in every pointer what is called a "firing interval"—the time lag between his impulse to fire the gun and the translation of this impulse into the act of pressing the firing button. A pointer, because of this reaction time, could not wait to fire the gun until the exact moment when the roll of the ship brought the sights onto the target; he had to will to fire a little before, while the sights were off the target. Since the firing interval was an individual matter, varying obviously from man to man, each pointer had to estimate, from long practice, his own interval and compensate for it accordingly.

These things, together with others we need not here investigate, conspired to make gunfire at sea relatively uncertain and ineffective. The pointer, on a moving platform, estimating range and firing interval, shooting while his sight was off the target, became in a sense an individual artist.

In 1898, many of the uncertainties were removed from the process, and the position of the gun pointer radically altered, by the introduction of continuous-aim firing. The major change was that which enabled the gun pointer to keep his sight and gun barrel on the target throughout the roll of the ship. This was accomplished by altering the gear ratio in the elevating gear to permit a pointer to compensate for the roll of the vessel by rapidly elevating and depressing the gun. From this change, another followed. With the possibility of maintaining the gun always on the target, the desirability of improved sights became immediately apparent. The advantages of the telescope sight, as opposed to the open sight, were for the first time fully realized. But the existing telescope sight, it will be recalled, moved with the recoil of the gun and jammed back against the eye of the gunner. To correct this, the sight was mounted on a sleeve that permitted the gun barrel to recoil through it without moving the telescope.

These two improvements—in elevating gear and sighting—eliminated the major uncertainties in gunfire at sea and greatly increased the possibilities of both accurate and rapid fire.

You must take my word for it that this changed naval gunnery from an art to a science, and that gunnery accuracy in the British and our Navy increased about 3,000 per cent in six years. This does not mean much except to suggest a great increase in accuracy. The following comparative figures may mean a little more. In 1899, five ships of the North Atlantic Squadron fired five minutes each at a lightship hulk at the conventional range of 1,600 yards. After twenty-five minutes of banging away, two hits had been made on the sails of the elderly vessel. Six years later, one naval gunner made fifteen hits in one minute at a target 75×25 feet at the same range; half of them hit in a bull's-eye 50 inches square.

Now, with the instruments (the gun, elevating gear, and telescope), the method, and the results of continuous-aim firing in mind, let us turn to the subject of major interest: How was the idea, obviously so simple an idea, of continuous-aim firing developed; who introduced it; and what was its reception?

Introduction of an Idea

The idea was the product of the fertile mind of the English officer Admiral Sir Percy Scott. He arrived at it in this way, while, in 1898, he was the Captain of H.M.S. *Scylla*. For the previous two or three years, he had given much thought, independently and almost alone in the British Navy, to means of improving gunnery. One rough day, when the ship, at target practice, was pitching and rolling violently, he walked up and down the gun deck watching his gun crews. Because of the heavy weather, they were making very bad scores. Scott noticed, however, that one pointer was appreciably more accurate than the rest. He watched this man with care and saw, after a time, that he was unconsciously working his elevating gear back and forth in a partially successful effort to compensate for the roll of the vessel. It flashed through Scott's mind at that moment that here was the sovereign remedy for the problems of inaccurate fire. What one man could do partially and unconsciously, perhaps all men could be trained to do consciously and completely.

Acting on this assumption, he did three things. First, in all the guns of the *Scylla*, he changed the gear ratio in the elevating gear, previously used only to set the gun in fixed position for range, so that a gunner could easily elevate and depress the gun to follow a target throughout the roll. Second, he rerigged his telescopes so that they would not be influenced by the recoil of the gun. Third, he rigged a small target at the mouth of the gun, which was moved up and down by a crank to simulate a moving target. By following this target as it moved, and firing at it with a subcaliber rifle rigged in the breech of the gun, the pointer could practice every day. Thus equipped, the ship became a training ground for gunners. Where before the good pointer was an individual artist, pointers now became trained technicians, fairly uniform in their capacity to shoot. The effect was immediately felt. Within a year the *Scylla* established records that were remarkable.

At this point, I should like to stop a minute to notice several things directly related to, and involved in, the process of innovation. First, the personality of the innovator. I wish there were space to say a good deal about Admiral Sir Percy Scott. He was a wonderful man. Three small bits of evidence must suffice, however. First, he had a certain mechanical ingenuity. Second, his personal life was shot through with frustration and bitterness. There was a divorce, and a quarrel with the ambitious Lord Charles Beresford—the sounds of which, Scott liked to recall, penetrated to the last outposts of empire. Finally, he possessed, like Swift, a savage indignation directed ordinarily at the inelastic intelligence of all constituted authority—especially the British Admiralty.

There are other points worth mention here. Notice first that Scott was not responsible for the invention of the basic instruments that made the reform in gunnery possible. This reform rested upon the gun itself, which as a rifle had been in existence on ships for at least forty years; the elevating gear, which had been, in the form Scott found it, a part of the rifled gun from the beginning; and the telescope sight, which had been on shipboard at least eight years. Scott's contribution was to bring these three elements, appropriately modified, into a combination that made continuous-aim firing possible for the first time. Notice also that he was allowed to bring these elements into combination by accident, by watching the unconscious action of a gun pointer endeavoring through the operation of his elevating gear to correct partially for the roll of his vessel.

The Prepared Mind Is Not Enough

Scott, as we have seen, had been interested in gunnery; he had thought about ways to increase accuracy by practice and improvement of existing machinery; but able as he was, he had not been able to produce on his own initiative and by his own thinking the essential idea and modify instruments to fit his purpose. Notice here, finally, the intricate interaction of chance, the intellectual climate, and Scott's mind. Fortune (in this case the unaware gun pointer) indeed favors the prepared mind, but even fortune and the prepared mind need a favorable environment before they can conspire to produce sudden change. No intelligence can proceed very far above the threshold of existing data or the binding combinations of existing data.

All these elements that enter into what may be called "original thinking" interest me as a teacher. Deeply rooted in the pedagogical mind often enough is a sterile infatuation with "inert ideas"; there is thus always present in the profession the tendency to be diverted from the *process* by which these ideas, or indeed any ideas, are really produced. I well remember with what contempt a class of mine, which was reading Leonardo da Vinci's *Notebooks,* dismissed the author because he appeared to know no more mechanics than, as one wit in the class observed, a Vermont Republican farmer of the present day. This is perhaps the result to be expected from a method of instruction that too frequently implies that the great generalizations were the result, on the one hand, of chance—an apple falling in an orchard or a teapot boiling on the hearth— or, on the other hand, of some towering intelligence proceeding in isolation inexorably toward some prefigured idea, like evolution, for example.

This process by which new concepts appear—the interaction of fortune, intellectual climate, and the prepared imaginative mind—is an interesting subject for examination offered by any case study of innovation. It was a subject that momentarily engaged the attention of Horace Walpole, whose lissome intelligence glided over the surface of so many ideas. In reflecting upon the part played by chance in the development of new concepts, he recalled the story of the three princes of Serendip who set out to find some interesting object on a journey through their realm. They did not find the particular object of their search; but along the way, they discovered many new things simply because they were looking for *something.* Walpole believed this intellectual method ought to be given a name—in honor of the founders—serendipity; and serendipity certainly exerts a considerable influence in what we call original thinking. There is an element of serendipity, for example, in Scott's chance discovery of continuous-aim firing, in that he was, and had been, looking for some means to improve his target practice and stumbled upon a solution, by observation, that had never entered his head.

Educating the Navy

It was in 1900 that Percy Scott went out to the China Station as commanding officer of H.M.S. *Terrible.* In that ship, he continued his training methods and his spectacular successes in naval gunnery. On the China Station, he met up with an American junior officer, William S. Sims. Sims had little of the mechanical ingenuity of Percy Scott, but the two were drawn together by temperamental similarities that are worth noticing here. Sims had the same intolerance for what is called "spit and polish" and the same contempt for bureaucratic inertia as his British brother officer. He had for some years been concerned, as had Scott, with what he took to be the inefficiency of his own Navy. Just before he met Scott, for example, he had shipped out to China in the brand-new pride of the fleet, the battleship *Kentucky.* After careful investigation and reflection, he had informed his superiors in Washington that she was not a battleship at all—"but a crime against the white race."

The spirit with which he pushed forward his efforts to reform the naval service can best be stated in his own words to a brother officer: "I am perfectly willing that those holding views different from mine should continue to live, but with every fiber of my being I loathe indirection and shiftiness, and where it occurs in high places, and is used to save face at the expense of the vital interests of our great service (in which silly people place such a childlike trust), I want that man's blood and I will have it no matter what it costs me personally."

From Scott, in 1900, Sims learned all there was to know about continuous-aim firing. He modified, with the Englishman's active assistance, the gear on his own ship and tried out the new system. After a few months' training, his experimental batteries began making remarkable records at target practice. Sure of the usefulness of his gunnery methods, Sims then turned to the task of educating the Navy at large. In thirteen great official reports, he documented the case for continuous-aim firing, supporting his arguments at every turn with a mass of factual data. Over a period of two years, he reiterated three principal points: First, he continually cited the records established by Scott's ships, the *Scylla* and the *Terrible,* and supported these with the accumulating data from his own tests on an American ship; second, he described the mechanisms used and the training procedures instituted by Scott and himself to obtain these records; third, he explained that our own mechanisms were not generally adequate without modification to meet the demands placed on them by continuous-aim firing. Our elevating gear, useful to raise or lower a gun slowly to fix it in position for the proper range, did not always work easily and rapidly enough to enable a gunner to follow a target with his gun throughout the roll of the ship. Sims also explained that such few telescope sights as there were on board our ships were useless. Their cross wires were so thick or coarse that they obscured the target, and the sights had been attached to the gun in such a way that the recoil system of the gun plunged the eyepiece against the eye of the gun pointer.

This was the substance not only of the first but of all the succeeding reports written on the subject of gunnery from the China Station. It will be interesting to see what response these met with in Washington. The response falls roughly into three easily indentifiable stages.

First stage: no response. Sims had directed his comments to the Bureau of Ordnance and the Bureau of Navigation; in both bureaus, there was dead silence. The thing—claims and records of continuous-aim firing—was not credible. The reports were simply filed away and forgotten. Some, indeed, it was later discovered to Sims's delight, were half eaten away by cockroaches.

Second stage: rebuttal. It is never pleasant for any man to have his best work left unnoticed by superiors, and it was an unpleasantness that Sims suffered extremely ill. In his later reports, besides the accumulating data he used to clinch his argument, he changed his tone. He used deliberately shocking language because, as he said: "They were furious at my first papers and stowed them away. I therefore made up my mind I would give these later papers such a form that they would be dangerous documents to leave neglected in the files." To another friend, he added: "I want scalps or nothing, and if I can't have 'em, I won't play."

Sims Gets Attention

Besides altering his tone, he took another step to be sure his views would receive attention. He sent copies of his reports to other officers in the fleet. Aware, as a result, that Sims's gunnery claims were being circulated and talked about, the men in Washington were then stirred to action. They responded—notably through the chief of the Bureau of Ordnance, who had general charge of the equipment used in gunnery practice—as follows: (1) Our equipment was in general as good as the British; (2) since our equipment was as good, the trouble must be with the men, but the gun pointers and the training of gun pointers were the responsibility of the officers on the ships; (3) and most significant—continuous-aim firing was impossible. Experiments had revealed that five men at work on the elevating gear of a six-inch gun could not produce the power necessary to compensate for a roll of five degrees in ten seconds. These experiments and calculations demonstrated beyond peradventure or doubt that Scott's system of gunfire was not possible.

Only one difficulty is discoverable in these arguments: They were wrong at important points. To begin with, while there was little difference between the standard British equipment and the standard U.S. equipment, the instruments on Scott's two ships, the *Scylla* and the *Terrible,* were far better than the standard equipment on our ships. Second, all the men could not be trained in continuous-aim firing until equipment was improved throughout the fleet. Third, the experiments with the elevating gear had been ingeniously contrived at the Washington Navy Yard—on solid ground. It had therefore been possible in the Bureau of Ordnance calculation, to dispense with Newton's first law of motion, which naturally operated at sea to assist the gunner in elevating or depressing a gun mounted on a moving ship. Another difficulty was, of course, that continuous-aim firing was in use on Scott's and some of our own ships at the time the chief of the Bureau of Ordnance was writing that it was a mathematical impossibility. In every way, I find this second stage, the apparent resort to reason, the most entertaining and instructive in our investigation of the responses to innovation.

Third stage: name calling. Sims, of course, by the high temperature he was running and by his calculated overstatement, invited this. He was told in official endorsements on his reports that there were others quite as sincere and loyal as he and far less difficult; he was dismissed as a crack-brain egotist; he was called a deliberate falsifier of evidence.

Sims Gets Action

The rising opposition and the character of the opposition was not calculated to discourage further efforts by Sims. It convinced him that he was being attacked by shifty, dishonest men who were the victims, as he said, of insufferable conceit and ignorance. He made up his mind, there-fore, that he was prepared to go to any extent to obtain the "scalps" and the "blood" he was after. Accordingly, he, a lieutenant, took the ex-traordinary step of writing the President of the United States, Theodore Roosevelt, to inform him of the remarkable records of Scott's ships, of the inadequacy of our own gunnery routines and records, and of the refusal of the Navy Department to act. Roosevelt, who always liked to respond to such appeals when he conveniently could, brought Sims back from China late in 1902 and installed him as Inspector of Target Practice, a post the naval officer held throughout the remaining six years of the administration.

With this sequence of events (the chronological account of the innova-tion of continuous-aim firing) in mind, it is possible now to examine the evidence to see what light it may throw on our present interest—the origins of and responses to change in a society.

First, the origins. We have already analyzed briefly the origins of the idea. We have seen how Scott arrived at his notion. We must now ask ourselves, I think, why Sims so actively sought, almost alone among his brother officers, to introduce the idea into his service. It is particularly interesting here to notice again that neither Scott nor Sims invented the instruments on which the innovation rested. They did not urge their proposal because of pride in the instruments of their own design.

The Engineer and the Entrepreneur

The telescope sight had first been placed on shipboard in 1892 by Bradley Fiske, an officer of great inventive capacity. In that year, Fiske had even sketched out on paper the vague possibility of continuous-aim firing, but his sight was condemned by his commanding officer, Robley D. Evans, as of no use. Instead of fighting for his telescope, Fiske turned his attention to a range finder. But six years later, Sims took over and became the engineer of the revolution.

I would suggest, with some reservations, this explanation: Fiske, as an inventor, took his pleasure in great part from the design of the device. He lacked not so much the energy as the overriding sense of social necessity that would have enabled him to *force* revolutionary ideas on the service. Sims possessed this sense. In Fiske, we may here find the familiar plight of the engineer who often enough must watch the products of his ingenuity being organized and promoted by other men. These other promotional men, when they appear in the world of commerce, are called entre-preneurs. In the world of ideas, they are still entrepreneurs.

Sims was one, a middle-aged man caught in the periphery (as a lieutenant) of the intricate webbing of a precisely organized society. Rank, the exact definition and limitation of a man's capacity at any given moment in his own career, prevented Sims from discharging all his exploding energies into the purely routine channels of the peacetime Navy. At the height of his powers, he was a junior officer standing watches on a ship cruising aimlessly in friendly foreign waters. The remarkable changes in systems of gunfire to which Scott introduced him gave him the opportunity to expend his energies quite legitimately against the encrusted hierarchy of his society. He was moved, it seems to me, in part by his genuine desire to improve his own profession but also in part by rebellion against tedium, against inefficiency from on high, and against the artificial limitations placed on his actions by the social structure—in his case, junior rank.

Responding to Change

Now, having briefly investigated the origins of the change, let us examine the reasons for what must be considered the weird response we have observed to this proposed change. Here was a reform that greatly and demonstrably increased the fighting effectiveness of a service that maintains itself almost exclusively to fight. Why, then, this refusal to accept so carefully documented a case, a case proved incontestably by records and experience? Why should virtually all the rulers of a society so resolutely seek to reject a change that so markedly improved its chances for survival in any contest with competing societies?

There are the obvious reasons that will occur to everyone—the source of the proposed reform was an obscure junior officer eight thousand miles away; he was, and this is a significant factor, criticizing gear and machinery designed by the very men in the bureaus to whom he was sending his criticisms. And furthermore, Sims was seeking to introduce what he claimed were improvements in a field where improvements appeared unnecessary. Superiority in war, as in other things, is a relative matter, and the Spanish-American War had been won by the old system of gunnery. Therefore, it was superior even though, of the 9,500 shots fired, at varying but close ranges, only 121 had found their mark.

A less obvious cause appears by far the most important one. It has to do with the fact that the Navy is not only an armed force; it is a society. In the forty years following the Civil War, this society had been forced to accommodate itself to a series of technological changes—the steam turbine, the electric motor, the rifled shell of great explosive power, case-hardened steel armor, and all the rest of it. These changes wrought extraordinary changes in ship design and, therefore, in the concepts of how ships were to be used, that is, in fleet tactics and even in naval strategy. The Navy of this period is a paradise for the historian or sociologist in search of evidence of a society's responses to change.

To these numerous innovations, producing as they did a spreading disorder throughout a service with heavy commitments to formal organization, the Navy responded with grudging pain. It is wrong to assume, as civilians frequently do, that this blind reaction to technological change springs exclusively from some causeless Bourbon distemper that invades the military mind. There is a sounder and more attractive base. The opposition, where it occurs, of the soldier and the sailor to such change springs from the normal human instinct to protect oneself and, more especially, one's way of life. Military organizations are societies built around and upon the prevailing weapon systems. Intuitively and quite correctly, the military man feels that a change in a weapon portends a change in the arrangements of his society.

Think of it this way. Since the time that the memory of man runneth not to the contrary, the naval society has been built upon the surface vessel. Daily routines, habits of mind, social organization, physical accommodations, convictions, rituals, spiritual allegiances have been conditioned by the essential fact of the ship. What, then, happens to your society if the ship is displaced as the principal element by such a radically different weapon as the plane? The mores and structure of the society are immediately placed in jeopardy. They may, in fact, be wholly destroyed. It was the witty cliché of the twenties that those naval officers who persisted in defending the battleship against the apparently superior claims of the carrier did so because the battleship was a more comfortable home. What, from one point of view, is a better argument?

This sentiment would appear to account in large part for the opposition to Sims; it was the product of an instinctive protective feeling, even if the reasons for this feeling were not overt or recognized. The years after 1902 proved how right, in their terms, the opposition was. From changes in gunnery flowed an extraordinary complex of changes: in shipboard routines, ship design, and fleet tactics. There was, too, a social change. In the days when gunnery was taken lightly, the gunnery officer was taken lightly. After 1903, he became one of the most significant and powerful members of a ship's company, and this shift of emphasis naturally was shortly reflected in promotion lists. Each one of these changes provoked a dislocation in the naval society; and with man's troubled foresight and natural indisposition to break up classic forms, the men in Washington withstood the Sims onslaught as long as they could. It is very significant that they withstood it until an agent from outside—outside and above— who was not clearly identified with the naval society, entered to force change.

This agent, the President of the United States, might reasonably and legitimately claim the credit for restoring our gunnery efficiency. But this restoration by *force majeure* was brought about at great cost to the service and men involved. Bitternesses, suspicions, wounds were caused that it was impossible to conceal or heal.

Now, this entire episode may be summed up in five separate points:

1. The essential idea for change occurred in part by chance, but in an environment that contained all the essential elements for change, and to a mind prepared to recognize the possibility of change.

2. The basic elements—the gun, gear, and sight—were put in the environment by other men—men interested in designing machinery to

serve different purposes, or simply interested in the instruments themselves.

3. These elements were brought into successful combination by minds not interested in the instruments for themselves, but in what they could do with them. These minds were, to be sure, interested in good gunnery, overtly and consciously. They may also, not so consciously, have been interested in the implied revolt that is present in the support of all change. Their temperaments and careers indeed support this view. From gunnery, Sims went on to attack ship designs, existing fleet tactics, and methods of promotion. He lived and died, as the service said, a stormy petrel, a man always on the attack against higher authority, a rebellious spirit.

4. He and his colleagues were opposed on this occasion by men who were apparently moved by three considerations: honest disbelief in the dramatic but substantiated claims of the new process, protection of the existing devices and instruments with which they identified themselves, and maintenance of the existing society with which they were identified.

5. The deadlock between those who sought change and those who sought to retain things as they were was broken only by an appeal to superior force—a force removed from and unidentified with the mores, conventions, devices of the society. This seems to me a very important point. The naval society in 1900 broke down in its effort to accommodate itself to a new situation. The appeal to Roosevelt is documentation for Mahan's great generalization that no military service should or can undertake to reform itself. It must seek assistance from outside.

Now, with these five summary points in mind, it may be possible to seek, as suggested at the outset, a few larger implications from this story. What, if anything, may it suggest about the general process by which any society attempts to meet changing conditions?

No Society Can Reform Itself?

There is, to begin with, a disturbing inference half concealed in Mahan's statement that no military organization can reform itself. Certainly, civilians would agree with this. We all know now that war and the preparation of war is too important, as Clemenceau said, to be left to the generals. But military organizations are really societies—more rigidly structured, more highly integrated than most communities, but still societies. What, then, if we make this phrase to read: "No society can reform itself"? Is the process of adaptation to change, for example, too important to be left to human beings? This is a discouraging thought; and historically, there is some cause to be discouraged.

This is a subject to which we may well address ourselves. Our society, especially, is built, as I have said, just as surely upon a changing technology as the Navy of the nineties was built upon changing weapon systems. How, then, can we find the means to accept with less pain to ourselves and less damage to our social organization the dislocations in our society that are produced by innovation? I cannot, of course, give any satisfying answer to these difficult questions. But in thinking about the case study before us, an idea occurred to me that at least might warrant further investigation by men far more qualified than I.

A primary source of conflict and tension in our case study appears to lie in this great word I have used so often in the summary—the word *identification*. It cannot have escaped notice that some men identified themselves with their creations—sights, guns, gear, and so forth—and thus obtained a presumed satisfaction from the thing itself, a satisfaction that prevented them from thinking too closely on either the use or the defects of the thing; that others identified themselves with a settled way of life they had inherited or accepted with minor modification and thus found their satisfaction in attempting to maintain that way of life unchanged; and that still others identified themselves as rebellious spirits, men of the insurgent cast of mind, and thus obtained a satisfaction from the act of revolt itself.

This purely personal identification with a concept, a convention, or an attitude would appear to be a powerful barrier in the way of easily acceptable change. Here is an interesting primitive example. In the years from 1864 to 1871, ten steel companies in the country began making steel by the new Bessemer process. All but one of them at the outset imported from Great Britain English workmen familiar with the process. One, the Cambria Company, did not. In the first few years, those companies with British labor established an initial superiority. But by the end of the seventies, Cambria had obtained a commanding lead over all competitors.

The Bessemer process, like any new technique, had been constantly improved and refined in this period from 1864 to 1871. The British laborers of Cambria's competitors, secure in the performance of their own original techniques, resisted and resented all change. The Pennsylvania farm boys, untrammeled by the rituals and traditions of their craft, happily and rapidly adapted themselves to the constantly changing process. They ended by creating an unassailable competitive position for their company.

How, then, can we modify the dangerous effects of this word *identification?* And how much can we tamper with this identifying process? Our security, much of it, after all, comes from giving our allegiance to something greater than ourselves. These are difficult questions to which only the most tentative and provisional answers may here be proposed for consideration.

The Danger of Limited Identifications

If one looks closely at this little case history, one discovers that the men involved were the victims of *severely limited* identifications. They were presumably all part of a society dedicated to the process of national defense, yet they persisted in aligning themselves with separate parts of that process—with the existing instruments of defense, with the existing customs of the society, or with the act of rebellion against the customs of the society. Of them all, the insurgents had the best of it. They could, and did, say that the process of defense was improved by a gun that shot straighter and faster, and since they wanted such guns, they were unique among their fellows—patriots who sought only the larger object of improved defense. But this beguiling statement—even when coupled with the recognition that these men were right, and extremely valuable and deserving of respect and admiration—cannot conceal the fact that they were interested too in scalps and blood. They were so interested, in fact, that they made their case a militant one and thus created an atmosphere in which self-respecting men could not capitulate without appearing either weak or wrong, or both. So these limited identifications brought men into conflict with each other, and the conflict prevented them from arriving at a common acceptance of a change that presumably, as men interested in our total national defense, they would all find desirable.

It appears, therefore, if I am correct in my assessment, that we might spend some time and thought on the possibility of enlarging the sphere of our identifications from the part to the whole. For example, those Pennsylvania farm boys at the Cambria Steel Company, were apparently much more interested in the manufacture of steel than in the preservation of any particular way of making steel. So I would suggest that in studying innovation, we look further into this possibility: the possibility that any group that exists for any purpose—the family, the factory, the educational institution—might begin by defining for itself its grand object, and see to it that that grand object is communicated to every member of the group. Thus defined and communicated, it might serve as a unifying agent against the disruptive local allegiances of the inevitable smaller elements that compose any group. It may also serve as a means to increase the acceptability of any change that would assist in the more efficient achievement of the grand object.

There appears also a second possible way to combat the untoward influence of limited identifications. We are, I may repeat, a society based on technology in a time of prodigious technological advance, and a civilization committed irrevocably to the theory of evolution. These things mean that we believe in change; they suggest that if we are to survive in good health, we must become an "adaptive society." By the word "adaptive" is meant the ability to extract the fullest possible returns from the opportunities at hand: the ability of Sir Percy Scott to select judiciously from the ideas and material presented both by the past and by the present, and to throw them into a new combination. "Adaptive," as here used, also means the kind of resilience that will enable us to accept fully and easily the best promises of changing circumstances without losing our sense of continuity or our essential integrity.

We are not yet emotionally an adaptive society, though we try systematically to develop forces that tend to make us one. We encourage the search for new inventions; we keep the mind stimulated, bright, and free to seek out fresh means of transport, communication, and energy; yet we remain, in part, appalled by the consequences of our ingenuity and, too frequently, try to find security through the shoring-up of ancient and irrelevant conventions, the extension of purely physical safeguards, or the delivery of decisions we ourselves should make into the keeping of superior authority like the state. These solutions are not necessarily unnatural or wrong; but historically, they have not been enough, and I suspect they never will be enough to give us the serenity and competence we seek.

A New View of Ourselves

If the preceding statements are correct, they suggest that we might give some attention to the construction of a new view of ourselves as a society which in time of great change identified itself with and obtained security and satisfaction from the wise and creative accommodation to change itself. Such a view rests, I think, upon a relatively greater reverence for the mere *process* of living in a society than we possess today, and a relatively smaller respect for and attachment to any special *product* of a society—a product either as finite as a bathroom fixture or as conceptual as a fixed and final definition of our Constitution or our democracy.

Historically, such an identification with *process* as opposed to *product*, with adventurous selection and adaptation as opposed to simple retention and possessiveness, has been difficult to achieve collectively. The Roman of the early republic, the Italian of the late fifteenth and early sixteenth century, and the Englishman of Elizabeth's time appear to have been most successful in seizing the new opportunities while conserving as much of the heritage of the past as they found relevant and useful to their purpose.

We seem to have fallen on times similar to theirs, when many of the existing forms and schemes have lost meaning in the face of dramatically altering circumstances. Like them, we may find at least part of our salvation in identifying ourselves with the adaptive process and thus share with them some of the joy, exuberance, satisfaction, and security with which they went out to meet their changing times.

QUESTIONS

1. Sum up Morison's conclusions as to why this useful innovation was so strongly resisted.
2. What is the primary source of conflict and tension in innovation, according to Morison? How can this source be combated?

3. The president of a major consumer metal container firm is aware of your study of innovation. He reports reluctance of his semiautonomous division managers to push for radically new products or materials. All divisions are doing reasonably well. Interpret to the president the significant elements of Morison's study and conclusions that might be useful in corporate life.

4. Study the history of a major innovation.
   a) What were the characteristics of the innovator?
   b) Under what conditions did innovation take place?
   c) Why and how did resistance occur?
   d) How can a corporation "define its grand purpose"? Give an example for a current firm.

The Inventor and His World

The fact is that born inventors do not, as a rule, join the research laboratories of manufacturing firms; and even when they do, the conditions under which they work are not conducive to production. The results obtained admit of no other interpretation. Yet it seems impossible to convince those responsible for the initiation and constitution of such laboratories for corporative research that matters are as they are, and might easily be improved.

The procedure adopted is to appoint as director some person of scientific attainments, who is instructed to engage at low salaries young persons of either sex pronounced by their college professors to be bright and promising, bind them by very strict long term agreements to assign all inventions to the company, and provide them with problems to work on, and facilities for work.

Unfortunately, people with original minds do not as a rule become employees on such terms unless they have little faith in themselves, or are driven by force of circumstances. If they do so, they resent very strongly being compelled to abandon the property in their own creative products which the law, in the first instance, guarantees to them. Everyone is perfectly familiar with this fact as regards creative work other than invention; in matters of art, music, and literature, the term of contempt used is "hack." Work under the conditions of most industrial research laboratories is hack-work in this sense. Insight into the psychology of the matter is gained by noting that the artist, writer, or composer feels no shame in accepting the support of a patron, dealer, or publisher, during the production of work of his own conception. He is still a free man, and not a wage slave.

The mistake arises in the case of invention largely from confusion with the position of pure scientific research, where creative work is unsaleable as such, and is maintained by paying its producers as teachers, and by grants-in-aid. The businessman who learns that Einstein or Rutherford drew smaller salaries than his own managers, yet turned out original

116

scientific work which is the wonder of the world, may be pardoned for supposing that if he catches their like young, by offering a little more than the academic rate of pay, they will turn out equally original work, but of a kind extremely profitable to his firm if protected by patents. The psychological errors involved in this view are too numerous to deal with here, but the businessman's psychological powers are best adapted to dealing with his own kind, and often fail completely when applied to the mentality of other human types. For one thing, he entirely fails to appreciate the fundamental difference between the pursuit of pure knowledge, every bit of which is of imperishable value, and technical invention, the value of which is largely transient.

But let the creative bird be caught in the net of the fowler, and duly caged. All experience goes to show that he rarely sings. Creative work is *over*-work; the steady round of 9 to 6, with lunch from 1 to 2:30, simply does not produce it. It needs sweating and worrying in the small hours of the night; it is monomania. The hope of fortune, the pressure of creditors, nay, even the battle with insufficient means and appliances, are the spurs that are needed.

H. STAFFORD HATFIELD

FROM: *The Inventor and His World* (New York: Penguin Press, 1933). Reproduced by permission of Routledge & Kegan Paul Ltd.

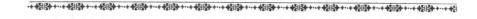

CREATIVE THINKING IN SCIENTIFIC WORK[1]

By E. I. Green

Vice President, Bell Telephone Laboratories

. . . "WHAT MANNER of person is a creative thinker?" Unfortunately, the answer is that no two creative thinkers are alike. Each one has his own capabilities, his own methods, his own idiosyncrasies. Notwithstanding this, a number of writers have concluded that two general types can be distinguished: the intuitive thinkers and the logical ones—the people who conceive a new idea and then test it, and the people who accumulate knowledge and analyze it until something new emerges. Considerable emphasis has been laid on these two types. The evidence indicates, however, that these are the extremes, and that most creative thinkers are mixtures of the two. It is suggested, therefore, that would-be creative thinkers exploit both approaches to the maximum extent possible.

To delve deeper into the characteristics of the creative thinker, attention is called next to a study carried out by Donald Walker at the University of Chicago. He devised tests for measuring five specific aptitudes which he felt might be essential to creative thinking, and applied these tests to a large group of chemists and mathematicians noted for their original contributions. Here are the aptitudes and the scores.

Ability	Approximate Percentage with High Score
Originality of response	28
Sensitivity to environment	22
Copious flow of ideas	33
Flexibility of approach	55
Ability to concentrate	39

Walker found that incidence of all five abilities in a single individual was extremely rare. He concluded that the best way to obtain creativity is not to depend on isolated original thinkers, but to assemble a group of individuals whose talents in these five areas are complementary, and train them for teamwork.

This analysis, while enlightening, leaves us wondering whether any more basic capabilities or propensities can be found in the make-up of the creative thinker. Search of the literature reveals a confusing array of such

---

[1] Condensed from *Electrical Engineering*, Vol. LXXIII (June, 1954), by permission of the author and the publisher.

factors. Those which have appealed to the writer as being most important follow.

To begin with, there is *knowledge*. Wisdom is the foundation of new ideas, and a certain threshold level of acquaintance with the subject is practically essential for creative thought.

In part, the necessary knowledge may be acquired through formal training. It seems to be true, however, that creative thinkers almost invariably possess an uncommon *capacity for self-instruction*.

Another cardinal requirement is *curiosity*. This refers, of course, not to a meddling interest in the affairs of others, but to scientific curiosity, that insatiable hunger to know how and why. This may well be the most valuable trait a scientist can have.

Next should be set down *observation*. This is somewhat the same as Walker's "sensitivity to environment." In particular, the creative thinker should be ever on the alert for exceptions, anomalies, and the like. A new uncertainty is apt to be more useful than an ancient verity.

Not far behind comes *memory*. Since creative thinking is frequently nothing more than the bringing-together of factors never before associated, the recollection of past observations and previous ideas may play a large part. Storing up old or unused ideas in the garret of the mind is a profitable habit.

Many writers say that *intellectual integrity* is the first quality of the scientific mind. In the words of Michael Faraday, the creative thinker should be "a man willing to listen to every suggestion, but determined to judge for himself. He should not be biased by appearances; have no favorite hypothesis; be of no school; and in doctrine have no master. He should not be a respecter of persons, but of things. Truth should be his primary object. If to these qualities be added industry, he may indeed hope to walk within the veil of the temple of nature."

Allied to integrity is the next factor, *skepticism*. However he may behave in private life, the creative thinker, in his technical world, must woo the unconventional. He must be an iconoclast, a breaker of idols, a discarder of trammels.

Nor should *imagination* be forgotten. On this, there is unanimous agreement among accepted authorities. But it is rather difficult to define as a trait. Maybe it is not too different from Walker's "copious flow of ideas."

Perhaps *enthusiasm* should have had a higher place on the list. Creative thinking is seldom process of the intellect alone. For maximum achievement, the mind must be inspired by the driving power of the emotions.

Coupled to this is *persistence*—the stubborn will to solve the problem despite maddening difficulties and frustrations. This is the quality which stands out in the records of creative thinkers, and the one which they themselves reiterate when counseling those who aspire to follow in their footsteps.

This brings the list of characteristics to ten, which seems a good place to stop. Though the list is impressive, no one should be frightened by it. Under no circumstance should anyone conclude that every creative thinker must embody an extreme measure of each one of these characteristics. If their presence in recognized creative thinkers could be determined, they surely would be found to occur in widely varying degree. So they should be regarded as desirable rather than essential qualities.

At this point, someone may ask: "Are not these characteristics inherent; are not creative thinkers born, not made?" The answer is: "To some extent, yes," but with the quickly added assertion that most people who have chosen science as their lifework do in fact possess a fair measure of the characteristics named, and the further thesis that latent powers of this kind can be developed and stimulated. . . .

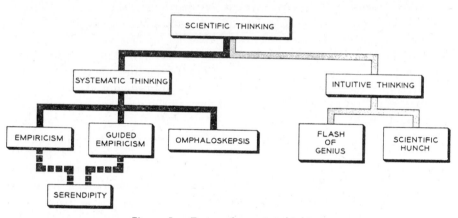

Figure 1.   Types of creative thinking

Types of Creative Thinking

Next, it is in order to consider the different types of creative thinking. Since each writer has a different classification, the author claims the privilege of devising his own. Like all the others, it is rather loose. To simplify things, it is put in the form of a family tree. See Figure 1.

At the opposite ends of what is conceived to be a continuum of creative thought lie *systematic thinking*, on the one hand, and *intuitive thinking*, on the other. The one is the deliberate act of the conscious mind, the other the gracious gift of the subconscious in return for the previous labors of the conscious mind.

To take intuitive thinking first, it has its spectacular form, the flash of genius, the sudden brilliant answer to a baffling problem. It has also its less pretentious form, which is herein termed the scientific "hunch."

Systematic thinking presents a greater diversity. There is, first, the pursuit of new knowledge by observation and experiment alone, without recourse to theory. This form was pursued so assiduously by Thomas

Edison that it often bears his name; a better name, however, is *empiricism*, from the Greek *en peira*, meaning "by trial."

Opposed to empiricism is the purely rational approach through formulation of theory. A British officer in India devised a delightful name for this process. He called it *omphaloskepsis*, meaning deep meditation, in oriental fashion, while gazing at the navel. The occidental style of gazing at feet on a desk is capable of producing a similar effect. Of course, the scientific method requires that any conclusions arrived at by either process be subjected to experimental verification.

In between empiricism and omphaloskepsis lies the invaluable hybrid combination of *guided empiricism*. Finally, there is one offshoot of experimentation, whose name derives from a fairy story about the three princes of Serendip (the old name for the island of Ceylon). These princes had the happy faculty of discovering something valuable by accident while searching for something else. To describe this gift, which is exemplified again and again in the annals of science, Horace Walpole coined the word *serendipity*.

A classic example of serendipity was the accident which led Dr. Alexander Fleming to the discovery of penicillin. While Fleming was studying new strains of bacteria, a culture plate which he had prepared became contaminated with a blue-green mold, *penicillium notatum*. He observed that the plate was covered with colonies of bacteria except for a clear space surrounding each spot of mold. The idea occurred to him that the mold produced something which interfered with multiplication of bacteria, and he went on with research which resulted in isolating penicillin. It is noteworthy that serendipity alone did not achieve the result, but was merely the starting point of a chain of creative thinking.

Processes

If the types of creative thought are difficult to analyze, the processes are more so. People are different; thought patterns are polymorphic. Whereas a number of types and blends of creative thinking were noted, the processes are even more numerous and varied. The one which has been studied the most is the flash of genius, so perhaps that is the place to start. In the literature on this subject, records of famous thinkers and inventors throughout history have been examined under high magnification. Contemporary thinkers have been analyzed and dissected by means of questionnaires. Out of all this has come a fairly clear picture of the steps or stages which can be distinguished in the flash-of-genius phenomenon. See Figure 2.

First comes the *conception of the problem* or perception of the need. This may occur in various ways. Frequently, it may be merely the realization or formulation of a need or problem of long standing. Back in the mid-twenties, many persons were aware of the necessity for a far better amplifier characteristic in order to achieve far-flung multichannel

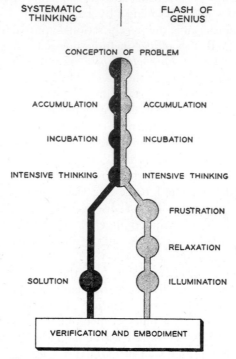

SYSTEMATIC THINKING | FLASH OF GENIUS

CONCEPTION OF PROBLEM

ACCUMULATION   ACCUMULATION

INCUBATION   INCUBATION

INTENSIVE THINKING   INTENSIVE THINKING

FRUSTRATION

RELAXATION

SOLUTION   ILLUMINATION

VERIFICATION AND EMBODIMENT

Figure 2.   Processes of creative thought

communication systems with great numbers of amplifiers in tandem. Harold S. Black stripped the problem down to the fundamental one of an amplifier output having an unwanted component not present in the input. This was the preliminary to years of study and approaches, out of which came the bold conception of an amplifier with large negative feedback, providing a new order of performance and bringing the problem of amplifier distortion within bounds.

Often the problem or need is thrust upon a person by the requirements of his job. But sometimes the genesis of the problem occurs in a flash of illumination which stems out of familiarity with an area of knowledge. Such an illumination of the problem, indeed, may be akin to the flash which later solves it.

The next stage is one of preparation or *accumulation*. The problem is investigated in all directions—by reading, by discussion with others, by experiment, if need be.

Frequently, there will follow a period of *incubation*, in which the mind digests and assimilates the information previously acquired. Some of this mental action may be subconscious.

Next comes the stage of deliberate, *intensive thinking* about the problem. Attempts are made to solve the problem by weaving ideas into new combinations. The reaches of memory are called upon. Reasoning is used to control the thought patterns, and judgment to determine their validity.

In the typical flash-of-genius case, there is a succession of trial solutions, each one bumping a dead end. Finally, the thinker runs out of ideas. He keeps on churning the old ones round and round, and winds up in a stage of *frustration*. It would even appear that a high degree of frustration may help to engender the subsequent revelation.

Usually, there ensues a time of *relaxation* of mental tensions, a period when the problem is turned over to the subconscious. On some occasion when the mind is free of obstructing interests, and concentrated attention has been succeeded by inattention or dispersed attention, the moment of *revelation* arrives. This is apt to be when the person is concerned with nothing of importance, when taking a walk, or riding on a train, or listening to music, or just letting his thoughts wander. Holidays and vacations are likely times. (It was while on vacation that J. R. Carson invented single-sideband transmission, which underlies efficient utilization of the frequency band in multichannel telephone systems.) Often the insight takes place near the fringe of consciousness, just before going to sleep or just after waking up. Just what actually happens inside the cranium when the flash of genius occurs is not definitely known. But at least enough is known to set the stage for the dramatic episode. Whatever the mechanism, the occasion for the revelation is the interval of calm following a period of intense and fruitless speculation which somehow conditions the subconscious channels.

Almost never is the flash of genius enough. Once in a blue moon the solution springs forth, like Minerva from the head of Jove, perfect in every detail. Even then, it must be committed to paper. But far more often the flash gives an imperfect solution, or just a new start. In any case, there are stern tasks to follow—days or weeks or months of confirmation by analysis or experiment, and of hammering the basic conception into practical form. This is the stage of *verification and embodiment.*

In the foregoing, the various stages which precede the flash of genius have been described as discrete entities. It will be understood, however, that in specific instances they may overlap, or become telescoped; or some, indeed, may be absent altogether.

Next come those minor manifestations of illumination referred to as scientific "hunches." These follow a less formal procedure. They are bread-and-butter things. They may occur at any time in the course of work, if pauses are made occasionally for a broad view of the situation.

Now, consider deliberate or systematic thinking. In reviewing the flash-of-genius procedure (see Fig. 2), it becomes apparent that the first four stages are, in fact, processes of deliberate thinking. These steps, namely, (1) conception of the problem, (2) accumulation of information, (3) incubation, and (4) intensive thinking, are the ones normally used in solving problems. Of course, the pattern may vary. Steps may be combined or repeated. There may be additional steps of refinement, improvement, correction, or extension. The real point is that, no matter how the answer is to come, a person starts out the same way. Usually, deliberate thinking does the job. Once in a long while, revelation does.

Guideposts

No doubt what the reader wants now is a set of rules of procedure for creative thinkers, a map which will enable him to reach the desired destination. Sad to say, the best that can be done is to indicate a few guideposts and a few road blocks. Each person must find his own way.

The first and most important guidepost is to *get the problem.* This does not sound very hard. Usually, the scientific worker is besieged by problems. The difficulty more often lies in selecting the important problems and prosecuting these without neglect of day-to-day job requirements. How does a person go about this? One way which has been tried with some success is to make up a list of things needed in one's own area of work: needed systems, needed devices, needed procedures, needed inventions, needed experiments, or whatever. These needed things are kept in mind and singled out for special attention as circumstances permit.

There was a famous Chautauqua lecture which, years before the days of radio and television, Russell A. Conwell delivered to 13 million Americans. This lecture, which was called "Acres of Diamonds," told of a man who sold his farm and wandered all over the world looking for diamonds. After he had failed in his search and died in poverty, the man who had bought the farm discovered on it a fabulous diamond mine. Just for good measure, Conwell went on to tell of other people who disposed of land rich with gold, or oil, or something, and spent their lives looking elsewhere for the thing they had abandoned. If Conwell were alive today, he surely would say that anyone in research and development work can find plenty of scientific riches in his *own back yard,* awaiting only interest and imagination. He might point out, too, that success in scientific work is not achieved in the traditional military pattern, where a subordinate waits for his supervisor to assign tasks, and that maximum satisfaction accrues from solving problems of one's own devising.

After finding the problem, the next thing is to *understand the problem.* The importance of such understanding most often becomes apparent after the fact. Suppose similar or identical problems are assigned to two men. One of them looks at the requirements separately, takes some things he knows, adds some appliques or excrescences, and comes up with a Rube Goldberg solution. The other one analyzes the problem, combines functions, strips off nonessentials, and emerges with an answer that gladdens the heart. Understanding of the problem usually is facilitated by *discussion with others.* This has the further benefit of bringing in ideas from different areas. A few gifted individuals can do creative thinking by purely mathematical processes. For most persons, however, a *physical insight* into the problem is a vast assistance.

In many cases the next step will consist in *association of ideas* in new ways. Indeed, some of the most striking examples of creative thought involve the finding of new relationships between known things or the finding of a new something which bears a given relationship to things already known. Poincaré, writing of the invention of a new class of functions, stated: "For two weeks I spent an hour or two each day at my working table, tried a great number of combinations but came to no solution. One evening, contrary to my custom, I drank some black coffee and could not sleep. Ideas crowded my mind; I felt them knocking together until two of them interlocked, making a stable combination."

So every creative thinker constantly needs to amass ideas and to seek for new combinations. Progress is made through trial associations. In dealing with a major problem, no idea should be rejected as irrelevant until it has been proved so. In particular, many ideas have been thrown on the ash heap because they did not fit a particular problem or because the means for utilizing them had not been perfected. These *rejected ideas* can become the cornerstones of new creations.

While chance may enter into creative thinking, this does not mean that the process should be haphazard. *Orderliness* is as important in tackling problems in creative thinking as in a mathematical exercise. Steps should be planned, records should be kept, and proper habits should be cultivated.

In planning excursions in creative thought, it should be borne in mind that a major instrument in scientific progress today is the organized, co-operative approach. Some ideas are small enough so that they can be worked out by one man. More often, however, a team attack is required. Uusually, the preferred type of *team attack* is not a regimented process, but one which affords opportunity for individual contributions, frequently of a high order. In all cases, whether it is a group problem or an individual one, a person can draw strength from his associates, just as Antaeus did from Mother Earth.

Much has been written on how to create and preserve the *working mood*. It seems reasonable to say that the subject has been overstressed. The best way to get in a working mood is to pick up a pencil and put something on paper, and the best way to preserve the mood is to keep on putting things down. Moreover, writing is a help to thought. It is a good exercise to tabulate different parts of the problem, different approaches, etc.

As already noted, *relaxation* can play an important part in creative thinking. Occasional pauses during the day are valuable. Sleeping over a difficult problem is a basically sound procedure. Occasionally, a longer period of relaxation is needed. But a person has to be careful. The process of relaxation is an enjoyable one, and it can be overdone. It is not too difficult to fall into what someone has termed a "plush-lined rut."

There is one important adjunct of creative thought which is seldom mentioned in the literature and which is neglected deplorably in scientific training. This is *vocabulary*. There is good evidence that most people think in words. If they do not know the words, they do not think. So the person who aspires to think creatively should expand his vocabulary in every possible way. He should make words his friends, dictionaries and glossaries a hobby.

And speaking of *hobbies,* there are several which are believed to be of value to the creative thinker. There include such things as puzzle solving, cryptography, chess, bridge, and other pursuits which require keen mental effort. This, of course, is not intended to belittle the benefits of other avocations which may contribute less directly to the development of creativity.

Road Blocks

What of the road blocks? To some extent, these are apparent from what has gone before. Perhaps the first is *limited intellectual capacity*. Fortunately, this is not beyond control. Not only can the human thinking machine be trained to work better; it has the amazing ability to train itself. Both brain and brawn develop by appropriate exercise.

Another road block is *limited knowledge*. The remedy is simple. When Alexander Graham Bell told Joseph Henry that he did not have the knowledge needed to invent the telephone, Henry replied: "Get it."

The next road block is *preconception* in its many forms. There is *wishful thinking*, that is, the ascribing to an idea or a device or a plan, especially one's own, virtues which we should like it to have, and the tendency to avoid evidence contrary to what we wish to believe. One way of lessening this tendency is by cultivating the habit of impartial use of multiple working hypotheses. Another type of preconception is *false associative thinking*, to wit, the conclusion that all properties are superlative, or the reverse, merely because one is. A familiar example is the tendency of the human male to overestimate the other attributes of a beautiful girl. Also antagonistic, if not fatal, to creative thought is *group thinking*, that is, thinking like the crowd, which reaches its extreme form in mob psychology.

Another kind of road block is *credulity*. This, in both scientific and popular circles, seems to have its greatest manifestation in *dramatized thinking*—the tendency to believe that anything new and striking is good or true. Slightly less common, but equally fatal to creative thought, is the antithesis: *unacceptance of the new*. Also, there is *superficiality*, which, as long as something looks good, accepts it without verification.

If, from those attributes listed as desirable in a creative thinker, it were required to single out one whose absence would be the greatest handicap of all, this almost surely would be enthusiasm. *Passivity* and creative processes are never on speaking terms with one another.

In contrast with these psychological road blocks is one of another sort, the *harassment of detail* which work pressures produce. The only answer is to set aside time for occasional reflection.

It is also worth noting that the creative thinker frequently must accept resistance and *discouragement* as his lot. After all, the innovator is a sort of transgressor; and even in a progressive organization, his way is sometimes hard. Unless he is willing to run the risk that his associates now and then may consider him eccentric and undependable, he had best eschew creativity.

Conclusion

So much, then, for the patterns and processes of creative thought, and related aids and difficulties. The factor of greatest significance is the strong evidence which exists that creativity can be enhanced alike by training and by conscious effort. And what of motivation? With science and technology so strongly in the ascendancy, some find their incentive in pride of contributions to society. Some have found it in the urge for fame or fortune. But for most creative workers the fountain spring of inspiration is the challenge of the difficult and the unknown, exciting an inner driving force that nothing short of complete solution can satisfy. The true scientist is generally content just to "walk within the veil of the temple of nature." The reward in terms of personal satisfaction is great. Dumas, the French chemist, pictured it as "the type of true happiness on earth."

QUESTIONS

1. What are the characteristics of creative thinkers, according to Green? Is this list complete and adequate in light of current research?
2. Is *serendipity* a common phenomenon in technological progress? If so, what is suggested for the planning and control of research and development work?
3. Compare the "creativity" of the following types:
    a) One who continually keeps abreast of the most advanced thinking, masters it, and attempts to apply it with some success to his current problems.
    b) One who has had one great concept in many years, but this concept is indubitably far ahead of current thinking and is brilliantly conceived.
    c) An individual who is noted for a flow of ideas, all of which represent slight but useful advances in current products.
    d) An individual who can be counted on to produce unique, unusual, bizarre, and radically different approaches to a problem, with varying degrees of success.
    e) An individual who is noted for a fast outpouring of wild or untested ideas, on any kind of problem, most of which prove to be useless. However, occasionally, one of his ideas is superbly effective.

4. Which types above would you favor for employment in an industrial research laboratory? An industrial development and engineering laboratory? As director of an R & D laboratory?

5. Describe the process of creative thought.

6. What are the road blocks to creative thinking? How can management help to minimize these road blocks?

7. How would you recruit a "creative" R & D staff?
   Suggestion: Explore this with industrial psychologists, sociologists, and leading scientists, engineers, and managers.

8. Examine histories of invention and development. What is the role played by serendipity? By empiricism? By omphaloskepsis? By flash of genius? By scientific "hunch"?

Creativity in Research Organizations

There are three common reasons why top management may not want creativity. One is that it seems an unnecessary burden. If business is good, if the company enjoys a strong financial position and is making good profits, there is great temptation on the part of management to coast along. Why get involved in discussions and tough decisions? Why take risks on new ideas when everything is going so well? Top executives may develop an almost superstitious aversion to change under such conditions—they may fear that any change in products or methods might somehow break the spell. . . .

A second reason may be that the top man is himself a very forceful and creative person. He may want an organization which carries out his ideas smoothly and efficiently rather than one which originates ideas. If he is a very able person, results may be quite good for a long while. Eventually, when he is gone, the organization may lose its ability to accomplish. Sometimes even while the top man remains this can happen. He grows older, loses his flexibility and flair but retains his stubbornness, surrounds himself with yes-men and gets rid of anyone who disagrees with him. The organization heads downhill.

A third reason may be that creativity in one area has stifled creativity in another. Research, production, marketing, and finance are all essential factors in modern industry. If top management overemphasizes any one of these, it may build up a talented, creative group in that area while relegating people in the other areas to servant status. A business may have a brilliantly creative research department and yet be unsuccessful if its marketing efforts are ineffective and expensive. In an organization dominated by advertising and marketing people, research may be expected merely to implement the specific requests which those people make, often for minor improvements or "gimmicks." Original suggestions by research people are not looked upon with favor.

IRVING REICH, Director of
Proprietary Research
Carter Products Company

FROM: "Creativity in Research Organizations," *Research Management*, Winter, 1960.

ON RESISTANCE TO TECHNOLOGICAL
INNOVATIONS

WHEN THE technologist—be he scientist, engineer, or inventor—and his financial supporters are convinced of the technological feasibility and economic merit of a new concept, they often tend to assume that the invention will be adopted by society in a reasonable time. Frequently, their personal involvement and sacrifices build such enthusiasm, belief, and stubbornness that their anticipations are highly optimistic. So it may be with the firm and its innovating group.

Anyone introducing a technological innovation is implicitly or explicitly predicting acceptance and a rate of adoption. The assumption seems to be that since the innovation provides greater service or a feeling of satisfaction to users than does its present equivalent, or because it is economically justified, it will be adopted. Yet a fact of technological history is that many innovations are subject to frustrating delays and deliberate resistances to adoption, so that the result is economic disaster. Concepts of inestimable value to mankind sometimes are not only unappreciated—they are bitterly attacked and rejected. Of course, there is the occasional experience of an innovation spreading more rapidly than even its protagonists had imagined. An innovation also may receive changing responses over time—a slow initial acceptance, and then a surging demand as the merit of the innovation is recognized. The reverse pattern also occurs—wild enthusiasm followed by rapid disillusionment.

While a complete analysis of the process of the adoption of *technological* innovations is beyond our present knowledge, it clearly depends upon many things, such as economic, cultural, technological, political, and social factors, and the response of the influential decision makers. There is, however, one aspect which deserves management's attention. This is the explicit act of resistance to technological innovation. By recognizing this possibility, and by considering means of minimizing or surmounting such resistance, the innovator may be able to achieve his goal more readily. Also, he may be able to delay or reduce the impact of a competitive innovation. These notes are intended to expand understanding of such resistance.

Before examining "resistance," let us consider whether resistance may not be desirable at times. There is a common inference that technological innovations are generally superior, beneficial, and of immediate or ultimate net value to society, to the innovating firm, or to industry. They are also claimed to be inevitable. Therefore, resistance to innovation is held to be "backward," if not downright reprehensible or foolish. But the idea that technological innovations are always desirable can certainly be challenged on moral grounds in many cases, and on social and political grounds in others. For management, there also may be immediate or ultimate economic effects that are negative and harmful to the firm, to individuals, or to society. We should not assume, therefore, that there is necessarily something morally wrong or economically unsound in opposing technological innovations at times. It may be a very wise managerial act to cling to the old and to delay the new.

Our point is that technological innovations may be resisted. This resistance may be foolish or wise, logical or illogical, obvious or unsuspected; but *its anticipation must become part of the manager's analysis.*

General Conditions Affecting Resistance

Resistance to technological innovations may stem from an individual, a firm, a community, an industry, or an institution such as the Church, a union, a government agency, or a formal act of a sovereign government. It also may be widespread within an institution, or be centered in an individual or a small departmental group. It may come from a special group having no formal associations other than opposition to the technological concept. However, the businessman can expect resistance to a given innovation to vary, depending upon whether the economy is expanding or contracting, and whether it is a time of great necessity (as in war), or locally or within a particular industry when economic depression exists.

Innovations do not seem to be so eagerly sought or welcomed when the intended *users* of the innovation are satisfied with and emotionally attached to the *status quo,* or when those who must *produce* the innovation are satisfied with the *status quo.* The apparent risk involved and the relationship of the resources that must be committed to the resources available also influence resistance by user and producer.

Resistance to technological innovation, we may assume, will be somewhat dependent upon general social and political conditions. A striking example was the change in public attitudes toward education, scientific research, development, and government support of such work after Sputnik I was launched in October, 1957.

Reasons for Resistance

There are many reasons why technological innovations are opposed:

1. To protect social status or prerogative.
2. To protect an existing way of life.
3. To prevent devaluation of capital invested in an existing facility, or in a supporting facility or service.

4. To prevent a reduction of livelihood because the innovation would devalue the knowledge or skill presently required.
5. To prevent the elimination of a job or profession.
6. To avoid expenditures such as the cost of replacing existing equipment, or of renovating and modifying existing systems to accommodate or to compete with the innovation.
7. Because the innovation opposes social customs, fashions and tastes, and the habits of everyday life.
8. Because the innovation conflicts with existing laws.
9. Because of rigidity inherent in large or bureaucratic organizations.
10. Because of personality, habit, fear, equilibrium between individuals or institutions, status, and similar social and psychological considerations.
11. Because of a tendency of organized groups to force conformity.
12. Because of reluctance of an individual or group to disturb the equilibrium of society or the business atmosphere.

The first question in a resistance study is to consider each of the above categories relative to the particular innovation. Then, having identified the possible sources, we can consider the means that may be employed to minimize resistance.

Means of Resisting Technological Innovations

One is startled upon reviewing the means by which technological innovations have been explicitly resisted. Again and again, the pattern is repeated. The same devices can be identified and often can be anticipated. Again and again, the innovator is caught flat-footed. In his enthusiasm and belief, he takes little account of the possible responses of those who will feel the impact of his innovation. Yet the same devices for resistance to technological innovation have been employed throughout history. They fall in the following areas:

Resistance through Legal Agencies and Political Devices. One common method is through obtaining a perpetual franchise for the existing system. Another is to obtain restrictive legislation or block permissive legislation concerning construction, application, or the mode and conditions of operation for the new devices. Patent litigation has often been used to forestall the innovation. Occasionally, the imposition of special taxes or tolls delays innovation. The use of legal strictures on transit or access rights is used to block the application or a necessary support service.

Action through a Business Activity to Resist the Innovation. These actions take the forms of the purchase and suppression of patents; conspiracy to prevent the sale, use, or distribution of the device; and advertising or "whispering" campaigns to discredit the innovation or to highlight the advantages of existing systems. There is also the refusal of financial support, or pressure brought to bear on financial agencies to cause them to withhold financial support. Another variation of this is to persuade the supplier of an essential material or service to withhold supply from the innovator. A reduction in the price of the existing system may be used to reduce the economic attractiveness of the innovation. Businessmen have not been above the use of violence to destroy the new system.

Resistance Emanating through Labor Groups.   In addition to legal devices and union contracts, we see innovations resisted by strikes, boycotts, violence, sabotage, and the refusal to use certain techniques or equipment. With the growth of large unions, some economic agreements, such as "automation funds" or fees paid to unions for each use, or the insistence on certain minimum crews, act as means of limiting innovation. Some automation funds are not intended to resist innovation so much as to compensate workers injured by innovation. However, the added economic burden may, in fact, delay adoption.

Propaganda and Pressure Group Efforts to Influence Public and Official Opinion.   The arguments traditionally are marshaled around the claims of physical dangers, of impracticality for scientific reasons, or as evidenced by "expert" testimony. Other arguments as to dignity, esthetic effect, morality, and religion are used. Opposition to the fluoridation of drinking water reveals illogical, fanatical, and "crackpot" response, but the resistance is powerful nevertheless. A favorite weapon is ridicule through the popular press, and another is condemnation from the pulpit. Bribery of government officials is well known. With businessmen, one of the deepest appeals lies in arguments as to the economic harm to existing organizations, supplemented by additional appeals to current job holders and unions.

Resistance Applied through Religious Groups as an Explicit Moral Position of the Church Body, or Opinion of the Local Religious Leader. The most timely example is the attitude of the Catholic Church on birth control techniques and devices. As another example, to this day the Amish (a religious sect of the Pennsylvania Dutch) have steadfastly refused to use power machinery of any type, including automobiles and tractors, in their excellent farming.

Observations on Resistance to Technological Innovations

1. Resistance will be somewhat in proportion to the extent to which institutions and individuals are threatened.

2. Resistances are lessened if only slight changes in behavior on the part of individuals, institutions, or organizations are demanded. Where private, individual users of the innovation are involved, the closer the new response required of the user parallels the old response, the less resistance is likely to be encountered. Does this suggest that an innovation should be introduced so that the consumer must change his behavior only by slight increments?

3. Innovations encounter less resistance in a firm, industry, or society where managers and workers are accustomed to frequent changes in the technical environment.

4. Those advocating innovations often tend to be overoptimistic as to the time and feasibility of accomplishment, although not necessarily as to

ultimate impact of their concept. Failure of their optimism to materialize can be regarded as an eventual cause of resistance. Unfilled claims are ridiculed with heavy sarcasm. Overoptimism also leads to misjudgment on the innovation. These misjudgments may be on cost, on the complexity of the device or the system employing the device, on the time needed to achieve successful commercial operation, on technical performance, or on the amount or degree of customer need or interest. Overoptimism also causes us to overlook or underestimate the progress of alternative ways of achieving the same service.

5. Resistance is aggravated or encouraged if the innovator is sarcastic, contemptuous, or insulting in his references to other devices and their advocates. Such actions naturally encourage defensiveness, although they may be useful in attracting attention.

Conclusions

The tone of this note might be construed as implying that technological innovations are *always* resisted. Of course, this is not so. Many firms, government agencies, and individuals are eagerly seeking radical technological improvements. Indeed, since Sputnik and the "moon race," one might question whether American society has not been too receptive to proposals for technological advances! Or a look at manufacturing automation shows that this field, like others, has its monuments to the overenthusiastic adoption of innovation.

Radical technological innovations carry with them a variety of benefits and liabilities, the importance of which varies with dozens of internal and external conditions. Thus the only proper management approach is one of respect and appreciation for the potential effects, as well as for the complexity of the interactions between the innovation and its environment. Formal recognition of resistance is a proper part of management's analysis. When the probable sources and means of resistance have been identified, we can make plans to minimize its impact.

QUESTIONS

1. Study the introduction of one or more technological innovations prior to 1920 in fields such as transportation, communications, military weapons, materials and processes, consumer products, agriculture, or home appliances. Analyze the reception for each innovation.
   a) What social, political, technological, and economic factors inhibited (or encouraged) adoption?
   b) How did the economic impact affect reception?
   c) To what extent did the personality, actions, and attitudes of key individuals affect the outcome?
   d) How did resistance materialize, and how was it overcome?
   e) Can you see any way in which the innovator might have speeded adoption of his concept?

2. Study any technological innovation introduced since 1945. Examine it through the questions listed under (1) above.

3. Assume that you are employed by a major mail-order house. You note the ability of mail-order houses to sell vitamins and toiletries by mail. Recent progress in dehydration and freeze-drying of foods, and the promise of irradiated foods, suggest that shelf life can and will be greatly extended, and that packaging cost, weight, and volume will be reduced. Consumer acceptability of such packaged foods seems to be growing. These technical developments are making mail delivery of many items feasible. You suspect that the mail-order house could find a substantial market in food distribution. Before putting your proposal before management, you decide to examine the potential sources of resistance to this concept, and to prepare an approach to surmounting these obstacles.

4. Examine the technological proposal in (3) above, assuming that you are employed by a large chain of food stores and are proposing the addition of a mail-order food department.

5. You are employed as an proposal analyst by the research laboratory of a supplier of aerospace control and power systems with sales of about $500 million annually. The laboratory has developed a fuel cell concept that shows efficiency far above anything in public knowledge. There appears to be a strong possibility of developing a power plant that will be moderately but distinctly superior to the gasoline engine in maintenance, smoothness, quietness, initial cost, and operating cost up to about 200 horsepower. The fuel cell will provide electric power by the interaction of two liquid components, neither of which is derived from petroleum. About five gallons of each fluid will be required per hundred miles of normal driving. This fuel cost to the consumer is presently indicated to be 10 per cent less per mile than current gasoline cost. Your technical associates and management confirm that, technologically and economically, the device can compete with small- and medium-sized gasoline engines. Your firm holds the critical patents, and your technical people cannot identify any other fuel cell concept that offers technological competition in the foreseeable future. Prepare an analysis on resistance problems that might have to be overcome in the introduction and diffusion of this power plant. What actions do you recommend to your management?

RELATED READINGS

Biographies of inventors, scientists, and industrial pioneers are replete with examples of resistance. Histories of major industries, products, and processes also provide examples. The student should read such works, applying the questions under (1) above.

Studies on the diffusion or rate of adoption of innovations frequently give insight on resistance. Worthwhile publications are:

MANSFIELD, EDWIN. "The Speed of Response of Firms to New Techniques," *Quarterly Journal of Economics*, 1963.

ROGERS, EVERETT M. *Diffusion of Innovations*. New York: Free Press of Glencoe, 1962.

The Case of the Conservative

Let us admit the case of the conservative: if we once start thinking no one can guarantee what will be the outcome, except that many objects, ends and institutions will be surely doomed. Every thinker puts some portion of an apparently stable world in peril, and no one can wholly predict what will emerge in its place.

JOHN DEWEY

FROM: *Characters and Events*, edited by Joseph Ratner (New York: Holt, Rinehart and Winston, Inc., 1929).

RIVERLAKE BELT CONVEYOR LINES, INC. (A)

IN MARCH, 1955, the House Committee on Commerce and Transportation of the Ohio legislature voted to table a bill which would have given the right of eminent domain to belt conveyor lines in Ohio. This was the third time the legislature had failed to take favorable action on this legislation. It was a serious setback for those associated with Riverlake Belt Conveyor Lines, Inc., chief proponent of the legislation. The company proposed to build a coal and ore conveyor belt line between Cleveland on Lake Erie and East Liverpool, Ohio, a port on the Ohio River, a distance of approximately one hundred miles, depending on the particular route selected. In the spring of 1955, H. B. Stewart, Jr., President of Riverlake, and also President of the Akron, Canton & Youngstown Railroad, was considering what action, if any, he should take prior to the next biennial session of the Ohio legislature in 1957 in connection with a fourth attempt to secure the legislation his company needed.

The idea for a belt conveyor line for coal and ore running between Lake Erie and East Liverpool on the Ohio River had its origin in some studies which the Akron, Canton & Youngstown Railroad had undertaken after World War II to determine the feasibility of expansion eastward. The railroad was a small carrier extending westward from Akron approximately 171 miles to Delphus, Ohio. No expansion of the railroad seemed feasible as a result of these studies, but Stewart's attention was drawn to the heavy north-south, two-way haul of ore and coal, and to the possibility that this traffic might be handled by a conveyor belt. His interest in such a project was stimulated by talks he had with friends in the Goodyear Tire & Rubber Company, a large manufacturer of belting, and in the various steel companies. Further conversations with Goodyear, with other manufacturers of conveyor belt equipment, and with potential shippers for the belt line—namely, coal companies, steel manufacturers, and electrical utilities which would provide power to the belt line along its proposed route—served to convince him of the probable practicability and economic soundness of the project.

Exploratory engineering analysis of the conveyor line was financed by the Akron, Canton & Youngstown Railroad in the form of advances during 1948 and early 1949. A preliminary six-month study of the project indicated that the project was feasible. Another six months was devoted to checking this conclusion and refining engineering data and cost estimates.

By February, 1949, the general feasibility of the undertaking had been sufficiently tested so that it was publicly announced. With the aid of a New York public relations firm, a presentation on the project was made to the press on February 9. The following day, an equally elaborate presentation was made to a group of approximately 150 potential shippers. News releases and feature stories appeared in the press the same day. The public announcement of the project aroused a substantial amount of public discussion and interest. In part, this appears to have been the result of adroit public relations and in part because of the intriguing nature of the project.

Simultaneously with the public announcement of the project, Riverlake Belt Conveyor Lines, Inc., was incorporated with the capitalization of $500 in stock, all of which was issued to Stewart. This company was charged with the promotion and construction of the line. In exchange for the advances which the Akron, Canton & Youngstown Railroad had made to the project, amounting to roughly $100,000, there was an understanding whereby if and when the line was built, the railroad would receive a contract for the management and operation of Riverlake at a management fee of 5 cents a ton of coal and ore handled.

Legislative Efforts in 1949

One of the problems confronting the backers of Riverlake was the necessity of securing the right of eminent domain for the belt line, so that it could condemn land over which it would have to pass. Without this right the building of the conveyor line would be impossible, since any individual or company owning land on the proposed right of way could either refuse to sell or at least charge an extortionate price for his land. Since the proposal would have diverted considerable traffic from the railroads, opposition to the line was early expected from them. And since, in many cases, it would be necessary to cross over the railroads, there was every reason to think that one or more railroads would block the building of the line unless it had the right of eminent domain. Under Ohio law the only transportation companies which have the right of eminent domain are a specific list of common carriers. Belt conveyor lines are not included in this list. In order to launch the project successfully, it was then necessary to get a bill passed by the Ohio legislature adding belt conveyor lines to the list of common carriers with the right of eminent domain. Such legislation was introduced into the biennial session of the Ohio legislature on February 12, 1949, two days after public announcement of the project.

In an effort to get this legislation passed, Stewart and various backers of Riverlake made a series of speeches around the state, talking before businessmen and other groups in the hope of arousing public support and understanding for the legislation. By the time the bill was acted upon in the spring of 1949, Stewart estimated that he and his friends had talked face to face to a total of 12,000 people. In addition, there had been a considerable public relations campaign through newspapers and other channels in support of the legislation. Nevertheless, the Ohio House Committee on Commerce and Transportation voted to table the bill by a vote of twelve to four. In the Senate the bill was tabled by the Committee by a vote of five to three. Since the Ohio legislature meets only every second year, the next opportunity for securing favorable legislation was 1951.

The Ohio legislature is made up of 133 House representatives and 33 senators. All members are elected every two years. As in many other states, the Ohio legislature appears to be a rural-dominated, with a high proportion of the members representing rural districts, despite the substantial number and size of industrial and urban communities in the state. Membership on legislative committees tends to go by seniority. There is a considerable amount of informal give-and-take among the legislative leaders and the senior members for positions on the "better"—i.e., more powerful—committees such as the Rules Committee. Because there is a heavy turnover of membership from session to session, the membership of the individual legislative committees tends to change rapidly.

In the 1949 session of the legislature, opposition to the bill granting Riverlake Belt Conveyor Lines common carrier status and the right of eminent domain came largely from the railroad industry, organized in the Ohio Railroad Association, whose secretary was Earl Shivley. He had represented the railroads successfully for many years at Columbus and was widely known in legislative circles. Direct railroad opposition to the legislation was organized in a Special Transportation Committee under the leadership of Frank Uible.

The principal arguments used by the railroads against the legislation may be briefly summarized as follows. The belt line was not in fact a "common carrier" but rather a contract carrier because it would not be open and available to all shippers and because it was limited to two commodities, coal and ore. A second argument was that Riverlake would deprive the railroads of a sufficiently large volume of tonnage, so that the railroads, already hard pressed financially, might be unable to continue to provide needed services unrelated to coal and ore. The railroads also argued that such curtailment of service would result in a heavy loss of jobs among railwoad workers and a drastic curtailment of railroad taxes.

Riverlake Engineering Council

In 1949, following the defeat in the legislature, the Riverlake Engineering Council was established. This Council was made up of various expert representatives from belting, electrical equipment, power, and materials-handling companies. Its task was to make a detailed engineering and cost study of the over-all feasibility of the project to verify or modify Riverlake's own preliminary study. The Council was broken down into various subcommittees dealing with such subjects as power, terminals, and conveyor engineering. The companies whose representatives sat on the Council were not promised the original equipment business for the line if it was built; in fact, they were advised that the Council might be enlarged at any time by the addition of representatives of possible competitors. It was generally agreed that if the line was built, the various phases of construction would be let out for bid to the lowest bidder. Nevertheless, a very considerable amount of technical talent was made available to the Riverlake Engineering Council. Companies with representatives on the Council included Goodyear, Link Belt, Westinghouse, General Electric, Dravo Corporation, Chain Belt, Jeffrey Manufacturing, Stephens-Adamson Manufacturing Company, Hewitt Robins, Wellman Engineering, and Ohio Edison. Other companies not actually represented on the Council gave technical advice and information. The various committees of the Council drew up reports on such questions as land valuation, the type of belting to be used, and the like. The Goodyear Tire & Rubber Company undertook the job of locating a line topographically, from a series of aerial stereopticon photographs.

The work of the Council was compiled into six volumes of engineering reports and estimates, and these volumes were turned over to the Stone & Webster Engineering Corporation for further analysis and appraisal. Late in 1950, as a result of a ten-month study of the work of the Council, Stone & Webster submitted a report which indicated that the line, as contem-

Exhibit 1

plated, could be built for a sum slightly in excess of $300 million. Including interest and taxes during the construction period, Stewart estimated that the total investment required in the line would be $320 million. It was on this basis that various rate estimates, which will be discussed below, were made.

Stewart felt that the estimates of the Council and Stone & Webster had been kept on a conservative basis. For example, belt life had been estimated at five years, assuming a belt speed of 600 feet a minute. In fact, Riverlake hoped that it would be able to get either substantially longer belt life, perhaps nine or ten years, or higher belt speeds up to 1,000 feet per minute.

As indicated in the photograph and diagram shown in Exhibits 1 and 2,

Exhibit 2

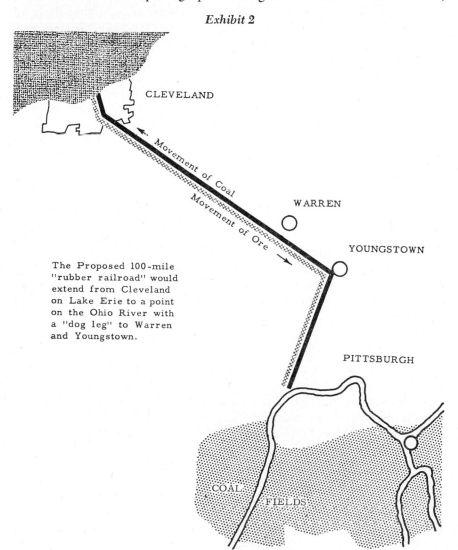

The Proposed 100-mile "rubber railroad" would extend from Cleveland on Lake Erie to a point on the Ohio River with a "dog leg" to Warren and Youngstown.

it was proposed to use a belt 48 inches wide to carry ore and a 72-inch belt to carry coal. These would run parallel to each other inside a covered tube. Actually, the line would consist of a series of belts feeding one into the other at transfer points. The distance between transfer points depended on the terrain, grade, and similar matters. Although originally it was proposed to have a straight line from East Liverpool, Ohio, to Lorain, a coal and ore port slightly west of Cleveland, later modification of the route called for a dog-leg between East Liverpool and Youngstown, Ohio, and thence northwest in a straight line to the Cleveland loading docks. Extensive coal- and ore-handling facilities would be available at Cleveland and East Liverpool; at Cleveland, coal and ore could be transferred from and to lake boats; while at East Liverpool, transfers could be made to and from Ohio River barges. At Youngstown, coal and ore would be dropped off to the various steel companies there; and in Cleveland and elsewhere along the line, it would be possible to drop off coal at the plants of various large utilities companies.

Although Stewart did not make any formal financing arrangements for the construction of the line, he did have a number of informal discussions with bankers and institutional investors. He was assured that if the right of eminent domain could be secured, and if the engineering work and cost estimates proved to be reasonably accurate when finally engineered, there would be no problem in financing the line on attractive terms. As far as the immediate expenses of Riverlake were concerned, these were financed initially by contributions amounting to approximately $300,000 from potential shippers and subsequently by contributions of a similar amount from potential equipment suppliers.

1951 Legislative Session

In part, this extensive engineering and cost-estimating work was done in anticipation of the 1951 session of the legislature. In addition, prior to the convening of the legislature, a considerable amount of lobbying and public relations activity was undertaken. Riverlake secured the services of several law firms in Columbus, familiar with the operations of the Ohio legislature, to represent it. On the public relations level a considerable amount of effort was expended in lining up various business and labor groups in support of the bill. With the exception of the railroad brotherhoods and certain of the coal unions, support of labor was secured for the bill. Active support was received from the various rubber workers' unions in and around Akron. Some support, much of it indirect, was also secured from the utilities and steel companies.

Because of the possible legal issue as to whether a belt conveyor line could or could not be properly classified as a common carrier entitled to the right of eminent domain, the bill which would have given such status to Riverlake was introduced initially in 1951 into the Senate Judiciary Committee. After a series of hearings, the efforts of Riverlake and its various representatives were successful in securing a favorable report on the bill by a vote of five to four. However, when the bill came before the Senate Rules Committee for a rule which would put it on the Senate Calendar, that Committee tabled it on the ground that the legislation was so controversial that it was impeding the balance of the legislative program. Since the Ohio Senate Rules Committee is a powerful body, its vote to table made it impossible to get the bill before the Senate. Because of the defeat in the Senate, it was felt that there was no object in attempting to get action on a bill in the House. Thus, for the second time the bill was defeated. As in the 1949 session, the Ohio Railroad Association was extremely active in its opposition to the legislation, first in the Senate Judiciary Committee and subsequently in the Senate Rules Committee.

Situation in 1953

Stewart thereupon determined that an effort should be made again in 1953. Additional public relations help was retained. A motion picture was prepared showing the major features and benefits of the belt line conveyor. This was widely exhibited throughout the state. Shortly before the 1953 legislative session was to convene, however, a detailed appraisal of the chances of receiving favorable action on Riverlake's bill was made by persons familiar with the Ohio legislature. It was determined that a major controversy in the 1953 session would be the axle-mile tax on trucks. It was felt that this controversy would take so much of the time and attention of the legislators that the Riverlake proposal would not receive adequate consideration. Accordingly, no Riverlake bill was introduced into the 1953 legislature, although considerable preliminary work had been done in anticipation of such a bill.

The 1955 Legislative Session

In preparation for the 1955 legislative session, however, considerable additional work was undertaken. The Riverlake Engineering Council was reconvened, and made a reappraisal and re-examination of its previous study. The revised study was again turned over to Stone & Webster Engineering Corporation for further analysis and appraisal. This work was not completed by the time the legislature convened. Principally, however, Riverlake concentrated attention on a public relations program at the grass-roots level. A working model of the proposed conveyor belt line was built for Riverlake by Goodyear and put in a trailer which toured the state. Because of the high proportion of rural representation in the legislature, a farm survey was made to determine the views of farmers on the idea of the belt line. Efforts, generally successful, were made to get farm bureaus along the right of way to pass resolutions supporting the belt line. Numerous speeches were given before luncheon groups; press releases, articles, and the like were written and sent to newspapers. On the whole, editorial comment appeared to be favorably disposed toward Riverlake (see Exhibits 3 and 4).

Exhibit 3

EDITORIAL, RAVENNA *RECORD*, JANUARY 8, 1955

CONVEYOR BELT

Whether we want to move people or products, northeastern Ohio is going to have adequate means of doing either.

We make that statement after looking briefly at the list of early bills tossed into the hopper at Columbus. The North-South turnpike, which will just miss Portage county, is practically assured. Besides that, we already have the east-west pike and the seaway. Now comes the conveyor belt.

After the rebuffs the idea has received at the hands of two or three legislators, we had about come to the conclusion that the beast was dead. Apparently not. It still lives. It still wants to do a transportation job for coal, steel and other products from Lake Erie to the Ohio river.

. . . .

Our point of view is favorable to the idea. Coal needs cheap transportation to make it again competitive as a fuel. Maybe this would provide that and thus revive an important Ohio industry. Besides that, many other bulk items could be moved that way, thus linking the Ohio and Mississippi with the Great Lakes system and the ocean.

There are other arguments, some for and some against. But we believe that the project would be just another boost to this great area in which we live and for that reason we'd like to see it tried.

There is no public gamble. It will all be done by private investment. That means jobs and greater productivity which in turn means more jobs. And that's what we need.

Northeastern Ohio appears to be destined to be a great transportation hub, which portends an even greater economic development for the area.

Exhibit 4

EDITORIAL,EAST LIVERPOOL *REVIEW*, JANUARY 7, 1955; STEUBENVILLE *HERALD-STAR*, JANUARY 7, 1955; MARION *STAR*, JANUARY 7, 1955; CANTON *REPOSITORY*, JANUARY 8, 1955; IRONTON *TRIBUNE*, JANUARY 10, 1955

WHOSE EMINENT DOMAIN?

The argument between railroads operating in Ohio and the backers of the proposed belt-line conveyor to carry coal and iron ore between Lake Erie and the Ohio River is going to be hot and heavy in this session of the Ohio General Assembly.

Twice the railroads have sidetracked the proposal in the Assembly without trouble, but this year Riverlake Belt Conveyor Lines, Inc., and its allies have taken steps to offset railroad pressure. It behooves Ohioans to understand what the issue is.

It is concerned wholly with eminent domain—whether the belt conveyor people would be given the right once given to railroads to acquire property in the public interest against individual opposition, provided reasonable compensation has been paid.

The people who want to build the belt conveyor must have this right for a special reason—because the conveyor would cross railroad rights-of-way. Since railroads do not want belt conveyor competition, they would refuse permission to cross their property even though it was acquired originally under the right of eminent domain too.

There is no other issue. Everything else that has been dragged into the discussion is unimportant. The conveyor would be economically feasible. It would be feasible as far as engineering is concerned. Its feasibility is so well established that it will be authorized eventually for the same reason the St. Lawrence Seaway was authorized eventually—because the railroads eventually will run out of delaying tactics.

The question is how long that will take.

How long will it take for members of the General Assembly to realize that the right of eminent domain belongs to the sovereign people and is delegated by them at will; that it does not belong to the railroads who were its first beneficiaries?

The railroads, for their part, were also extremely active. They made a motion picture entitled "Decision for Ohio," depicting in graphic terms the hardship which the Riverlake belt conveyor line would impose upon the railroads and upon Ohio communities through loss of jobs, taxes, and railroad service. Railroads also increased their lobbying pressure. They prevailed on the membership of the various railroad brotherhoods, who numbered approximately 85,000, to send letters opposing the conveyor belt to their representatives.

Among the steps which Stewart took was to write a series of letters to members of the Ohio legislature. Beginning in October, 1954, they appeared approximately weekly thereafter. Each one-page letter discussed in an informal way the issues involved in the Riverlake belt conveyor controversy. Samples of these letters are included as Exhibits 5–8. During the 1955 campaign, Stewart and his associates handled many of the direct contacts at Columbus and relied less on Columbus lawyers and lobbyists. In addition, however, a New York firm of public relations experts was employed to handle general public relations work.

From the outset, Stewart had laid down a firm policy that no individual connected with Riverlake should make direct or indirect campaign contributions to any of the members of the legislature or to any prospective members of the legislature. (As is the case at the federal level, Ohio law makes it illegal for corporations to contribute directly to campaigns.) It had been Stewart's feeling that giving campaign contributions, whether to legislative candidates who were friendly to Riverlake, to candidates who might be neutral, or alternatively to opponents, was not desirable. He was not certain what policy the railroads were following in regard to campaign contributions.

A serious effort was made during the 1955 campaign to secure the support of various Ohio political leaders in both parties. Some of these leaders had in the past been closely identified with railroad interests—for example, as counsel for one or another railroad or railroad group. Generally speaking, it had not been possible to gain the active support for

Exhibit 5

RIVERLAKE BELT CONVEYOR LINES, INC.

Akron, Ohio

November 19, 1954

DEAR MR. LEGISLATOR:

"You aren't a common carrier because you won't be able to carry strawberries!"

Yes, that statement actually was made just last month in table conversation at a Columbus meeting. The speaker was explaining why he believed belt conveyors shouldn't have the same privileges as other forms of transportation. He was talking with an Akron belt conveyor proponent attending the same convention.

As patiently as he could, the Akron man tried to set him right. At the risk of boring you with facts you already know, here is what he told him:

Many kinds of common carriers in Ohio carry only one thing, yet have been declared "common carriers" by the Legislature. For example:

A pipeline company transports only petroleum.
A gas pipeline company moves only gas.
Power lines handle only electricity.
A water company limits itself to water.
A telephone or telegraph company handles only communications.

And in 1951 the Ohio General Assembly declared *coal pipelines* common carriers and granted them the right of eminent domain!

Yes, carriers may be common carriers even if they carry only two commodities, iron ore and coal, as Riverlake plans to do.

Volume 9, *American Jurisprudence*, page 432, says:

"Every common carrier has the right to determine what particular line of business he will follow, and his obligation to carry is coextensive with and limited by his holding out or profession as to the subjects of carriage. . . . If he holds himself out as a carrier of a particular kind of freight generally, prepared for carriage in a particular way, he will be bound to carry only to the extent and in the manner proposed."

Sincerely,

(*Signed*) H. B. STEWART, JR.

Copy to friends of Riverlake

Exhibit 6

RIVERLAKE BELT CONVEYOR LINES, INC.

Akron, Ohio

January 13, 1955

DEAR MR. LEGISLATOR:

If we were going to build a conveyor belt through your farm, naturally you would be the first person we would consult on the subject.

Late last summer Riverlake asked Stanley Howard, a farmer near Salem, to find out how the owners of farm property in Northeastern Ohio felt about our proposed conveyor.

Stan Howard started out in the six counties through which the conveyor will pass. He explained the project and answered questions.

Then he branched out into ten adjoining counties and did the same thing, working in a total of sixteen. And what were the results?

When the annual meetings of the Farm Bureaus of those counties were held in October and November, fifteen urged action on conveyor legislation. *The six counties through which Riverlake will pass led the way.*

Twelve were unqualified endorsements of belt conveyor legislation. Two urged a legislative floor vote on the subject. One urged that the measure be studied.

That's how the farmer in Northeastern Ohio feels about progress in transportation. We are encouraged by his attitude.

Sincerely,

(*Signed*) H. B. STEWART, JR.

Copy to friends of Riverlake

Exhibit 7

RIVERLAKE BELT CONVEYOR LINES, INC.

Akron, Ohio

January 27, 1955

DEAR MR. LEGISLATOR:

If you find this letter in that welter of anticonveyor belt legislation post cards the well-organized railroaders are sending you, it will be a major triumph. It's amazing how much clamor can come from just one per cent of the state's population.

My nugget for this week has to do with proof of our contention that diversion of certain iron ore and coal traffic to conveyor belts isn't going to increase rail rates on other commodities. That threat of a price increase has been one of the railroad arguments against us, as you know, just as it was one of their arguments against the St. Lawrence Seaway, etc., etc.

Last week a national news analyst featured the "freight rate war" now looming up between the Seaway, the railroads and the trucks. He said rail rates already have been cut on heavy machinery shipped from Chicago to Baltimore. His major point was that, because of the Seaway, many shippers, including rail shippers, will save money. Of course, that is inevitable. History proves it.

It's the simple old law of supply and demand. The railroad is just like the corner grocer. If a competitor moves in across the street, he lowers his prices. If the fellow moves out, he raises them.

What creates this railroad neurosis every time a new form of competition comes along? It is merely the handing down from generation to generation of railroad managements the policy (admittedly human) that it is easier to defeat than it is to compete. For generations an old and efficient lobby has always been readily available for such purpose.

Sincerely,

(*Signed*) H. B. STEWART, JR.

Copy to friends of Riverlake

Exhibit 8

RIVERLAKE BELT CONVEYOR LINES, INC.

Akron, Ohio

February 24, 1955

DEAR MR. LEGISLATOR:

Solicitude is a very touching virtue, and the railroad lobbyists, bless them, are dripping with concern about Riverlake these days in Columbus.

They are worried for fear we will "go broke."

Now, I know it isn't smart to broadcast your opponents' propaganda but I can't refrain from reassuring them on this point. After all, we don't want them to worry too much.

Of course, they admit that when Riverlake is built and "goes broke," it will mean real trouble to them because the defunct company then will be bought up for about ten cents on the dollar and will thus be a very competitive thorn in their sides.

But how in the name of common sense do they think we can get investment bankers interested in a project which might cost as much as $300 million dollars if it competitively were not a sure thing as a money maker?

If they ask you to share their worries please tell them Riverlake won't be a "widows and orphans" stock issue type of deal. And please tell them that maybe the same bankers and insurance companies who finance the railroads will finance Riverlake also. Many of the same brains will be involved.

If their fears did materialize who would like to buy Riverlake at ten cents on the dollar? You guessed it! The railroads, of course.

Sincerely,

(*Signed*) H. B. STEWART, JR.

Copy to friends of Riverlake

Riverlake of those prominent in the party hierarchy. But in virtually all cases, it was possible to secure from party leaders a "hands off" agreement, so that they would not actively support either the railroad's or Riverlake's point of view.

A bill which, if passed, would give Riverlake the right of eminent domain was introduced early in the 1955 session as House Bill No. 6 and was referred to the House Committee on Commerce and Transportation. Late in February the bill came on for hearing. Witnesses supporting the bill testified first and were as follows:

> Newton B. Chapman, General Counsel, Riverlake Belt Conveyor Lines, Inc.
> Paul M. Zeis, Vice President, Riverlake Belt Conveyor Lines, Inc., and principal economic witness
> Stanley G. Howard, farmer and former field representative of the Ohio Farm Bureau
> Robert S. Wilson, Vice President, Goodyear Tire & Rubber Company
> Lincoln O. Gries, Vice President, May Department Stores
> A. T. Wood, President, Wilson Transit Company of Cleveland; and past President, Lake Carriers Association
> E. J. Burger, Division Manager, Ohio Edison Company
> Kenneth Lloyd, Mahoning Valley Industrial Council
> C. W. Maloney, Stone & Webster Engineering Corporation
> J. O. Cross, Assistant General Counsel, United Cork, Rubber, Linoleum, and Plastic Workers of America, CIO
> H. B. Stewart, Jr., President, Riverlake Belt Conveyor Lines, Inc., and Akron, Canton & Youngstown Railroad

Several of the potential Riverlake shippers who were strongly in favor of the belt line proposal nevertheless did not, as a matter of policy, care to support Riverlake overtly in its battle with the railroads. But in addition to the support of the Ohio Edison Company, as represented by the testimony of E. J. Burger (listed above), and industry in general as represented by the testimony of Kenneth Lloyd of the Mahoning Valley Industrial Council, Riverlake also received outright support from Republic Steel Corporation in the form of a letter from its president, C. M. White (Exhibit 9).

The list of opposition witnesses to the Riverlake legislation is as follows:

> Frank Uible, of the Special Transportation Committee, composed of all the railroads serving Ohio with the exception of the Akron, Canton & Youngstown. These railroads include the Baltimore & Ohio; the Chesapeake & Ohio; the Bessemer & Lake Erie; the Detroit, Toledo & Ironton; the Big Four; the Erie; the New York Central; the Norfolk & Western; the Nickle Plate; the Pennsylvania; the Pittsburgh & Lake Erie; the Pittsburgh & West Virginia; and the Wabash.
> Mr. Crumlauf, Ohio Railroad Association
> Arnold Lamm, Vice President, Sunny Hill Coal Sales Company
> Edele Pacifico, United Mine Workers, District No. 6
> Clarence Krueger, Ohio Grange
> Lee Ferguson, United Mine Workers, Local No. 50
> Roy Denman, President, Longshoremen's Union

Exhibit 9

REPUBLIC STEEL CORPORATION
Republic Building, Cleveland 1, Ohio

Honorable C. Stanley Mechem,   C. M. White
President Pro Tem, Ohio State Senate,   President
State House,   February 28, 1955
Columbus, Ohio.

Dear Mr. Mechem:

You are aware of the importance of the St. Lawrence Seaway to the economy of our country. You are also aware of its value to the steel industry. You realize, I am sure, the importance of transportation to our whole scheme of things. You know of the importance of competition and the basic right to compete. You know that no particular form of transportation has a vested interest in our economy and our free country. If such were so there would be no Panama Canal, no modern canalized rivers, no pipelines, no over-the-road trucks, perhaps no highways and certainly no Seaway, the very things so vital to the growth, prosperity and strength of our country, including the railroads. There is a place for every form of transportation. Surely each will be needed to its capacity to meet the demands of progress and our continued growth and prosperity.

You are familiar with the efforts toward enabling legislation in Ohio which would make possible the construction of belt conveyor lines as commercial carriers of bulk materials, as first proposed to the Legislature almost six years ago. Next possibly to the Seaway I consider there is nothing of greater importance to the industrial growth of Ohio. Surely there should be no further delay.

The great industrial midwest has developed largely because of the Great Lakes and their accessibility to iron ore. The British, the French and our forefathers fought bitter battles for the possession of this great inland waterway. Contributing to the growth of the Great Lakes states has been the Ohio River System running through the greatest coal deposits in this country. While Ohio is graced geographically in that it provides the shortest portage between the Ohio River and the Great Lakes, only in recent years has an economically sound means been developed whereby our State could capitalize more fully on its location. At long last has come the proposed 100-mile belt conveyor. With private capital it will bring essential coal and iron ore more closely together by cheap modern transportation at huge savings and tax benefits. With such advantage and with the Seaway-conveyor combination no other state can be so well situated to enjoy the huge economic growth to come to this country through increased population, progressive and competitive enterprise. With merely the Seaway, Ohio's ability to compete with other Great Lakes states would be substantially status quo. However, with the conveyor, too, surely our advantages will be paramount. Greater industrial growth for Ohio can be assured with a conveyor linking Lake Erie and the Ohio River. The advantages will be almost immeasurable.

I sincerely hope that you can support this measure which is so important to the State of Ohio.

Sincerely yours,

(*Signed*) C. M. White

L. A. Daniels, Transport Workers of America, Railroad Division, CIO
Mr. Rupp, Baltimore & Ohio Railroad
General Breen, transportation consultant
Roy Kern, Chairman, Coal, Coke and Iron Ore Committee of the Central
  Territory Railroads
L. G. Walker, Manager, Ore and Coal Exchange, Cleveland, Ohio

The principal arguments used by the railroads against Riverlake in 1955 were substantially similar to those used in the 1949 and 1951 sessions of the legislature. It was argued that the belt line was not a common carrier because of the limited number of commodities and customers that it would handle; that it was technically unfeasible because of such difficulties as the freezing of the ore and coal in transit, the pulverization of coal, and the like; that the loss of revenue to the railroads which the line would bring about would seriously impair the railroads' economic stability and would result in loss of jobs, loss of taxes, and the like. It was further argued by opposition witnesses that because of technical difficulties and an underestimation of costs, the line was economically unsound and was doomed to bankruptcy. The railroads argued that when reorganized, the line would be bought at a low valuation and, because of low fixed charges, would be able to offer uneconomically low rates in unfair competition with the railroads.

In opposition to these arguments, Riverlake stressed the fact that the common carrier status and the right of eminent domain had been given to a coal pipe line and other forms of transportation handling a limited number of commodities; that the technical and economic feasibility of Riverlake had been demonstrated by the strong participation and support of various highly reputable companies making up the Riverlake Engineering Council; and that the Council's technical and economic work in turn had been validated by the Stone & Webster Engineering Corporation, a highly regarded engineering firm. The validated costs would make possible a schedule of freight rates which were approximately 50–60 per cent of the rail rate on coal, approximately three quarters of the railroad rate on storage ore, and roughly 80–90 per cent of the rail rate on direct-shipment ore (see Exhibit 10). Riverlake's witnesses argued that they would secure long-term contracts for guaranteed minimum tonnages from certain large users, and that these contracts would guarantee the financial stability of the belt line. Because of the savings in freight charges, the belt line would appreciable improve the competitive status of the steel industry in Ohio and western Pennsylvania, and would also be of substantial assistance to the coal industry. The line would make a natural extension to the St. Lawrence Seaway for bringing in domestic and Labrador ores to the steel industry at reduced cost. Thus, although the railroads might lose some of their coal and ore traffic, they would gain traffic in finished steel products and from other finished goods built in Ohio plants attracted by low coal rates.

The hearings on the bill consumed twelve sessions of the Committee and were completed early in March, 1955. The first vote of the Committee on reporting the bill was nine to nine, with one member absent. Subsequently, it was found that this member was opposed to the bill, and the

Exhibit 10

COMPARISON OF RAIL RATES WITH PROJECTED BELT CONVEYOR RATES AT A 40-MILLION-TON ANNUAL OPERATION LEVEL ON A PER TON BASIS

ORE—CLEVELAND TO MAHONING VALLEY (YOUNGSTOWN)

Rail:
Direct-shipment ore.....................................$1.6549
Storage ore... 2.0844
Conveyor:
Direct-shipment ore................................... 1.40
Storage ore... 1.45
Savings via Riverlake:
Direct-shipment ore.................................. 0.25
Storage ore... 0.63

COAL—CONNELLSVILLE TO CLEVELAND

Rail... $3.2794
Conveyor... 1.20
Barge... 0.64
Combined Riverlake-barge............................. 1.84
Savings via Riverlake................................ 1.44

* Rates include transfer charges from vessels absorbed by rails or conveyor, as the case may be.

Committee thereupon voted to table the legislation. Thus, for the third time the legislation necessary to get Riverlake started was killed. The next session of the legislature was not until early 1957.

In the spring of 1955, Stewart, who had no disposition to give up, was considering what program of action he should develop in anticipation of the 1957 legislative session. The legislative activity and the various engineering studies and reports had cost approximately $700,000 to date, of which roughly $200,000 had been expended on the 1955 effort. Stewart believed that with the assistance of interested shippers and equipment manufacturers, it would be possible to finance at least one more round in the controversy. He was interested, however, in taking all steps necessary in order to make successful the fourth attempt to get the right of eminent domain for Riverlake.

SECTION II

Case Studies in Research, Development and Technological Innovation

PHOTON, INC. (A)

INTRODUCTION

ON APRIL 7, 1950, William W. Garth, President of Lithomat Corporation, and the directors of the Graphic Arts Research Foundation met with a Technical Advisory Board of fourteen men from the printing industry (1) to review the research work that had been done on the Higonnet-Moyroud photocomposing machine and (2) to determine what would be the ideal characteristics of this machine for the printing industry. The second item was most important to the research team of Lithomat and the Research Foundation. Much argument had developed between the engineers and scientists about what specific features the machine should have, and it was hoped that the Advisory Board would settle the question.

Lithomat Corporation, the predecessor to Photon, Inc., had decided in 1946 to back Rene A. Higonnet and Louis Moyroud in the development of the photocomposing machine, which was expected to replace the Linotype machine in common use in the printing industry. Lithomat had been formed in 1940 to manufacture and market offset duplicating supplies and equipment which were developed from the ideas of J. E. Gilligan. Lithomat's sales for the year ended December 31, 1949, stood at $874,496, and net income after taxes was $1,011. (Financial statements are shown in Exhibits 1 and 2.)

The Graphic Arts Research Foundation was founded in July, 1949, as a nonprofit, industry-supported organization which was designed to support printing research in general and to give financial and technical aid in the development of the photocomposing machine. The Foundation was the first independent research organization in the printing industry and was regarded by many as a vitally necessary and long-overdue step toward technical improvements in printing.

Character of the Printing Industry

Until recently, the printing industry has not been particularly research-oriented. Inventions have usually arisen under pressure from needs, rather than from a scientific or technological base. Most of the inventions have been improvements on existing processes instead of radical innovations. Metal type, cast type, the Stanhope press, photoengraving, paper feeders, and rotogravure presses were outgrowths of and improvements on old processes. (A brief list of printing innovations is presented in Exhibit 3.)

Exhibit 1

LITHOMAT CORPORATION

Income Statements

	June 30, 1946	June 30, 1947	June 30, 1948	December 31, 1949*
Net sales	$537,104	$910,842	$1,032,644	$874,496
Cost of sales	309,980	615,792	730,508	655,389
Gross profit	$227,124	$295,050	$302,136	$219,107
Selling, general, and administrative expenses	289,220	233,290	286,494	219,447
Profit (loss) from operations	($ 62,096)	$ 61,760	$ 15,642	($ 340)
Other income:				
Reduction of federal taxes on income provision—prior period	$14,502			
Miscellaneous	3,746	8,391	4,360	7,751
	18,248	$8,391	$4,360	$7,751
Total Other Income	($ 43,848)	$ 70,151	$ 20,002	$ 7,411
Other charges:				
Interest on bank loan and other indebtedness	6,674	8,382	9,459	6,257
Net income (loss) before provision for federal taxes	($ 50,522)	$ 61,769	$ 10,543	$ 1,154
Provision for federal taxes	18,502	22,858	5,601	143
Net income (loss) before refund	($ 69,024)	$ 38,911	$ 4,942	$ 1,011
Refundable excess profits—prior year	84,668			
Consolidated net income (loss)	$ 15,644	$ 38,911	$ 4,942	$ 1,011

* Fiscal year changed.

Exhibit 2

LITHOMAT CORPORATION
Balance Sheets

	June 30, 1946	June 30, 1947	June 30, 1948	December 31, 1949
ASSETS				
Current assets:				
Cash in banks and on hand	$ 61,920	$ 33,321	$ 24,588	$ 22,212
Accounts and notes receivable (net)	190,273	112,862	149,351	149,678
Inventories (lower of cost or market):				
Finished goods	$ 35,790	$ 56,833	$ 42,012	$ 44,818
Work in process	24,816	52,745	52,672	71,155
Raw materials and packages	83,048	144,212	116,592	78,766
(total inventories)	143,654	253,790	211,276	194,739
Total Current Assets	$395,847	$399,973	$385,215	$366,629
Property, plant, and equipment at reproduction cost	$184,137	$285,476	$293,277	$308,205
Reserve for depreciation	43,354	69,464	87,535	106,617
(net)	140,783	216,012	205,742	201,588
Prepaid and deferred items	4,741	5,198	4,123	7,701
Development costs of machines	1	21,369	44,259	40,437
Patents and patent rights		1	1	54,941
Excess of acquisition cost over net asset value of subsidiary		2,707		
Total Assets	$541,372	$645,260	$639,340	$671,296
LIABILITIES				
Current liabilities:				
Accounts payable and accrued items	$ 25,012	$ 39,622	$ 79,867	$ 48,284
Commissions payable	4,005			
Notes payable:				
Bank	10,000	54,000	50,167	35,500
Mortgage		10,000		5,000
Other		3,414	8,338	5,360
Provisions for federal income tax	86,796	58,794	46,870	44,540
Taxes on income (other than federal)	4,938	11,619	8,341	6,431
Provisions for redemption of returnable containers	7,048	3,999	3,218	3,056
Total Current Liabilities	$137,799	$181,448	$196,801	$148,171
Long-term debt	112,000	84,000	67,500	34,422
CAPITAL				
Common stock, no par value, authorized shares outstanding, $200,000	157,000 shares	162,000 shares	162,000 shares	169,194 shares
	31,400	86,400	86,400	129,016
5 per cent cumulative convertible preferred stock, $100 par value, 3,000 shares authorized, 1,006 shares outstanding				100,600
Capital surplus	78,504	72,832	63,117	53,106
Earned surplus	181,669	220,580	225,522	205,981
Total Capital Stock and Surplus	$291,573	$379,812	$375,039	$488,703
Total Liabilities	$541,372	$645,260	$639,340	$671,296

Exhibit 3

HISTORY OF INNOVATIONS

The following is a brief summary of the major technological innovations in the printing industry.

A.D. 100:   Papermaking appeared in China and was confined to the Chinese Empire until the end of the seventh century.

Sixth century: Wood-block printing began in China.

Eleventh century: Movable wooden characters for type began to be used in China.

Circa 1390:   Movable metal type was developed in Korea.

1470:   Nicolas Jensen added lower case type to the existing capital letters and provided the basis for modern type design.

Middle of eighteenth century: The stereotype process was invented.

1798:   Aloys Senefelder discovered the principle of lithography in Germany.

1800:   The Earl of Stanhope developed the all-iron press.

1803:   Fourdrinier invented a papermaking machine which made cheap paper for newsprint available for the first time.

1811:   Freiderich Koenig develop the first power-driven press.

1814:   Koenig invented the continuously revolving cylinder press.

1822:   Dr. William Church in Boston took out patents on the first type-composing machine.

1835:   Sir Roland Hill developed a method of printing on both sides of the paper.

1840:   Electrotypes and engravings were developed.

1850:   The wood-pulp process for papermaking was developed. Pulp paper was much less expensive than paper made from rags.

1855:   Color and halftone printing was developed.

1865:   First web-fed press was developed; this increased the press speed.

1878:   Ottmar Mergenthaler built the first slug-casting machine, which was the forerunner of the Linotype machine. By 1890 the Mergenthaler Linotype was in common use.

1898:   A. G. Harris developed the offset process for printing lithographically.

Early twentieth century: Rotogravure presses, photolithography, and the multilith process were developed to increase the speed and variety of printing.

1915:   W. C. Huebner developed a photocomposing machine which was designed for letterpress work, but could be used only for lithography.

1915–29:   Single-color, two-color, and finally four-color offset presses were developed.

1921–40:   Many laboratory models of photocomposing machines were built, but none were put into commercial production.

The lack of research orientation in the industry was perhaps due to the fact that publishers, more concerned with the content and presentation of the reading matter, did not worry much about the production costs. The main competitive advantage for a magazine or newspaper lay in the gathering, writing, and editing of material. The production department of a typical newspaper or publishing house has been made up of men who began as craftsmen. The production heads are usually men who worked their way up by knowing more about the existing processes than anyone else.

Unions have had a strong position in the industry beginning with the founding of the International Typographical Union in 1852. They have held great power because of the peculiar perishability of the printing

Exhibit 4

The Linotype Machine*

Ottmar Mergenthaler invented his Linotype machine in 1878, and it came into common use in the 1890's. The machine substitutes a keyboard operation for hand typesetting and automatic distribution for hand sorting of used type.

The Linotype is actually not a typesetting machine. No types are used in it. It composes with matrices—small brass units having characters indented in the edges—hence the name "matrix." These matrices are assembled into justified lines. From the matrix line the Linotype automatically casts a solid bar, or line, of type. This bar is known as the linotype slug and is ready for use when it leaves the machine.

The Linotype has four major divisions: (1) The magazines which contain the matrices—they represent type cases. A magazine is compact and light, and an operator can produce a variety of composition by simply changing magazines. (2) The keyboard and related parts—this controls the release of matrices from the magazines in the order in which the characters are desired. The operator's duties are limited to operating the keyboard keys—justification of the lines and distribution of the matrices are mechanically automatic. (3) The casting mechanism—this division of the machine makes the linotype-equipped printer his own type founder. The justified line of matrices is presented automatically to the casting mechanism; molten type metal is forced into the indented characters on the edges of the matrices; and the cast line, a single unit with a new type face, is delivered to the galley on the machine, precisely trimmed, and ready to go into the form. (4) The distributing mechanism—when a line of matrices has served for casting the line of type, it is lifted automatically and carried to the top of the magazine, where, by a simple though ingenious system, each matrix is delivered to its proper place in the magazine, and is ready to serve again.

The Linotype is, in simplest terms, a machine for (1) assembling a number of these matrices in a row, or line; (2) automatically spacing that line to a desired length, or justification, (3) holding the indented characters of this line up against a casting mechanism, of which they become a part and which molds the line of printing characters on a bar or slug; and (4) transferring this line of matrices to their original positions in the magazine, where they may be used again.

---

* Summarized from *The Big Scheme of Simple Operation* (Brooklyn: Mergenthaler Linotype Co., 1940).

industry's product. This is particularly true of newspapers. If an issue is late, it is worthless in terms of market value. The loss in business due to a strike cannot be made up in increased sales after the strike is over. Publishers, then, have not often been anxious to fight union demands and take the loss of a strike.

For an example of the printing industry's reaction to change, Ottmar Mergenthaler's Linotype machine was a radical innovation in 1886. (A description of the Linotype is given in Exhibit 4.) This machine threatened to displace many employees in the printing industry because it greatly increased typesetting speed. At first, there was tremendous opposition to the machine in the individual shops. As the machine proved its efficiency and gradually became widely used, the unions realized that they could not prevent its introduction. The unions then began a series of jurisdictional disputes among themselves over which union should operate the machine. The International Typographical Union claimed jurisdiction and urged its members to learn how to operate the machine. They sought to soften the impact of the machine by installing an apprentice system, by limiting the number of apprentices, and by keeping the apprentice period from four to six years. They attempted to limit the use of the new machines in their labor contracts and tried intentional slowdowns on the equipment to maintain jobs. A movement for shorter hours has been a continuous fight in the industry ever since.

Statistics, Processes, and Trends

The printing and publishing industry is one of the major industrial groups in the United States. In 1947, it ranked third in the number of establishments, with 28,986 units. It ranked ninth in number of employees, with 715,450 people. The value added by manufacture stood at $4.2 billion, and this ranked ninth among the major groups. The industry is made up of a number of different groups such as newspapers, periodicals, book publishing and printing, and commercial printing. Of the three major processes used, letterpress accounts for 80 per cent of the printing; lithography, for 13 per cent; and gravure, for 5 per cent.

Letterpress printing uses raised type. Ink is spread on the surface, and the type is pressed against paper to produce an image transfer.

Lithography uses printing areas that are flush with the surface. The plate is alternately dampened with water and inked. Water adheres to the nonimage areas due to surface tension and repels the ink. The image area is greasy and repels water but accepts the ink. When the plate is pressed against paper, the ink is transferred. In offset lithography the plate is pressed against a rubber cylinder. The image is transferred to it, and the cylinder is then pressed against the paper.

In gravure printing the image is sunk into the plate by means of many tiny holes or depressions. The plate is covered with ink, and then the surface is scraped. The ink remaining in the sunken image areas is transferred to the paper when the plate is pressed against it.

During the war a trend of seriously rising costs of production and distribution began, and has continued. For the first time, the publishers had to concern themselves with the costs and efficiency of the printing operation. When the publishers turned to the production departments for help, production managers were presented with a new problem. The production manager's success had always depended on his knowledge of the machines and the process, and on his leadership ability. He was usually not trained in, and had little experience with, cost control and cost cutting. It is anticipated that this trend of rising costs will continue.

SOURCE OF INVENTION

Rene A. Higonnet got the idea for a photocomposing machine when he was an engineer employed by International Telephone and Telegraph Company in France in 1944. He had no experience with printing and made his first visit to a printing plant in Lyon to discuss the publication of a book. Since the plant only had offset presses, Linotype machines were used to set type for printing one page. This page was then photographed, and the film was used to prepare the offset plate. Higonnet noted the difficulty of working with hot lead to form the lines of type. He also noticed that the completed banks of type were extremely heavy and difficult to move.

It seemed to Higonnet that there should be a simpler and more direct method of setting type on film for the preparation of an offset plate. A year before, he had seen a paper on the use of flash tubes to study high-speed mechanisms such as aircraft propellers. Since Higonnet had an old interest in photography, it occurred to him that this flash tube could be used to project a clear image from a continuously moving film. After seeing the printing plant, Higonnet thought he had an application for his moving film idea. He believed that if this film contained letters of type, a machine could be constructed to set type on film without the use of the Linotype machines.

Higonnet discussed his idea with a friend, Louis Moyroud, and Moyroud persuaded him to build a prototype out of cardboard to demonstrate the principle. By early 1945 the inventors had built a simple machine to demonstrate the moving film principle for photocomposition. This machine showed that the flash was fast enough to project on a plate a clear image of a character on a revolving disc. The inventors took this machine to a school of printing in Paris, Ecole Etienne, and to a commercial printer for evaluation. The machine excited great interest, and the inventors felt that they were on the right track. The inventors then devoted their time to developing a solution to a second important problem —line justification. If the machine was to be useful, it would have to justify

Exhibit 5

THE INVENTORS' PHOTOGRAPH OF THEIR FIRST
PHOTOCOMPOSING MACHINE

lines of print quickly and easily (i.e., adjust the space between words and letters so that the lines are of equal length).

The inventors completed the construction of their prototype model by April, 1946. This model demonstrated the composition of lines on film with a selection of 82 letters or characters and with a means for automatic justification (see Exhibit 5). The main components of this machine were:

1. A manual typewriter with permutation bars and contacts to give each of the characters a binary code.
2. A memory register in the form of a revolving drum with sliding pins controlled by solenoids. Each pin could be set in either of two positions (to record the binary code).
3. A counter justifier to accumulate the widths of the characters and determine the justification increment after each line had been completely typed.
4. A control circuitry made of telephone relays.
5. A photographic unit made up of a film carriage and a continuously rotating disc with 82 transparent characters on an opaque background. The flash lamp was controlled by an electronic circuit made up of a rotating switch with brushes and 82 terminals, one terminal for each character. Each terminal, and therefore each character, could be selected by the relay circuitry.

In May of 1946, ITT sent Higonnet to the United States for a short trip. He decided to bring pictures and drawings along to try to interest

United States investors in the machine. He contacted Dr. Burchard at Massachusetts Institute of Technology, who suggested that Higonnet take the machine to William W. Garth, President of Lithomat Corporation. Lithomat made office offset duplicating plates and chemicals, and had an active research program for new products.

LITHOMAT'S INVOLVEMENT

Around 1934, J. E. Gilligan conceived the idea which subsequently was the basis for the Lithomat Corporation. Gilligan had worked for some years in the office duplication business and saw large profits made by companies introducing successful innovations in the industry. He thought there was potential in a lithographic plate made of paper which could be used for office duplication equipment. The conventional metal plates were impractical. Two other engineers helped him, and he was financed for some time by a large office equipment manufacturer. By 1939 the office equipment manufacturer had dropped the idea, and outside capital was obtained. Lithomat was incorporated in 1940 to draw together all the interests.

Garth and others invested in it in 1942, when the company still had not been profitable. Garth was elected President in 1942. Fiscal 1944 (June, 1943, to June, 1944, was profitable for the first time. Net income before federal and excess profits tax was $708,000. The after-tax income was $206,000. Lithomat's sales, however, were primarily to the government. Garth carried Lithomat through the difficult period of postwar adjustment, when private customers had to be found. The financial statements for 1946 show the effect of this adjustment (see Exhibits 1 and 2).

The Lithomat Corporation then, having been formed as a result of an inventor's ideas, and having struggled through a decade of development problems, had experience in working with innovations.

Early in 1946, Higonnet met Garth and showed him the drawings and pictures of the photocomposing machine (Exhibit 5). Although Garth knew little about commercial printing or the newspaper business, from his experience in the office offset duplication field he knew that the machine definitely had potential if it could photocompose and justify lines. Since it was difficult to evaluate the invention from the drawings, Garth and Higonnet decided to bring Louis Moyroud to the United States with the prototype, each covering 50 per cent of the travel expenses.

When Moyroud arrived in the summer of 1946, Garth contacted Dr. Samuel Caldwell at MIT for technical advice and had him study the machine. Dr. Caldwell verified that the machine would photocompose and justify lines. From a technical standpoint, it looked as though this prototype had the potential for a commercial photocomposing machine. The inventors estimated that it would take about a year and cost about $10,000 to bring the machine to the commercial prototype stage.

Exhibit 6

THE SECOND PHOTOCOMPOSITION MACHINE—1948

Lithomat and the inventors signed a contract which gave Lithomat an option on the western hemispheric rights for manufacturing and distribution of the machine for $10,000. The inventors returned to France to complete the commercial model in November, 1946.

The inventors returned to the United States in July, 1948, with their second model (see Exhibit 6). Although this model was based on the same principles as the 1946 model, it represented major improvements in the design of the components. It was no longer necessary to wait for one line to be transcribed on film before typing the next line. Therefore, typing of lines could be done at much greater speed than with the first machine. This model had 88 characters in its alphabet, and it could compose lines of one size up to five or six inches long with a maximum capacity of 75 characters per line.

The typewriter was an Electromatic Commercial Controls electric typewriter, the first electric typewriter developed in this country. Permutation bars were installed by the inventors under the electric typewriter to obtain a code in binary form. In this machine, contrary to the 1946 machine, the computation for justification was made entirely in the binary system. Since no binary counters were available at the time, the inventors had to develop and manufacture their own binary switches. They also had to design their own circuit for accumulation of character widths and for the division of the line shortage (or overage) by the number of interword spaces in the line. A variable escapement mechanism was used, which provided the choice of eighteen character widths. This represented considerable progress over the 1946 model, which had a maximum number of eight character widths.

In July, 1948, this machine was shown to Robert B. Choate, publisher of the *Boston Herald,* and to Henry A. Laughlin, President, Houghton Mifflin Company. They immediately recognized that the machine was of vital importance to their industries and to the entire printing world. The machine was later shown to C. M. Flint, Research Director, American Newspaper Publishing Association, and to Dr. Vannevar Bush, President, Carnegie Institute in Washington.

It was suggested at this latter meeting that the machine could be the basis for starting a nonprofit, industry-controlled independent research organization which could command industry interest and support. This would be the first independent research organization in the printing industry. The proposal appeared attractive to Lithomat because it would publicize the photocomposing machine and would contribute financial support for its development. Work was begun in the summer of 1948 to interest industry leaders.

In July of 1948 a prominent Boston patent attorney advised Lithomat that it would probably take $125,000 to bring the photocomposing machine to the market. This estimate appeared high, but Lithomat also wanted to acquire the patents of W. G. Mullen for other commercial printing improvements, so a package of convertible preferred and common stock was offered to the stockholders in the summer of 1948. The eventual proceeds of this offering were about $125,000.

During an ANPA convention in New York in April, 1949, the photocomposing machine was exhibited at the Waldorf Astoria. Competitors were strictly excluded, and identification had to be shown to gain entrance to the exhibit. Interest in the machine was excited throughout the printing industry. The exhibition was very helpful in attaining support for the Research Foundation.

On July 14, 1949, the Graphic Arts Research Foundation was founded as a nonprofit research organization. The printing industry was to contribute $100,000 annually for three years to support printing research in general and mainly to support the development of the photocomposing machine. Lithomat was to assign its patent rights for the machine to the Foundation in return for a license to produce it commercially.

The Foundation began with little space, inadequate equipment, and a technical staff of three engineers. The first six months were devoted to space, staff, and equipment requirements and, most important, to the training of new personnel in the principles and circuitry of the existing machine. In March of 1950 the Graphic Arts Research Foundation (GARF) moved into permanent headquarters near the Lithomat manufacturing facilities. The staff had been increased to ten, i.e., the two inventors plus machinists and technicians experienced in electronics, electrical engineering, mechanics, optics, photography, and design. So much progress had been made in the development of the machine that the Research Foundation and Lithomat expected to produce three production models for field test by the summer of 1950.

Difficulty developed, however, on what specific characteristics the machine should have. The scientists and engineers of Lithomat and the GARF personnel did not have experience with the commercial printing field and did not know what people in printing production wanted. Industry people did not understand the problems of scientific research and development. To solve this language barrier, a Technical Advisory Board of fourteen men from the printing industry was invited to meet with the GARF and Lithomat staff to review the development progress to date and to define the characteristics of the photographic type-composing machine that should be developed. They met on April 7, 1950, at the new headquarters of the Graphic Arts Research Foundation.

FINDINGS AND RECOMMENDATION OF THE ADVISORY BOARD

The Board carefully reviewed the progress of the Graphic Arts Research Foundation up to April 7, 1950, and made the following statement to the subscribers of the Foundation:

We have examined in detail the work done by the Foundation since the beginning of its operation in August 1949, and we have examined the estimates made by the staff of the Foundation on the degree of completion of various elements of their program. We believe the attached chart correctly represents a measure of the progress made [see Exhibit 7]. On the basis of manpower available and the work still to be done, it now appears reasonable to expect an operating prototype machine to be ready in July or August of 1950, which is approximately the schedule planned.[1]

The second purpose of the meeting was to solve the problem of what to develop, and to advise the scientists and engineers of the Foundation and of Lithomat Corporation what specific features of the machine were

---

[1] Quoted from *Report to the Subscribers of the Graphic Arts Research Foundation* for the period August 1, 1949, to March 31, 1950.

Exhibit 7

PROGRESS CHART
(Shading Indicates Work Completed)

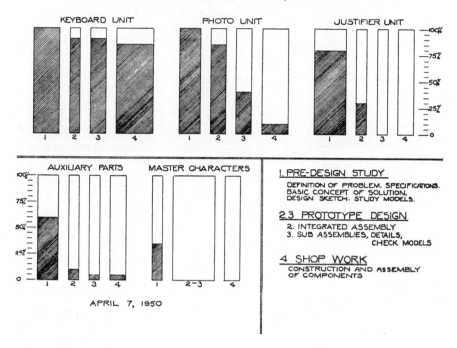

APRIL 7, 1950

I. PRE-DESIGN STUDY

DEFINITION OF PROBLEM. SPECIFICATIONS.
BASIC CONCEPT OF SOLUTION,
DESIGN SKETCH. STUDY MODELS.

2,3 PROTOTYPE DESIGN

2. INTEGRATED ASSEMBLY
3. SUB ASSEMBLIES, DETAILS,
                        CHECK MODELS

4 SHOP WORK

CONSTRUCTION AND ASSEMBLY
OF COMPONENTS

necessary to have it fully versatile and useful to the printing industry. "The discussion covered composition requirements in the various fields of printing, and existing typesetting methods, their limitations and their problems."[2]

The meeting of the Advisory Board was most constructive on the matter of requirements. Agreement was obtained on the following specifications:

1. The machine should operate from a standard typewriter keyboard.
   a) All controls should be at the keyboard position.
   b) The speed should be that of an electric typewriter.
2. The machine should justify the lines automatically.
   a) Justification should be from a single typing.
   b) Any line up to 42 picas should be possible.
   c) Line length should be under dial control.
   d) Provision should be made for production of unjustified lines.
3. The machine should allow mixing of type in the same line.
   a) Provision should be made for mixing families and styles.
   b) Provision should be made for mixing different set-widths.
   c) Provisions should be made for mixing point sizes.
   d) Mixing should not affect justification or character alignment.

[2] Quoted from *ibid.*, July 1, 1952.

e) Master character matrices should be interchangeable.
4. The machine should be capable of variable leading between lines.
   a) Automatic leading of selected amount.
   b) Fixed leading of specific amount.
   c) A key should allow repeated insertion of selected leading.
5. The machine should be capable of making corrections.
   a) Corrections should be possible on an individual character basis.
   b) It should be possible to "kill" entire lines.
6. The machine should contain the following controls:
   a) Provision for automatic left or right quadding.
   b) Provision for automatic centering.
   c) Provision for fixed space insertion.[3]

Many of these requirements went far beyond the features anticipated by the Foundation staff, on which the original three-year program was predicated. Only those specifications covered by items 1(*a*), 2(*a*), 2(*d*), 4(*b*), 5(*a*), and 5(*b*) had been demonstrated in operating form—six out of nineteen general features.

An argument developed between various members of the Lithomat and Research Foundation staff as to whether the new features should be incorporated into the design or not.

On the one hand, it was pointed out that no compromise with the new specifications was necessary from a technical standpoint because research already conducted indicated that all the features could be achieved. It was felt that incorporation of the features would make the machine more versatile and would enable it to fulfill the requirements of a greater number of printing and publishing establishments. The patent structure was thought to be adequate at present, and some of the staff believed the machine was five years ahead of anything the competition had.

From the financial standpoint, it was pointed out that by April of 1950, 148 concerns had contributed $100,850 to the Graphic Arts Research Foundation, and it was expected that $150,000 would be obtained annually for the three years requested. The 148 concerns were made up of the following:

97 Newspapers	$ 63,050
19 Book publishers	12,550
6 Book manufacturers	12,500
15 Newsprint manufacturers	6,000
5 Typographers	2,500
2 Lithographers	1,000
4 Miscellaneous concerns	3,250
148	$100,850

Furthermore, it was felt that the great interest displayed in the machine at the 1949 showing indicated that Lithomat could sell more stock, if necessary.

The men on the opposite side of the argument pointed to the develop-

[3] *Ibid.*

ment work that had been done to date (Exhibit 7) and stressed the fact that even though research had shown that the new features would be technically possible, these changes would require drastic revision and complete reshaping of the technical program. The changes would extend the development program for at least another year and perhaps longer. It was felt that the delay might antagonize some contributors to the Foundation.

Furthermore, even though contributions had come in to the Foundation, Lithomat expected to continue to bear two thirds of the development costs of the machine. In spite of the interest shown in the machine, Lithomat could not sell stock indefinitely without showing an operating profit. Some men felt very strongly that design should be frozen for production just as soon as possible, so that the machines could be marketed while interest was high. They felt that "perfection" of the machine would make it too expensive and too versatile to be used on over-all composing operations.

It was pointed out that the printing machine industry was dominated by two or three large manufacturers, such as the Mergenthaler Linotype Company, with great financial strength; and they would be bringing out competing machines eventually.

There seemed to be no successful way to resolve the two sides of the argument, and yet a decision had to be made on this problem immediately.

Will Established Industries Propose Innovations?

The history of the turbojet makes it very clear that the engine industry can by no means be counted on to propose development of a radical innovation as soon as it is technically practicable to do so. This is as it should be, since to a large extent the efficiency and effectiveness of the engine industry come from its specialization in the task of improving existing types of engines by continual refinement. If the engine builders were to divert a large part of their efforts to studying and experimenting with every new type of engine to be suggested, they would be unable to carry out their essential task.

The fact that innovations are more likely than not to come from outside the established industry means, however, that the government must not look with prejudice upon schemes for the new engines which come from sources with no experience in engine development. Such prejudice would be more than natural, since the services have been continually harassed by proposals for new types of engines (and for new types of aeronautical materiel of all sorts) from sources obviously incompetent to produce a sound proposal, let alone to develop it. The services have in the past maintained a very open mind concerning such proposals and have probably erred in the direction of supporting too many "cats and dogs" rather than in giving support only to the established companies. The important thing is to recognize that despite the high ratio of failures to successes, this open-minded policy must be continued.

ROBERT SCHLAIFER

FROM: *Development of Aircraft Engines and Fuels* (Boston: Harvard Business School, 1950).

CLARK EQUIPMENT COMPANY

Background

When Clark closed its 1962 books, a 19 per cent performance improvement was evident. Sales had climbed to over $206 million, and earnings had gone from $1.62 per share in 1961 to $2.64. From corporate offices in Buchanan, Michigan, Clark management co-ordinated four independent manufacturing divisions, each with a good position in its field (see Exhibit 1):

Division	*Product Line*
Industrial Truck (Battle Creek, Michigan)	Fork lift trucks, hand pallet trucks, towing tractors, straddle carriers
Automotive Division (Buchanan and Jackson, Michigan)	Transmissions, axles, torque converters, and heavy-duty automotive components
Construction Machinery (Benton Harbor, Michigan)	Tractor shovels and bulldozers, tractor scrapers, logging equipment
Brown Trailer (Michigan City, Indiana)	Freight, platform, and insulated truck trailers, shipping containers

The Central Parts Division in Chicago supplied spare parts for all products. This warehouse was noted for an advanced, computer-controlled inventory and order-processing system. Clark's Credit Corporation financed more than $130 million of equipment for Clark's dealers and customers. Canadian Clark, Ltd., was a wholly owned manufacturing subsidiary.

Overseas the Clark Equipment International, C.A., a wholly owned subsidiary, produced sales of $87 million, of which $65 million were sales of overseas affiliates and licencees—"in every country of the free world."

Clark's business began in fork lift trucks and automotive parts prior to World War II. The war gave a great boost to mechanized handling of packaged goods, which spread into manufacturing and warehousing after the war. In the 1950's, Clark's steady program of expansion and acquisition in other fields overcame a leveling-off of the fork lift truck market

Exhibit 1

PRODUCTS OF CLARK EQUIPMENT COMPANY: (*A*) INDUSTRIAL TRUCKS; (*B*) BROWN TRAILER DIVISION; (*C*) CONSTRUCTION MACHINERY DIVISION; (*D*) AUTOMOTIVE DIVISION; (*F*) CLARK'S CENTRAL PARTS DIVISION AT CHICAGO

Exhibit 2

PERFORMANCE REVIEW*

The following is a tabulation of our annual sales, earnings, dividends, and net worth averaged over three-year periods beginning with World War II, and showing a steady increase in our performance.

Period	Average Annual Sales	Average Annual Earnings	Average Annual Dividends	Average Year-End Net Worth
1939–41............	$ 22,095,000	$1,634,000	$ 820,000	$ 9,262,000
1942–44............	67,700,000	2,169,000	803,000	12,925,000
1945–47............	50,745,000	2,159,000	1,001,000	15,979,000
1948–50............	62,184,000	4,293,000	1,290,000	25,036,000
1951–53............	119,647,000	5,319,000	2,602,000	35,585,000
1954–56............	122,581,000	8,216,000	4,204,000	48,740,000
1957–59............	164,622,000	9,027,000	5,118,000	62,892,000
1960–62............	192,129,000	9,117,000	5,776,000	74,571,000

* Quoted from the 1962 annual report.

Exhibit 3

FINANCIAL HIGHLIGHTS*

	1962	1961
Sales of products and services.........................	$206,299,000	$173,320,000
Income before federal income tax....................	23,989,000	11,921,000
Federal income tax................................	11,200,000	4,100,000
Net income.....................................	12,789,000	7,821,000
Net income per dollar of sales......................	6.2¢	4.5¢
Net income per share of common stock..............	$2.64	$1.62
Income tax per share of common stock...............	2.31	0.85
Dividends paid in cash per share of common stock......	1.20	1.20
Working capital at end of year......................	52,455,000	48,623,000
Properties and equipment (less depreciation)...........	31,557,000	32,080,000
Depreciation of plant and equipment..................	3,247,000	3,083,000
Ratio of current assets to current liabilities............	2.7 to 1	3.7 to 1
Share owners' investment at end of year..............	$80,319,000	$73,040,000
Shares outstanding at end of year....................	4,842,552	4,830,866
Book value per share of common stock at end of year...	$16.59	$15.12
Number of employees..............................	8,635	8,170
Number of share owners............................	8,727	7,989

* Quoted from the 1962 annual report.

(although Clark had grown to do about 50 per cent of the aggregate industrial truck business). Exhibit 2 shows the firm's twenty-five-year record. Exhibit 3 gives highlights from the 1962 annual report. Clark's outstanding performance was largely credited, inside and outside the company, to the driving leadership of George Spatta, President. Spatta was known as a man who made his own decisions and who ran the company with a firm hand. Over the years, he had built up a team of division executives with proven ability.

Although Clark's position was strong, each Division operated in a severely competitive field. As of 1960–62, a rough appraisal might have looked like this:

Industrial Truck Division. Market apparently leveling off around 30,000–35,000 units annually for the total industry. Chief competitors were Yale & Towne, Hyster, Towmotor, and Allis Chalmers. Specialized competition from small, owner-held firms like Lewis-Shephard, Elwell-Parker, and Raymond Corporation. Clark's position in the industry very strong, due to its volume and marketing organization.

Construction Machinery Division. Up against International Harvester, Caterpillar Tractor, Westinghouse-Euclid Division of General Motors, J. I. Case, Allis Chalmers, LeTourneau, and a variety of small manufacturers of mobile cranes and other special units.

Brown Trailer Division. Clark's purchased company, Brown Trailer, was a solid organization, but competed with Fruehauf Trailer and many others. Trends toward containerization systems that integrated road, rail, air, and marine carriers, and were based upon special handling devices, looked promising.

Automotive Division. Strong competition from many large and small producers. The trend for the automobile companies to make their own parts was evident. However, growth in the construction equipment and special vehicle field promised heavy-duty parts business.

Clearly, this product environment was not static, and Clark had achieved its growth only by shrewd acquisition and aggressive development, production, and marketing. It was apparent to Clark management that future growth in existing divisions would depend heavily upon finding new developments and new product fields. Clark divisions were expected to develop new ideas and improved products to add to their lines. Division managers were expected to be aggressively searching for new products.

In 1959, management organized the Clark Development Division, headed by Bruce Rogers, 35, a former development engineer from the Industrial Truck Division. The mission of the new division was to explore concepts and promising product ideas that would not normally be undertaken by another division. Meanwhile, top management turned up many potential product areas and passed them on to appropriate divisions for study.

THE KURT FRUIT HARVESTER

In the fall of 1962, Clark Equipment Company's Industrial Truck Division became interested in mechanical harvesting of tree-borne crops through a contact with Herman Kurt. Kurt had been in the business of building his own tree shakers and harvesting frames. He approached Clark because it was too costly for him to continue a long-range development program. The Industrial Truck Division was aggressively searching for new products and markets, since its materials-handling market was highly competitive and appeared to have leveled off.

The agreement called for Clark to evaluate Kurt's design and to incorporate some of the improvements he suggested. Meanwhile, Kurt was hired as a consultant to make a survey of the present and potential

Exhibit 4

ENGINEERING DEPARTMENT
November 5, 1962

To: Ralph Jensen, Accounting
From: D. W. McKee
Subject: Kurt Fruit Harvester

You are aware that we are currently undertaking the design and manufacture of two complete Kurt harvesting machines. Each harvesting machine consists of two self-propelled parts and a catching frame.

I would like you to take out a development number of this program in which you would account for at least the following items:

1. 300 hours of engineering design time.
2. 200 hours of engineering test time.
3. Approximately $30,000 in development costs which would be split 50% labor and 50% materials.
4. Jim Schell's salary for a six months period and the assumption that he will be involved in travel and living away from home for three months of this period at about $15 per diem, plus travel.
5. A provision for $9,000 of consulting fees to Herman Kurt and his per diem for six months at $15 per day, plus travel.
6. In addition, this ultimately will require two shaking devices at approximately $2,000 each. Presently these should be handled as purchased items.

This complete program should be written up as a formal project estimate. Our first task in the description of the project estimate is to build and evaluate two Kurt Fruit Harvesting devices—one for use in the California market with a target delivery in California of February 1. The second unit is intended for the Florida citrus operation with delivery as soon after February 1 as practical.

The following areas are to be investigated for improved design:

1. Flotation
   a) Requires improvement for California—look at four-wheel drive, four-wheel steer. Will probably require added horsepower.
2. Lower profile at tree side and outboard side.
3. Hydraulically raise and lower side deflectors. (Required for hillside operation.)
4. Manually raise and lower main deflectors—slip tube connector.
5. All surfaces and moving deflector areas have to be strong enough to walk on.
6. Improve hydraulic plumbing (change to hose and tube).
7. Simplify frame chassis (use deeper channels, not boxed).

On November 15 we intend to make a decision to the practicability of incorporating these design revisions into the sample machines. Immediately after the 15th, we will start to order material for the manufacture of those items in the Experimental Shop.

One additional thing must be done prior to the 15th and that is to ascertain the best method of ordering and expediting the materials for Buchanan Shop so that we don't have our usual problem with lost or unordered parts. The time schedule will not permit.

cc: W. Norlander
     J. Schell
     H. Kurt

market for mechanical tree-harvesting equipment, assisted by company engineers and market researchers.

The engineering study was launched in November, 1962, by the head of the Engineering Department, Dale McKee (see Exhibit 4). James Schell, a development engineer, was assigned project responsibility, including co-ordination of the market survey field work. Schell's first step was to lay out a development-field survey program, as outlined in Exhibit 5.

Exhibit 5

ENGINEERING DEPARTMENT
November 19, 1962

To: D. W. McKee
         W. A. Norlander
         H. Kurt

From: J. D. Schell

Subject: Engineering Program for the Self-Propelled Catching Frames
         Used for Mechanical Harvesting

In a meeting held November 19, 1962 it was decided to plan and run the engineering program according to the steps listed below:

1. Eliminate two (2) samples by February 15, 1963.
2. If it is necessary to have a machine for Prune Day, February 8, purchase a used machine on West Coast and rework it for this show. This decision to be made in the next week or two.
3. Do engineering studies on paper until market survey is completed.
   a) Build sample machine for summer 1963 for California.
4. If market survey and sample indicate "Go" build ten (10) machines for June 1964 California season.
5. Full production will depend on success of item 4 above.
6. Study citrus applications and write a specification for a citrus machine in fall of 1963.
7. If item 6 looks O.K. and preliminary survey indicates interest and possibilities, build prototype for 1963–1964 season demonstration.

These seven items pretty well outline our position and program. These steps can either be eliminated or extended in time as our program and results progress.

By mid-December, Schell and Kurt, accompanied at times by Bill Norlander from Engineering, had spent several weeks in California and Florida calling on various agricultural agencies and users of tree-harvesting equipment. Based on findings described in Exhibits 6, 7, and 8, the program was altered.

Exhibit 6

EXTRACTS FROM CALIFORNIA TRIP REPORT,
NOVEMBER 4–11

. . . On Monday morning I met with Dr. Ralph R. Parks, Extension Agricultural Engineer, University of California, at Davis, California, to discuss what has been done and what needs to be done in the bulk handling of agricultural products. Dr. Parks has spent a great deal of time and effort in this area, and because he works almost entirely out in the field with the farm people, he knows pretty much what is going on. First of all, Dr. Parks pointed out that there already is a lot of bulk or bin handling in use, and it is increasing every year. More and more research is being done on the various fruits to determine at what depths they can be piled in bins and also what damages occur when these products are hauled to processing. Presently, more of the fruits being handled in bins are for processing. Dr. Parks also stated that with the present trend toward mechanical harvesting, the bulk handling problems will increase and will certainly need more equipment and study. He feels that right now any new methods of handling will not be evident until the harvesting methods have been completely ironed out.

Dr. Parks said that with the use of mechanical harvesting equipment, productivity has been increased up to 1,000% and 600–800% is common. In addition to this harvesting, labor can be cut 70–80%. This, of course, could be a real savings if a farmer has enough fruit to warrant the purchase of the harvesting equipment. I believe that these are ideal figures he is quoting.

Dr. Parks had nice things to say about Mr. Kurt. . . . One thing that should be pointed out here is the fact that the University is always in favor of someone who pursues and spends money on the areas that cover their own interests. I'm trying to say that I'm sure Dr. Parks is sincere in what he said, but his own personal convictions could have tempered the statements.

I spent the rest of the day talking with various members of the staff at the University asking similar questions of each of them. In general, they all tend to lean toward Dr. Parks in that mechanical harvesting will eventually become reality. How quick it comes about depends a great deal on the labor supply and costs of it. It is interesting to note that the labor supply was more plentiful this year because of a couple of labor strikes in some areas, and this apparently has an effect on how fast this trend moves. It seems apparent that the rush to mechanical harvesting has not been as fast this past year.

One of the gentlemen I visited with was Lloyd Lamouria of the Agricultural Engineering Department. Dr. Lamouria has been working with shaking olives for the past four or five years and is now making some progress, but not enough yet. Dr. Lamouria very definitely thinks that mechanical harvesting with the present self-propelled catching frame is a marginal program if it costs over $8 to $8.50 per square foot, this square foot area being the frame area under the tree. This is food for thought!

Also talked with Bob Fridley, Agricultural Engineer, who is the man who worked on the development of the inertia tree-shaker. He stated

Exhibit 6 (Continued)

that, although he liked the rotating weight-type inertia shaker, it is almost necessary to go to the crankshaft-driven inertia shaker in order to get the necessary amount of stroke. This means that the Kurt shaker will need a redesign.

My talk with Mike O'Brien did not reveal much except that he feels bulk-handling and mechanical harvesting are going to increase and eventually be widespread. Dr. O'Brien is a farm shop instructor for future Vocational-Agriculture teachers, but has done a lot of work with bin-dumpers and bin-samplers. He was the most cautious of any of the men, but appears to have a good background.

On Tuesday I drove with Herman Kurt to about 200 miles north of Sacramento, to visit with Paul Smith, who is the owner of the last Kurt machine built by the King Company. Mr. Smith has not been very well satisfied with the machine due to the many problems he encountered. He indicated that owning the machine was financial disaster for him this year, and he is now making plans to try and persuade King to take the machine back and refund his money. Some of the problems he had were:

1. Hydraulic leaks and hose breakage.
2. The tree deflector squashes fruit when retracing.
3. Tree-side deflector too high at tree.
4. Not enough angle to tree-side deflector, fruit will not roll.
5. Rear conveyor speed too fast.
6. Poor steering. Too fast and no way to see wheel.
7. Marginal tractive effort.
8. Shaker slide too hard to operate and too long.
9. No covers for area where tree slide works, causing loss of fruit.
10. Other small areas where there were openings left uncovered, which allowed fruit to fall out.
11. Line sizes too small for shaker—too much pressure loss.
12. No hand throttle to engine.
13. Difficulty with the trough on the top conveyor that empties into bulk bin—clogged up with fruit.
14. Could use more flotation.
15. Poor maneuverability.
16. Poor workmanship in general—this can't be blamed on the machine.
17. Front overhang too much—drags or digs in ground on humps.

. . . In spite of all the problems Mr. Smith said he had, he was still able to harvest about 45 acres of prunes, which is about par for the machine. From what I understand, the average prune picking season is about 20 days, and you can harvest about 2½ acres per day. One of Mr. Smith's complaints with the machine was that he was unable to pick 150 acres that he had contracted to pick outside. The way I figure, he picked all he could with one machine and certainly could not have done another 150 acres.

We went to the Wend Farms. At this ranch they have a pair of XYZ catching frames. They have used these frames two years and seem to be entirely satisfied with them. In addition, they leased a machine this year to help out. The cost of leasing was $10 per ton. The concept of the XYZ

Exhibit 6 (Continued)

is quite a bit different than the Kurt machine. It is better designed, better built and simpler than the Kurt. They have less moving parts and gadgets and build only one basic machine rather than one right hand and one left hand. Then they drive one down the row and back the other one down the other row. All the extension into the tree is accomplished from only one frame. They use a shaker on each frame eliminating the slide mechanism, using only a rotary joint connection. Steering is manual radi-arc steering. The fruit removal is accomplished out over the outboard side in the center of the frame. The fruit is conveyed into the center by two belts running from each end into the middle where it is picked up by the cross belt running out over the side into the bin. This looks pretty good although it causes the fruit to change directions and it always is necessary to drive the machine in the same direction in order to unload the bulk bins. They paid in the neighborhood of $17,000 for this rig with a shaker on each half. It is powered by a Wisconsin engine and a hydro-static chain drive, much neater than the Kurt machine. It has four drive wheels, two sets of duals mounted on a walking beam under the cross conveyor that runs the fruit out to the boxes. I'll attach a copy of their sales literature to this report. There are some good and some bad features about their machine, and I'll list them as I see them:

Good Features
1. Lower profile at tree.
2. One basic unit for both sides.
3. Better designed from mechanical and structural standpoint.
4. Deflectors much simpler and better supported.
5. Engine shock-mounted.
6. Good clean drive set-up.

Poor Features
1. Small steering wheels.
2. Radi-arc steering could allow you to get next to tree with no way to get out.
3. Manual steering.
4. Change in direction of fruit—could cause excess damage.
5. Extremely high at outside edge that runs in aisle.
6. Excessive height on main deflectors causes the shaker to be mounted high which seems difficult to operate.

From this short observation, I'm certainly not in a position to evaluate this approach vs. the Kurt approach, but it is apparent that the XYZ machine was designed with considerable thought and effort.

. . . The Wend Ranch also had two of the Kurt cable shakers which they used up until they got the inertia shakers mounted on the catching frames. Apparently they did a good job for them although they had several service problems. From what I can gather, these are probably declining in use and popularity.

From Red Bluff we drove to Napa where we visited the Charles Tone ranches. They have the first King-built machine which had some better workmanship, but many weak spots. They have had problems, but have

Exhibit 6 (Continued)

reworked and pretty much corrected the machine themselves. One serious problem was with the steer wheels and tires. The wheels did not hold up and the tires were far too small. They solved this temporarily by installing duals. The main frame was weak enough that it bucked when the front end of the machine was picked up. These people are good ranchers and, in general, seemed pretty well satisfied with the results. They apparently feel that, with a new product and concept you must expect to have problems and that it will be necessary to improve the characteristics over a period of time.

. . . From Napa we drove to Fairfield to the Georgiana ranch. These people have a 1961 model machine. The movies we saw were taken of this machine. When this machine was built, it had side transfer belts to the center conveyor. This did not work out, so for the 1962 season they rebuilt the machine to nearly a 1962 model. They have spent a great deal of time and money to correct the faults of the unit, but do not seem unhappy or dissatisfied. With the acquisition of the machine, they were able to become a "family" operation and avoid any labor problems. They feel that mechanical harvesting is a necessity and have been preparing their orchards for this over the past few years. Presently, they are harvesting both prunes and apricots. Their shaking is done with a tractor-mounted Johnson shaker run by compressed air. This is probably the most loyal customer that Kurt has, and I believe Mr. Georgiani has been pretty well satisfied with the machines in spite of their obvious shortcomings. Of all the ranches I visited, these people take the best care of their equipment and do by far the best job of remodeling and reworking. These machines also have very small steer wheels and have proven troublesome. They now have larger wheels and tires to install before next season. They seemed to feel that the machines had adequate power.

From Fairfield we went to San Jose to the Harry Selnak ranch. They also have a 1961 model with the crossways conveyor belts that move fruit into the center into a conveyor that puts it out the back into a bulk bin. They have not removed the crossbelts yet, but intend to do so as they are troublesome and are not generally satisfactory. This and the Georgiana machines were built in the Kurt shop and appear to be a bit sturdier, and the workmanship is better. Mr. Selnak feels that if maneuverability could be improved, it would be a desirable improvement. The steer wheels are far too small and seriously hamper general flotation and tractive effort. Mr. Selnak indicated that he was going to try and sell part interest in his machines to enable him to get money enough to make the improvements he feels are necessary for better operation. Generally, these improvements would be the removal of the side delivery belts and improved flotation on the front axle. Of the two machines that Mr. Selnak has, one has a 10 HP engine and the other has an 18 HP engine. They both seem to perform about equally as well, but the one with the smaller engine seems to have more road speed.

On Thursday we met Bill Norlander and took him back over the same route we had gone and tried to show him all that we had seen. There was no harvesting taking place, but we did have a chance to drive and evaluate the machines. In addition, we were able to see several kinds of shakes. However, we only saw one in operation—this being the one

Exhibit 6 (Continued)

at the Smith farm. This was an inertia shaker with a hydraulic motor driving a crankshaft. The shaker seemed to operate pretty good except that it appeared lacking in power. We did not study the shakers very much in detail as we felt our immediate problems were with the catching frame.

From the short exposure I've had with these machines, I can't truthfully comment on the market potential of them. There does appear to be a great deal of interest in mechanical harvesting and certainly the labor situations have contributed to this.

There are several questions in my mind concerning the machines. These are as follows:

1. As near as I can tell the majority of the work being done is in prunes. The work with peaches and apricots is little, and some is experimental only.
2. There are no very large growers who have jumped into this. Why not?
3. Cost comparisons between the hand-catching frames and the self-propelled.
4. The specialty of each crop may prove to be too much for one machine to overcome.
5. The machines sold to date are very limited in number and have to be reworked each year to do the job.
6. I'm not sure it will ever work in Florida citrus.

After observing the Kurt machines, I would like to point out a few areas that I feel should be redesigned and engineered before any effort is made to build any samples.

1. The drive train needs analyzing and components properly matched.
2. The engine needs to be shock mounted.
3. Four-wheel drive and steer, if necessary, installed.
4. Things in general must be redesigned.

This entails quite a bit of work, but I'm sure that we wouldn't care to show or market any product like this until we've done the necessary work. Up to now, the ranchers have rebuilt and reworked their machines, on their own, to make them operate properly. I don't think Clark could depend on this. My recommendations, if you want them, would be to spend some design time, during the time the market survey is being made; and when the survey is complete, analyze what we have and then build our samples. If we sold 10 machines this year, we couldn't deliver them anyway.

The job looks interesting, and I'm willing to pitch in and make it go. I just want everyone to be sure to know that the machines need to be gone completely through and redesigned. Once this is established, I feel that we can continue with the program and the market survey should tell the rest.

cc: D. W. McKee
       W. A. Norlander

James D. Schell

Exhibit 7

EXTRACTS FROM CALIFORNIA TRIP REPORT,
NOVEMBER 4–11

ENGINEERING DEPARTMENT
November 16, 1962

To: D. W. McKee

From: W. Norlander

Subject: Kurt Fruit Harvester Trip Report

Together with Jim Schell and Herman Kurt, I was able to see three of the Kurt units and one competitive XYZ Harvester. In my opinion the Kurt units that have been built fall far short of a universal machine for fruit harvesting. I believe, as a small manufacturer dealing with small individual owners, he has been able to produce a marginal unit that they have been willing to modify to suit their needs. I am sure we would have these machines back at our dealerships if this were our unit.

The following deficiencies were apparent to me; however, some of these were pointed out to us by Kurt in the summary we made in your office so they aren't new:

1. Too high a profile at the tree—

    . . . .

    The growers do not want to raise the height of the first crotch in the tree because the tree then becomes more susceptible to wind damage. From what little I have seen of citrus groves in Florida, I believe this unit wouldn't have a chance from this standpoint.

2. Inadequate Flotation—
    Competitive unit that doesn't look too much heavier has a lot more rubber under it.

    Even in California prune orchards the ground under the trees is loosely cultivated so that fruit that drops off early can drop without damage. Every Kurt unit I saw had different steer tires on it, and one owner said flotation is completely inadequate. Incidentally he was cleaning his unit up to try to return to King because it wouldn't do his job. We won't know if we can correct this until we finish some more layout work.

3. Tractive Effort Inadequate—
    This is by my rough calculation of what he has according to prints. I can't seem to pin Kurt down on what pressures he has in system, but if he has 1,000 psi at motor, gradeability is only about 4 to 5%. This means engine size will have to be increased.

4. Frame Too Weak—
    Every frame we saw was taking a set one place or another or had been beefed up. This can be corrected by redesign. Steer axle oscillation would help relieve this.

5. Engine Vibration Too Severe—
    Engine needs to be shock mounted.

Exhibit 7 (*Continued*)

6. Steering Control Inadequate—
   Can't see the steer tires so you don't know where they are and unit steers too fast. A separate pump for steering will help this but I believe at least a wheel position indicator is required.
7. Extendable Deflector Motion—
   Extension cylinders go into a cock putting a bad bending moment on the rod. This will require considerable redesign.
8. Needs disconnect in drive for towing.
9. Prunes are main fruit these machines have been used on and then only by the smaller operators. If the unit has so much merit, why haven't the big operators tried the unit?

I don't know what Kurt has sold Clark as far as his present unit being ready for production is concerned, but in my opinion we are nearly starting from scratch engineering-wise. I believe every fruit crop will require something different in a machine so that no big production of anything will ensue. Even within the State of California, the difference in farm tillage tools is so bad that John Deere and IH set up small plants out there to compete with the local blacksmiths. This is to protect their tractor sales—we don't have any other machine sale to protect.

I would recommend we drop this project now, but I suppose we have gone too far to do this. If we proceed, I would like Kurt to go on record with answers to the attached questionnaire so our own engineers don't become the victims of a failing program because we modified the design. I also see no hope of getting a sample ready for "Prune Day" in February. If we want to check the market at this show, why not rent one of his existing units and show it?

I think Schell and Kurt should go to Florida as planned to get growers' comments, but I think the citrus groves will have to be regrown around the machine to make it work. Most groves I have seen have branches hanging down to the ground or within a few inches of it. With the low profile and resulting underclearance required we can never cross irrigation ditches or even cross over a reasonable hump in terrain.

I made no survey of the market potential other than to arrive at the fact that one machine should be able to harvest about 50 acres of prunes in the 25-day picking time allowable. The cost savings in harvesting should make the initial cost feasible.

W. NORLANDER

Exhibit 8

EXTRACTS FROM NOTES ON FLORIDA TRIP,
DECEMBER 3, 1962

From Tampa we went to the Lake Alfred Citrus Experiment Station to talk with Glenn Coppock, Agricultural Engineer for the Citrus Commission; Scott Hedden, Agricultural Engineer for the USDA; and Pierre Jutras, Agricultural Engineer for the Experiment Station.

These gentlemen are working jointly on the problem of mechanical harvesting for the three agencies. To date, most of their work has been done with the removal of the fruit from the tree in one way or another, but most recently with the tree shaker and a wind machine. Neither of these methods is entirely satisfactory, but offers enough encouragement to warrant continued work and experimentation.

Glenn Coppock has been working on a catching frame for use in trials this year. They have been making shaking trials and this is their first attempt at the catching frame and they are making only one side for their tests. Their unit is tractor towed and operated by the power take-off from the tractor. The frame moves sideways 54″ into the tree by use of slides and cylinders. They have pretty much copied their idea from the new Troy machine which also shifts sideways. This seems to be the easiest way to get a low profile at the tree. This also causes a change in the conveying direction of fruit and may or may not be desirable. When the machine starts to work, I hope to get some pictures of it.

Their experiences with shaking and blowing fruit from the tree have not been entirely satisfactory, but they are the only means of mechanical removal that seem to offer any real economic advantage. It is felt that the fruit might be removed easier if a spray could be developed that would work on the abscission layer and cause the fruit to drop off easier. This, in combination with shaking or blowing seems to be the best answer. This year should provide a lot more information than has been provided in the past. I'll keep in touch with these men so that we can keep up to date. It is apparent that interest is high in this area as they are devoting a great deal of time and money toward solving the problem. They are not as far along as they are in other fruit areas, but they probably will catch up in a hurry.

If the fruit can be removed by mechanical means economically, the rest will come in a hurry. In general, the opinions are that it is essential to remove a great deal of fruit in a short period in order for a machine to be economical. For example, a $6,000 machine that could only increase a man's productivity by 50%–60% would certainly not be considered practical at this stage of the game. Anyway, there is considerable interest in the area of fruit removal from the tree and, without exception, when the question, "What is your biggest problem?" is asked, the answer is always, "The picker."

Rather than write a long complicated report, I'll just comment in general on the situation the way I see it and some of the changes that are taking place since we were there last. As I have already indicated, there appears to be considerable interest in fruit removal. In general, the people we talked with felt that either shaking or blowing the fruit off was the answer. These methods seem to best fulfill the speed requirements.

Exhibit 8 (Continued)

In addition to removing fruit mechanically for processing, there doesn't seem to be much doubt but what the same practices and methods can well be used for fresh fruit removal, too. It seems that an orange is a lot less susceptible to damage than most people realized. A freshly picked orange apparently is almost impossible to bruise to any great extent. This is true to such an extent that I saw at least two operations where fresh packed fruit was actually being picked in the grove in the "Lightning Loader" 10-box wire containers and then dumped into the hi-lift truck body and further dumped into the bulk fruit trailer. It is my understanding that the only real problem is the sand and this, in most cases, is no more than with the normal field box.

This all indicates the great interest in reducing costs of picking and handling the fruit. We also saw at least one new operation using 10-box bulk bins, plywood construction, in the groves and then running this bin directly into the packing house. This has been so successful that tangerines are included, something that, when we were down there two years ago, everyone thought could never be done successfully. It is apparent that the change is rapid, and I think in the right direction. This one bulk operation is using 4,000 lb. lift trucks in the grove. They now have six of them in their fleet, and they are apparently happy with them.

Minute Maid indicated that they were going to build a new packing house and that it would probably be a bulk bin operation. They are now studying the various systems in use and seem to think they want to use wooden bulk bins in the grove, load them with a fork truck, or boom, and bring them into this packing house. I told Mr. Dwight Lucas that we were still interested in the problems and would be happy to work with them, but that we were by no means interested in sponsoring any programs to prove or disprove their theories. However, if they were sure of the direction they wanted to go and how they wanted to get there, we could help. I wanted him to be sure to understand that we weren't willing to sponsor their guesses.

I'm sure that the freeze in the Florida area will slow down some of the progress this year. If they've been hurt badly, they won't be willing to spend any money. If the fruit removal problem is solved in the near future, there will no doubt be considerable market for some type of catching device. The labor situation will be a factor in how rapidly the situation develops and moves ahead.

JAMES D. SCHELL

Exhibit 9

EXTRACTS FROM MARKET SURVEY REPORT, "MECHANICAL HARVESTING, FRUITS AND NUTS," BY HERMAN KURT, ASSISTED BY DOYLE VERGON, MARKET RESEARCH DEPARTMENT, CLARK EQUIPMENT COMPANY

Summary and Conclusions

From the standpoint of Clark Equipment Company, the field of mechanical harvesting seems to be divided into three related parts. They are:

1. The design and manufacture of suitable machines for the job of crop removal into containers at the tree.
2. The study and appraisal of the best method of distribution (sales and service) open to Clark for this specialized equipment. Also, consideration of the practicality of leasing such equipment.
3. Combining the harvesting machines at the tree with existing Clark material handling equipment, in order to get the crop out of the field.

1. This report deals only with the harvesting machines, and the study of the market for them. Emphasis is on the catching frames, bearing in mind that two tree shakers will probably be sold for every set of frames.

2. Also, the study indicates that the potential market can be divided into three phases of development over the next 10 years. These phases are outlined [below], and our interest now is in Phase I where complete mechanical harvesting has already been successful.

SCOPE

Phase I. Principal first use in: Apricots, Peaches, Prunes, Cherries. Complete Mechanical Harvesting—By Shake and Catch Method.

Some use in: Almonds, Walnuts, Pecans.

Phase II. Oranges, Plums, Freestone Peaches. Harvesting Aids.

Phase III. Apples, Pears, Oranges, Plums, Olives. Harvesting equipment for all processed fruit and some fresh fruit, requires:

a) Proper fruit removal method.

b) Shaping the tree.

c) Perfecting the catching and handling equipment.

3. Machines, the farmer's most important ally, accelerate yield at an astonishing pace; in just one decade they have nearly doubled the individual U.S. farm worker's average production. If American farmers today used 1940 methods and equipment, it would cost them $13 billion more to grow the country's food.[1]

Mechanical harvesting by shaking a tree and gathering the crop has moved fom nuts like almonds, pecans, and walnuts, to successful machines which collect soft fruits such as apricots, cherries, peaches, and

---

[1] "Bounty of Food," *Life Magazine*, November 23, 1962.

Exhibit 9 (Continued)

prunes, in bulk containers holding up to 1,500 pounds. This fruit remains suitable in quality to satisfy the sometimes critical doorman at the processing plant.

"We harvest faster, with fewer people, and get a cleaner product."[2]

4. There are about 779,000 acres of citrus in the United States. The two highest cost factors connected with this fruit are: (1) Transportation from field to plant. (2) Hand picking off the tree. Great strides have been made in material handling citrus for processing, but it is only in the past two years that bulk container systems have come into being for fresh fruit. Probably less than 5% of the fresh fruit is bulk handled—now indications are that eventually all of it will be.

So far, shaking citrus off the tree is not satisfactory. The fruit requires up to 30 pounds pull to break the stem. Tree shakers tend to damage the tree before removing the fruit. However, the Department of Agriculture, several chemical companies, and the Florida Citrus Commission, are working to develop a spray material that will loosen the fruit for shaking. "Catching frames, tree shakers, combined with a spray operation a few hours before harvest, seem to be the method we are counting on!"[3]

5. One suggested use for the catching frames as a harvesting aid in citrus prior to the time when a suitable fruit removal method is perfected, would be as a platform on which four to six hand pickers would ride. This would eliminate ladders, speed up the harvest, especially if means are provided to reach the tops of the tree.[4]

6. Thus, picking aids of one kind or another will be the "next step in mechanizing the harvest of citrus," a statement from A. E. Newitt, Exeter Citrus Association, Exeter, California. Mr. Newitt was the first Sunkist plant manager to spend $250,000 on bulk handling, and now expects to get his investment back within four years, in spite of poor crops.

Therefore, trials of the early soft fruit harvesters will be made in citrus starting in 1963, the Florida Citrus Commission having made their first experimental catching frame. Phase II may have a market developing earlier than we think.

7. The market potential for catchers and tree shakers in the harvest of nut crops is not discussed here in Phase I report. However, it should be pointed out that several prune and apricot harvesters are now used successfully in almonds and walnuts. There are 190,000 tons of nuts produced in the United States having a value of $119,664,000. Tree shakers were first used in the harvest of nut crops, and this usage will continue as a substantial market with probable need for catching equipment similar to that required for soft fruits. Catchers certainly will find use in areas where the trees are not too large, and the nuts stick on the tree sufficiently to require machine shaking for removal.

---

[2] Alfred Tisch, a partner in Mills Orchards, Hamilton City, California, in *Fortune Magazine*, January, 1963.

[3] A. H. Reppard, Vice President and General Manager, Pasco Packing Co., Dade City, Florida (second largest processor), also Chairman of the Harvesting Committee for the Citrus Commission.

[4] *California Citrograph*, December, 1962.

Exhibit 9 (Continued)

8. By far the most important reason for the growing interest in mechanical harvesting is the pressure from uncertain migrant labor, which, when unavailable, or lacking in skilled desire to work, costs the farmer so much headache and money that it hardly seems worthwhile being in business. Especially, when that business is producing a commodity which knows not how to rest its cycle to maturity, and rarely waits for storage without loss.

9. Large sums of money are being spent on machines for research and development in harvesting fruits more economically, for this is the most important remaining area in which the farmer's costs can be reduced, his profit margins made higher. The United States Department of Agriculture, Florida Citrus Commission, Michigan State University, Cornell University, University of California, name only a few of the people who conclude that shaking a tree and conveying the fruit into large containers is the likely method to harvest all fruits for processing, which is about 1,300,000 tons annually.

10. The second prime reason for a growing need to mechanize fruit harvest is, therefore, the economics of doing the job faster, with fewer people. The savings over the old method, hand-pick and small-field-box handling is indeed encouraging. Apricots and cherries indicate approximately five to one ratio in harvest cost savings, peaches and prunes approximately four to one.

If mechanical harvesting costs can be kept below the costs of hand picking, it will be economical.

An economic analysis of mechanical harvesting is possible with estimates of these factors: (*a*) Initial equipment costs, (*b*) depreciation rates, (*c*) operational costs, (*d*) labor force required, and wage rates, (*e*) actual rate of harvest, and (*f*) hours of annual use. Enough research has been done in the past three years to provide a guide and enough actual harvesting data to substantiate the assumption in the following tables.

11. With an investment of $16,000,[5] the farmer can purchase a soft-fruit harvester consisting of a set (two halves) of self-propelled catching frames and two tree shakers attached. On this assumption of machinery cost we can determine the economics of mechanizing each of the first fruit crops to be changed from the old way.

12. Many areas will adopt a two-shift day (8–10 hours per shift) for their mechanical harvest, in which case the use of the specialized equipment will be improved, and the savings per ton harvested greatly increased.

13. The tables show the optimum number of machines required to do the job in each fruit. Thus, on the basis of acreage and production needed to justify the expense of a machine, we can draw some conclusions. However, it must be pointed out that farmers are sometimes slow to make changes. They often take a wait-and-see attitude, but in this case labor unions knocking on the farm workers' door, shortages of dependable work forces, minimum wage laws, politics about importing foreign help, all point to pressures that seem to indicate a stepped-up trend to mechanize.

[5] See "Cost Analysis for Machine Harvest," Appendix, p. 194.

Exhibit 9 (Continued)

SUMMATION OF PHASE I

	Acres	Machine Use Maximum Number
Apricots	40,000	800
Cherries	43,000	1,100
Peaches	49,000	500
Prunes	132,000	2,640
Total	264,000	5,040

1. The problem of determining market potential in numbers of machines is difficult. By comparing the maximum usage that is indicated for each crop with a realistic guess as to how fast complete mechanization will come to fruition, perhaps we can arrive at a summation. Such a conclusion, however well thought out, must, because of the newness of fruit harvesting by machine, be considered an estimate only.

The above table seems to indicate that a fair machine potential would be one-half the figure 5,040 or approximately 2,500 machines in the next five years. Also, it can be emphasized that mechanical harvesters will be improved as techniques are perfected, causing a continuing market.

2. The many factors which have created the need for mechanical harvesting today will invite much competition. The principal manufacturers of tree shakers and/or catching frames at present are:

1. XYZ Corporation, California
2. Troy Brothers, California
3. J & J Manufacturing Company, California
4. August Tractor Company, Michigan
5. Willard Brothers, California
6. Burton Company, California

All of the above manufacturers are producing tree shakers with the exception of XYZ and J & J. The principal makers of self-propelled catching frames have been XYZ, Troy, and J & J, in addition to the Kurt equipment now being considered in this report. These catching frame manufacturers have produced about ten sets of harvesters each to date.

1962 prices for equipment ranged from a high of $17,000 for XYZ machines, Troy and Kurt about $16,000, J & J $8,500, and August about $6,500 for one self-propelled unit with shaker and hand-operated frame included.

. . . .

Appendix to Exhibit 9[1]

PEACHES

The clingstone peach varieties for canning, and possibly some freestone fruit for drying, will be the first to mechanize. Selectivity (shaking the ripe fruit and leaving the green) is a major problem in peaches. Also, most of the early types of catchers have caused excessive damage to the peaches either when they fall and hit unsuitable padding or when they are conveyed. These problems will be overcome and "mechanization of most clingstone peach harvesting as well as thinning and pruning, is practically inevitable within a few years."[2]

32,000[3] pickers are needed to harvest the California cling peach crop, some 548,000 tons, over an eight-week[4] period.

Rate of Harvest	Cost to Hand-Pick (12 Men)[5]	Cost to Machine-Pick (4 Men)
160 trees per 8-hour day......35 tons	$210.00 144.00 ——— $ 66.00 Saving per 8-hour day	$144.00[6]

Use of each harvesting unit for more than one 8-hour shift (2-acre rate) is indicated.[7]

Capacity for each machine is indicated at 96 acres. This capacity seems high unless the fruit matures over a long period. About 500 mechanical harvesters can be assumed proper for optimum in peaches.

CHERRIES

There are approximately 70,000 workers required to harvest the nation's crop of tart cherries, at an annual cost of about $10,000,000—one-half the value of the crop.

The harvest period varies, but can be said to equal twenty-four 8-hour days. A set of machines harvesting at the rate of 15 trees per hour, could handle 2,880 trees in one season on a one-shift per day basis. If the machine is used sixteen hours per day, the per-pound equipment cost is reduced almost one-half.

---

[1] The Appendix contained similar data sheets on apricots (and national production figures by areas, and reference readings).

[2] *American Fruit Grower*, May, 1961.

[3] *California Annual Farm Labor Report*, 1961.

[4] *California Fruit and Nut Crops*, Manual 20.

[5] One man, 80 boxes at 15 cents, $12.

[6] Appendix cost analysis (48 eight-hour days, $18 per hour, $144 per day).

[7] Approximately 4.5 boxes per tree, selective two-time harvest.

Appendix to Exhibit 9 (Continued)

Rate of Harvest	Cost to Hand-Pick (32 Men)	Cost to Machine-Pick (4 Men)
120 trees per day (100 lbs. per tree)[8] . . . . 12,000 lbs. @ .03	$360.00[9] 244.00	$244.00[10]
	$116.00 Difference per day	

The national production of processed cherries is 170,300 tons per year. Each machine can harvest 12,000 lbs. per 8-hour day or 144 tons per 24-day harvest season. Therefore, it might be said 1,100 machines could be used for processed cherries. This, of course, would be the maximum number.

PRUNES

In California, the number of workers required to harvest the 1961 crop was about 30,000;[11] other areas probably require another 5,000 people in the field to pick the processed prunes and plums. There are more $10,000 to $17,000 mechanical catching frames working in this fruit than any other; a fair estimate is 50 machines. Tree shakers removing prunes number in the hundreds. This is the first and largest market for combined shakers and catchers and Ralph R. Parks, University of California agricultural engineer, estimates 2,000 machines will be in use some day, in California.

Rate of Harvest	Cost to Hand-Pick (32 Men)	Machine Harvest (4 Men)
240 trees, or 3 acres per day, averaging 4 boxes per tree . . . . 24 Tons @ $16 per ton[12]—$384		$244.00[13]
	244	
	$140 Difference per day	

One man can pick about 30 field boxes per day costing about $16 per ton. The machines pick for about $4 per ton, not counting depreciation.

[8] One hundred pounds per tree may be a low figure; some growers report 300 to 700 pounds. Michigan State University cites: 150–200-pound average (Gordon Monroe, USDA). Levin, *et al.* article 42–60 example is 100 pounds. Cornell University, Markwardt uses 80-pound example.

[9] *Does not include* expense of ladders, buckets, and housing for approximately thirty-two men that would be required.

[10] Includes depreciation, interest, taxes, insurance, and maintenance. For breakdown, see Appendix, "Cost Analysis."

[11] *Annual Farm Labor Report*, 1961.

[12] Forty boxes—one ton, 24 tons—960 boxes.

[13] See Appendix, page 194, and note that a two-shift-per-day harvest will indicate payment for one machine in approximately two years.

Appendix to Exhibit 9 (Continued)

There are 132,000 acres, and if every 50 acres needed a machine, 2,640 units would be required. Here, again, a maximum.

NUT CROP

Type and Major Regions	Acres[14]	Production[15] (Tons)	Crop Value[16]
Almonds (California)	102,470	40,000	$ 25,376,000
Pecans (Southern States)	N.A.	75,000	56,012,000
Walnuts (California)	137,614	75,000	38,276,000
Total	N.A.	190,000	$119,664,000

COST ANALYSIS FOR MACHINE HARVEST

One Set (2 Halves) Self-Propelled Catching Frames $13,000
Two (each) Tree Shakers Mounted on Frames 3,000

 a) *Farmer investment:*   16,000
 Annual charges:

      Depreciation 20%
      Interest 6%
      Taxes 2%
      Insurance 2%
      Maintenance 3%

 b) *Yearly depreciation figured at 30%* $4,800
 Machine use:

      24 8-hour days—$25.00 per hour
      48 8-hour days— 12.50 per hour
      96 8-hour days— 6.25 per hour

 c) *Cost to operate (per hour):*

      Labor, 3 men @ $1.25 per hour $3.75
              1 man @ 1.75 per hour 1.75
      Total labor per hour $5.50
    Machine, used 24 8-hour days ($4,800 ÷ 24 = $200 ÷ 8) $25.00
      Total hour rate $30.50
                                                 8
      Cost per 8 hours $244.00

Basically, Schell's group decided to postpone the building of samples until the market survey was completed. During this time, they made "paper designs" to reflect their combined thinking and collective experience. They also compared specifications with those of competitive equipment to see what advantages they might have.

In January 1963 Mr. Kurt submitted his report, "Mechanical Harvesting, Fruit and Nuts" (assisted by Mr. Vergon of Clark's Market Research Department). Various extracts from this report are shown in

---

[14] 1953 acreage from *California Fruit and Nut Crops*, Manual 20.

[15] 1949–58 average U.S.D.A.

[16] 1960 value.

Exhibit 9. More field visits by Schell and other Clark personnel continued during these months. During a "Prune Day," held February 8, 1963, at the Agriculture Branch of the University of California, Davis, California, some pictures of the newest competitive equipment were taken, and further rough comparisons of equipment performance were made.

Meanwhile, Kurt continued to gather marketing information. He reported that customary dealer discounts on agricultural implements ranged between 20 and 25 per cent off list. However, about half of the nine producers of tree shakers and catching frames seemed to be dealing directly with consumers, while three also dealt through dealers, and two dealt only through dealers. Clark's San Francisco office studied the local marketing methods and on March 13, 1963, provided answers to specific questions raised by Battle Creek. Their reply said, in part:

The following will answer the specific questions which you have listed—

1. With the exception of XYZ and Troy, all manufacturers market their product directly to the user. These utilize a dealer organization for the distribution of their products. (These two used farm implement dealers.)
2. With the exception of XYZ and Troy these manufacturers have less than 10 employees.
3. It is recommended that farm implement dealers be used to distribute these products.
4. The following is a tabulation of the estimated sales for Shakers only—

> 1960—10 units
> 1961—25 units
> 1962—35 units

5. The following is a tabulation of the estimated sales for Catchers only—

> 1960—10 units
> 1961—25 units
> 1962—35 units

This type of equipment is being used and promoted primarily for the harvesting of prunes. There are approximately 90,000 acres under cultivation—40,000 acres are identified as coastal prunes. The Shaker and Catcher mechanisms are not being used in harvesting this type. The balance of 50,000 acres is located in the Sacramento Valley. The harvest period for prunes is approximately 20 to 25 days, and runs from late August to early September.

A Shaker and Catcher mechanism services approximately 40 trees per hour, and on the basis of an eight hour day can harvest prunes from 320 trees, which is approximately 4 acres. The amount of time required to move the Shaker and Catcher from one tree to another is approximately 20 seconds. Assuming a 25 day season, one machine could harvest 100 acres. On the basis of 100 acres per machine, and a 50,000 acre potential this would indicate a minimum requirement of 500 machines in the Sacramento Valley if all growers mechanized their operations.

The second most important market in California is for handling Cling peaches. There are approximately 50,000 acres of Cling peaches in California, which are composed of several varieties. The harvest period of these several varieties runs for approximately six weeks, commencing in July and running to the middle or last part of August. It is estimated that a Shaker-Catcher mechanism could harvest approximately 75 acres during the harvest season.

The third most important market is the apricot market which consists of approximately 40,000 acres in California. The harvest period is 10 to 14 days —running from mid June to late June. It is estimated that a Shaker-Catcher mechanism can service approximately 50 acres during this harvest season.

The fourth and final market is the cherry market. There are approximately 10,000 acres under cultivation in California.

The Economic Study which I am requesting indicates that it costs the Prune Growers 35¢ per box, using the knock and pick method. This same study indicates that the Shaker and Catcher method should reduce their cost to 16¢ a box. On this basis a grower with 100 acres could recover the cost of the Shaker and Catcher mechanism in approximately three years. The life expectancy of these units is estimated at eight years. The Shaker units presently being offered sell for approximately $2,500.00, and are of the frame mounted type. The Catcher mechanisms cost approximately $10,000 per unit (one pair).

About this time the Director of Marketing for the Industrial Truck Division, J. Mitchell, and the Chief Engineer (McKee) discussed the results of the preliminary research. They prepared Exhibits 10 and 11 for the manager of the Industrial Truck Division, B. E. Phillips. Concurrently, Schell and Kurt visited Florida. On March 19, Schell submitted a report to McKee, which concluded:

It remains apparent that interest is high in mechanical harvesting. Many organizations are spending money to further develop this means and will continue until such a time that most of the problems are solved. I wish that I was able to determine how much total business would be available if, and when, the problems are solved. I'm convinced that eventually the "shake and catch" method will become reality through the country.

I'll repeat earlier statements that I've made—I feel that if Clark is truly interested in this or any other agricultural area, I think we must get into it and stay—perhaps not in a big expensive way, but enough to stay abreast of, and improve, any areas we might be interested in. If we're not interested, then perhaps we should stay out. I think it's a fascinating field and the only really untapped source yet, but we may not be interested in sticking with it long enough to benefit from anything. I'm sure that as harvesting progresses many new concepts in handling will also come about.

I'd like to further suggest that if we wish to investigate any other new areas such as this, it is not necessary to hire a consultant to do this for us. I respect and admire Mr. Kurt but feel that we have people right here that are willing and able to do just as good and complete a job. I feel confident that we can study, evaluate, and present a proposal and survey as good as anyone. I think that Daryl and I had a great deal to offer this program; and I'm positive, without a doubt, that the machine we offered is far superior to the one that was brought here, and, if built, would sell and perform much better.

Jim Schell prepared a summary report for the record of the engineering projects. In the conclusion, he said:

We went through several design ideas during this period and finally settled on one basic design, similar to most of the competition. This basic approach seemed to offer the most advantages of any approach. We tried to continue with the Kurt design, but were unable to accomplish some of the very impor-

Exhibit 10

MARKETING OPINION

March 11, 1963

To: B. E. Phillips
     D. W. McKee

SUBJECT: Mechanical Harvester—Kurt Development

We have done some preliminary research on the market for this product with a view toward determining the advisability of proceeding with this project.

There are five major competitors in the business. I believe that Kurt's estimated potential of 2,500 units over the next five years is a very optimistic one. Assuming that it is reasonable, the mathematics of this business for us do not look encouraging. If we could sell a hundred units a year of Kurt's figure of approximately $16,000 per unit, we are talking about approximately one and a quarter million dollars potential of factor sales price, per annum.

Such a product should not be put into our present dealer organization and therefore a new distribution system would have to be established to enter this market. I would also like to point out that the estimated costs established by Kurt for a self-propelled vehicle of this type are also very optimistic and probably our selling price would have to be considerably higher than the $16,000 figure.

I recommend that we drop this project.

J. E. MITCHELL

---

tant things this way. This design was relatively simple and had some good advantages, but in our opinion it was best suited in areas where the trees were pruned quite high. For this reason, we felt that if we stayed with his design we could not service enough trees to make any headway into the market.

Our final design (Exhibit 12) offered several advantages over our competitors, and we feel that even in the areas where we might be weak, we are still in good shape. Some of our advantages are:

1. Good tire sizes—both standard and optional.
2. Four-wheel drive and steer (radi-arc-crab and two-wheel).
3. Optional limited spin differential.
4. Mechanical disconnect hubs for towing.
* 5. Match components—well engineered.
6. Good weight distribution.
7. Excellent gradeability—25% +.
8. Adequate speed—3.5 MPH, maximum.
9. Universal harvester—closest to being used in all fruits and nuts.

---

* With the exception of XYZ Corporation, I feel that we have probably done a better job of selecting and matching components to do the job than any other manufacturer.

Exhibit 11

ENGINEERING OPINION

March 14, 1963

To: B. E. Phillips
From: D. W. McKee
Subject: Fruit Harvesting Machine

Engineering has pretty much concluded their design study on this program. Herman Kurt has written a preliminary report on market research assisted by Doyle Vergon in Buchanan.

My conclusions from the development program are:

1. We can design a machine that will have more competitive features than anything that is currently on the market.
2. I am certain that there will be increased utilization of this type of equipment in the near future.
3. I am afraid of the cost of our product inasmuch as Kurt has indicated a selling price, including two halves and shakers at about $16,000, and our preliminary cost analysis would indicate our machine based on IT mark-up, would have to sell for about $16,000 to which would have to be added approximately $3,000 for shakers.
4. Our engineers have indicated that it would cost approximately $65,-000 to build and test one of these machines or about $90,000 to build and test two of them.

   I do not believe that these numbers are completely realistic and I would guess that it would cost us close to $80,000 for one machine and approximately $110,000 for two machines. It would be my recommendation that we build the second machine if we decide to go ahead with the program.
5. There is a possibility that some of the larger harvesters would share in the development program at least to [the extent of] underwriting part of the cost and doing the test work for us.
6. We would have to continue our consulting arrangement with Kurt (which is expensive in itself), for at least another year.

Conclusion

In conclusion, I do not feel that this is the kind of undertaking that we should be getting in on. Mitchell has concurred in this opinion; however, I don't feel that either of us have given you sufficient data for you to carry this cost back to top management. I would like to know what you require in the way of information for such a presentation.

I am trying not to be influenced in my decision by other things which I feel are much more pressing in our development program.

As of this date the cost estimator's figures are not really firm and he tells me they won't be until the end of this week.

I intend to stop the work on this program until I have some sort of direction from you and if you agree in principle to my conclusions, Kurt should be notified according to the terms of our contract

cc: J. E. Mitchell
     File (2)

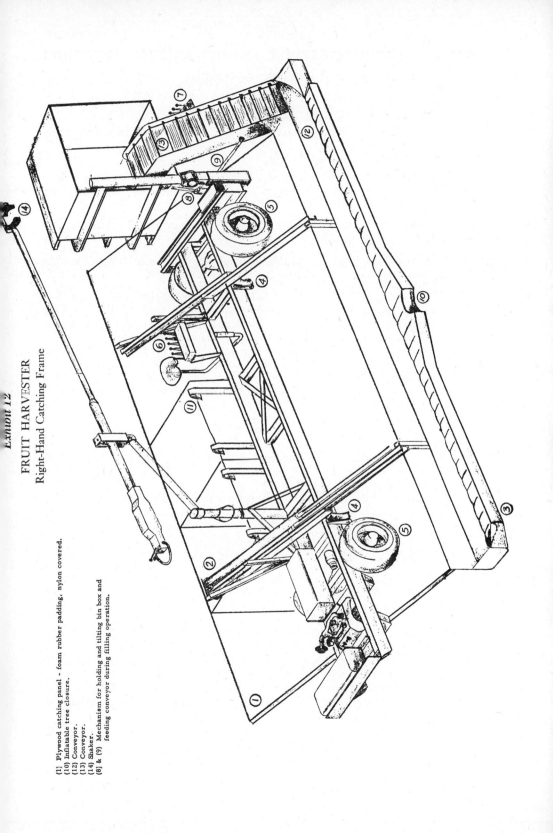

Exhibit 12

FRUIT HARVESTER
Right-Hand Catching Frame

(1) Plywood catching panel – foam rubber padding, nylon covered.
(10) Inflatable tree closure.
(12) Conveyor.
(13) Conveyor.
(14) Shaker.
(8) & (9) Mechanism for holding and tilting bin box and
feeding conveyor during filling operation.

10. Reducible to 95.5″ over-all width for shipping.
11. Inflatable tree seal.
12. Box rotation for soft fruit handling.
13. Simple design with minimum of pieces.
14. Good control features on tree side deflector and conveyor—raise, lower, and extension.
15. Good treeside conveyor height.

We feel that our proposal offered a better machine with more advantages than any other machine; and if there is a universal machine, ours is closer than that of any competitor.

Kurt, too, submitted a last opinion to McKee on March 25. His memorandum said, in part:

I wish to point out a few more facts which might be considered favorable to the harvesting equipment program.

1. The Florida trip March 13–15 indicated to both Schell and to me that the use of catching frames in citrus, especially early and mid-season grapefruit and oranges (other than the difficult-to-remove Valencia which comprises about 50% of the citrus) has progressed further because of the research machine now operating at the Florida Citrus Association. Harvest cost savings are considered about 4:1 ratio compared to hand-pick methods. General harvesting is still dependent on the method of fruit removal. So far the shakers used are inadequate. When these are perfected, an estimate of the potential use of complete harvesters in Florida would be 1,000–1,500 machines.
2. If Clark makes two prototype catchers this year, I am quite sure I can dispose of these at nearly cost should the program be dropped later. Or, perhaps people like Borden Company in New York and Mariani Packing Company in California would contract for the use of Clark's first machines.
3. Potential sales of catchers only can, I am sure, reach $1,500,000 by 1965, and if tree shakers are also manufactured by Clark, I think we can look to at least $3,000,000 in sales three years from now. In five years a $5 million to $7 million market should be our goal.
4. Mechanical harvesting of fruits and nuts will, I am convinced, lead to a sales volume of many times the above $5,000,000 estimate during the next 20 and more years. I do not limit this product line to a mere $1,500,000 in sales annually; however, I cannot help repeating my belief that we have to develop the machines to the obvious needs, and this is not a short-term program.
5. I do not feel the preliminary market survey I submitted to you in February is complete because it does not include the estimate of machines required for automation of the phases II and III as outlined. I can complete this part if you wish for future reference, but there would be many assumptions and a lot of guess-work involved at this time, and I hadn't felt this was necessary to the furtherance of the program for 1963–1964.

On March 26 the cost estimator finished his study of the final "paper design" fruit harvester (Exhibit 12). Based upon building ten units, his cost for a four-wheel-drive, four-wheel-steer unit with no-spin differential and locking hubs, using the standard markup for industrial trucks, indicated a list selling price of $16,406 (two catching frame units like the one shown in Exhibit 12). A stripped-down two-wheel-drive model would have to sell for $15,000. Over 66 per cent of the cost of either model would be purchased parts, not using Clark's manufacturing facilities.

With this background, Phillips and his staff met on March 27, 1963, to finalize a decision.

A Philosophy for Development

Give them the third best to go on. The best never comes, and the second best comes too late.

SIR ROBERT WATSON-WATT

His philosophy in his development of radar, as expressed to a Harvard Business School class, November, 1962.

EARLY IN 1950, the decision was made to incorporate the new features (see Photon, Inc. [A], page 169) into the machine. In spite of the many drawbacks of changing the development program, it was felt that the new features would make the machine fully versatile and enable it to appeal to the greatest number of firms in the printing industry.

Work was begun immediately to design and build the new machine. Each new specification required new design, the construction of test ponents, and, ultimately, the operation of all these together as a co-ordinated machine.

To obtain more capital for the new development work, 21,568 shares were sold (average price, $11.42 per share) to two private investors in June of 1950 for a net to the company of $246,306. The office offset portion of the business was sold to A. B. Dick Company of Chicago for $675,000 on October 13, 1950. This was the original Lithomat undertaking in the manufacture of paper lithograph plates, supplies, and chemicals for office duplication.

On November 14, 1950, Lithomat Corporation changed its name to Photon, Inc., better to reflect its major operation, the Photon photocomposing machine.

By April of 1951, every requirement of the Technical Advisory Board was met; and in addition, important new features had been added. The passage from the establishment of the specifications in April, 1950, to one model of the fully versatile machine took one year. This preproduction model, affectionately called "Petunia" by the Graphic Arts Research Foundation and Photon staff, was exhibited at the convention of the American Newspaper Publishing Association at the Waldorf Astoria in April, 1951. It operated for five days and demonstrated to the printing industry the advantages of photocomposition (see Exhibit 1).

The machine attracted much attention at the show; and many firms in the printing industry, which had been hearing about the machine for two years or more, began to show some impatience for a commercial model. Impatience was particularly shown by some contributors to the Graphic Arts Research Foundation and by some Photon stockholders. In response to this pressure, it was decided to produce an initial lot of ten machines.

In June of 1951, Photon began assembling and training personnel for its engineering and production staff. The preparation of production drawings

Exhibit 1

Figure 1.   The Photon machine as exhibited at ANPA convention, 1951.

The electric typewriter transmits information to the storage unit, as well as making a "hard copy" on white paper so the operator can see what has been typed into the machine. The control console is used to select the various styles and sizes of type, and to control the positioning of the characters vertically or horizontally on the film.

The two knobs to the right of the keyboard control the selection of type styles and sizes. Sixteen different styles, such as Baskerville, Techno Bold, and Granite, can be chosen by the customer for each matrix disc. Each style contains a 90-character alphabet (26 lower case letters, 26 upper case letters, 10 numerals, 23 symbols, and five ligatures). Therefore the operator has a choice

Exhibit 1 (Continued)

among 1,440 different characters for each matrix disc used. Styles may be changed readily in the middle of the line—for example, to insert an italicized word.

Each of the 16 matrix disc styles can be printed in twelve sizes (from five to 72 points [one inch]). Size variations are achieved by changing lenses and not by different-size characters on the disc. A particular style and size make up a "font," and the operator therefore has 192 fonts, or (90 × 192) different characters, available at his fingertips. He may mix a variety of styles and sizes in the same line without affecting alignment or justification of the lines on the film.

Other controls to the top and left of the keyboard allow the operator to accomplish the following operations:

a) "Center"—automatically center a line.
b) "Flush right or left"—automatically position a line to the extreme right or left margin of a page.
c) "Tighten and loosen"—stretch or squeeze a line by inserting or deleting interwords spacings.
d) "Lead control"—control the lead between lines and the length of lines up to 54 picas in units of 0.06 picas.
e) "Insertions"—automatically insert periods, dashes, lines, or blanks to fill a selected space.

The control console also has a panel of lights to indicate a mistake by the operator or a malfunction in the machine.

The memory unit and computer stores each character typed until the end of the line; justifies the line (adjusts the spacing of characters); and sends the line, character by character, to the photo unit. This storage arrangement allows a character to be erased (by backspacing the typewriter) or the entire line to be "killed" before it is sent to the photo unit.

The photo unit is the heart of the Photon machine.

The position of the lens turret is selected by the lever on the control board according to the type size desired. Each lens has a different magnification and thus produces a different-size image on the film. The position of the matrix disc is adjusted by a lever on the control board so that the proper band of characters for the style desired is opposite the shutter.

The glass matrix disc spins at 12,000 revolutions per minute. At the instant when the desired character on the disc is lined up with the shutter, the strobe light flashes. The image of the character is projected through the lens and prism onto the film or paper. The prism determines the placement of the character on the film. The computer tells the prism how much to move between characters in order to obtain a properly justified line. At the end of each line the film indexes, and the prism returns to begin the next line.

The film or photographic paper contained in a magazine can be up to 50 feet long, permitting long periods of uninterrupted operation. The film is developed in the normal manner and used to produce a photographic plate.

and the training of personnel required complete data on the mechanical, optical, electrical, and electronic components of the composing machine and their interrelation. Four months of test operation, together with subsequent dismantling and reassembling of the prototype, provided the training and knowledge for Photon's engineers to begin to prepare detail drawings of all the machine parts.

Figure 2.   The Photon photo unit.

Once the production drawings were started, Photon began the job of establishing adequate production facilities, deciding what parts would be subcontracted, and arranging for the manufacture of the subcontracted materials.

Net sales for 1951, as shown in Exhibit 2A, were $842,834. These were sales of the Chemical Products Division only and represented a considerable increase over this subsidiary's previous sales. Due to the heavy expenditures on the Photon machine, loss from operations was $6,051.

In January, 1952, 7,600 shares of common stock were sold for a net to the company of $201,400.

By April, 1952, Photon had assembled and trained a complete staff, had set up its production facilities, and had established all its sources of subcontracted materials. Four departments were set up in Cambridge: machine component manufacture, electrical assembly, matrix disc preparation, and engineering. Research on design improvements continued during this time.

There is scarcely a subassembly in the composing machine design, "frozen" for production in June 1951, where improvement possibilities have not been found. Some of these involve fundamental changes which derive from very recent technological progress. For example, (1) the transistor was hardly known in 1949. Now it offers the opportunity to perform complex computation and control operations with compact, light, and rugged circuits. (2) Improvements in magnetic recording techniques and materials make this process a likely substitute for the present mechanical memory unit.[1]

Improvements were also being considered for the justification component and for the photographic process.

By the end of 1952, expenditures on photocomposition totaled $900,000. The Graphic Arts Research Foundation had contributed $360,000, and Photon had contributed the balance. Photon's operating loss, Exhibit 2, for the year 1952 was $133,642. Again, the expenditures on the photocomposing machine exceeded the earnings from the chemical subsidiary.

By the spring of 1953 the initial lot of 10 machines was near to completion. One commercial machine was exhibited at the ANPA convention in the Waldorf Astoria on April 20–23. A priority list of customers interested in purchasing the photocomposing machine was begun. This list totaled sixty firms after this showing. To insure that this demand could be filled once production began, Photon increased its inventory build-up of subassemblies of manufactured and subcontracted parts for the Photon machine.

In July, 1953, Photon sold 15,000 shares of common stock at an average price of $37.75 per share for a net of $566,250.

For the year 1953, sales of the Chemical Division were up 36 per cent to

---

[1] From the *1952 Report to the Subscribers of the Graphic Arts Research Foundation.*

Exhibit 2A

INCOME STATEMENTS

	December 31, 1950	December 31, 1951	December 31, 1952	December 31, 1953	December 31, 1954	December 31, 1955
Net sales	$982,966	$842,834	$915,671	$1,250,026		$ 9,629
Cost of sales	707,128	626,727	712,186	939,707		5,454
Gross profit	$275,838	$216,107	$203,485	$ 310,319		$ 4,175
Selling and general and administrative expenses	261,028	222,158	337,127	444,085	$292,524	393,989
Operating profit (loss)	$ 14,810	($ 6,051)	($133,642)	($ 133,766)	($292,524)	($389,814)
Other income:						
Interest—government securities	$6,336					
Gain on sale of assets	$478,714*	$7,056				
Adjustment of prior taxes	980			$277,860†		
Discounts earned	5,283	1,224				
Miscellaneous	1,133	2,755	11,035	5,501	279,925	3,039
	945	14,677		$5,501		$3,039
	3,463					
	482,177					
	$496,987	$ 8,626	($122,607)	($ 128,265)	($ 12,599)	($386,775)
Interest on indebtedness	4,420	3,329	3,330			
Net income (loss)	$492,567	$ 5,297	($125,937)	($ 128,265)	($ 12,599)	($386,775)
Provision for taxes	133,638	6,037	7,100	10,838		9,150
To earned surplus	$358,929	($ 740)	($133,037)	($ 139,103)	($ 12,599)	($395,925)

* Sale of offset duplication business.
† Sale of chemical business.

Exhibit 2A (Continued)

	December 31, 1956	December 31, 1957	December 31, 1958	December 31, 1959
Income—sales and rentals	$ 155,859	$1,555,010	$1,379,261	$1,430,065
Other income	3,616	6,325	549	3,196
Total income	$ 159,475	$1,561,335	$1,379,810	$1,433,261
Costs, including cost of sales, engineering and development, and selling and general and administrative expenses	$1,903,055	$1,715,925	$1,915,109	$1,831,873
Depreciation of plant, equipment, and machines	40,473	75,478	118,200	153,763
State tax		11,888	14,300	11,502
Interest of bank loans	6,355	10,146	22,732	10,325
Total expenses	1,949,883	1,813,437	2,070,341	2,007,463
Profit (loss) for year	($1,790,408)	($ 252,102)	($ 690,531)	($ 574,202)

Exhibit 2B

BALANCE SHEETS

	December 31, 1950	December 31, 1951	December 31, 1952	December 31, 1953	December 31, 1954	December 31, 1955
Current assets:						
Cash	$ 262,663	$ 41,543	$ 87,678	$ 376,569	$ 13,937	$ 24,470
U.S. Treasury notes	500,569	401,470	201,401		391,614	666,402
Accounts receivable. Net of reserve	123,074	93,067	123,698	213,289	1,308	7,956
Inventories:						
Finished goods	$ 28,524	$ 43,167	$ 62,761	$ 50,990		
Work in process	23,324	34,391	202,122	408,193		
Raw materials	194,963	236,999	177,349	205,112		
	246,811	314,557	442,232	664,295	379,761	460,349
Total Current Assets	$1,133,117	$ 850,637	$ 855,009	$1,254,153	$ 786,620	$1,159,177
Cash value—life insurance		2,659	5,214	9,943	14,800	20,162
Accounts receivable—other	43,799	43,799	43,799	43,799	116,491	168,710
Property, plant, and equipment	$302,687	$406,471	$472,456	$566,978	$ 282,447	$ 351,620
Reserve for depreciation	110,915	127,174	143,610	173,474	34,657	59,435
	191,772	279,297	328,846	393,504	247,790	292,185
Deferred Photon machine costs					203,258	500,017
Development costs, Mullen dampening system				32,572	32,484	32,484
Prepaid and deferred items	12,048	42,240	43,443	53,852	42,260	62,321
Good will	1	1		1	1	1
	$1,380,737	$1,218,633	$1,275,312	$1,787,824	$1,443,703	$2,235,056
Current liabilities:						
Accounts payable	$ 102,218	$ 45,422	$ 56,367	$ 136,179	$ 30,104	$ 38,958
Notes payable—bank		25,000				
Provision for federal taxes	155,327	51,232	54,387	20,348	12,393	18,617
Taxes—other than federal	32,955	10,506	14,753			
Provision for redemption of returnable containers	4,617	8,166	10,909	13,698		
Total Current Liabilities	$ 295,117	$ 140,426	$ 136,416	$ 170,225	$ 42,497	$ 57,575
Capital stock and surplus:						
Common stock	$199,600	$207,200	$222,875	$ 235,475	$ 270,001	
Common stock	$199,600	319,170	506,297	1,063,041	1,148,820	2,276,494
Capital surplus	325,842	559,437	426,399	331,683	26,911	(369,014)
Earned surplus	560,178					
Total Capital Stock and Surplus	1,085,620	1,078,207	1,139,896	1,617,599	1,401,206	2,177,481
	$1,380,737	$1,218,633	$1,276,312	$1,787,824	$1,443,703	$2,235,056

Exhibit 2B (Continued)

	December 31, 1956	December 31, 1957	December 31, 1958	December 31, 1959
Current assets:				
Cash	$ 62,845	$ 58,332	$ 318,769	$ 52,916
U.S. Treasury notes	......	......	204,781	155,774
Accounts receivable—net	46,801	217,510	1,501,368	1,351,948
Inventories:				
Finished goods				
Work in process				
Raw materials	373,949	1,304,337		
Total Current Assets	$ 483,595	$1,580,179	$2,024,918	$1,560,638
Cash value—life insurance	25,149	30,187	35,332	40,017
Accounts receivable—other	199,414	236,987	250,095	184,475
Plant and equipment	$ 548,281	820,838	$1,101,207	$1,018,855
Reserve for depreciation	98,372	171,659	285,936	424,899
(Net plant and equipment)	449,909	649,179	725,271	593,956
Prepaid and deferred items	47,081	62,897	69,074	67,143
	$1,205,148	$2,559,429	$3,104,690	$2,446,229
Current liabilities:				
Accounts payable	$ 93,478	$ 212,853	$ 77,569	$ 111,227
Notes payable—bank	400,000	270,000	350,000	175,000
Provision for federal taxes				
Taxes—other than federal	26,005			
Provision for redemption of returnable containers		66,500	42,362	45,166
Accrued payroll, taxes, and other expenses				
Total Current Liabilities	$ 519,483	$ 549,353	$ 469,931	$ 331,393
Customer prepayments and deferred rental income	134,967	95,955	132,474	141,753
Capital stock and surplus:				
Common stock	$ 277,801	$ 338,500	$ 390,625	$ 392,875
Capital surplus	2,432,319	3,987,145	5,213,715	5,256,465
Earned surplus	(2,159,422)	(2,411,524)	(3,102,055)	(3,676,257)
Total Capital Stock and Surplus	550,698	1,914,121	2,502,285	1,973,083
Total Capital Stock and Surplus	$1,205,148	$2,559,429	$3,104,690	$2,446,229

$1,250,026. Due to heavy expenditures on Photon machine production, the loss for the year was $128,265 before taxes.

By May 12, 1954, three "competitive" photocomposing machines had appeared but were not yet in commercial production. These machines were called Fotosetter, Monophoto, and Linofilm. The Linofilm was produced by the Mergenthaler Linotype Company. Due to Photon's technical lead and strong patent position, the competing machines, in the opinion of Photon management, did not approach the Photon machine in productivity, versatility, or economy. The three competitive machines were brought out by large suppliers of machinery to the printing and publishing industry.

On October 14, 1954, the Chemical Products Division was sold for $709,776. This step was taken as an opportunity for Photon to realize gains on its initial investment in the chemical subsidiaries and to provide funds for the manufacture of the photocomposing machine.

On September 1, 1954, the first of the Photon machines was installed in the production department of the *Quincy Patriot-Ledger*, Quincy, Massachusetts. (See Exhibit 7.)

By April 8, 1955, four machines in all had been installed—two at the *Quincy Patriot-Ledger*, one at the Machine Composition Company in Boston, and one at Massachusetts Institute of Technology. Five more machines were installed at various firms in the Boston area shortly afterward. All the machines were placed on a rental basis, and rents of $400 per month were charged for each machine.

The Photon machine demonstrated its great productivity advantage and versatility to those pioneering firms who were the first to try it out.

For example, one major advantage of this machine was that all characters were stored on a small matrix disc, instead of in magazines of cold-metal type. Sixteen fonts, or styles of type, and 1,440 separate characters were available in each disc. In addition, through the system of automatic lens changes, each character could be photographed in twelve different sizes; 17,280 combinations of character and point sizes were available to the operator at the keyboard. The disc weighed one pound and a half, and was eight inches in diameter. It replaced 4,000 pounds of cold-metal type, which would cost $25,000 and would require 90 cubic feet of storage space.

A second advantage was that the operator could control entire lines easily. Any desired length of line was set by pushing buttons, and a similar control adjusted the vertical spacing between lines. Line justification was handled automatically without any effort or thought required by the operator. Other keys directed the machine to execute automatically instructions such as "flush left," "flush right," and "center."

There were many problems, however, which developed under operating conditions with this new machine. The major one was maintenance.

Exhibit 3

INDEPENDENT STUDY BY EASTMAN KODAK COMPANY, SHOWING ANNUAL COST COMPARISON FOR TYPICAL METROPOLITAN NEWSPAPER*

3A. News (Lead)—Ads (Lead)

	Capital Costs	Annual Equipment Depreciation	Number of Men	Annual Direct Labor	Annual Film, Paper and Chemicals Cost	Total Annual Materials Cost	Total Annual Cost
Copy desk	$ 200	$ 20	2	$ 12,800			$ 12,820
News Linotypes	363,000	18,150	45	288,000		$ 24,988	331,138
News Linotype maintenance			8	51,200			51,200
Correction bank	400	40	2	12,520			12,560
Proof press	7,000	700	2	12,520			13,220
Proofreaders	600	60	12	75,120			75,180
Page make-up	29,600	2,960	22	137,720			140,680
			93				
			+29 = 122				
Added men to man news composition				185,600			185,600
Ad markup	800	80	7	44,800			44,880
Ad Linotypes	208,130	10,407	26	166,400		8,153	184,960
Ad Linotype maintenance			4	25,600			25,600
Correction bank	400	40	2	12,520			12,560
Proof press	3,500	350	2	12,520			12,870
Proofreaders	300	30	5	31,300			31,330
Ad assembly	46,700	4,670	39	249,600			254,270
Other maintenance			4	25,600			25,600
			89				
			+28 = 117				
Added men to man ad composition				179,200			179,200
Process camera	56,250	5,625	8	47,600	(Film) $20,322 (Chemical) 1,372	21,694	74,919
Contact print	1,500	150	4	27,400		13,588 (Metal)	41,138
Fast etch	18,200	1,820	4	27,400		3,260 (Chemical)	32,480
Rout and proof	10,700	1,070	4	27,400			28,470
			20				
			+6 = 26				
Added men to man Engraving Department				41,100			41,100
Flat Caster	40,800	4,080	9	40,410			44,490
Mat press	30,400	3,040	9	40,410		18,009	61,459
Stereo caster	218,000	21,800	12	77,880		20,904	120,584
			30				
			+9 = 39				
Added men to man Stereo Department				58,410			58,410
Subtotal	$1,036,480	$75,092	304	$1,911,030	$21,694	$110,596	$2,096,718
Benefits at $431 per man			...	131,024		....	131,024
Total	$1,036,480	$75,092	304†	$2,042,054	$21,694	$110,596	$2,227,742

Lead system annual cost = $2,227,742
Combined system annual cost = $1,973,895
Net annual cost reduction = $ 253,847

$$\frac{\$253,847}{\$254,400} = 100 \text{ per cent return}$$

Exhibit 3 (Continued)

3B. News (Lead)—Ads (Photon)

	Added Capital Costs	Annual Equipment Depreciation	Number of Men	Annual Direct Labor	Annual Film, Paper, and Chemicals Cost	Total Annual Materials Cost	Total Annual Cost
Copy desk		$ 20	2	$ 12,800		$ 24,988	$ 12,820
News Linotypes		18,150	45	288,000			331,138
News Linotype Maintenance			8	51,200			51,200
Correction bank		40	2	12,520			12,560
Proof press		700	2	12,520			13,220
Proofreaders		60	12	75,120			75,180
Page make-up		2,960	22	137,720			140,680
			93 +29 = 122				
Added men to man news composition				185,600			185,600
Ad markup	$ 200	100	10	64,000			64,100
Ad Photon	316,400	31,640	14	89,600	$25,718 (Film and Chemical)	25,718	146,958
Photon Maintenance			2	12,800			12,800
Photon darkroom	3,500	350	1	6,400			6,750
Proofreaders	1,200	150	7	43,820			43,970
Film assembly	1,100	110	4	25,600			25,710
Ad assembly metal paste-up		4,670	12	76,800			81,470
Other maintenance			4	25,600			25,600
			54 +17 = 71				
Added men to man ad composition				108,800			108,800
Process camera		5,625	8	47,600	(Film) 20,322 } 1,372 (Chemical)	21,694	74,919
Contact print		150	4	27,400	5,741	31,714	59,264
Fast etch		1,820	4	27,400	(Film and Chemical)	35,445	35,445
Rout and proof		1,070	4	27,400		6,225	28,470
			20 +6 = 26				
Added men to man Engraving Department				41,100			41,100
Flat caster		4,080	9	40,410			44,490
Mat press		3,040	9	40,410		18,009	61,459
Stereo caster		21,800	12	77,880		20,904	120,584
			30 +9 = 39				
Added men to man Stereo Department				58,410			58,410
Subtotal	$ 322,400	$96,535	258	$1,616,910	$53,153	$149,252	$1,862,697
Benefits at $431 per man		......	...	111,198	......	......	111,198
Total	$ 322,400	$96,535	258†	$1,728,108	$53,153	$149,252	$1,973,895
Less: Ad Linotype trade-in, 17 Linotypes at $4,000	−68,000						
Net added capital cost	$ 254,400						

* Exhibit 3 shows summary of annual costs using Photon machines (3B) for advertising work in comparison with lead (Linotype machines) (3A) for advertising work in a newspaper with combined daily circulation of approximately 400,000 over 312 days per year.

† The added men are required for vacations, holidays, and the six-day work week: lead system—232 + 72 added men = 304 total men required; combined system—197 + 61 added men = 258 total men required.

Operation required the proper functioning of a myriad of electromechanical systems. A malfunction was extremely difficult to locate, and the machine was built so compactly that many circuits and mechanisms were not easily accessible.

The machine proved to be not flexible enough. Changing from one style of type to another was awkward and required the replacement of one mechanical component by another. Trouble developed with the variable escapement mechanism which spaced the characters the proper distance apart on the film. Operators complained that the design of the keyboard and the positioning of certain controls made operation of the machine more difficult than necessary.

It was decided, in the spring of 1955, to redesign the machine and bring out a new model, taking into account actual operating and service experience. A new design would enable Photon to add many improvements which research had come up with since the construction of the first machine was frozen. From the operating experience gained, greater margins of security could be built into the mechanical, optical, and electrical components. These components could be production-engineered for simpler and easier manufacturing. Operator controls could also be arranged for maximum efficiency based on the new information available.

During the rest of 1955, all efforts were directed to the development of the new model, called the 200 series. The sale in 1955 of 44,526 shares of common stock for net proceeds of $1,159,152 provided additional funds for this work.

The 1955 loss before taxes was $386,775, and reflected heavy engineering and development expenses. Since Photon, Inc., had sold its operating divisions, income for the year was negligible. The sales of $9,629 consisted of supplies and accessories for the Photon machines in commercial use.

Most of the year 1956 was spent on testing and initiating production of the 200 series machine. The first machine was delivered to the Machine Composition Company of Boston early in December, 1956, for a price of $48,000. One more machine was delivered that month (see Exhibit 8, page 227).

At the end of 1956 the priority list of customers interested in the Photon machine stood at over one hundred firms. To insure that this indicated demand could be met, management had made the decision in 1955 to use its limited resources for an inventory build-up of the necessary parts for full production. As a result, Photon, in December, 1956, had the capacity to produce one machine per week. It was felt that funds should not be spent on developing an extensive sales engineering force until the initial demand was met.

Operating loss for the year 1956 was $507,230. In addition, since full production had finally been achieved, management decided to write off the entire development expense, which totaled $1,283,178. The total loss was thus shown as $1,790,408 for 1956.

Shipments of one unit per week continued through the spring of 1957,

PROCESS CHART FOR EXHIBIT 3A—MANPOWER BASED ON AVERAGE
DAILY REQUIREMENTS, USING LINOTYPE, FOR 47 MILLION AGATE
LINES OF ADVERTISING PER YEAR

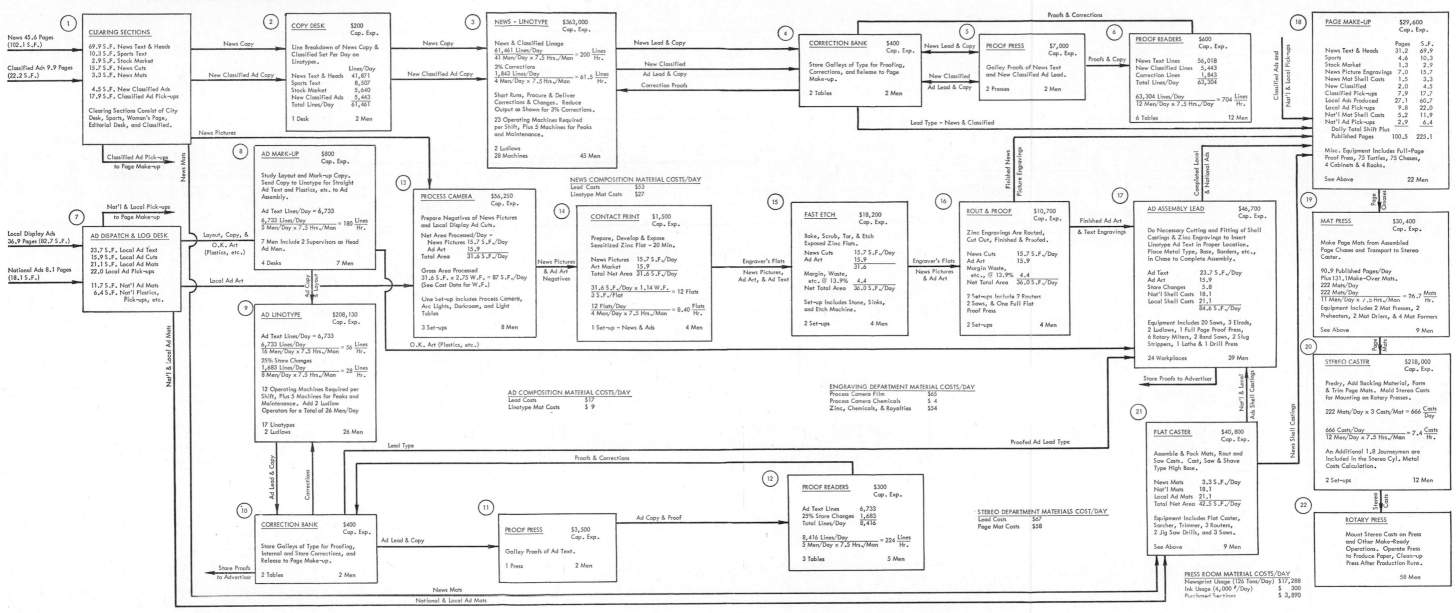

PROCESS CHART FOR EXHIBIT 3B—MANPOWER BASED ON AVERAGE DAILY REQUIREMENTS, USING PHOTON, FOR 47 MILLION AGATE LINES OF ADVERTISING PER YEAR

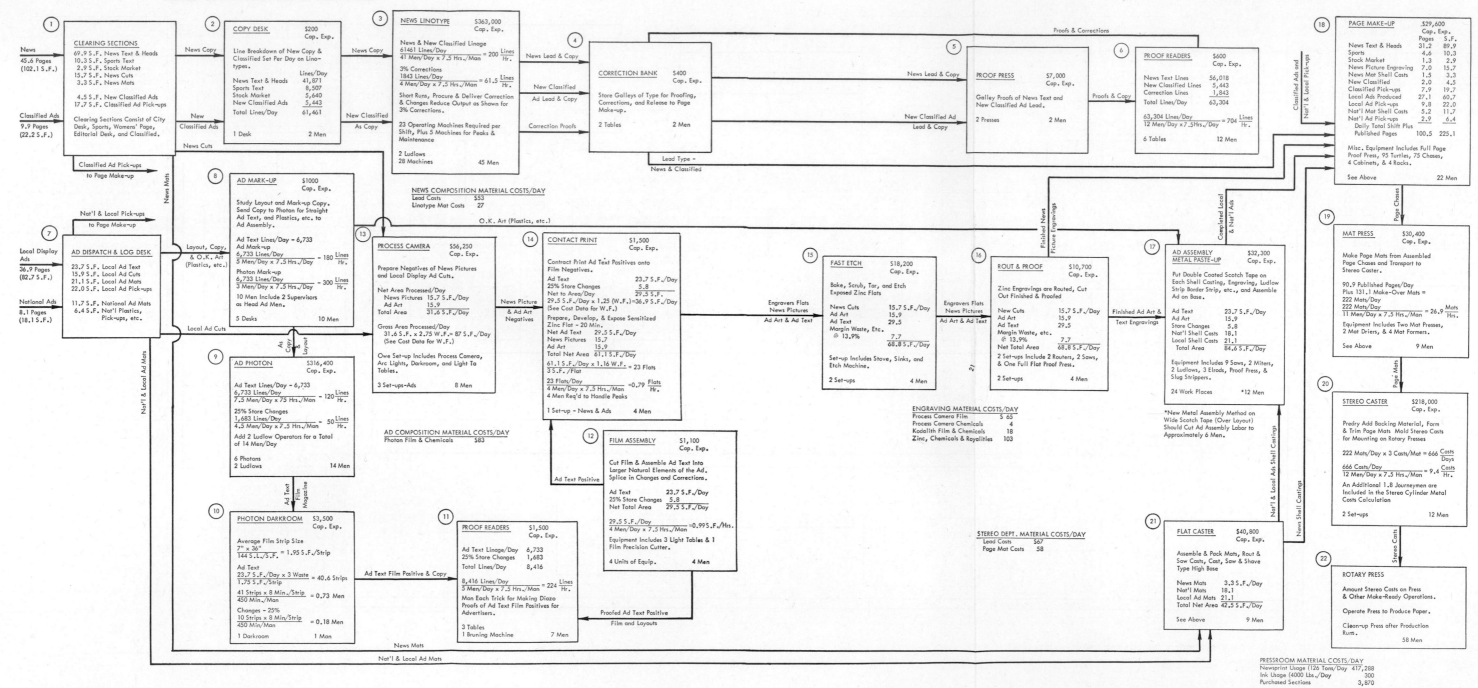

so that management anticipated that sales for 1957 would be at $2.5 million. These sales did not materialize, however, due to an abrupt downturn in business conditions. Furthermore, many of the customers on the priority list adopted a "wait and see" attitude when they saw that the price of the machine was $48,000. They thought that the price was too high to take a chance and wanted to see how the machine proved out.

A total of twenty-six machines was sold in 1957 for total sales of $1,555,010. The break-even level had not been reached, however, and the loss was $252,102.

The business recession continued through 1958, and management felt that it accentuated the normal conservatism of the printing industry toward new equipment. Customers' reaction to the Photon machine was generally very good. This was especially true on the part of the firms which had first received the Photon machine and had pioneered its usage. Some customers, however, who had purchased machines only after hearing of others' success with it, were disappointed and found it difficult to produce the savings which were so much talked about. One Florida newspaper which bought a Photon machine found that its union insisted on assigning operators to the machine. The men who were assigned were very slow to learn, and the newspaper found it extremely difficult to get proper production from its Photon.

It was difficult to evaluate the machine properly because installing it not only required new skills on the part of the operator, but also required a complete change in the entire production process and organization. The Eastman Kodak Company initiated a six-month study of the machine in the summer of 1958 to try properly to evaluate the savings that could be gained. It was hoped that this independent study would be useful in selling the Photon machines.

Twenty-five machines were invoiced in 1958, and total sales were $1,379,261. The operating loss was $690,531. Management said that operating expenses were higher because of the time lag between the decision, made in the year 1957, to curtail programs of expansion and the actual realization of expense reduction. An intense program of cost reduction was being pursued. Early in 1959, Photon had only 184 employees, as opposed to the peak of 308 employees in 1958.

It was hoped that this cost-cutting program would show results in the operating figures for 1959.

In late February, 1959, the results of the Kodak study were presented to Photon. This study was made on an installation of six Photon machines at the *St. Louis Courier Dispatch*. This newspaper was selected as a typical metropolitan newspaper, and the savings shown were startling. Exhibits 3A and 3B show that $253,847 in annual cost savings were obtained on an investment of $254,400 by the newspaper with a circulation of 400,000 papers daily. Exhibits 4A and 4B compare the work flow and manning of the two processes.

In the spring of 1959 a major stockholder initiated a study of consumer reactions to the machine at his own expense. Excerpts from this report are presented in Exhibit 5.

Exhibit 5

EXCERPTS FROM A MAJOR STOCKHOLDER'S STUDY
OF CONSUMER REACTION

"Allentown Call-Chronicle"—Mr. Miller and Mr. Marsteller

Both believe that photocomposition has a bright future for both newspapers and the printing industry. It offers definite savings in labor and saves the large investment in type.

The newspaper is now running 20% of their display advertising on the two Photon machines and expects to expand to 75%. They have been converting slowly for labor reasons.

The Photon machines have been very satisfactory. No problem in training operators and maintenance has been very easy. Only once was it necessary to send for a factory representative as most difficulties can be solved by a phone call. The machines are operating 27 hours per week.

No regrets for having selected Photon; both feel it is the most versatile machine. It does in one operation what Linofilm machine does in three.

Mr. Miller estimates 30% of 1,800 newspapers in the country could use one or more Photon Machines.

"Quincy Patriot-Ledger"—Mr. Allen

Mr. Allen was a very enthusiastic user of the Photon machines and a great believer in photocomposition. At the present time 80% of the display advertising is being run on the Photon machine.

Mr. Allen felt that the machine is easy to operate, easy to maintain especially if a good maintenance man can be trained and does regular preventive maintenance. It has been very seldom that it has been necessary to send for factory representative.

Mr. Allen feels that Photon and Linofilm are the only machines on the market worth considering. He thought that the introduction of the production model Linofilm machine would broaden the photocomposition field and thus help Photon sell more machines.

Westchester County Newspapers, Inc., White Plains—Mr. William Fanning

Mr. Fanning has been busy with labor troubles since December 1957 when the union called a strike. They got in new employees and have been publishing the papers without union members.

He definitely believes that photocomposition is the coming thing for the newspaper industry, especially when the present drawbacks are solved. Due to labor difficulties he has not made cost studies of the hot and cold methods, therefore cannot say which one is cheaper.

He has two Photon machines and also two Fotosetters. He has been using the four machines equally, to do slightly more than 50% of their display advertising. He is more or less forced to run the two type machines equally due to having just enough trained operators for both type machines. He would not say which type machine he considered the better. They have been proceeding rather slowly waiting for new developments and better techniques.

Exhibit 5 (Continued)

The Photon machines have been very satisfactory. They are not too diffi-cult to run and maintain. The company has given excellent service. In three hours a man is available and just recently the new modifications have been installed.

The one problem with photocomposition is the cost of proofs. With the hot method, they are run on waste news stock that costs nothing. The Ozalid and Bruning machines make them cost too much.

He thought the use of photocomposition for the news copy was a long way off. Display advertising and gravure were the only places it could be used successfully at the present.

"Philadelphia Bulletin"—Mr. Spendlove

Mr. Spendlove believes photocomposition is the coming process especially adapted to display advertising and gravure. He has watched and studied its development for two years. He feels it has arrived at a point where a large newspaper should start using it. Some advertisements use both methods. Smaller newspapers (less than 25,000 circulation) could not use photocomposi-tion because of large investment for needed engraving department.

He studied the field carefully and decided to purchase two Photon ma-chines. Fotosetter was too similar to old method, thus outdated; therefore choice was between Linofilm and Photon. His reasons for selecting Photon were as follows:

1. Best machine for *Bulletin*'s system and does what they want done.
2. He does in one operation what Linofilm takes three operations to accomplish, thus cheaper to operate.
3. Photon is more flexible with wider range. The ad can be spaced and set on the Photon machine, which other machine does not do.

Bulletin would require six Photon machines to convert completely to photocomposition.

Mr. Spendlove has studied the photocomposition operations at the *New York News, Times* and Louisville newspapers. He discounts the Louisville survey figures[1] as he thinks the cost studies were made under ideal conditions instead of actual conditions with corrections, etc. He feels four Photons will do the work of seven old hot metal machines.

One drawback to photocomposition is large quantity of proofs requested by the department stores. Ozalid type too costly in quantity and not good enough. He feels photocomposition has possible future for smaller news-papers (50,000 circulation and less) if the experimental offset press is per-fected. Then whole newspaper would use photocomposition. This method would not be practical for large newspaper as there is no way to make extra plates from original. Smaller paper would only need one while *Bulletin* would need eleven.

Mr. Spendlove has received calls from brokers about Photon stock. He thinks the *Bulletin* purchase will help sell others. The company is small competing with large one; may have to merge. He understands Photon is now suing Linotype for patent infringement. (Photon statement on his desk.)

"New York Times"—Mr. Tewlow

Mr. Tewlow feels that photocomposition will have a place in the news-paper industry but has some reservations as to how soon it will develop. He

---

[1] This survey was not available at the time this case was written.

Exhibit 5 (Continued)

feels there are some definite problems that have to be worked out as yet. He estimates that in time at least the larger daily newspapers will be running a large percentage of their display advertising and gravure on photocomposition.

The *Times* has two Photon machines which are working well but doing less than 10% of the display advertising. The main reason for the delay in shifting more of the work to the Photon machines has been due to the fact that the *Times* does not have a deadline for accepting advertiser's copy. Also the bogus problem and the fact that they only have two machines so that any breakdown or illness of operators would seriously curtail the output, have also been deterring factors. In July the *Times* will install a deadline and then Mr. Tewlow expects to step up the photocomposition output. He would need more machines but does not think that he would ever go to photocomposition completely as hot metal is still better for some work.

He has no cost figures showing a comparison of the two methods. There are so many variations that make cost figures very difficult to obtain. He would not feel qualified to comment on the 16% to 17% saving the Louisville cost study shows. He is now conducting a hot metal cost study at the *Times*.

The Photon machine runs satisfactorily if you have trained operators and good maintenance men. The two-week training course at the factory is not enough. He feels Photon is making a mistake by telling prospective customers the machines are easy to operate. The prospects seem dissappointed when they hear a different story at the *Times*. The company should also do applied research in addition to machine research, but evidently the financial condition of the company makes it impossible. He feels the selling techniques of the company could be improved.

Mr. Tewlow feels the Photon machine is superior to the Linofilm as it is electro-mechanical while Linofilm is electronic; thus Photon should be easier to maintain. Also Linofilm is too limited and will not space the advertisements. It might be better for straight type because of the greater speed with use of tape being run on three keyboards and fed into one photo unit. He thought Photon was developing the same setup. Linofilm was limited in different sizes of type on the same line.

One of the problems in photocomposition was the furnishing of proof to the advertiser. He had worked out a paper plate to use in running proofs and did not know whether it was superior to the Louisville system.

He thought great progress was being made in the development of an offset press for printing newspapers. The method would advance photocomposition materially.

He thought eventually some company would offer the newspaper publishers an integrated system including all the necessary machines to do the complete job. He said RCA was getting into the printing field and might be the company to do the job. They might be interested in the Photon machine as a part of their integrated system.

Regency Thermographers—Mr. Fugasse

Mr. Fugasse felt that photocomposition had a definite place in his particular phase of the printing industry. Photocomposition's main contribution has been higher quality of workmanship. He feels it is possibly slightly cheaper and faster but quality is the main reason for shifting. His firm processes a large quantity of small orders a day with the average run only 150, such items as invitations, business cards, etc.

They have one Photon machine which has proved to be very satisfactory.

Exhibit 5 (Continued)

They have well-trained operators and maintenance men and have no trouble keeping the machine running. The service from the company has been excellent. They run the machine only on one shift so one machine is all they would require.

He feels that Photon is far superior to any machine on the market. He doubts the claims being made for the new Linofilm machine.

American Chemical Society

I talked to Mr. La Rose, the operator. He feels the machine did not operate properly at the start. Certain parts broke and the down time was very discouraging. He felt the parts that broke were defective and not his fault. Service men hinted to him that certain things were wrong with the machine. He resented Photon blaming him and not the machine. Service men from the factory have not put the machine in operating form.

He operated for me but it soon broke down and he seemed confident he could fix it, although he was not able to do so while I was there. He did seem young and inexperienced. He is making up the type for a new disc. He summed up his remarks by saying that the machine did good work but was quite complicated. They have been using it for special chemical formulas.

Walter Conway Associates, Inc.

Mr. Conway was out of town so talked with the operator of the machine. He has no difficulty operating and maintaining the machine. It is satisfactory in every way. Most difficulties can be corrected by phone call to the factory.

The machine did not replace any other but opened up new type of work for the company. Operator feels it is the best one on the market although he is not too familiar with the others.

He was not too impressed with Photon factory while taking his training course. He thought they should turn out more machines. However, he did feel they were well made.

He feels that it would be helpful to have a service man in area, although he has not needed him as yet.

Knight Press—Mr. Bulmark's Assistant

The Knight Press prints small shopping guide type newspapers and circulars with runs up to 150,000.

In 1955 they converted from letterpress to offset type printing and now do not use any hot type. The shift has been very satisfactory as it proved to be quicker, cheaper and better.

A Photon machine was purchased in 1957 after studying the various machines available. The Photon machine operates very well with no maintenance problems. Mr. Bulmark does his own repair and maintenance and experiences no difficulty keeping the machine running constantly. All display advertising is done on the machine including the setting of the ad. Straight type is put on tape with a flexiwriter and then run through the Photon machine. In this way machine can be running display advertising during first shift, then the tape is run on the second shift at a faster rate than the typist could put it in the machine. In this fashion they are getting full utilization of the machine.

They are dependent on one Photon machine and have experienced no difficulty. They have gotten good service and cooperation from the Photon company.

Exhibit 5 (Continued)

Machine Composition Company—Mr. Miller

Mr. Miller expressed the opinion that photocomposition was the new method and would grow as new users come into the field. The method had many advantages. They had made the plates for a big dictionary with many different type letters and the Photon method had enabled them to do the job cheaper and better.

Mr. Miller had not experienced any difficulty training operators for the Photon machines, nor had any trouble keeping the machines running. The maintenance was no problem.

He felt Photon should be constantly developing new uses and methods for their machine.

"Boston Globe"—William Taylor

Mr. Taylor believes that photocomposition is definitely the coming process. The *Globe* expects to do 10% of their display advertising and all gravure by photocomposition.

They have selected the Linofilm machine based on a visit to the *New York Daily News*. They were well satisfied with the operation and results of the machine in use there.

Their reasons for not selecting Photon were:

1. Photon is too complicated a machine to operate.
2. Photon necessitated high maintenance cost.
3. Constantly need factory repair man to keep machine running.
4. Higher cost—the number of Photon machines needed would cost $250,-000 as against $80,000 for Linofilm.
5. Linofilm's lease with option to buy with rent being deducted from sale price more attractive than Photon price policy.

The above objections were observations from Photon users.

The next choice would probably be the new Fotosetter when available in six months.

Mr. Taylor felt that Photon was well represented saleswise. He had not gone to Quincy despite friendship and regard for Mr. Lowe.

Mr. Taylor was in the midst of labor negotiations and anticipated some difficulty with the union on the switch to photocomposition.

"Camden Courier-Post"—Mr. Dyer

He thinks photocomposition will eventually prove cheaper and quicker than hot metal. However, he feels that newspapers will be slow to convert and will tend to wait for improvements and better techniques. They will let others do the pioneer work.

The reasons for the slow change will be the difficulty in training new personnel with the union objections. Also, engraving departments are necessary. Improvements such as the Dow etched plates are helping.

Accurate costs of the hot and cold methods are difficult to secure as no two newspapers have exactly the same methods and types of advertisements vary greatly.

Mr. Dyer is not ready to put in photocomposition as yet. He studies his man-hours per page throughout the year and it shows his costs going down slightly so he feels he has a rather efficient operation. Thus he will wait further developments before shifting.

Of the machines he has studied he thinks Photon is probably the best. It is a

Exhibit 5 (Concluded)

very versatile machine and should prove an even greater asset in offset printing.

"Lancaster New Era–Intelligence Journal"—Mr. Finney

He believes photocomposition will be the coming method for display advertising and gravure and he has been studying the field before making his recommendations to management. He must show savings in writing before management will buy.

He is waiting to see a production Linofilm machine in operation before making his decision.

He is leaning toward Linofilm for these reasons;

1. He likes Linotype Company which makes good machines and is a nice company to do business with.
2. Linofilm uses tape and plain keyboard so three lesser paid operators can run tape on two shifts; then the photocomposition part can be done later with skilled operator. Photon possibly requires a journeyman to operate. Linofilm should be cheaper to operate; three unskilled and one skilled vs. three semiskilled and one skilled.

He understands Photon is in poor financial condition and would not be surprised if Mergenthaler bought the company.

Photon has good sales representative. Mr. Finney has visited South Bend, Allentown and *New York News*. He wants to go to Louisville as he was impressed with survey. He would like to have copy of survey for his file.

"Philadelphia Inquirer"—Mr. Fazio

Mr. Fazio feels photocomposition is the new method for display advertising and gravure work and will revolutionize his department in the next few years.

He studied the field for two years and narrowed his choice down to Linofilm and Photon. He finally selected Linofilm based on visits to *New York News* and Louisville newspapers. The reasons for his choice were as follows:

1. He bought a system not a machine and felt Linofilm had the best system for his department.
2. He felt there was an advantage costwise in having three lesser paid operators prepare the tape on the second and third shifts if necessary, then run the tape through the photocomposition unit on the regular shift and complete the operation with more skilled people.
3. Tape can be used again if any mistake occurs in later operation such as paste-up; while with Photon machine it is necessary to start over.
4. Linofilm is simpler machine to operate and maintain. Photon does more but is too good a machine for the newspaper industry. Newspapers do not need to do as fine printing; thus Photon's advantages are wasted on the newspaper field.
5. Mr. Fazio doubted the claims of Photon's wide variation of type sizes.
6. Photon disc is too delicate, easy to scratch, or break. Linofilm disc much more durable.

The *Inquirer* production engineer confirmed Mr. Fazio's selection from a maintenance point of view. Linofilm simple to operate and keep running.

Inquirer will use photocomposition for display advertising and gravure.

Photon made a good sales presentation. He is not wedded to Linotype Company. Would have selected Photon if better machine. In printing work Photon might prove better machine.

Due to the poor operating results in 1958, and because of the success of the Kodak study, it was decided to raise the price of the Photon machine 15 per cent, to $55,600, on May 1, 1959.

In the summer of 1959 the results of a consulting firm's study were made available to the Photon management. Excerpts from this report are shown in Exhibit 6.

Exhibit 6

EXCERPTS FROM CONSULTANT'S REPORT

The Phototypesetting Technique[1]

A. Current Status of Phototypesetting

    1. Machines in use:

        a) Fotosetter.........250 + placed since 1950.........about $33,000 each
        b) Photon............62 placed since Dec. 1956........about $55,000 each
        c) Monophoto........estimate 6 now in use............about $35,000 each
        d) Linofilm..........delivery just starting..........Keyboard....$17,000
                                             Photo Unit.. 40,000
                                             Corrector.... 5,000
                                             Composer... 7,500
        e) ATF typesetter.....20–25 sold since Jan. 1958
                            (may be low)................about $14,000 each

    2. Rate of acceptance compared to slug casting machines:

Years since Introduction	Slug-Casters	Photo-typesetters
2.............................	50	...
6.............................	1,000	...
10............................	3,000	300

    Ratio of productivity:

                Hand setting............1
                Slug casters.............4
                Phototypesetters.........about 8 currently

    3. Statistics on machine use:

        a) Estimated. 310 Photons and Fotosetters in use now. Distributed as follows (in per cent):

	Photon	Fotosetter	Combined
Newspapers............................	50%	14%	23%
Typographers.........................	22	21	21
Printers and lithographers..............	8	18	16
Business forms.	8	10	8
Foreign...............................	3	15	13
U.S. government......................	2	6	5
Job printers and miscellaneous............	7	16	14
	100%	100%	100%

---

[1] From a report by Arthur D. Little, Inc., to a corporation which was considering the purchase of Photon, Inc.

Exhibit 6 (Continued)

B. Comparison of Phototypesetting with Hot-Metal Typesetting

1. Phototype *Advantages*

   a) High quality
   b) Rapid face and size change
   c) Compose on machine (versatility)
   d) Eliminates type metal inventory
   e) Eliminates proof presses
   f) Theoretically high speeds attainable
   g) Easier page make-up with complex composition—white space free
   h) Much broader availability of type styles and sizes from keyboard

   Disadvantages

   a) Requires more skilled markup (training a problem)
   b) Requires more skilled setting (training a problem)
   c) Cost of materials
   d) Cost of machine
   e) Little demonstrated savings yet
   f) Corrections tough
   g) Proofs are difficult and expensive
   h) Little increase in speed over hot-metal machines
   i) Cannot print directly from machine product

C. The Potential of Phototypography

1. Comparative economics
   a) Economic results depend on the specific "local situation," the users' requirements and how phototype is integrated into existing processes.
   b) Few studies done before purchase.
      (1) Not enough experience to estimate costs reliably.
      (2) Managements are not detail-cost conscious.
      (3) Other owners tend to justify own decision—buyers mistrust their statements.
   c) Managements will not often release figures they have compiled.
      (1) They don't want to help potential competition.
      (2) They hesitate to release superficial studies.
   d) What figures we could dig up showed that:
      (1) Savings must be calculated for total chain of events, not just composition. (May have to spend more on part of system to achieve over-all savings.)
      (2) Management often used both photo and hot metal for a given category of work (such as advertisements), choice depending on difficulty of job.
      (3) Cost savings from typesetting varied widely according to comprehensiveness of systems change and efficiency of old hot-metal operation. Reported results ranged from cost of savings of 18% to 40% higher costs.

2. Negative influences on rate of acceptance of phototype
   a) Cost of machines is high; capital is limited in this fragmented industry.
   b) Little improvement in speed over present.
   c) Buyers don't like paying for abilities they're not going to use.
   d) Buyers waiting to see what market will offer.
   e) Correction ability poor (this is of primary importance in some cases).
   f) Difficulty of getting reliable performance and cost data before a machine is purchased.
   g) Proofing is difficult and costly.
   h) Managerial reluctance to change—conservatism.

3. Positive influences on rate of acceptance
   a) Technology developments due within a year or two
      (1) New letterpress plates—flexible, reduce make-ready, fast etch, on routing.

Exhibit 6 (Continued)

    (2) New Litho plates—print directly from film—expose inside machine?
    (3) Presses designed for (1) and (2) above—web-fed, automatic folding of signatures.
    (4) Rise of offset lithography.
  b) Changing attitudes of management
    (1) Gradually increasing interest in new technology is apparent.
    (2) A gradual influx of engineering talent in industry.
    (3) Faith in future technology prevails—research departments and associations and donations.
    (4) Owners merely ask for a machine designed specifically to meet their uses.
  c) Rising pressure to reduce rising costs and the squeeze on profits.
  d) Inherent speed and flexibility advantages of phototype over hot metal.
  e) Trend toward increased use of photographic techniques in printing.

D. Principal Markets for Phototypesetting Equipment in Near Future
  1. Advertising typesetting for all media
    a) In general, the more complex the ad, the greater the savings.
  2. Offset book typography
    a) These are largely illustrated children's books or complicated textbooks—makes phototypesetting advantageous.
  3. Straight matter—editorial copy, books, etc.
    a) Current low speeds and high costs of phototypesetters eliminate this market.
  4. Business forms
    a) Volume of forms composition not yet known. Estimate minimum of 100,000 sq. ft. per year.
  5. Opening new vistas—announcements, engraving, TV titles, electronic circuit diagrams.

E. Market Size: 800–1,000 Machines/Yr.

Estimate #1

Market	Sq. Ft./Day	Estimated Composition Time/Sq. Ft. (Hrs.)		Machines Required
Newspaper local ads (50% type)	74,500	1.5	Run two 7 hr. shifts 7 days/wk.	3,500
Typographers—national ads	13,700	4.0	Run two 8 hr. shifts 5 days/wk.	3,400
Books—offset	1,500	1.5	Run 8 hrs./day 5 days/wk.	280
Business forms	400	2.0	Run 8 hrs./day 5 days/wk.	100
Commercial printing	6,000	3.0	Run 12 hrs./day 5 days/wk.	1,500
Total Market for Current Machines				8,800
Yearly Market (Estimated 10-Year Life of Machines)				880 machs./yr.

Note: Estimate should be conservative since no allowance yet made for stand-by capacity or capacity for revisions, corrections, bogus, etc.

Exhibit 6 (Continued)

Estimate #2

85,000 slug-casting machines in U.S.

    30,000 in newspapers; $\frac{1}{3}$ of these in ad alley. Estimated efficiency of phototype at 2. times hot metal. Therefore, newspaper ads potential is 5,000 machines.

    Typographer volume of ad setting estimated same as newspapers since he sets 90% of magazine ads as well as 25% of newspaper ads. This adds another 5,000 machines.

    Total Market = 10,000 machines

Yearly Market (10-year life of equipment): 1,000 machines per year.

A. Evaluation of the Photon System

  1. State of the art

    a) No system yet meets market needs in best manner.

    b) All phototype equipment has attempted to be sufficiently versatile to meet all typographic needs. Economically questionable.

    c) Probable that evolution will lead to perhaps several types of more specialized and less versatile systems.

    d) Minimum of text and display composition systems.

  2. Comparison with other major phototypesetting systems

    a) Fotosetter and Monophoto—no significant threat. Certain short-term advantages of familiarity but incorporate most of inherent limitations of present hot-metal equipment—circulating matrix, moving type case, etc.

    b) ATF Typesetter and new Filmotype machine probably not competitive—much cheaper, slower and less versatile equipment.

    c) "Cold-type" and photolettering equipment in different league.

    d) New Harris-Intertype equipment—unknown quantity. Suspect similar to Linofilm system.

    e) Photon and Linofilm appear approximately comparable—each has certain strong points. Particular application probably will determine which is best fitted.

    f) Attempt to rate Photon, Linofilm and Fotosetter on major performance parameters:

	Photon	*Linofilm*	*Fotosetter*
Keyboard speed.......................1	1	2
Human engineering....................2	1	3
Typographic quality..................3	1	2
Pi character availability.................2	2	1
Mix set widths within a line..............1	2	3
Error correction......................1	2	3
Character availability—keyboard.........1	2	3
Character availability—type library.......3	2	1

    g) Single (Photon) vs. multiunit (Linofilm) system still unresolved. Lean towards multiunit concept because of potential for greater flexibility and balance between units.

B. Maintenance of Photon

  1. Machine has been forced to perform in absence of field service force.

  2. Reliability—most companies report good luck and a few are disappointed.

Exhibit 6 (*Continued*)

3. Experience good where preventive maintenance practiced.
4. Maintenance and downtime usually no greater than for hot-metal machines.
5. Modular design aids maintenance enough but replacement of parts sometimes difficult.
6. Pick repair men carefully—Photon is at their mercy in field. Train them better.
7. Most problems seem to be mechanical.

C. Questionable Features of Photon

1. Excessive use of mechanics in design.
2. Disc idea—16 fonts. Limits flexibility.
3. Disc idea—implies limited top speed and multiple flash on large letters.
4. Too many features on machine that some customers don't want to pay for.
5. Keyboard complexity—operator training time high.
6. Pi character device not really usable.
7. Disc availability is poor: slow, expensive, low quality type library.
8. Separate keyboard with perforated tape. Intermediary product desirable?
9. Very expensive parts prices.
10. Slow changeover from film to paper.
11. Letter-fit poor.

D. Projection of Photon's Sales and Market Share

1. Annual sales of phototypesetting systems

Year	Photon	Foto	Lino	ATF	H-I	Total
1958 (in use)	60	220	...	...	...	280
59	25	25*	10	40	...	100
60	35	10*	35	50	...	130
61	50	...	50	50	10	160
62	100	−20	80	75	30	265
63	150	−50	100	75	100	475
Total in use	420	185	275	290†	140	1,410

*Net of sales less returns.
†Film usage about half that of other machines.

2. Above projections based on following judgments and assumptions:
   a) Photon will develop a sound marketing program.
   b) Photon, Linofilm and unannounced Harris-Intertype systems approximately equal in terms of meeting market needs.
   c) Photon will be given sufficient backing to correct present impression of "lack of substance" to trade.
   d) Trade will hold back to see performance of Linofilm and Harris-Intertype systems.
   e) Technical advances, particularly in platemaking will become available to enhance use of phototype.
   f) Fotosetter will fade out of picture and Monophoto will not have significant sales.
   g) ATF system only partially competitive at most.

At the stockholders' meeting in the summer of 1959, the Board of Directors of Photon, Inc., was reconstituted as a result of discussion with certain stockholder interests. Policy differences developed within the new Board of Directors. Some of the directors felt that a merger with a large

Exhibit 7

THE PHOTON MACHINE—100 SERIES, 1953

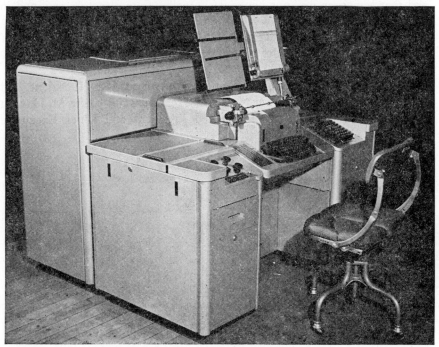

Exhibit 8

THE PHOTON MODEL 200

company was necessary to give Photon increased financial backing. Others believed that Photon, Inc., was not far from operating profitably and that a merger was not necessary. Finally, four directors resigned in November of 1959.

Sales for the year 1959 were $1,430,065 and did not reach the level of profitable operations. Only nineteen machines were shipped, and the operating loss was $574,202.

On February 28, 1960, William Garth resigned as President and Treasurer. Frank L. Tucker was elected Treasurer, and Kurtz M. Hanson was appointed a Director and elected President and Chief Executive Officer.

The Decision Making Problem in Development

. . . [I]t may also be true that the forces making for efficiency in the narrower sense are deeply engrained in our society and stand in the way of more rapid progress. While economists have probably had little influence on business practices in research and development, the same cannot be said of cost accountants, management experts, and the growing army of business school graduates in general. And to their influence must be added the influence of the engineers. Despite the rise of experimental physics, a good many engineers are still trained in the tradition that it is sinful to design anything that might later have to be changed.

Burton Klein

FROM: "The Decision Making Problem in Development," *Sources of Inventive Activity* (Princeton: Princeton University Press, 1962).

HERMAN KURT

ENGINEERING DEPARTMENT
March 28, 1963

To: D. W. McKee
From: H. Kurt

This will summarize our Fruit Harvester program since last November, in which we engineered a self-propelled catching frame, and conducted a market survey in the field of mechanical harvesting of soft fruits and nuts.

I. The Clark-Kurt machine seems to be the most outstanding design offered to date. It can be used in cherries and oranges, as well as apricots, prunes, and peaches. Maneuverability and gradability exceed competition, making our unit capable of handling these problems in almost any type of orchard or grove. Also included are the features of soft-padding and bin-tilt to make the Clark-Kurt harvester the most desirable for handling soft fruit.

Price-wise the Clark-Kurt machine at $18,406 is slightly higher than the major competition of XYZ and Troy, but it is a better machine. Our economy version equals price competition favorably.

II. Management at Battle Creek reached the decision on March 27 to discontinue this project for the following reasons:

1. The indicated market volume of about 2,500 machines in the next five years seemed too small to warrant the expenditure of $150,000 per year required.
2. It will be a long time before wide use of these machines will be found in the eight major deciduous fruits grown in the U.S. These fruits are: apples, peaches, pears, grapes, cherries, plums, prunes, apricots, composing 1,718,500 acres—citrus fruits, nondeciduous, comprise 779,100 acres.
3. Clark would be entering the agricultural field with a fringe line product without established distribution.
4. Clark analysis at this time shows 68.47% of these first machines to be purchased manufacturing.

III. My opinion of the situation at this time is as follows:

1. Price will not be the deciding factor, the best machines will capture the early market.
2. Distribution should at first be handled direct to the consumer, using specialized service while retaining the profits—no dealers. Consideration should be given to rentals and contract harvest.
3. Every section in the U.S. that has producing trees recognizes the need for mechanized harvesting. The savings with machines ranges from 2:1 to 5:1. Millions of dollars are now being spent on research and development in this field. Large companies like Borden in New York, California Packing Corporation in the West, will be forced to mechanize and they will start in 1963.

4. The market will develop faster and be larger than we have judged in this program. Prunes are the first crop to be harvested mechanically starting with self-propelled catchers only three years ago. Apricots and cherries and peaches will follow.

IV. My recommendations are that if Clark decides in the future to offer products to agriculture, in the way of machines to improve harvest methods, they should do so with a line of tools. In this case, catchers and tree shakers, also attachments for lift trucks such as pruning platforms, scoops, and shaker mounts, and a special distribution program should be established.

cc: B. E. Phillips
      J. D. Schell

PHOTON, INC. (C)

When Kurtz M. Hanson became President of Photon on February 28, 1960, he began his job by studying the company's current position and identifying matters that required immediate attention. Two problems seemed paramount: First, to continue operations through 1960, there was an urgent need for additional capital in excess of $500,000. Second, further to improve Photon's financial position and to put the company on a firmer foundation, sales had to be increased and costs reduced. However, Hanson realized that improving sales would be difficult until more money was available. A third and interrelated problem was that during the previous four years, Photon's image had steadily deteriorated because of its shaky financial condition and because the prior management had often publicly made overoptimistic claims about present and future products. This reputation of insolvency and exaggeration made both raising money and selling machines difficult.

Solving these problems became Hanson's principal objective. To help establish a better corporate image, he instituted a new policy whereby all Photon's claims about present products would be conservative. Furthermore, absolutely no mention would be made about a future product until a reliable, operating model had been produced.

Hanson began traveling extensively, using his knowledge and influence in the graphic arts industry to sell both the company and its products. Concurrently, he carried out a search for additional sources of capital. He investigated several merger possibilities but found none of them to be in the best interests of the stockholders.

To reduce the cash drain on the company, Hanson cut the number of employees from 170 to about 100. Most of the layoffs were in the production department, many of the supervisors being downgraded to assembly jobs. He also initiated a program to reduce inventories over the coming year.

In March, 1960, just as Hanson's new program was getting underway, the Harris-Intertype Corporation filed a suit against Photon and one of Photon's customers for patent infringement. The suit involved the rotating matrix disc of the photo unit, which is one of the essential components of the Photon machine. Loss of the suit would remove Photon's main technological advantage over competing companies. Therefore the immediate effect of the legal action was an increase in customer sales resistance caused by even greater uncertainty about the company's future. In addition, Photon's management believed that a derogatory whispering campaign was being carried on by some competitors, who had salesmen calling on everyone in the printing industry.

Despite these unfavorable developments, Hanson continued his search for capital; and during April, he was able to raise $206,000 in eight-year notes. This money was to be used as working capital to sustain

Exhibit 1

FINANCIAL STATEMENTS FOR YEAR ENDED
DECEMBER 31, 1960

BALANCE SHEET

ASSETS

Current assets:		
Cash..		$ 41,517
Accounts and notes receivable...................		
Less reserve for doubtful accounts..............		47,858
Inventories—at lower of cost or market...........		861,829
Total Current Assets.........................		$ 951,204
Accounts receivable—other........................		219,075
Plant and equipment—at cost.....................$	673,994	
Less allowance for depreciation..................	274,414	399,580
Prepaid and deferred items.......................		36,971
Total....................................		$1,606,830

LIABILITIES AND STOCKHOLDERS' EQUITY

Current liabilities:		
Notes payable to banks...........................		$ 175,000
Accounts payable................................		74,743
Accrued royalties................................		50,974
Accrued payroll, taxes and other expenses........		41,784
Total Current Liabilities......................		$ 342,501
Convertible subordinated 6 per cent note payable.....		206,000
Customers' prepayments and deferred rental income...		191,347
Stockholders' equity:		
Common stock...............................$	392,875	
Capital surplus.............................	5,256,465	
	$5,649,340	
Deficit.......................................	(4,782,358)	
Total Stockholders' Equity....................		866,982
Total.................................		$1,606,830

INCOME STATEMENT

Gross income from sales, service, and rentals........		$ 974,186
Costs, including cost of sales; service engineering; administrative, selling, and general expenses—exclusive of depreciation.....................$	1,670,656	
Loss on disposal of obsolete equipment and other assets	228,169	
Provisions for:		
Depreciation of plant, equipment, and rental machines..................................	155,881	
State tax.....................................	6,666	
Interest on bank loans...........................	18,915	
Total Costs and Expenses......................		2,080,287
Loss for the Year...........................		($1,106,101)

operations in the immediate future. In spite of his energetic attempts to sell machines and to improve the company's image, his efforts were more than offset by the lawsuit. Consequently, during 1960, only 10 machines were sold. The sales volume of $974,186 was accompanied by a loss of $1,106,101, which was twice as large as the loss in 1959 (see Exhibit 1).

Exhibit 2

DESCRIPTION OF THE PHOTOTYPESETTING AND PHOTOCOMPOSITION PROCESSES

Strictly speaking, the terms "phototypesetting" and "photocomposition" have different meanings, although they are often used interchangeably.

Phototypesetting is the process of photographically putting images of type characters on a photographic film or paper. The Photon machine does this by projecting the type image directly on the film or paper.

There are other methods of putting images on film or paper; for example, in the "bright type" process, a form (metal type arranged in sentences and paragraphs) is prepared, the type is sprayed with carbon black, and the faces are wiped clean. A photograph is then taken which, when developed, shows only the "bright" faces of the type. Another method of transferring the type face image to film is by "reproduction proofs." In this process the form of metal type is inked, and its image is carefully transferred onto paper. A photograph is then taken of the paper. Images can also be put on films by nonphotographic means, such as by pressing a transparent acetate sheet against an inked type in a form. These processes vary in the quality of image achieved on the film. In general, the direct projection of the image (the process that Photon uses) gives the highest quality of reproduction, and the nonphotographic method gives the lowest quality of reproduction.

Photocomposition, in contrast to phototypesetting, describes the complete system of putting an image on a photographic film or paper and then transferring the image to the plate which is used in the actual printing process. Once the film has been exposed (using one of the processes described above), it is developed, placed on a specially prepared metal plate, and exposed to light. The light causes a change in the special chemical coating on the plate, the nature of the change depending on the type of plate being produced.

In some printing processes a negative (or reverse-reading) image is needed on the plate; in other printing processes a positive image is needed on the plate. Accordingly, the chemical coating is either hardened or decomposed on the areas of the plate which receive light through the film (since the film is opaque in places, the rest of the plate's area is not exposed to light). The image has now been transferred to the plate, and the plate is treated to preserve this image by washing away the undesired coating.

The three common printing processes use different types of plates:

1. In the *letterpress* process a negative image is transferred to the plate, and the background is etched away so that the image stands in relief above the plate surface. This image is coated with ink and applied directly to the paper.
2. In the *offset process* a plate with a "right-reading" (positive) image is used, and both the image and the nonimage surfaces are on the same level. The image area is specially treated to absorb ink; the nonimage area is treated to absorb water. In the printing process the plate is pressed against a water-soaked roller (which coats the nonimage area with water) and then against an ink roller (where the image area is coated with ink). The plate is then pressed against a rubber-covered cylinder, the inked image is transferred to the cylinder, and the rubber cylinder impresses the image upon the paper (hence the name "offset").
3. In the *gravure process* a negative plate is prepared, on which the image area is *below* the surface of the plate. In the printing process a layer of ink is applied to the plate, a "doctor blade" scrapes the ink from the nonimage areas, and the plate is pressed to the paper, transferring the inked image.

Early in 1961, Hanson closely examined the potential in each sector of the market for phototypesetting machines in order more accurately to direct Photon's sales efforts.[1]

He estimated the total market potential to be more than 1,000 units per year, broken down as follows:

Newspapers............................... 400 machines
Typographers............................ 400
Other commercial printing................. 170
Book publishers.......................... 35
Business forms........................... 10
    Total............................1,015 machines

Despite the size of this large potential market, Photon was able to sell only 10 units; and the two chief competitors, Harris-Intertype and Mergenthaler Linotype, sold only about 25 machines each during 1960. These two companies offered the only effective competition for Photon's machine. Both Harris and Mergenthaler had been for many years the principal suppliers of hot-metal typesetting equipment, and within the last few years had introduced phototypesetting units. Harris' machine, called the Fotosetter, sold for $40,000, while Mergenthaler's machine, called the Linofilm, was priced at $70,000. Although their prices were comparable to the cost of the Photon machine, Photon people were sure that neither of these products had the flexibility, capabilities, or reliability of the 200 model. (Exhibit 3 compares the performance characteristics of the three machines according to Photon.)

In spite of the competitive disadvantages of their products, Harris-Intertype and Mergenthaler Linotype were a serious threat to Photon's future because of their vastly superior financial resources to apply to research and development, sales, promotion, and manufacturing efficiency. Harris' annual sales were over $70 million, and Mergenthaler's were in excess of $45 million. Because of many years' service to the printing industry through an extensive sales network, both had excellent corporate images.

Several smaller companies claimed to have phototypesetting machines, but the machines had limited capabilities. Because of the large investment required to compete effectively in the phototypesetting field (initial development costs in excess of $2 million and investment in a type library of over $1 million), these small companies were not expected to pose a serious threat to Photon.

In view of Photon's poor sales performance in a large potential market, and because of the competition, Hanson decided a new sales strategy was

---

[1] Although the term "photocomposition" was used in "Photon, Inc. (A) and (B)," the particular function of Photon's equipment is more accurately described as phototypesetting. See Exhibit 2 for a complete definition of the two words and a description of the processes.

Exhibit 3

COMPARISON OF PHOTON'S 200 MODEL, MERGENTHALER LINOTYPE'S LINOFILM, AND HARRIS-INTERTYPE'S FOTOSETTER, AS PREPARED BY PHOTON

	200 Model	*Linofilm*	*Fotosetter*
Mixing facilities:			
Number of different point sizes available from one matrix...............	21	6	4 or 6
Number of faces available at keyboard.............	16	6	2
Size range of machine (points)..............	4 to 72	6 to 36	4 to 72
Total keyboard mixing capacity (sizes × faces)...	12 × 16 = 192	13 × 6 = 78	14 × 2 = 28
Mixing of sizes and faces in one operation..........	Unlimited and automatic	Faces only	Two faces only, limited size mixing with special mats
Horizontal spacing:			
Maximum line length in picas	54	42	30–42
Justification...............	Positive; depends on line shortage *and* number of interword spaces	Justification warning *does not* take into account number of spaces	Letter spacing only
Automatic insertion of leaders and blanks in justified line..............	Yes	No	No
Automatic multiple justification for tables, columnar work, etc..............	Yes	No	No
Vertical spacing:			
Film feed reversing means	Yes	None	None
Keyboard features:			
Record of composition (hard copy).................	Yes	Yes	No
Correction possible at keyboard................	Delete one or several characters by back spacing, or kill entire line	Kill line only	Kill line or correct in assembler
Special functions:			
Special functions for display composition:			
Counter off.............	Yes	No	No
Register off.............	Yes	No	No
Nonphoto..............	Yes	No	No
Leading repeat..........	Yes	No	No
Feedback checks to operator:			
Proper font.............	Yes	No	No
Proper size.............	Yes	No	No
Correct justification......	Yes	No	No
Magazine in place........	Yes	No	No
Tape operation:			
Tape size and source.......	Limited to straight matter (can be modified to accept standard teletypesetter or flexo-tape)	Sixteen-level tape	Yes
Miscellaneous			
Number of steps necessary to produce a complete display and markup.......	2 Keyboard Develop and dry	7 Punch tape Process through photo unit Develop and dry Make negative Develop and dry Process through composer Develop and dry	2 Keyboard Develop and dry
Photo speed...............	Eight or 10 characters per second; very fast size or face shifts	Approximately 10 characters per second; slow size or face shifts	Six to eight characters per second
Power requirements........	115 volts, 12 amperes	115 volts, 55 amperes	N.A.
Air conditioning...........	Indifferent	Strongly recommended	Indifferent

Note: This information prepared by Photon, Inc., for its product comparison study.

needed. Since the nature of the selling job required that considerable time be spent with any customer before a sale could be made, it was decided that a concentrated sales effort confined to selected customers in the northeastern part of the United States would best utilize Photon's limited sales force. To further implement this program for increasing sales, the previous sales manager was replaced by Mr. Godshall, who had joined Photon in 1957 after long experience in the printing industry. Godshall had been manager of the Fotosetter Field Division of Harris-Intertype Corporation from 1949 to 1957. Another man, previously personnel manager, was assigned as Godshall's assistant. Hanson continued to devote a large amount of his efforts to selling Photon's machine.

On February 28, 1961, the Graphic Arts Research Foundation, which had jointly supported the development of Photon's products for more than twelve years, decided that it wanted to terminate its connection with Photon. Therefore, Photon canceled the $175,000 in receivables due from GARF and agreed to pay GARF a total of $350,000 in royalties in exchange for severance of all obligations.

Partially to offset this loss of $175,000 in receivables and to provide working capital, Hanson again turned his attention to finding money. In May, he was able to raise $800,000 from officers, directors, and other stockholders in the form of short- and intermediate-term loans. The financial position of Photon was also improved by the success of the inventory reduction program, inventories having dropped from $1.4 million to $814,000 in eighteen months.

Later in May, Robert M. Campbell, a previous associate of Hanson, was hired as an Executive Vice President. His assignment was to concentrate on production, cost control, and other internal aspects of the company, while Hanson largely occupied himself with the external aspects. In effect, the company was now to be run by this two-man team.

Now that additional working capital was available, the decision was made further to emphasize marketing; and during the early part of July, five new salesmen were hired. All the men had experience in the printing industry, many in the composing room; they were therefore able to understand the problems of the printer and were conversant with the language peculiar to the industry. To develop their ability to act as sales engineers, they received instruction in the capabilities and application of the Photon machine. Also, they were directed to use a cost analysis approach and show each customer a cost study that had been made on operations similar to his own.[2] If the customer was important, a special cost analysis would be done, showing how the use of a Photon machine could reduce the cost of his operations.

To insure that Hanson's "rifle shot" marketing policy was followed and that the salesmen's efforts were put to optimum use, a prospect list of 150 companies was drawn up. This list consisted of the most promising

[2] The Eastman Kodak cost study, contained in Exhibits 3A and 3B (p. 212–213), "Photon, Inc. (B)," is typical of such a cost study.

customers for phototypesetting in the East and Northeast, i.e. printers who were known to be progressive in thought and who seemed to be "style setters." Several such companies on the list were the *Post Times* in Florida, the *New York Daily News*, and the *Kingsport Daily News*. Campbell helped considerably in the decisions for deployment of the sales force; and based on the prospects list, salesmen were placed in Chicago, New York, New Jersey, Washington, D.C., and the South. In addition, Campbell took the primary responsibility for Photon's promotional activities.

Later in July, Hanson and Campbell met to discuss in greater depth how to improve the marketing program and increase sales. Photon now had a competent sales force in the field, and money was available for a limited amount of promotion. The Photon machine had been improved to a high degree of reliability. In their opinion, it was the best phototypesetting machine on the market. For the first time, Hanson's work load was reduced so that he could effectively implement the sales effort. It was vital that these factors be utilized to produce an effective marketing program.

After considerable discussion, they reached the major conclusion that being able to offer only one machine to a potential customer was a serious handicap to Photon. A new product would add breadth to the company's product line and help establish Photon as a progressive company which was interested in satisfying the individual needs of customers in each segment of the printing industry. Therefore, several criteria for a new product were established, the most important ones being (1) that minimal cost be involved, (2) that the period of development be short, and (3) that it be in the phototypesetting field.

One possibility for a new product was the development of a high-speed phototypesetting machine (later called the ZIP machine) which would be capable of operating at a rate of 300–500 characters per second. The original idea for such a machine had been conceived by the Photon inventors, Higonnet and Moyroud, in 1957. At that time, they visualized the product as filling the need of small printers for low-cost phototypesetting. It could be installed in a service center similar to IBM's computer service centers. The customer would bring his copy to the service center, where it would be typed by one of the twenty-five typists feeding each ZIP machine. The resulting film would then be taken back to the printer's plant for use. Hanson and Campbell recognized that this product would greatly improve Photon's reputation, since it represented a tremendous technological advance over the present phototypesetting speed of 10 characters per second. However, the cost and time to develop this machine and set up service centers would be very high. (An estimate was made of $200,000 and one year's time to develop the machine alone.)

Another possible new product that interested Hanson and Campbell was a punched-tape-operated phototypesetting machine. They were aware of the tremendous growth in the use of punched tape during the past decade for such applications as controlling machine tools. They felt that tape carried with it an aura of progressiveness and efficiency. Another feature of tape, important in the printing industry, was that it provided a permanent means of storing information. At this point the two men decided to break up their meeting and investigate further possibilities for new products.

Shortly afterward, during a discussion of the meeting with Higonnet and Moyroud, Campbell discovered that they had proposed a tape machine in 1957. The inventors went on to state that with a slight change in the circuitry and reader of the present 200 model, it could be adapted to punched tape. The cost of developing such a unit, they felt, would be quite reasonable, especially since it would not be necessary to redesign the photo unit. Higonnet said that while a tape machine would not be as flexible as the 200 machine, it would be less complicated and probably cost less.

After further discussion a definite design was agreed upon. The photo unit would be fitted with an adapter and sold without a keyboard. The customer could then use his present TTS [3] or Monotype keyboard in conjunction with the photo unit to produce phototypeset film. The two managers estimated that developing a unit for handling TTS tape and one for handling Monotype tape would involve about three months' time and $35,000 or $40,000 for each unit. Campbell realized that such a machine would allow the printers to try phototypesetting at a much lower investment than now possible, and that it would be particularly well suited to the small print shop. On the other hand, Photon's present marketing program was directed toward large printers, who might not appreciate this type of machine. Another consideration was that the composing flexibility and capabilities of this "phototypesetting adapter" would be restricted by the limited capabilities of the TTS or Monotype keyboard. This product might not prove attractive, therefore, to much of the industry.

Armed with this additional information, Hanson and Campbell met on July 21 to decide which of four alternatives should be followed. The alternatives were:

1. Apply all resources to selling the 200 machine.
2. Develop the "phototypesetting adapter" which would accept the punched-tape output of a TTS or Monotype keyboard.
3. Develop the high-speed ZIP machine, and establish phototypesetting centers.
4. Undertake a combination of the above.

[3] Teletypesetter.

We Need More Engineers and Fewer Scientists

The proposition that engineers should be paid more than scientists is worth defending. Engineers refer to those who are engaged in the conception, design and production of physical devices which have economic value, and scientists refer to those who are uncovering new knowledge with a purely intellectual motivation.

To some extent, the proposition is merely a defense of the status quo, since on the average those who are engaged in engineering work do receive more remuneration than those engaged in pure research. However, in academic circles, a curious intellectual hierarchy exists familiarly known as the academic pecking order, which is roughly the inverse of the economic one. Thus the person with the greatest intellectual status is the pure mathematician, the man who can rejoice when he has discovered a theorem so abstract that it will never be used in a practical problem. Next to him ranks the applied mathematician and under the mathematicians come the physicists. The theoretical physicist is the most revered. Under him comes the experimental physicist and at the bottom of the physics list comes the applied physicist. Beneath the physicists come the engineers with the research engineer at the top, the production engineer at the middle and the sales engineer at the bottom.

One defense of the intellectual order is that the increasing prestige in passing from the sales engineer to the pure mathematician compensates for the decreasing salary levels. Another statement of this same concept is the theorem of Psychic Income. This theorem states "The non-monetary satisfactions of any job can be converted to an equivalent dollar value, and the sum of the real income and the psychic income gives the true income for any job." According to this view, the pure mathematician must be willing to take some of his income in cash and some in personal satisfaction.

FROM: An editorial reproduced by permission from *The Reflector*, Boston, October 1, 1962.

Pressures have been exerted recently, particularly from Government sources, to disturb this natural order. It is felt that we must increase the amount of basic science which is produced and that the way to do so is to increase the salaries of the scientists doing basic work. By this means, more people will be drawn into the area of basic science, and more new results will be discovered. Unfortunately, however, this argument ignores the true nature of the scientific hierarchy. The reason that pure scientists receive less money than applied scientists is that they, on the average, are worth less to society. For every pure scientist who makes a significant discovery, there are hundreds whose lives are essentially wasted. They merely look into the unknown and see nothing. Society must average out all these failures with the few successes and for this reason must pay the average pure scientist a relatively small wage.

The engineer, on the other hand, is producing a product which can be used directly by society and which always has an economic value. Even the mediocre engineer is doing useful work and producing new values for society. The mediocre scientist is worse than useless. His work may actually hinder the advance of science, and at best is completely negated by the superior work of someone else.

The danger in increasing the salaries of pure scientists is that more mediocre people will be attracted into the area. They will only clutter it up and may actually impede the development of new ideas. We do not need more pure scientists. We need fewer and better ones. A single Einstein can trigger the work of a generation of engineers, and mere money does not produce an Einstein. We do, however, need more engineers. We can never raise the industrial level of the country too high, and each engineer contributes to this end. The salaries of engineers should, therefore, be raised relative to those of scientists, and other means should be sought for uncovering the Einsteins among us.

RONALD E. SCOTT

DALLAS CHEMICAL CORPORATION[1]

In the spring of 1959, Dr. Caldwell, Director of Research at Dallas Chemical Corporation, called a meeting of laboratory management to discuss the problem of formal recognition of scientists who stayed in research work. Attending the meeting were the personnel manager, Mr. Keats, and the two laboratory directors, Dr. Faulkner and Dr. Maughan. Six months before, Dallas' Research Division had initiated a "technical ladder of advancement" for those scientists who chose to remain in direct scientific work rather than assume research management positions. The purpose of this meeting was to analyze the effects of this technical ladder and arrive at some decisions on future action in this area.

The research laboratories of the Dallas Chemical Corporation were a separate entity and maintained only loose ties with any of the other corporate divisions. They had been located in a small university town for the past fifteen years, and much of the academic atmosphere pervaded the laboratories. No development work or engineering was done by the professional staff of four hundred persons; they were strictly basic researchers in all areas of Dallas' interests.

Dr. Caldwell opened the meeting by reviewing the events leading up to the company's initiation of the technical ladder of advancement.

DR. CALDWELL: Let me briefly review the events which led up to our decision last year to initiate a technical ladder. Our interest, as you may recall, was stimulated about a year and a half ago by both internal and external forces. You may recall the loss of several highly regarded individuals to other companies for reasons that appeared to be better positions and increased status. At the same time, there appeared in the literature several articles pertaining to various methods of rewarding technical personnel. At that time, Mr. Keats made a study of the procedures and policies used by several other laboratories comparable in size and work scope, and he presented a plan to our Research Council for the adoption of the title of Fellow of the Technical Staff. This was to be the only step in the ladder and was to be the highest status our technical men could obtain. Six months ago, we made a public announcement of this position plus the appointment of eight of our best scientists as Fellows. These men are, as you are well aware, outstanding in their fields and also our most senior men. Now that six months have passed, I would like to hear from you any reactions of your own or your men concerning the position plus your recommendations for the next step to be taken.

MR. KEATS: Since I made the original study at the time we adopted the Fellow title, I have been doing a lot of thinking and talking with outsiders on this action. When I first presented our plans to the Research Council, I ration-

---

[1] All names are disguised.

alized this move on the basis of having a desire to show to everyone associated with these labs that management wants to reward those men who have contributed to the company's benefit over the years. The other reason was a desire to remove the lack-of-a-title stimulus which drives some of our good men out of research. Let me explain this last one in more detail. For years, we have done our best to give the researchers whatever they wanted within reason. One very selfish reason we have done this was because the researcher who saw a difference between his present job and a job in management or a research job at another company would be much more prone to leave for this reason. One of the areas in which these differences occur is the title and status of the job. Before this dual ladder was conceived, this was one area in which research was particularly weak. Ours is a management-oriented society where a man's position depends upon his title. When I say this was our weak area, I mean we were losing men to other labs and to nonresearch work when everything but the title was the same. Thus, our introduction of the technical ladder was our first attempt at correcting the title problem.

DR. FAULKNER: Six months ago, when this idea was originally presented, I agreed with you; but from reactions to the dual ladder in my lab, I conclude that this is not practical at Dallas Research. Let me show you where these arguments fail when applied to our research staff. In my lab, recognition of men is primarily through the work they are doing and the articles they have published. Management cannot confer prestige and recognition; it can only hope to recognize formally this "position" of these men who have done well in their profession. In fact, our first action of conferring the title of Fellow on those eight outstanding men was primarily for the purpose of borrowing some of their prestige for the title. This earned recognition which I am speaking of pertains only to the laboratory and the scientists as a professional group. Certainly, this title has an effect; but upon whom? Obviously upon the people who cannot recognize a man for what he has done, but only for the title he wears. This comprises most of the rest of the Corporation plus the outside world, the man's family, and his friends. Perhaps this is the group we want to please, but I think not. What does it matter what they think of you? This is hollow prestige praise for a title, not for the man or the accomplishments. As far as removing the title difference which might motivate good researchers out of science, I doubt that this is important; the good researcher has such a strong motivation to contribute that the quest for a title is a comparatively weak force.

DR. MAUGHAN: Without appearing to be a fool, I would like to agree with both you and Keats. I think you are both correct but that you are talking about different people. Perhaps we have diagnosed the problem correctly but treated the wrong patient. By that I mean that the eight men who have received the titles were the last ones to need them. They had recognition, money, honors, and whatever else was needed. The Fellow title was only frosting. However, there *is* a group which is drastically affected by management's attitude toward titles, and that is the younger men; these are the ones who have not yet received formal recognition and are most prone to leave the lab because of their poor status. At this point, I want to disagree with Dr. Faulkner on the importance of being recognized outside the professional group. Many of these men have families and friends who are important and are interested in how they are doing; and to these people, "how they are doing" is equated with their title. The older men, their wives, and their families have learned to live with their position; but to the young men, it is doubly hard, for they see their friends in business and the universities climbing the various ladders, and they have no signs of progress to show. As a generalization, I also think that the younger generation is more title-conscious. To state my position fully, I think that the need for a title provides a motivational force of varying intensity for the individual, but on the whole stronger in our younger and less well-recognized colleagues. I think that the pressure from the outside can be strong enough in some cases to veer a good researcher from strictly scientific work in our labs to other labs or nonscientific work. As an aside, I think that the size of the lab has grown to the point where a man may no longer be recognized for his accomplishments alone, as all of our Fellows were. It now may take the formal approval of the lab management before a man is recognized for his work, even within the lab.

MR. KEATS: If we accept your hypothesis of the value of the title being dependent upon the position of the man receiving it, this would tie in nicely with the results I have observed. For one thing, the results have been very negligible; no one is either very pleased or very displeased. Most of the staff are waiting to see if any other titles are introduced and who will be recognized in the next few years. By giving more men recognition and recognizing the younger men, management will make a real contribution to their position both within and outside the labs.

DR. FAULKNER: Yes, and it is these younger men who may be hurt the most by this system of giving titles. We haven't mentioned any of the ill effects of this ladder. My men have commented that one of the big advantages to our lab is its democracy, and they are worried that formal titles would result in a stratification detrimental to communication. One or two of them left labs just because of this; for example, they don't like to see all the senior scientists eating together and loss of first-name intimacy. Many also fear that the granting of titles will produce a harmful competition for titles which could endanger the co-operation and communication between our scientists. One of our big selling points in recruiting men has been this lack of competition which created a different atmosphere than at many labs. The final thing I think we should consider is what the effect of not receiving a title is. How will it affect the performance of the man who doesn't get the title, both the mediocre one who doesn't rate one and the good man whom we misjudge? I realize that the first step has been taken and we can't turn back, but I certainly think we should go slow in the future, first comparing the advantages that have been mentioned against the liabilities of each new step.

MR. KEATS: I have to agree with most of your points, but the problem is, what can be done about this reaction? How can we even measure it? To your list of problems with the technical ladder, I would like to add one more. A major complaint is that we give the men a title only and no other rewards such as a bonus, a raise, or many of the little trappings they expect with high management positions. It is difficult to tell the younger men that the Fellows have been on the same financial level as members of the laboratory management for years. I have tried to point out that it is our policy to pay a man equally for his contribution whether he is in a research management position or actual scientific work. Most of the younger men don't believe this, and it is impossible to prove this with our policy of salary secrecy. As far as the trappings of the position go, you all recognize that our policy has been to minimize the trappings in the entire laboratory. We have no private parking lots or dining rooms; and researchers obtain space, service personnel, and equipment only when they can show a need. This puts us in a definite bind as compared to other labs or even some product divisions of our own company, in which salary increases and all sorts of little trappings are included in a promotion or new title.

DR. CALDWELL: As I have been sitting here listening to the arguments both pro and con for this technical ladder, it strikes me that we are involved in a problem much more complex than originally anticipated. If we accept the hypothesis of Dr. Maughan that the real effects of this title business are felt most strongly in the middle echelons, then we can concede that our first efforts have been negligible because they were misdirected. These top men had all the recognition they needed; the Fellow title was frosting on the cake. However, these first efforts were not entirely wasted, for two reasons: We had a definite desire and duty to recognize these men for their contribution to Dallas' research; secondly, this move has acquainted the entire technical staff with the knowledge that management wants to recognize them formally and their time will come. As I see it, we are now progressing to more reactive material—those men who have not been widely recognized. Selection of these men will be much more controversial. The reactions here to our actions should be much more substantial, and we need to give careful thought and planning to the situation to make sure that reaction is favorable. As to the problem of not providing any physical rewards with the title, I think much of this may be solved by my explaining our salary policy of not associating a raise with a promotion, but publicizing the fact that the top salary barriers have been removed for this group of men.

Specifically, what I would like to see come out of this meeting is a decision as to what our next step should be—naming more Fellows or initiating a new position for younger men, or both. This entire problem has suddenly been exposed, like an iceberg, with the most dangerous part hidden. I do not think it appropriate or possible to arrive at a decision immediately. Let's meet again next week at this time. That will give you some time to sound out the men in your groups. I hope by next week we can detail a course of action on this subject.

UNION OIL COMPANY OF CALIFORNIA (A)

On January 31, 1955, the Shale Oil Committee which had been formed four months previously to study the question of how best to exploit Union Oil Company's substantial Colorado oil shale holdings submitted its report to the Board of Directors.

The essence of the Committee report was this: The prospective economic gain from a large-scale commercial operation of producing oil from oil shale appeared to be at least as good as the average return on finding, developing, and producing domestic crude oil. However, several unknowns remained to be resolved. The importance of the venture was such that the Committee recommended a special research program with these aims:

1. Develop and prove out a full-scale model of the oil shale retort designed by Union's Research Department.
2. Determine the optimum manufacturing method for producing marketable products from shale oil.
3. Obtain accurate estimates of capital and operating costs for a commercial shale oil operation.

It was estimated that the research program would cost about $5 million and would take from two to two and a half years. Because of the magnitude of the expenditure, it was recommended that a special appropriation apart from the normal research budget be made for the oil shale project.

UNION OIL COMPANY'S OPERATIONS

The Union Oil Company owned 40,000 acres of rich oil-shale-bearing lands located in the Piceance Creek Basin situated near the Rifle–Grand Valley area of western Colorado. The shale rock in these holdings contained approximately five billion barrels of recoverable shale oil, or about ten times the Company's proven crude oil reserve.

Union Oil was one of the major oil companies in the United States. Its principal marketing area was in the western United States, Alaska, and Hawaii. In this area a full line of petroleum products was sold. Throughout the rest of the nation and western Canada, special products, such as lubricating oil and waxes, were sold under the Company's brand names. A limited line of products was sold through distributors in northwestern Mexico. In addition, bulk sales were made to marketers in western Canada,

246

Exhibit 1

CONSOLIDATED FINANCIAL POSITION, DECEMBER 31 (IN THOUSANDS)

	1954	1953	1952	1951	1950	1949	1948	1947	1946	1945
CURRENT ASSETS										
Cash	$33370	$37881	$30843	$21049	$32896	$16736	$22126	$25267	$15780	$21997
Gov't & other securities	158	8125	8766	203	394	15371	2429	2392	7626	18023
Accounts Receivable (net)	62098	50215	40847	38530	30122	25325	25869	21088	17606	14622
Inventories										
Crude Oil	2987	3547	4076	3343	3055	4438	5990	4099	3459	1862
Pet & chem. pdts.	26848	28333	21006	18094	21858	22785	19352	13964	14789	9373
Mat'l & Supplies	3451	4255	4015	3932	2542	2088	3269	4084(1)	4652(1)	3450(1)
TOTAL CURRENT ASSETS	128912	132356	109553	85151	90867	86743	79033	70894	63912	69327
CURRENT LIABILITIES										
Accounts Payable	25628	22124	23259	23506	17326	15465	15790	13681	11150	8191
Excise tax collected for Gov't	4967	4884	4269	3859	3245	3382	2841	3142	2143	1633
Taxes Payable (Ex. Inc. Tax)	4637	4249	3833	3271	3048	2814	2488	1775	1852	1620
Dividends Payable	3996	2905	2633	2633	2633	2633	2917	1633	1167	1167
Interest Accrued	283	467	455	274	275	291	92	73	57	57
Due on S.F. & purch agreements	2615	1415	1303	803	300	300	200	200	---	---
Provision for Inc. Tax (net.)	6378	3157	734	703	6405	3187	7076	4261	2277	171
TOTAL CURRENT LIABILITIES	48504	39201	36486	35049	33232	28072	31404	24765	18646	12839
WORKING CAPITAL	$80408	$93155	$73067	$50102	$57635	$58671	$47629	$46129	$45266	$56488
PROPERTIES										
Properties - at cost	712343	654023	618975	574164	525535	503631	431125	398077	376576	354845
Less Depreciation	353506	331339	313538	293497	271034	254259	234525	219669	209754	200208
Net Investment	358837	322684	305437	280667	254501	249372	196600	178408	166822	154638
OTHER ASSETS										
Invest. in non-consol. majority										
owned companies	629	731	1754	5334	5161	5413	3378	3374	3375	344
Invest. in other securities										
and advances	15699	13406	12827	5609	4738	3618	2110	1961	1428	1475
Less allowance for loss	2510	2500	2500	2500	2370	2565	1965	1000	---	---
	13828	11637	12081	8443	7529	6466	3523	4335	4803	1819
Prepaid Taxes & Insur.	6138	5271	4340	4611	3917	2942	2779	2301	1923	1991
Other ppd. expenses & def.chgs	3523	4100	3625	2405	1478	2024	1574	982	1165	743
Proceeds from sale of Prom.note							14907(2)	14907		
Total Working Capital, Properties										
& Other Assets	462734	436847	398550	346228	325060	319475	267012	247062	219979	215679
LESS:										
Long Term Debt	93997	122111	118203	84907	79400	79700	54400	54600	40000	40000
Allowance for Self-Ins. Risk	2854	2541	2238	2052	1990	1670	1508	1331	1222	1123
Deferred Earnings	2742	2939	3135	---	---	---	---	---	---	---
Total	99593	127591	123576	86959	81390	81370	55908	55931	41222	41123
SHARE OWNERS EQUITY	$363141	$309256	$274974	$259269	$243670	$238105	$211104	$191131	$178757	$174556
Preferred Shares	23250	23450	23788	23765	24010	24255	24500	24500	24500	24500
Common Shares	166472	145235	131657	131657	131657	131657	116657	116657	116657	116657
Capital Surplus-Common	27173	14451	8529	8529	8536	7299	3699	3699	3699	3699
Capital Surplus-Preferred	286	282	260	245	245	245	---	---	---	---
NET EARNINGS RETAINED	145960	125838	110740	95073	79222	74649	66248	46275	33901	29700
TOTAL SHARE OWNERS										
EQUITY	$363141	$309256	$274974	$259269	$243670	$238105	$211104	$191131	$178757	$174556

(1) Years 1945, 1946, 1947 are not comparable with succeeding years, as construction materials are included in these years.

(2) Transferred to Cash resources in 1949   *S.F. is Sinking Fund on Bonds

Mexico, Japan, and other countries. A wholly owned subsidiary, Brea Chemicals, Inc., manufactured and sold ammonia, ammonia-based fertilizers, and various industrial chemicals throughout the western United States and in Mexico and Hawaii.

Exploration activities were carried out in western Canada, western and southwestern United States, Cuba, Costa Rica, and Guatemala. About 70 per cent of the Company's crude oil production came from fields located in California, and about 70 per cent of the Company's proven crude oil reserve was also in this area.

Three of the Company's five refineries were located in California: at Olcum (near San Francisco), Bakersfield, and Los Angeles. The others

Exhibit 2

CONSOLIDATED EARNINGS (IN THOUSANDS)

	1954	1953	1952	1951	1950	1949	1948	1947	1946	1945
GROSS INCOME										
Sales of petroleum pdts.(net)	$334253	$305819	$269811	$261712	$208948	$200396	$203859	$165701	$117488	$134792
Other operating income	15415	18668	15730	13141	7800	4951	4494	5677	4185	3720
Sale of property (1)	1484	354(2)	1996	1208	376	239	259	648	84	---
Other income	570	263	560	23	409	365	632	409	1181	437
TOTAL	$351722	$325104	$288097	$276084	$217533	$205957	$209244	$172435	$122938	$138949
COSTS & EXPENSES										
Raw Mat'l, Pdt. purch & Operating costs	$208590	$182911	$170951	$152882	$130049	$122451	$113078	$96705	$65711	$82054
Selling and Admin. Exp.	38219	35164	31927	31727	28138	26567	24783	23029	21800	17944
Depletion, Depreciation & Amortization	33677	33381	27765	23916	21702	25200	25590	23888	17975	22843
Dry Hole & Land Relinquished Losses (3)	15800	14200	14050	16350	5600	---	---	---	---	---
Taxes, other than Income	10224	9235	8131	7733	7263	6513	5250	4149	4360	3901
Interest & Other Debt Exp	2724	3363	2893	2180	2203	2169	1550	1153	1137	1406
Provision for loss on invest. & advances	---	---	---	---	---	600	1500	1000	---	---
Est. Fed & other Income Taxes	6600	8750	4800	14000	5400	2100	6200	3600	2150	1600
TOTAL	$315834	$287004	$260517	$248788	$200355	$185600	$177951	$153524	$113133	$129748
NET EARNINGS	$ 35888	$ 38100	$ 27580	$ 27296	$ 17178	$ 20357	$ 31293	$ 18911	$ 9805	$ 9201

(1) Up to 1951 gains on sale of property were offset against Depletion, Depreciation and Amortization and only the net figure reported. Statements from 1946 to 1951 have been adjusted to make them comparable to later years. Amount of gain from sale of property in 1945 unknown.

(2) This figure includes $7.6 million capital gain, after income taxes, from the sales of the Company's investment in capital stock of the Trans Mountain Oil Pipe Line Company and the Company's fleet of six tankships.

(3) Previous to 1950 this amount was included with Depletion, Depreciation and Amortization.

were at Edmonds, Washington, and Cut Bank, Montana. A 20,000-barrel-per-day coking plant was under construction at Santa Maria, California. Union Oil was also operating nearly a thousand miles of oil pipe line and several coastwise tankers for the transportation of crude oil and petroleum products.

Balance sheets and income statements are shown in Exhibits 1 and 2. Other statistical data on the Company's operations are given in Exhibit 3.

THE WEST COAST PETROLEUM INDUSTRY

The period between 1947 and 1953 saw the West Coast petroleum industry[1] clearly shift from the role of a surplus producer of crude oil to that of a net importer. See Exhibit 4. The basic causes were these:

1. The West became one of the nation's fastest growing regions in the postwar period. This growth particularly stimulated the demand for gasoline.
2. California's oil provinces no longer offered the profitable drilling opportunities they once did. Existing oil fields were declining steadily—reflecting, in part, the very high production rates required to meet the needs of World War II.
3. California's oil was of a lower gravity than the nation's average, thus yielding a high proportion of residual fuel oil and a low proportion of gasoline. Prior to the end of World War II, this production met West Coast needs, since the area was a big consumer of residual fuel oil. Local supplies of coal and natural gas were insufficient. However, in 1947 the demand for fuel oil started falling as railroad dieselization began, and the first of several large natural gas pipe lines was completed from Texas to California. With gasoline demand rising and fuel oil demand falling, California crude oil was no longer able, without expensive refinery modifications, to meet the required product balance. The need was for a higher gravity crude oil, such as that produced in the Middle East, the Far East, South America, and Canada.
4. Several of the West Coast majors owned substantial foreign crude oil reserves.
5. Following the end of the Korean War, oil tankers were in surplus.

Between 1947 and 1953, imports of light crude oil increased from virtually zero to 80,000 barrels per day. In addition, West Coast refiners invested several millions of dollars in new cracking equipment in an effort to balance product output with the changing demand pattern. They also, from time to time, continued to sell surplus residual fuel oil at low prices in foreign markets and other United States markets.

Total West Coast demand for all petroleum products except fuel oil increased by 7 per cent per year for the first five years following World War II. Industry forecasts called for substantial future increases in demand, though at a slower rate. Little or no increase was expected in fuel oil demand.

---

[1] This term refers to all operations of the petroleum industry of Arizona, California, Nevada, Oregon, and Washington.

Exhibit 3

TEN-YEAR STATISTICAL SUMMARY

ASSETS *at year end*	1945	1946	1947
Crude oil reserves—barrels (a):			
California	329,100,000	356,100,000	356,300,000
Other States and Canada	54,500,000	54,400,000	62,900,000
Net investment in properties, plants and equipment (b):			
Production (including natural gasoline plants)	$86,755,964	$90,086,040	$98,049,276
Transportation (pipe lines, tankships, etc.)	14,077,650	17,478,230	16,926,897
Manufacturing	37,254,560	39,334,889	39,456,864
Research	245,096	382,827	417,031
Marketing	15,580,396	18,846,481	22,929,458
Miscellaneous	724,253	693,974	627,973
Total	$154,637,919	$166,822,441	$178,407,499
Working Capital—Funds available for current operations	$56,487,921	$45,265,932	$46,129,154
Ratio of current assets to current liabilities	5.4 to 1	3.4 to 1	2.9 to 1
Share owners' equity per common share (adjusted for 1953 share dividend of 10%)	$29.13	$29.95	$32.36

OPERATIONS *barrels handled*			
Crude oil production (a):			
California	22,797,000	21,408,000	23,265,000
Other States and Canada	3,583,000	4,109,000	4,478,000
Crude oil processed at refineries	41,246,000	34,352,000	36,976,000
Percent supplied from Company production	64.0	74.3	75.0
Sales of crude oil and products:			
Crude oil	4,711,000	5,791,000	7,559,000
Petroleum products:			
Domestic and foreign	24,664,000	26,292,000	34,562,000
United States Government	18,431,000	4,081,000	5,788,000

FINANCIAL SUMMARY			
Gross revenue	$138,948,960	$122,937,835	$172,435,222
Total costs and expense	129,747,837	113,133,312	153,524,362
Net earnings from operations	9,201,123	9,804,523	18,910,860
Net earnings per common share (c)	$1.70	$1.73	$3.50
Nonrecurring gains (or losses) from sales of properties, etc., reflected directly in net earnings retained in business	(1,791,250)		
Charges to cover replacement of underground crude oil reserves and "tools" used in operations, and to meet contingencies, plus book value of properties sold	32,564,896	17,891,208	25,704,791
Net proceeds from borrowing, from sale of preferred shares, and from issuances of common shares in exchange for assets, less purchases and redemptions	9,608,346		14,600,000
TOTAL FUNDS AVAILABLE	$49,583,115	$27,695,731	$59,215,651
Cash dividends declared on:			
$3.75 Cumulative preferred shares	$401,048	$937,500	$937,500
Common shares	4,666,270	4,666,270	5,599,524
Expenditures for replacement and expansion of properties and facilities:			
Production (including natural gasoline plants)	13,664,353	15,131,590	24,881,370
Transportation (pipe lines, tankships, etc.)	1,665,867	4,833,088	1,122,580
Manufacturing and Research	4,786,395	5,285,274	4,055,596
Marketing	897,692	4,614,679	6,058,184
Miscellaneous	88,994	214,022	172,119
Total	21,103,301	30,078,653	36,289,849
Increase (decrease) in investments, etc., including, in 1949, acquisition of capital stock of Los Nietos Company, $41,000,000	1,281,701	3,235,297	15,525,556
TOTAL EXPENDITURES AND DISTRIBUTIONS	$27,452,320	$38,917,720	$58,352,429
BALANCE ADDED TO (or drawn from) WORKING CAPITAL	$22,130,795	($11,221,989)	$863,222

NOTES: (a) After deducting interests of others.

(b) After deducting accumulated charges for exhaustion of oil and gas properties, wear and tear, obsolescence, etc.

Exhibit 3 (Continued)

1948	1949	1950	1951	1952	1953	1954	TEN YEARS 1945-1954
360,100,000	403,200,000	391,600,000	408,800,000	431,600,000	423,800,000	399,000,000	
65,000,000	70,300,000	67,200,000	72,500,000	72,000,000	85,800,000	96,000,000	
$109,882,618	$151,892,915	$153,370,862	$170,289,122	$183,010,324	$204,218,320	$208,246,536	
16,387,484	17,247,021	17,365,731	17,685,597	17,846,576	14,175,403	18,397,227	
42,982,307	48,746,623	47,309,984	52,471,428	67,181,129	64,620,403	89,016,331	
497,890	583,742	3,490,055	4,564,385	4,623,086	4,539,284	4,483,889	
24,148,436	27,794,326	29,439,350	31,393,692	29,962,370	31,863,633	33,041,620	
603,206	3,107,642	3,524,978	4,262,541	2,813,676	3,266,863	5,651,319	
$194,501,941	$249,372,269	$254,500,960	$280,666,765	$305,437,161	$322,683,906	$358,836,922	
$47,629,536	$58,670,963	$57,635,576	$50,101,535	$73,066,554	$93,154,778	$80,408,037	
2.5 to 1	3.1 to 1	2.7 to 1	2.4 to 1	3.0 to 1	3.4 to 1	2.7 to 1	
$36.25	$36.82	$37.83	$40.56	$43.35	$49.19	$51.04	
24,874,000	20,992,000	21,585,000	25,744,000	27,074,000	29,930,000	29,635,000	247,304,000
5,073,000	5,040,000	5,561,000	6,263,000	6,594,000	7,618,000	7,529,000	55,848,000
40,989,000	42,829,000	43,461,000	47,307,000	49,840,000	51,554,000	53,552,000	442,106,000
73.1	60.8	62.5	67.7	67.6	72.8	69.4	68.6
7,300,000	7,258,000	10,560,000	11,243,000	11,660,000	13,604,000	15,279,000	94,965,000
35,034,000	36,151,000	38,937,000	40,524,000	45,715,000	44,075,000	44,745,000	370,699,000
3,902,000	4,796,000	5,283,000	9,631,000	4,244,000	7,123,000	11,010,000	74,289,000
$209,243,953	$205,957,148	$217,532,601	$276,083,666	$288,096,950	$325,103,778	$351,721,678	$2,308,061,791
177,950,806	185,600,202	200,355,054	248,787,695	260,517,191	287,004,176	315,833,758	2,072,454,393
31,293,147	20,356,946	17,177,547	27,295,971	27,579,759	38,099,602	35,887,920	235,607,398
$5.92	$3.35	$2.81	$4.55	$4.02	$5.59	$5.26	
					7,646,178		5,854,928
27,327,588	26,195,875	28,830,040	42,161,672	45,909,165	54,471,747	54,734,002	355,790,984
(200,000)	43,673,140	(458,744)	(652,300)	33,558,301	4,014,832	7,012,040	111,155,615
$58,420,735	$90,225,961	$45,548,843	$68,805,343	$107,047,225	$104,232,359	$97,633,962	$708,408,925
$937,500	$930,469	$921,094	$911,719	$900,408	$886,359	$874,688	$8,638,285
10,382,451	10,799,108	10,532,540	10,532,540	10,532,540	10,804,104(d)	14,890,862	93,406,209
29,414,187	23,385,245	19,624,630	42,968,996	45,841,777	57,370,539	45,695,882	317,978,569
1,030,255	2,430,020	1,801,131	2,600,607	1,947,261	2,086,665	3,033,689	22,551,163
7,627,573	10,148,100	5,416,910	10,444,496	20,222,422	5,946,608	33,236,776	107,170,150
3,681,651	4,412,284	5,280,826	5,214,915	2,782,224	5,459,994	6,485,218	44,887,667
168,364	602,341	598,210	1,191,914	589,219	723,037	3,249,992	7,598,212
41,922,030	40,977,990	32,721,707	62,420,928	71,382,903	71,586,843	91,701,557	500,185,761
1,580,721	30,086,405	2,857,267	2,474,197	1,266,355	866,829	2,913,596	62,087,924
$54,822,702	$82,793,972	$47,032,608	$76,339,384	$84,082,206	$84,144,135	$110,380,703	$664,318,179
$3,598,033	$7,431,989	($1,483,765)	($7,534,041)	$22,965,019	$20,088,224	($12,746,741)	$44,090,746

(c) Based on shares outstanding at year end, adjusted for 10% share dividend paid in 1953, and also adjusted in 1952 and 1953 for additional shares issued in 1954 as a result of conversion of debentures sold in 1952.

(d) In addition, a share dividend of one common share for each ten common shares held was paid in December, 1953.

Exhibit 4

PETROLEUM SUPPLY AND DEMAND POSITION IN DISTRICT FIVE, (1) 1945-53

	Supply				Foreign and Intercoastal Shipments			Increase or Decrease In Stocks	Demand			
		Receipts from Outside Dist 5 (2)		Total Current New Supply					Domestic Demand & Losses(3)	Military Demand	Civilian Inc. Losses	Total Demand Inc. Losses
Year	Production All Liquid Hydrocarbons	Total	Crude		Total	Crude	Other		Total Inc. Losses	Net		
1945	952	46	18	993	23	11	12	-38	1,007	294	713	1,031
1946	923	17	4	940	59	14	45	+42	839	78	761	898
1947	982	14	4	997	76	17	59	+8	914	67	847	990
1948	1,001	15	3	1,016	72	19	53	+44	900	88	812	973
1949	986	23	6	1,009	73	18	55	+50	886	76	810	959
1950	975	16	4	991	142(3)	29(3)	113	-76	925(4)	83(4)	842(4)	1,067
1951	1,052	37	14	1,090	110	23	87	-37	1,017	112	905	1,126
1952	1,064	79	41	1,143	86	18	68	+37	1,020	78	942	1,106
1953	1,085	135	84	1,220	92	16	76	+70	1,060	93	967	1,152

(1) District Five of Bureau of Mines includes California, Oregon, Washington, Arizona, and Nevada.

(2) Includes both imports and receipts from other U.S. districts.

(3) Includes demand in District Five, shipments to Alaska and Hawaii, and rail and truck shipments to U.S. points outside District Five. Losses have averaged about 1% of total for this period.

(4) Adjusted by FRB of San Francisco to remove certain shipments to Japan included by Bureau of Mines in Military Demand, Domestic. The amount has been included in Foreign shipments by FRB.

Source: FRB of San Francisco and Bureau of Mines

THE HISTORY OF SHALE OIL

The Nature of Oil Shale

Strictly speaking, the rock commonly called "oil shale" is not a shale, nor does it contain any oil as such. It is a laminated, sedimentary rock technically classified as a marlstone—that is, a limestone with a mixture of minerals. The rock was formed by deposits of clay, mud, and other sediment and contains an organic material usually called "kerogen," from which appreciable amounts of oil can be extracted by the application of heat.

The relationship between the formation of crude oil deposits and oil shale is not well defined. Geologists generally agree that the origin of both can be traced back to the decomposition of plant and animal remains deposited in muds and other sediments. There are, however, many different opinions as to why one deposit became a liquid while the other remained a solid. One widely held view is that the oil shale deposit is merely an "unfinished" crude oil field.

Location of Oil Shale Deposits

Although oil shale deposits have been found throughout most of the world, the majority of them have little economic significance at this time. In many cases the shales assay less than 15 gallons of oil per ton and are considered too lean for commercial operations. In a few countries, shales yielding nearly 100 gallons per ton exist, but the deposits are too small to mine profitably.

With due allowance for the lack of adequate geologic data, the upper limit of the recoverable shale oil in the world, excepting the United States and Brazil, has been placed at about five billion barrels. About half of these deposits are located in Europe. These reserves, although large, are insignificant when compared to the reserves that exist in the United States and Brazil.

Brazil's largest deposit is known to be over 250 miles long and from 100 to 300 feet thick. Even though the richness and extent of this and other beds are not fully known, geologists have estimated Brazil's recoverable shale oil reserve to be in the order of 300 billion barrels.

The oil shale beds found in the United States vary considerably both in quality and in quantity. See Exhibit 5. The most important single area is the Green River formation found in the Rocky Mountain region of Colorado, Utah, and Wyoming. The sections in Utah and Wyoming contain some 55 billion barrels of recoverable shale oil, but the section in Colorado known as the Piceance Creek Basin has rich, thick beds known to contain about one *trillion* barrels.[2] The beds of shale here vary from 200

---

[2] This compares to the United States *proven* crude oil reserves of about 30 billion barrels.

Exhibit 5A

PRINCIPAL OIL SHALE RESOURCES IN THE UNITED STATES

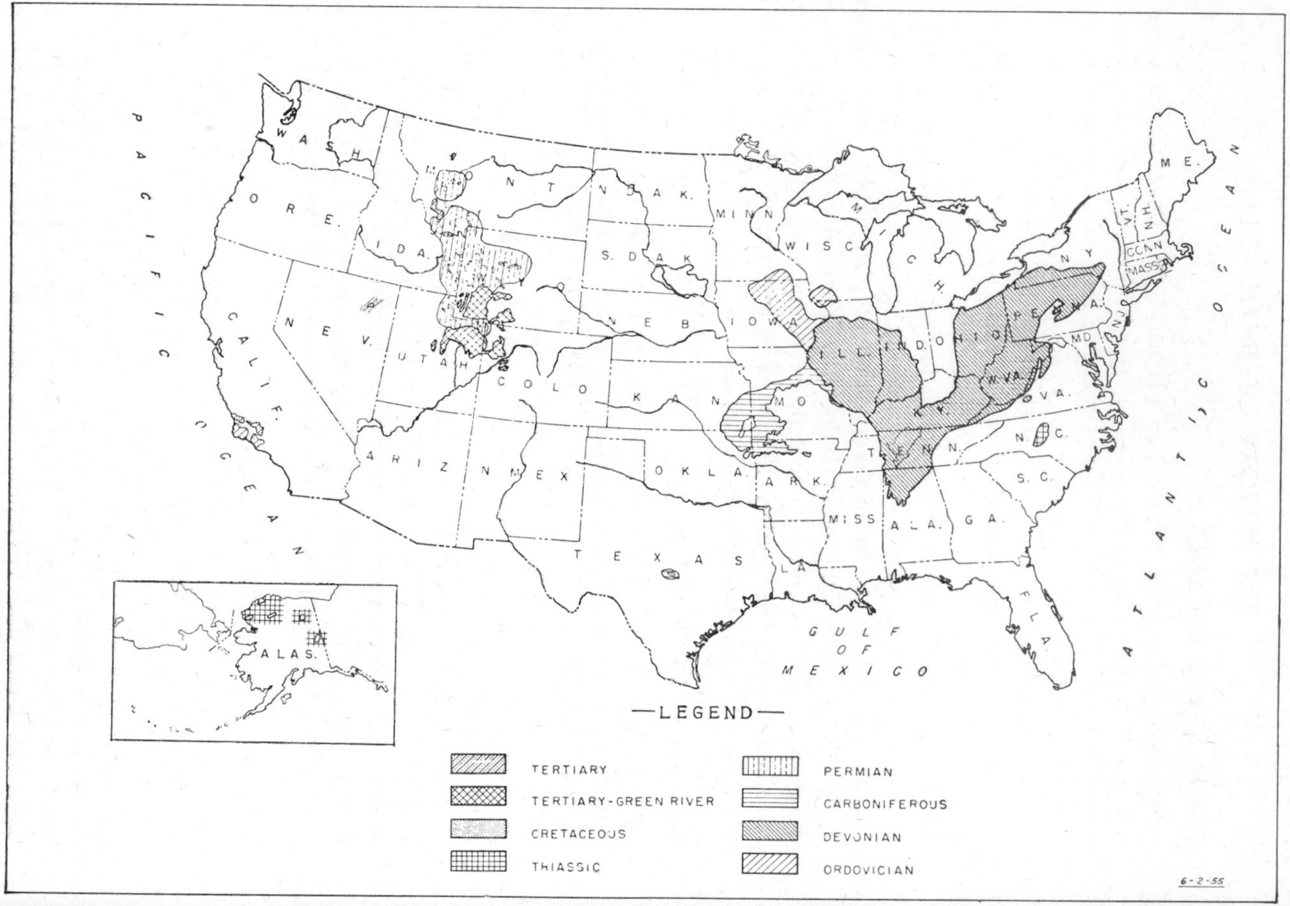

— LEGEND —

TERTIARY
TERTIARY-GREEN RIVER
CRETACEOUS
TRIASSIC

PERMIAN
CARBONIFEROUS
DEVONIAN
ORDOVICIAN

6-2-55

State	Formation	Age	Est. Area Sq. Miles	Approx. Thickness Feet	Gal. Per Ton	Short Ton Million	Bbl. Oil Million	Author	Reference Publisher	Volume
Ala.	Chattanooga	Devonian	8,900	2 to 20	28 to 122	20,670		Butts	Ala.G.S.	Ala.Geol. Bull. 797C
Alaska		Triassic						Mertie	U.S.G.S.	Bull. 130-
Ariz.								Butler	Ariz.B.M.	
Ark.	Chattanooga	Devonian	2,700	5 to 70	1.5	63,000	1,500	Adams	U.S.G.S.	Pyt'ville F.
	Fayetteville	Carboniferous		8 to 200				White	U.S.G.S.	Bull. 691
Calif.	Miocene	Tertiary	3,070	1400	3 to 30	960,000	70,000	Winchester	C.S.S.M.QT.*	Vol.17 #4
		Tertiary						Hoots	U.S.G.S.	P.P. 154
Colo.	Green River	Cretaceous	2,592	83 to 2,300	25	210,000	125,000	Winchester	C.S.S.M.QT.*	Vol.17 #4
		Tertiary			10	1,785,000	494,000	Belser	U.S.B.M.	R.I. 4769
Georgia	Chattanooga	Devonian	210	1 to 45		45,570		Smith	Ga.G.S.	Bulls.23,45
	Floyd	Carboniferous				4,300		Smith	Ga.G.S.	Bulls.23,45
Idaho	Phosphoria	Permian	200	50 to 200	1 to 6	5,000	360	Mansfield	A.I.M.E.	Lindgren
	Frontier	Cretaceous		2 to 20	2 to 20			Winchester	U.S.G.S.	Bull. 729
	Along Bear River	Quaternary						Winchester	U.S.G.S.	Bull. 729
Illinois	Maquoketa	Ordovician	615	1		143		White	Ill.G.S.	Bull. 21
	Chattanooga	Devonian	46,470	5	0 to 16	535,000	76,000	Winchester	U.S.G.S.	Bull. 729
	Pottsville	Carboniferous		2 to 6	5 to 49			Barret	U.S.G.S.	Bull. 34
Iowa	Maquoketa	Ordovician	19,600	1	10	45,570		Howell	Iowa G.S.	Vol.28
Indiana	New Albany	Devonian	16,000	15 to 100	12 to 15	420,000	100,000	Ashley	C.S.S.M.QT.*	Vol.17 #4
		Carboniferous		9				Winchester	C.S.S.M.QT.*	Vol.17 #4
Kansas	Chattanooga	Carboniferous	6,400	40 to 50	5 to 21	505,000	50,000	Lee	Kans.U.	Bull. 73
Kentucky	Chattanooga	Devonian	30,750	20 to 245	10 to 50	100,000		Jilson	Ky.G.S.	S.6,Vol.11-12
	Sunbury	Carboniferous		15	14			Lee	Ky.G.S.	S.5,Bull.12
	Pottsville	Carboniferous		5				Miller	Ky.G.S.	Bull. 64
Maryland	Genesee	Devonian	922	3 to 100		21,000		Clark	Md.G.S.	UppDevonian
	Magothy	Cretaceous		4				Wood	U.S.G.S.	Bull.691
Missouri	Chattanooga	Devonian	15,800	25 to 45	2 to 3	915,000	44,000	Wilson	Mo.G.S.	S.2, Vol.16
	Cherokee	Carboniferous						Wilson	Mo.G.S.	S.2, Vol.16
Montana	Three Forks	Devonian	50?	5 to 18	1 to 10	580	72	Bowen	U.S.G.S.	Bull. 691
	Quadrant	Carboniferous	50?	0 to 60	3 to 8	3,600	700	Bowen	U.S.G.S.	Bull. 691
	Phosphoria	Permian	100	50 to 75	2 to 21	7,000	1,700	Mansfield	A.I.M.E.	Lindgren
	Colo. Shale	Cretaceous	130	15 to 25	1 to 2	3,000	75	Winchester	U.S.G.S.	Bull. 661
	Muddy Creek	Tertiary	120	5 to 1000	8 to 76	2,800	460	Condit	U.S.G.S.	Bull. 711
Nevada	Green River	Tertiary	16	60	5 to 87	72	26	Winchester	U.S.G.S.	Bull. 729
New York	Genesee	Devonian	10,400		3			Vilbrant	N.Y.S.Museum	Clay & Shale
N. C.	Deep River	Triassic	1,500	51 in 5 beds	11 to 70	1,000	643	Vilbrant	U.of N.C.	Ec.P.59
Ohio	Chillicothe	Devonian	21,500	300	5 to 8	6,450,000	1,075,000	Ashley	Ohio G.S.	Bull. 64
				5				Stout	Ohio G.S.	S.4,Bull. 30
								Stout	Ohio G.S.	S.1,Bull. 30
Okla.	Sunbury	Carboniferous		15 to 35	11	153,000	11,000	Weldman	Okla.G.S.	Bull. 56
	Lalthina Chert	Ordovician	3,300					Weldman	Okla.G.S.	Bull. 56
	Chattanooga	Devonian		2				Winchester	Okla.G.S.	Bull. 691
Pa.	Genesee	Carboniferous	32,000	2 to 10	2 to 40	371,000	37,000	Ashley	Pa.G.S.	Bull.C-1
	Pottsville	Carboniferous		1 to 10	5 to 25			Ashley	Pa.G.S.	Bull.C-1
S. Dak.	Pierre	Cretaceous	11,070	10		287,000	12,300	Rothrock	S.Dak.S.M.	Bull. 15,16
Tenn.	Chattanooga	Devonian	12,900	12 to 500	4 to 14	898,800	140,000	Bassler	Tenn.D.G.	Bull. 38
	Cumberland	Carboniferous	1,230	20 to 40	4	700	66	Winchester	C.S.S.M.QT.*	Vol.17 #4
Texas	Lampasas	Cretaceous						Schuh	U.of Tex.	Bull.66
		Tertiary						Winchester	C.S.S.M.QT.*	Vol.17 #4
		Cretaceous						Winchester	C.S.S.M.QT.*	Vol.17 #4
Utah	Cannel Coal	Cretaceous	100	20 to 100	1	21,000	500	Winchester	C.S.S.M.QT.*	Vol.17 #4
	Phosphoria	Permian	4,680	10 to 2,950	5 to 55	92,000	33,000	Mansfield	A.I.M.E.	Lindgren
	Green River	Tertiary	3,700	50 to 1,100				Winchester	U.S.G.S.	Bull. 729
Virginia	Chattanooga	Devonian		50 to 200				Bassler	Tenn.D.G.	Bull. 38
W. Va.	Genesee	Devonian	22,100	10 to 500	7	2,566,000	266,000	Price	W.Va.G.S.	Vol.10-1938
	Onondaga	Carboniferous						Ashley	U.S.G.S.	Bull. 691
Wisc.	Maquoketa	Ordovician	1,830	1		4,250		Howell	Iowa G.S.	Vol.29
	Phosphoria	Permian	100	50 to 150	1 to 3	11,615	285	Mansfield	A.I.M.E.	Lindgren
Wyo.	Mowry	Cretaceous		11				Winchester	U.S.G.S.	Bull. 691
	Green River	Tertiary	9,192	30 to 900	5 to 40	7,176	2,560	Winchester	U.S.G.S.	Bull. 729

*Colorado School of Mines Quarterly

to 2,000 feet thick. Corings have indicated an average depth of 1,300 feet of shale that assays more than 15 gallons per ton, and some thick strata assay more than 30 gallons per ton. Exhibit 6 lists approximate recoverable

Exhibit 6

RECOVERABLE RESERVES OF MAJOR LANDHOLDERS IN THE PICEANCE CREEK BASIN

Company	Estimated Recoverable Shale Oil Reserves (in Thousands of Barrels)*
Union Oil Company	5,700,000
Standard of California	4,800,000
Getty Oil	2,800,000
Dow Chemical	1,500,000
Equity Oil	1,400,000
Socony-Mobil Oil	1,400,000
Texas Company	1,100,000
Cities Service	1,000,000
Sinclair Oil	600,000
Continental Oil	180,000
Shell Oil	170,000
Honolulu Oil	137,000
Gulf Oil	89,000
Pure Oil	16,000

* Estimated recoverable amounts from minable sections yielding 25 gallons per ton or greater.

Source: Barron's.

reserves of shale oil from shale assaying over 25 gallons per ton of companies that are major landholders in this area.

Chemical and Physical Properties of Shale Oil

After the kerogen has been converted to raw shale oil by thermal decomposition, or "retorting," as it is commonly called, the end oil product still bears little resemblance to typical crude oils. Raw shale oil is a black, highly viscous oil that contains appreciable amounts of nitrogen and sulfur. Below about 80 degrees Fahrenheit the oil becomes a gelatinous mass due to the high wax content, but above this temperature the oil will flow easily. Another major difference is that shale oil contains many "unstable" molecules that tend to react with each other and form gums and other undesirable compounds. These molecules are also present in crude oil but not in sufficient quantity to cause the same processing problems they do in shale oil. Exhibit 7 contains a comparison of the characteristics of raw shale oil and Santa Maria Valley crude oil, a typical California high-sulfur, heavy crude oil. In practice, the refining techniques for both would be quite similar.

Shale Oil Production

The shale oil industry had its beginning in western Europe around 1830, but it was never competitive with crude oil except under severely

Exhibit 7

COMPARISON OF TYPICAL CHARACTERISTICS OF RAW SHALE
OIL AND CALIFORNIA HEAVY CRUDE OIL

Characteristic	Raw Shale Oil	Santa Maria Valley Crude Oil
Gravity, API at 60 degrees Fahrenheit.............. 21		14
Pour point, degrees Fahrenheit.................+90		+20
Viscosity, SSU at 122 degrees Fahrenheit.......... 175		215
Sulfur, percentage by weight.................. 0.7		5.0
Nitrogen, percentage by weight.............. 1.8		0.6
Coke yield, percentage weight of total feed (typical)..... 10		15

limited conditions. European shale oil industries that have survived have done so only because of government subsidies or the relatively short local supply of competing fuels. In Scotland, where a plant has operated since 1850, shale oil production was under 3,000 barrels per day in 1954.

During World War II a modern shale oil plant was built in Sweden at government expense. This plant is still in operation, but its output of some 3,000 barrels per day is only a small fraction of that country's requirements of about 200,000 barrels per day. A small plant producing less than 1,000 barrels per day has been operating profitably in South Africa, apparently because of its distance from other sources of oil. The world's largest shale oil plant, which once processed about 10,000 tons of shale daily, was in operation during the 1930's in Manchuria. Its postwar status is unknown.

In the United States the shale oil industry enjoyed a brief existence along the Atlantic Coast until the completion of Drake's well near Titusville, Pennsylvania, in 1859. This well set off the world's first crude oil boom and put an end to shale oil production. The industry lay dormant, except for a flurry of oil shale land activity in Colorado during the early 1920's, until the beginning of World War II. Only sporadic research on retorting methods was done during this period.

In 1944, Congress, faced with an increasing wartime oil scarcity, passed the Synthetic Liquid Fuels Act. This Act directed the Bureau of Mines to conduct research and development work on methods of producing petroleum products from shale oil and coal. About this time the Union Oil Company resumed its experimental work on shale retorting.

Engineers from the Bureau of Mines started work in 1944 at the Navy's oil shale reserve in the Piceance Creek area near Rifle, Colorado. These reserve lands include about one half of the "Mahogany Ledge," a rich substratum which lies under an overburden of about 1,000 feet in depth. This substratum is from 70 to 90 feet thick and assays to about 30 gallons per ton. The name of the substratum is derived from the distinct mahogany color of the newly mined shale. Work in the Mahogany Ledge led the Bureau to develop a low-cost room-and-pillar mining technique.

Before this method was developed, mining experts estimated that use of conventional open-pit mining methods and equipment would result in a cost of $4.50 a ton to deliver shale to the crushers. At 30 gallons per ton assay, this amounted to 15 cents per gallon of shale oil. This cost was greater than the wholesale price of refined gasoline.

In the room-and-pillar method, as the mining equipment advanced into the face of the shale, pillars of shale 60 feet square were left standing to support the mine roof. These pillars were staggered at intervals of 60 feet. See Exhibit 8. Bolts six feet long and one inch in diameter were driven into

Exhibit 8

ROOM-AND-PILLAR MINING

 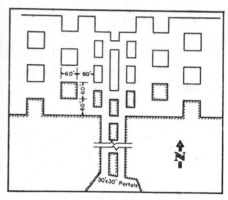

Bureau of Mines Room-and-Pillar Mine   Plan View—Room-and-Pillar Mine

the mine roof to "staple" the upper layers of rock together. This method, which allowed recovery of 75 per cent of the available shale, resulted in mining costs of between 50 and 60 cents a ton.

The greatest variable and unknown factor in producing oil products from oil shale is the retorting process. During the period from 1850 to 1945, over two thousand patents were issued relating to oil shale retorts. Only a very few, however, ever reached the working model stage, and many of these had little commercial value.

Generally, the retorts used in Europe can be characterized as follows:

1. They are relatively small in capacity, ranging from a fraction of a ton to 50 tons per day. This requires a large number of individual retorts to do a sizable job.
2. They are either batch or semicontinuous in their operation, and as such, have inherent disadvantages, including a large labor requirement.
3. They require that the shale be crushed to a relatively small diameter for successful operation. This means increased crushing and screening costs as well as shale losses, since the smallest shale particles (called "fines") are generally not retortable.
4. They require expensive external condensing equipment. This is a particular disadvantage where cooling water is costly or scarce.

Around 1950, Bureau of Mines engineers at Rifle, Colorado, developed an experimental retort called the "gas-combustion retort." This retort was gravity-fed, fully continuous, and internally heated. In experimental test runs, pilot plant models retorted shale ranging in size from three eighths of an inch to three inches. A description of its operation is given in Exhibit 9.

Three pilot plant gas-combustion retorts were built and operated having rated capacities of six tons per day, 25 tons per day, and 150 tons per day. The latter plant operated successfully, although intermittently, in excess of 200 tons per day. From these plants a commercial design had been scaled and developed by Bureau engineers. This retort had a capacity of 2,000 tons per day, but had not yet been constructed.

Since about 1950, the Sinclair Oil Company had been experimenting with an *in situ* burning process to recover shale oil without mining the rock. Their experiments and results, however, were a closely guarded secret. During this same period, Esso Research and the Bureau of Mines were individually experimenting with a method of retorting called "fluidizing." In this method, shale was crushed very fine and retorted by injecting it into a stream of superheated air or steam. This method was not far enough developed to make any prediction as to its success.

UNION OIL'S SHALE DEVELOPMENTS

Immediately following World War I, there was widespread concern that the nation was "running out of oil." As a hedge against possible future oil scarcity, Union Oil in 1920 purchased in fee and at very low cost approximately 8,000 acres of rich oil shale land in the Mahogany Ledge near Grand Valley, Colorado. Later selective purchases raised the total to about 40,000 acres. Since Union Oil was the first major oil company to purchase in this area, it was able to acquire some of the richest and most accessible deposits available.

By the mid-1920's, oil discoveries in California, Oklahoma, and Texas dispelled any fear of a near-term oil shortage. Finally, the 1930 discovery of the giant East Texas field made it abundantly clear that the real problem facing the oil industry was not a shortage, but rather how to handle the enormous oil glut that had developed. Although a limited amount of shale research was done by Union and others in the early 1920's, by 1930 all such work was shelved. Since Union's capital investment in shale was relatively minor and the land could be leased for enough to pay real estate taxes, the Company kept the properties.

At the request of A. C. Rubel, Vice President for Exploration and Production, the Research Department began working on the problem of oil shale retorting during the early years of World War II. This effort led, in the mid-1940's, to the development of a continuously operating retort. This small pilot plant had a capacity of two tons per day. Its most unusual feature was that the shale entered from the bottom. A brief description of its operations is given in Exhibit 10.

Exhibit 9

BUREAU OF MINES RETORT

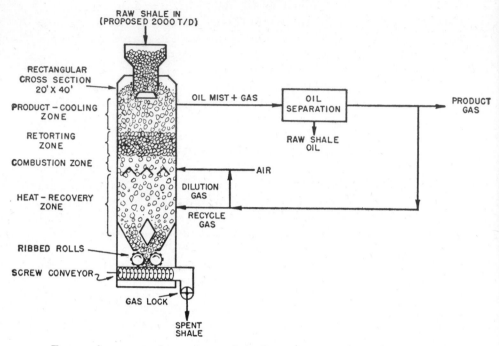

From a hopper at the top, raw shale flows downward by gravity through the retort as a moving bed. It is heated to retorting temperature by direct contact with an ascending stream of hot gas from the gas-combustion zone. After leaving the gas-combustion zone, the hot shale ash is cooled by the countercurrent flow of colder gas in the lower part of the retort before being discharged at the bottom.

The gas used to cool the shale in the lower section of the retort is a portion of the cold product-gas stream. It contains combustible components which, when preheated by contact with the hot retorted shale, burn readily when air is supplied. To control combustion zone temperatures, the rate of recycle gas is controlled, and a portion of the recycle gas is not preheated, but mixed externally with air.

This air-gas mixture is introduced into the downward-moving shale bed at the bottom of the gas-combustion zone. Combustion then takes place in the shale bed at the point of the introduction of the air-gas stream.

Hot flue gas from the gas-combustion zone passes upward through the shale bed, heating the shale to retorting temperature in the retorting zone. Shale oil vapors and gas are swept upward and out of the retort at the top by the ascending hot flue gas stream. This vapor stream and gas are cooled by the incoming shale in the product-cooling zone, where the oil vapors are condensed as a stable "oil mist" in the gas stream. The product passes from the retort into the oil mist collection system. The oil is separated from the non-condensible products in a two-stage process, first in a cyclone and then in an electrostatic precipitator. The retort operates at essentially atmospheric pressure, and maximum temperatures are held between 1400 and 1600 degrees Fahrenheit.

Exhibit 10

UNION OIL RETORT

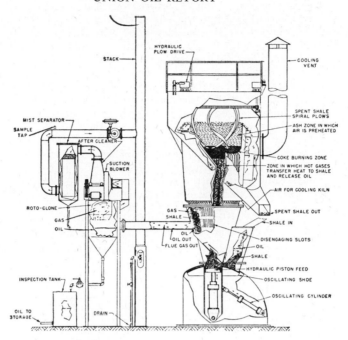

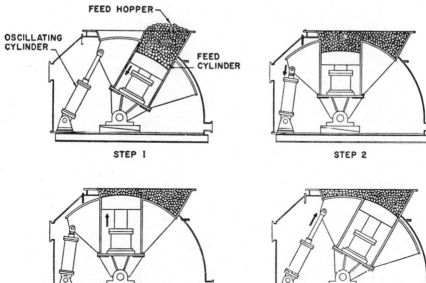

STEP 1

STEP 2

STEP 3

STEP 4

The "rock pump" in the Union Oil Company retort requires four operations: (1) It takes a fresh charge of shale, (2) moves into pumping position, (3) pumps shale into the retort, and (4) returns for the next charge of shale.

Raw shale, introduced into the kiln at the bottom, passes through a liquid seal and drops into the feeder mechanism by gravity. It is then forced upward by the rock pump (see drawing) through a slotted cone and, above that, through the expanding shell of the kiln itself. Thus the shale progressively passes through a preheating zone, a retorting zone, a coke burn-off zone, and finally a cooling zone at the top. The spent shale is then broken up by a rotating plow and discharged into an annular collecting chute.

A blower draws air downward through the upward-moving shale. The air, preheated by the hot shale ash, burns off the residual carbon, which in turn supplies heat for the distillation process in the retorting zone. The distilled oil, along with the combustion gases, is cooled to nearly atmospheric temperature by heat exchange, with the cold shale being moved upward. The oil and gases are removed from the retort through the slotted cone and drawn through a rotoclone, where the oil is separated from the gases.

All necessary heat for the retorting process was generated internally and no cooling water was required. The retort could tolerate some shale fines, and it was expected that a commercial-sized unit could process shale of up to six-inch size.

Between 1948 and 1950, Dr. Tell Ertl was employed as a mining engineer and geologist with the Union Oil Company. During this time, he made detailed mining studies of Union's shale deposits. Dr. Ertl had formerly worked for the Bureau of Mines at Rifle, Colorado, where he had assisted in the design of the room-and-pillar mine. Though he later became Chairman of the Department of Mining and Petroleum Engineering at Ohio State University, he continued his interest both in Union Oil and in oil shale. It was at his suggestion that Union's Executive Committee formed the Shale Oil Committee in 1954 to study the question of how best to exploit Union's shale holdings. He indicated in a special report in mid-1954 that there was strong evidence to support the belief that oil from shale could now be produced at a cost competitive with crude oil.

After several years of work the Research Department developed, in 1954, a hydrogenation process widely licensed under the name "Unifining." This process used a cobalt-molybdate catalyst to "rearrange" undesirable molecules in oil into stable, easily refined hydrocarbons. Though it was originally developed to upgrade high-sulfur, heavy California crude oils, it also provided an excellent technique for upgrading raw shale oil to the point where it was indistinguishable from a very high-gravity (e.g., 40 degrees API) crude oil.

By 1954 the Research Department had constructed and demonstrated a 50-ton-per-day oil shale pilot plant retort. This design was scaled from the smaller two-ton-per-day pilot plant.

THE NATIONAL PETROLEUM COUNCIL STUDY

A detailed study of shale oil capital and operating costs was made in 1951 by the Committee on Synthetic Liquid Fuels Production Costs of the

National Petroleum Council. The NPC, which is composed of many prominent members of the petroleum industry, served as a semiofficial advisory committee to various government agencies. This study was undertaken at the request of the Secretary of the Interior, Oscar L. Chapman. Selected data from this report are shown in Exhibit 11.

Several features of the NPC report and its conclusion should be noted:

1. For the 200,000-barrel-per-day case (Exhibit 11B) the price of gasoline in Los Angeles, including a profit of 6 per cent on the *initial* investment, was estimated at about 14 cents per gallon. This compares with a 1951 refinery selling price of slightly under 12 cents per gallon. Since a 6 per cent profit on the initial investment is approximately 12 per cent on the *average* investment, this suggested that shale oil was not too far from being competitive with crude oil as a source of gasoline.
2. No allowance was made for cost of the land or for mineral depletion.
3. The study was based on a scaled-up version (1,000 tons per day per retort) of the Union Oil retort.
4. The product mix used for the refinery design was based on wartime needs and was not necessarily comparable to civilian requirements.

As indicated, the NPC Committee selected a scaled-up version of the Union Oil retort rather than the scaled-up Bureau of Mines retort. The Committee felt that on the basis of public pilot plant operations the Union retort was more reliable and closer to being a commercial success.

For the NPC study the Union design engineers scaled their retort in the following manner: The rock pump from the 50-ton-per-day pilot plant was increased in diameter by a factor of three. Four of these units were then "joined" to make a 1,000-ton-per-day retort.[3] This was purely a paper design, and although the engineers foresaw some difficulties in translating it to a workable commercial unit, they did not feel that these difficulties were insurmountable. A plant producing 100,000 barrels per day of oil would require about 165 such separate retorts.

THE UNION OIL COMPANY SHALE OIL COMMITTEE STUDY

Early in October, 1954, the Executive Committee of Union Oil established a special Committee with the objective of determining the best way to exploit the Company's shale holdings. The Shale Oil Committee membership was as follows:

W. L. Stewart, Jr., Committee Chairman—Executive Vice President[4]
E. L. Hiatt, Vice President, Transportation and Supply
K. E. Kingman, Vice President, Manufacturing
Max Lorimore, Assistant Comptroller
C. F. Parker, Assistant Treasurer
A. C. Rubel, Vice President, Exploration and Production[4]
A. C. Stewart, Vice President, Marketing[4]
C. E. Swift, Vice President, Research[5]

---

[3] Rated capacity is a nonlinear function of rock pump diameter and kiln shape.

[4] Also member of the Executive Committee and the Board of Directors.

[5] Swift retired at the end of 1954 and was replaced by F. L. Hartley, General Manager of Research.

Exhibit 11A

SUMMARIZED ECONOMIC CALCULATIONS FOR 39,700 B/CD (BARRELS PER CALENDAR DAY) OF REFINED PRODUCTS FROM SHALE OIL PLANT (1951)

PRODUCT YIELDS AND BY-PRODUCT INCOME	Units/CD	Price	$/CD
Liquid Fuels			
Motor Gasoline, Bbls.	25,380	--	--
Diesel Fuel, Bbls.	12,200	--	--
Residual Fuel Oil Bbls.	340	$1.60/Bbl.	$ 544
LPG, Bbls.	1,780	5.30¢/Gal.	3,962
Total Liquid Fuels, Bbls.	39,700	--	--
Other Products			
Ammonia, Tons	92	$80.00/Ton	7,360
Sulfur, Tons	43	$20.50/Ton	882
Coke, Tons	1,180	$ 4.00/Ton	4,720
Fuel Gas (1,060 Btu/SCF), MSCF	24,830	7.0¢/MSCF	1,738
By-Product Income, $/CD	--	--	$19,206

OPERATING EXPENSE	Basis	$/CD
RETORTING, REFINING, & PIPELINE FACILITIES		
Labor		
Operating	612 Employees @ $1.98/Hr.	$ 6,921
Maintenance	1.81% per Yr. of $214,655,000 Investment	10,620
Unit Supervision & Clerical	Detailed in Engineering Report	1,100
Payroll Extras	20% of above three items	3,728
Material		
Operating	Detailed in Engineering Report	1,470
Maintenance	1.39% per Yr. of $214,655,000 Investment	8,190
Utilities	See Footnote *	-2,260
Catalysts and Chemicals	Detailed in Engineering Report	3,890
Tetraethyl Lead	1.5 cc per Gallon @ 0.224¢/cc	3,582
Total Direct Expense		$37,241
General Overhead (Plant Burden) & Administration Overhead	50% of Material and Labor less Payroll Extras	14,150
Research & Development	$1,000,000 per Year	2,740
State, County & Local Taxes and Insurance	1.5% per Year of $230,220,000 Investment	9,461
Total Plant and Pipeline Expense Excluding Depreciation		$63,592
OIL SHALE MINE (76,800 T/CD)		
Labor		
Total Mine Labor	1,156 Total Employees	$15,116
Payroll Extras	Basis Given in Oil Shale Mining Report	2,700
Utilities	Purchased from Shale Oil Plant	3,050
Total Supplies	Detailed in Oil Shale Mining Report	10,949
Administrative Overhead	10% of Total Labor Cost	1,780
State, County, & Local Taxes and Insurance	1.08% per Year of Mine Investment	792
Depletion and Royalty	(None Estimated)	--
Total Mine Expense Excluding Depreciation		$34,387
Total Operating Expense Excluding Depreciation		$97,979

INVESTMENT	Case *** A	B	C	D
Total Plants and Pipeline	$214,660,000	$214,660,000	$214,660,000	$214,660,000
Construction Labor Premium	15,570,000	15,570,000	15,570,000	15,570,000
Oil Shale Mines	26,020,000	26,020,000	26,020,000	26,020,000
Process Royalties	11,730,000	11,730,000	11,730,000	11,730,000
Start-Up Expense	9,400,000	9,400,000	9,400,000	9,400,000
Working Capital	27,700,000	27,700,000	27,700,000	27,700,000
Total Investment Excluding Housing	$305,080,000	$305,080,000	$305,080,000	$305,080,000
Housing for Employees	--	22,000,000	22,000,000	--
Housing for Tradespeople & Others	--	15,400,000	--	--
General Community Facilities	--	5,500,000	5,500,000	5,500,000
Commercial Buildings	--	6,100,000	--	--
Total Investment	$305,080,000	$354,080,000	$332,580,000	$310,580,000

ECONOMICS $/CD	A	B	C	D
Total Operating Expense	$ 97,979	$ 97,979	$ 97,979	$ 97,979
Depreciation of Operating Facilities (Plants and Pipeline, Labor Premium and Oil Shale Mines)	38,614	38,614	38,614	38,614
Amortization of Process Royalties & Start-Up Expense	2,895	2,895	2,895	2,895
Depreciation of Housing Facilities	-	6,712	3,767	753
Sub-Total	$139,488	$146,200	$143,255	$140,241
Credit for By-Products	-19,206	-19,206	-19,206	-19,206
Income from Electricity Sold to Community	---	- 440	- 259	0
Rental Income from Housing Facilities	---	-6,282	-2,712	0
Cost of Major Products Before Profit	$120,282	$120,272	$121,078	$121,035
Return on Investment @ 6% per Yr. of Total Investment	50,150	58,205	54,670	51,054
Federal Income Taxes @ 50% Rate	50,150	58,205	54,670	51,054
Cost of Major Products Including Return	$220,582	$236,682	$230,418	$223,143
Cost of Equivalent Gasoline**, ¢/Gal.	15.5	16.6	16.2	15.7

Los Angeles refinery price of gasoline, ¢/gal.   11.7

* Utilities purchased from outside sources for pipeline and California refining facilities equal $790/CD; credit for utilities sold to mine is $3,050/CD.

** Equivalent gasoline volume is comprised of 100% of gasoline plus 70% of diesel fuel, which basis represents relative value of these two products.

*** A) No housing or community development
B) Complete housing and community development including (1) housing for employees, (2) housing for trades people, teachers, etc., (3) general community facilities comprised of streets, utilities, schools, etc., and (4) commercial buildings
C) Housing for employees and general community facilities
D) General community facilities

Exhibit 11B

SUMMARIZED ECONOMIC CALCULATIONS FOR 200,000 B/CD OF REFINED PRODUCTS FROM SHALE OIL PLANT (1951)

PRODUCT YIELDS AND BY-PRODUCT INCOME	Units/CD	Price	$/CD
Liquid Fuels			
Motor Gasoline, Bbls.	126,900	--	--
Diesel Fuel, Bbls.	62,360	--	--
Residual Fuel Oil, Bbls.	3,050	$1.60/Bbl.	$ 4,880
LPG, Bbls.	8,920	5.30¢/Gal.	19,856
Total Liquid Fuels, Bbls.	201,230	--	--
Other Products			
Ammonia, Tons	460	$77.50/Ton	35,650
Sulfur, Tons	215	$20.50/Ton	4,408
Coke, Tons	5,900	$ 4.00/Ton	23,600
Fuel Gas (1,060 Btu/SCF), MSCF	124,150	7.0¢/MSCF	8,690
By-Product Income, $/CD	--	--	$97,084

OPERATING EXPENSE	Basis	$/CD
RETORTING, REFINING, & PIPELINE FACILITIES		
Labor		
Operating	2,539 Employees @ $1.98/Hr.	$ 28,750
Maintenance	1.8% per Yr. of $953,772,000 Investment	$ 48,800
Unit Supervision & Clerical	Detailed in Engineering Report	4,250
Payroll Extras	20% of above three items	16,360
Material		
Operating	Detailed in Engineering Report	6,410
Maintenance	1.48% per Yr. of $953,772,000 Investment	38,740
Utilities	See Footnote *	-12,690
Catalysts and Chemicals	Detailed in Engineering Report	19,430
Tetraethyl Lead	1.5 cc per Gallon @ 0.224¢/cc	17,908
Total Direct Expense		$167,958
General Overhead (Plant Burden) & Administrative Overhead	50% of Material and Labor less Payroll Extras	63,475
Research & Development	$5,000,000 per Year	13,700
State, County, & Local Taxes and Insurance	1.5% per Yr. of $1,026,108,000 Investment	41,565
Total Plant and Pipeline Expense		
Excluding Depreciation		$286,698
OIL SHALE MINE (384,000 T/CD)		
Labor		
Total Mine Labor	5,780 Total Employees	$ 75,580
Payroll Extras	Basis Given in Oil Shale Mining Report	13,500
Utilities	Purchased from Shale Oil Plant	15,260
Total Supplies	Detailed in Oil Shale Mining Report	54,740
Administrative Overhead	10% of Total Labor Cost	8,910
State, County, & Local Taxes and Insurance	1.08% per Year of Mine Investment	3,960
Depletion and Royalty	(None Estimated)	--
Total Mine Expense Excluding Depreciation		$171,950
Total Operating Expense Excluding Depreciation		$458,648

	Case ***			
INVESTMENT	A	B	C	D
Total Plants and Pipeline	$ 953,770,000	$ 953,770,000	$ 953,770,000	$ 953,770,000
Construction Labor Premium	72,340,000	72,340,000	72,340,000	72,340,000
Oil Shale Mines	130,100,000	130,100,000	130,100,000	130,100,000
Process Royalties	58,650,000	58,650,000	58,650,000	58,650,000
Start-Up Expense	27,800,000	27,800,000	27,800,000	27,800,000
Working Capital	122,700,000	122,700,000	122,700,000	122,700,000
Total Investment Excluding Housing	$1,365,360,000	$1,365,360,000	$1,365,360,000	$1,365,360,000
Housing for Employees	--	121,600,000	121,600,000	--
Housing for Tradespeople & Others	--	85,100,000	--	--
General Community Facilities	--	30,500,000	30,500,000	30,500,000
Commercial Buildings	--	33,600,000	--	--
Total Investment	$1,365,360,000	$1,636,160,000	$1,517,460,000	$1,395,860,000
ECONOMICS $/CD				
Total Operating Expense	$ 458,648	$ 458,648	$ 458,648	$ 458,648
Depreciation of Operating Facilities (Plants and Pipeline, Labor Premium and Oil Shale Mines)	175,943	175,943	175,943	175,943
Amortization of Process Royalties & Start-Up Expense	11,842	11,842	11,842	11,842
Depreciation of Housing Facilities	--	--	20,836	4,178
Sub-Total	$ 646,433	$ 683,529	$ 667,269	$ 650,611
Credit for By-Products	-97,084	-97,084	-97,084	-97,084
Income from Electricity Sold to Community	--	- 2,440	- 1,435	0
Rental Income from Housing Facilities	--	- 35,853	-14,992	0
Cost of Major Products Before Profit	$ 549,349	$ 548,152	$ 553,758	$ 553,527
Return on Investment @ 6% per Yr. of Total Investment	224,443	268,958	249,446	229,457
Federal Income Taxes @ 50% Rate	224,443	268,958	249,446	229,457
Cost of Major Products Including Return	$ 998,235	$1,086,068	$1,052,650	$1,012,441
Cost of Equivalent Gasoline **, ¢/Gal.	13.9	15.2	14.7	14.1

Los Angeles refinery price of gasoline, ¢/gal.   11.7

* Utilities purchased from outside sources for pipeline and California refining facilities equal $2,570/CD;
  credit for utilities sold to mine is $15,260/CD.
** Equivalent gasoline volume is comprised of 100% of gasoline plus 70% of diesel fuel, which basis
   represents relative value of these two products.
*** See note previous page.

C. S. Brinegar, Committee Secretary—Assistant to C. F. Parker[6]
Tell Ertl, Consultant[6]

The Committee met weekly during the next three months. Questions studied included:

1. What was known and what was unknown insofar as technology needed to produce marketable products from Colorado oil shale?
2. What promises were there of technological gains by intensive research?
3. In what markets could shale oil products compete, and what was the long-term supply, demand, and price outlook in these markets?
4. What, in general terms, was the future world energy outlook?
5. Making various assumptions as to size of operation, cost of equipment, prices of products, etc., what were the ranges of prospective rates of return on a commercial shale oil investment?
6. How did these rates compare with alternative uses of the capital?

The Committee reported to the Executive Committee in December that, based on apparently reasonable assumptions, a commercial shale oil operation of 15,000–50,000 barrels per day and costing from $50 to $150 million in capital could be as profitable, on the average, as investments then being made in searching for domestic crude oil. In addition, a combination of rising finding and developing costs for crude oil (see Exhibit 12) and possible technological gains in shale oil production

Exhibit 12

FOOTAGE DRILLED, NET RESERVES, AND DISCOVERY AND DEVELOP-
MENT COSTS IN THE UNITED STATES, 1940–54

	Footage Drilled (1) (Million Feet)	Net Reserves, (2) Discovered & Dev. Total (million bbl.)	Per Ft. of Hole Drilled	Estimate Approx. cost (3) Total (millions)	Per Ft. Drilled	Est. Development and Delivery Cost/Bbl.
1940	89	1657	18.5	$1,050	$11.80	63.4¢
1941	90	1723	19.3	1,103	12.30	64.0
1942	60	1644	27.5	871	14.50	53.0
1943	65	1300	23.6	830	15.10	63.8
1944	74	1810	24.3	1,031	14.00	57.2
1945	83	1846	22.4	1,035	12.50	56.1
1946	90	2326	25.8	1,315	14.60	56.5
1947	102	2377	23.5	1,521	14.90	64.2
1948	127	3733	29.3	1,820	14.35	48.9
1949	128	3128	24.3	2,036	15.90	65.0
1950	150	2912	19.4	2,424	16.20	83.3
1951	164	4495	27.4	2,815	17.10	62.6
1952	175	2893	16.5	3,101	17.75	107.5
1953	182	3535	19.4	3,333	18.30	94.5
1954	197	2607	13.2	3,390	17.25	130.0

(1) Total footage drilled in U.S. including oil wells, injection wells and dry holes but excluding gas wells.
Source: World Oil

(2) One-eighth royalty has been deducted from API annual estimates of crude oil and natural gas liquids added to U.S. reserves through new discoveries, extensions and revisions of previous estimates.

(3) Includes cost of drilling and equipping wells, dry holes, lease bonuses and rentals, overhead, land geological and geophysical expense.
Source: Harold's Petroleum Outlook

---

[6] Nonvoting member of Committee.

suggested further profit improvements, relative to domestic crude oil, in the years ahead. However, the venture was of such magnitude that certain technical steps (notably retorting) had to be fully developed and proved *in advance* of any attempt at commercial operations.

The Committee recommended a special research project, to cost about $5 million and to last from two to two and a half years. The research was aimed to accomplish the following:

1. Develop and prove out a full-scale model of the oil shale retort designed by Union's Research Department (about 70 per cent of the research cost).
2. Determine the optimum manufacturing method for producing marketable products from shale oil (about 20 per cent).
3. Obtain accurate estimates of capital and operating costs for a commercial shale oil operation (about 10 per cent).

Only when this research work was completed and evaluated did the Committee feel that a proper decision could be made regarding a full-

Exhibit 13

ENERGY REQUIREMENTS AND PETROLEUM SUPPLY FOR THE WORLD, THE UNITED STATES, AND CALIFORNIA

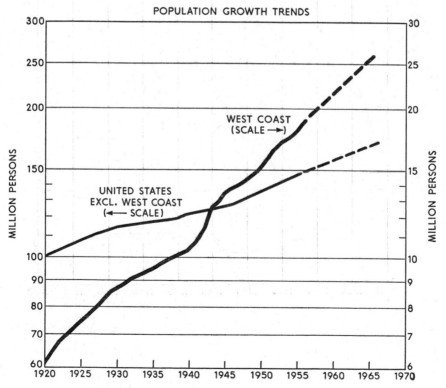

Source: Chase Manhattan Bank (all diagrams).

Exhibit 13 (Continued)

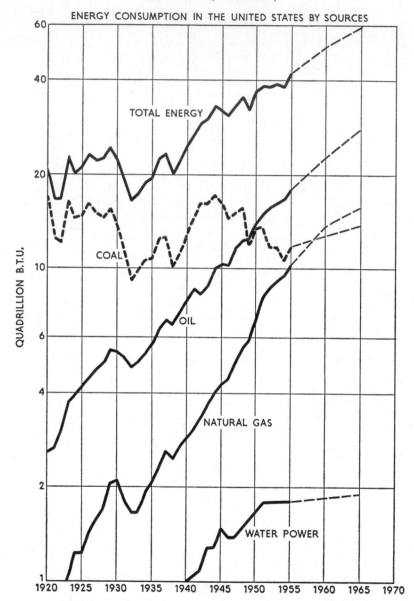

ENERGY CONSUMPTION IN THE UNITED STATES BY SOURCES

Exhibit 13 (Continued)

PAST GROWTH TRENDS FOR PETROLEUM DEMAND
WITH PROJECTIONS TO 1965

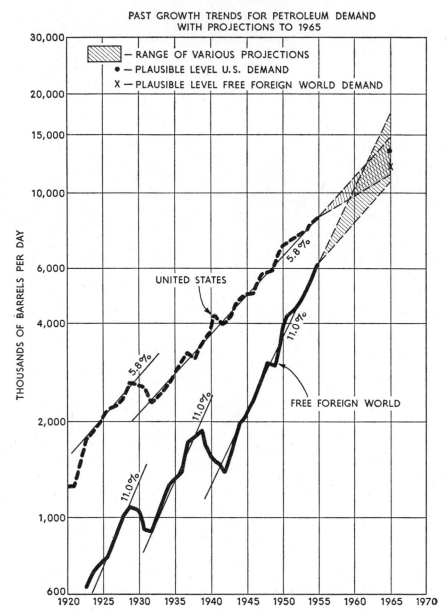

Exhibit 13 (Continued)

WEST COAST DEMAND FOR ENERGY
TRILLION B.T.U.

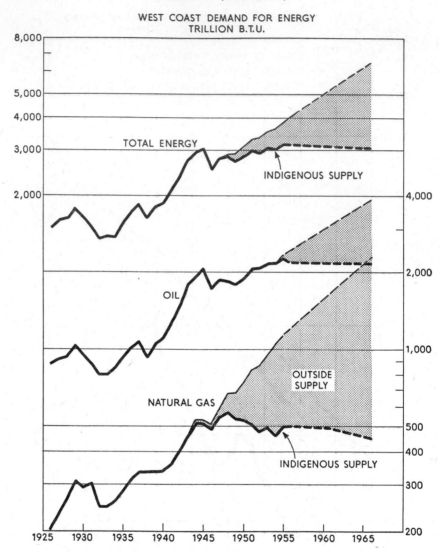

Exhibit 13 (Continued)

TREND AND PROJECTION OF DEMAND IN THE UNITED STATES
FOR PRINCIPAL PETROLEUM PRODUCTS

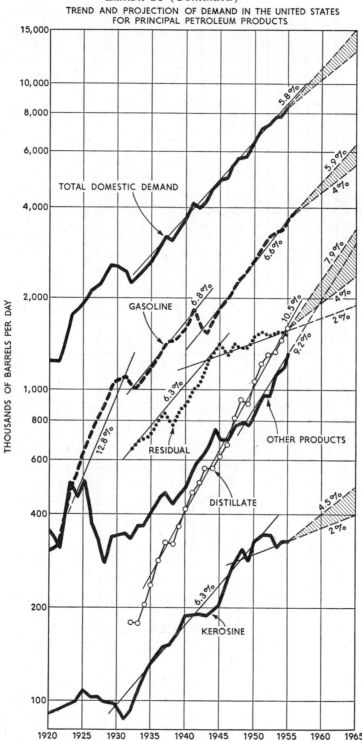

Exhibit 13 (Continued)

COMPUTED PATTERN OF CRUDE OIL PRODUCTION IN THE UNITED STATES

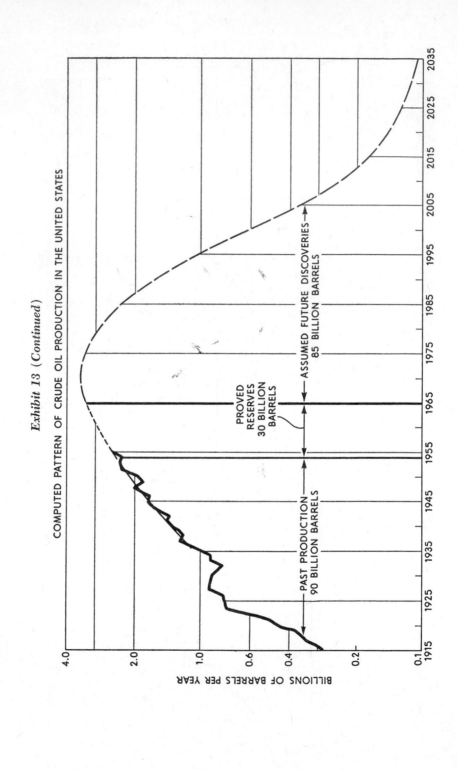

Exhibit 13 (Continued)

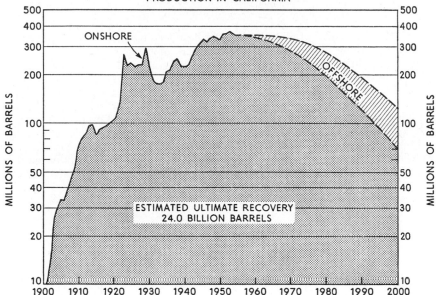

COMPUTED PATTERN OF CRUDE OIL
PRODUCTION IN CALIFORNIA

ONSHORE

OFFSHORE

MILLIONS OF BARRELS

ESTIMATED ULTIMATE RECOVERY
24.0 BILLION BARRELS

1900 1910 1920 1930 1940 1950 1960 1970 1980 1990 2000

scale commercial venture. However, the Committee did believe that prospective profits, including the promise of "unlocking" a five-billion-barrel oil reserve, clearly justified the special research expenditure.

The Executive Committee agreed with this recommendation, and requested that the Shale Oil Committee present it formally to the Board of Directors on January 31, 1955.

The presentation to the Board was as follows:

1. W. L. Stewart, Jr., outlined the Committee's work and its conclusions in broad terms.
2. Dr. Tell Ertl discussed the history of shale oil, its technology, and the current "state of the art."
3. Dr. Claude Brinegar described the results of the detailed economic calculations that had been made and the assumptions underlying them. The supply, demand, and price outlook for crude oil, both in the United States and abroad, were also considered. (Exhibit 13 illustrates the type of supply and demand data discussed.)
4. G. H. Hemmen, Chief Research Engineer, listed the specific research questions to be studied if the project was approved. He also outlined the present conception of a commercial shale oil operation.
5. Stewart then recommended that the Board of Directors approve the project as a special expenditure apart from the regular Research Department budget.

Exhibit 14 has been supplied by the case writer to sum up the depletion allowance controversy as of 1955.

Exhibit 14

DEPLETION ALLOWANCE CONTROVERSY

In 1955 the depletion allowance for shale oil conversion was 15 per cent, applied to *mining* costs only. Several members of Congress were in favor of raising this allowance to 27½ per cent (the same as crude oil) or having the allowance applied after the retorting process. Their argument was that crushed shale rock had no intrinsic value, and therefore the first marketable product was raw shale oil. They claimed that this would be comparable to the applying of the 27½ per cent allowance against the wellhead price of crude oil.

Since raw shale oil is not readily transportable, some people in the oil industry and some Colorado legislators argued that the allowance should be applied after some preliminary refining operations. Other members of the oil industry opposed any increased depletion allowance for shale oil recovery on the ground that it was a mining operation and hence did not involve the same degree of risk as crude oil exploration and development.

The great contribution of physical science to social science is the realization that there is no guilt to failure.

Dr. EDWIN LAND, President
Polaroid Corporation

FROM: An informal talk to students in the Technological Innovation Course at Harvard Business School, December, 1961.

PHOTON, INC. (D)

AT THE meeting on July 21, 1961, Kurtz M. Hanson and Robert M. Campbell decided to undertake the development of the "phototypesetting adapter" which could be used in conjunction with TTS[1] or Monotype keyboards. Even though they doubted that this product would become a sales leader, they agreed that it fulfilled the marketing objective of broadening the Photon product line with a minimum investment in development expense and time.

The decision was also made to shelve the ZIP project.[2] This was done for two reasons: (1) The service center application made the project undesirable in the foreseeable future, since it implied a tremendous capital investment; and (2) such a service center would be competing against present owners of Photon equipment and would therefore make future sales more difficult. Since the basic technical idea was sound, the two men considered other possible uses for a high-speed phototypesetter. They agreed that a possible application would be the printing of computer output. Here was a market that was growing faster than any market which Photon now serviced. In addition, the computer manufacturers probably would be more receptive to adding a complex phototypesetting read-out mechanism to an already intricate system than the printers would be to installing such a device in their production process, since the printers had worked with relatively simple equipment for years. However, despite this promising potential for the ZIP machine, Hanson and Campbell decided that the cost of development was too large for Photon to take on at the present time.

Within several days after the meeting, the development engineers began work on two tape-operated machines, one to handle TTS tape (510 series) and the other to handle Monotype tape (520 series). Exhibit 1 is a description of these two models. By the first of November, 1961, the two units were ready for production, the entire development for each machine taking about three and one-half months and costing about $40,000. They were shown at the November trade show in Milwaukee and received favorable comments from the printing industry.

During the development of the models (510 and 520), the officers and inventors of Photon realized that tape offered another promising modification of the original Photon machine. With tape carrying information

---

[1] Teletypesetter.

[2] Necessary background can be found in Photon, Inc. (A), (B), and (C).

Exhibit 1

DESCRIPTION OF PHOTON MODEL 510 AND 520

PHOTOTYPESETTING MACHINES

The 510 and 520 models are modifications of the 200 model machine, which was Photon's original product. The modification consisted of "removing" the 200 model's keyboard and modifying the circuitry so that the photo unit would accept input from a paper tape. Two different kinds of tape are used: TTS tape (six channels), and Monotype tape (thirty-one channels). These tapes are the normal output for the TTS keyboards and Monotype keyboards that are in common use for hot-metal typesetting throughout the industry. The model 510 (or 520), therefore, is used to adapt a TTS keyboard (or Monotype keyboard) so that it provides a photocomposed film instead of a form of metal type. Installation of a 510 or 520 model on a keyboard does not prevent its being used for hot-metal typesetting.

Because of the limitations of the TTS and Monotype keyboards and tapes, the 510 and 520 model machines have less flexibility and fewer capabilities than the 200 model. However, they have considerably greater capability than the hot-type application of the TTS or Monotype systems.

The operational specifications of the machine are as follows:

	510 Model	*520 Model*
Composing speed	10 characters per second; 15 newspaper lines per minute	10 characters per second; 12 newspaper lines per minute
Maximum line length	42 picas (7 inches)	42 picas (7 inches)
Point sizes:		
Standard	5 through 18 point	5 through 18 point
Special	Up to 72 point	Up to 72 point
Type face selection:		
Standard	two or four faces	225, 255, or 324 characters (depending on keyboards)
Special	Additional faces	

Photon offers extra attachments which will increase the capabilities and flexibility of either the 510 or the 520 model. (When extras are added, the third digit of the model number is changed, i.e., 510, 511, 512, etc.). Among these are additional type sizes and faces, equipment for automatically changing type sizes and mixing type faces, automatic quadding, etc. In addition, extra matrix discs may be purchased for the photo units of the 510 and 520 models. As an example of how these attachments add to the basic models, the Photon 513 model (a 510 model with all extras) has about 80 per cent of the performance capabilities of the 200 model.

from the keyboard to the photo unit, it would be possible to design a machine in which two or three keyboards all feed one photo unit.

In this way the full speed potential of the photo unit (ten characters per second) would not be limited by the speed of a single operator (maximum about three or four characters per second). Such a machine would be only slightly less flexible than the 200 model, but the investment for the customer per unit of output would be much less. With this system, three keyboards and one photo unit would have almost the same capacity as three 200 models (in which the keyboard and photo unit are integrated in one unit).

The time and expense to develop this design would be greater than was the case with the 510 or 520 models, because an entirely new control mechanism and an extensive modification of the circuitry would be necessary. More specifically, Hanson estimated that it would take about five months and from $90,000 to $100,000 to develop an operational model. While the machine undoubtedly would improve the product line, Hanson and Campbell feared that it might severely cut into the market for the 200 model, rather than serve a market of its own. By the middle of December, no decision had been reached concerning the possible new product.

At this time, General Electric announced that it was asking for bids on a contract to develop a high-speed computer print-out. This device would be used in conjunction with a GE-developed data-processing system to be installed in the National Library of Medicine. Other companies which were expected to submit bids included CBS Laboratories, Mergenthaler Linotype, A. B. Dick, Eastman Kodak, and Stromberg-Carlson. The managers of Photon recognized that this was an obvious application for the ZIP design, which had been shelved in July. Since Photon already had patents covering the basic components of the ZIP machine, they would be able to use all the knowledge gained from a development contract. Furthermore, obtaining the contract would enable Photon to get a considerable lead on the large companies working on designs for the same application.

Hanson realized that if Photon bid on the contract, it would involve violating his policy of not revealing information concerning new products until they are operational. Exactly how serious such a disclosure would be in this instance Hanson did not know, but he felt it deserved careful thought. In addition, if the contract was awarded to Photon, he questioned whether the present engineering staff would be able to handle the contract plus its normal duties of modifying present products and getting the 510 and 520 models into production. Winning the GE contract would probably mean hiring new men and familiarizing them with Photon's designs and secrets, and then laying them off when the contract was completed if new projects were not available. Since Hanson considered employee security quite important, hiring new engineers worried him.

While studying the multikeyboard tape unit and the GE contract, Hanson wondered whether it might not be wise to put off further new-product development and concentrate on selling the present products. This would give the engineers an opportunity to refine the current

Exhibit 2

FINANCIAL STATEMENTS FOR YEAR ENDING DECEMBER 31, 1961

BALANCE SHEET

ASSETS

Current assets:

Cash..		$ 878,418
Accounts receivable, less reserve for doubtful accounts.................................		139,454
Inventories, at lower of cost or market...........		753,801
Prepaid expenses...............................		17,618
Total Current Assets......................		$1,789,291
Accounts receivable, noncurrent...................		10,413
Plant and equipment, at cost.....................	$ 436,291	
Less: Accumulated depreciation.................	246,473	189,818
Patent license, at cost, less amortization...........		9,890
Deferred debenture issue expenses.................		77,400
		$2,076,812

LIABILITIES AND STOCKHOLDERS' EQUITY

Current liabilities:

Note payable to bank...........................		$ 120,786
Accounts payable..............................		42,106
Accrued royalties..............................		20,788
Accrued payroll, taxes, and other expenses........		43,436
Advance payments by customers.................		19,959
Total Current Liabilities...................		$ 247,075
Deferred rental income...........................		5,761
Long-term debt:		
Convertible subordinated 6% note payable........		206,000
5% convertible subordinated income debentures due December 1, 1971......................		1,785,000
Commitments and contingent liabilities:		
Stockholders' equity:		
Common stock...........................	$ 396,675	
Capital surplus..........................	5,277,765	
	$5,674,440	
Deficit.................................	(5,841,464)	(167,024)
		$2,076,812

INCOME STATEMENT

Net sales.......................................		$ 725,879
Cost of sales...................................		689,257
Gross profit on sales.......................		$ 36,622
Other costs and expenses:		
Engineering, research, and development..........	$ 204,361	
Selling.....................................	277,699	
General and administrative.....................	220,696	
Provision for bad debts.......................	1,175	
Excess of cost of used machines over their realizable value after deducting estimated cost to recondition and sell.........................	183,101	
Account receivable from Graphic Arts Research Foundation, discharged in connection with acquisition of patent license rights.........	178,735	
Interest on notes payable to banks and others.......	32,758	
Other income—net............................	(2,797)	
Total Other Costs and Expenses............		1,095,728
Loss for Year........................		($1,059,106)

products to achieve improved performance and greater reliability. Also, it would leave Hanson and Campbell with more time to make several necessary improvements in the economic side of Photon's operations. (Exhibit 2 shows Photon's financial position as of the end of 1961.)

During 1961, marketing expenses jumped to 74 per cent of sales and contributed to the loss of $1,059,106. The total annual 1961 sales figure of $725,879 consisted of 70 per cent machine sales, 19 per cent installation and service, 8 per cent parts and accessories, and 3 per cent film.

As 1961 came to a close, Hanson decided that a definite decision must be made on whether or not to develop another product during 1962. Accordingly, in December, Hanson and Campbell met to decide which of the following alternative courses of action would contribute most to Photon's future success:

1. To develop the new tape-controlled machine which would have separate keyboards feeding into one photo unit.
2. To bid on the General Electric contract in expectation of using the ZIP design if the bid was accepted.
3. To concentrate efforts on selling the 510, 520, and 200 models, deferring work on any new products until marketing and production are improved.
4. To undertake several of the above.

Management Crises in Development

Nearly all major development projects pass through three or four managerial crises—usually resulting in a change of manager after much confusion, unhappiness and lost time. These situations arise as the result of circumstances which repeat themselves so often as to constitute a law of nature. Change is inevitable in management of a project for reasons discussed in the preceding paragraph. Individuals who are qualified by knowledge, originality, and experience to guide an advanced project through its formative stages of scientific exploration and feasibility and who aim the project toward a difficult but achievable target, are almost certainly not qualified to manage it much beyond this point; even if they were qualified and willing, their talent is so rare it should be applied to other advanced efforts. Each phase of a project presents different major problems. The change of managers to meet these requirements should be an accepted, routine event, anticipated and carried out without disruption of work. Unfortunately, the inevitable change of manager is usually delayed until a crisis in performance, schedule, money, or personnel forces the issue, to the discredit of the outgoing project manager, when the basic fault was failure on the part of the higher management to recognize the symptoms early and to plan a replacement in time.

M. P. O'BRIEN

FROM: "Technological Planning and Misplanning," *Technological Planning on the Corporate Level* (Boston: Harvard Business School, 1961).

THERMAL DYNAMICS CORPORATION (A)

THE THERMAL Dynamics Corporation specialized in finding industrial applications for plasma technology.[1] The company had investigated a wide range of applications in which extremely high temperatures were useful and manufactured a general purpose plasma torch which was sold to research laboratories interested in investigating plasma.

The company was located in Lebanon, New Hampshire, about five miles from the campus of Dartmouth College. In 1959, total sales were about $420,000.

In December, 1959, the management of TDC was considering whether to undertake a new development project. It would involve trying to develop a device which would utilize plasma for industrial cutting purposes; the product would probably be called a plasma flame cutter.

Company Background

The founder of the company was James Browning, who, by arrangement with the Thayer School of Engineering at Dartmouth College, divided his attention between his work as Professor of Mechanical Engineering at the Thayer School and as an executive of the Thermal Dynamics Corporation. In 1955, he and several other engineers organized Combustion Products Research, a consulting firm which specialized in investigating problems associated with combustion and high temperatures. In 1956 the consulting firm received a contract to investigate the application of plasma technology to "metallizing," a process by means of which materials with high melting points could be sprayed; thereafter, Browning and his associates became increasingly involved in investigating applications of plasma.

In January, 1958, Combustion Products Research ceased to exist as an active business organization, and the Thermal Dynamics Corporation was formed to concentrate upon applications of plasma technology. The new company had total personnel of twelve, including four engineers, and total capitalization of $1,000. James Browning was President of the company and divided his time between administrative duties and laboratory work.

---

[1] Plasma—a substance in which the individual atoms have been broken down into ions and free electrons. This condition is brought about by the application of extremely high energy levels to a substance (and in the TDC investigations brought about by temperatures from 5,000 to 60,000 degrees Fahrenheit).

TDC had several research contracts, which provided all of the company's revenue during the first six months of 1958. However, during this same period, TDC developed its first product, a general purpose plasma torch with certain accessory equipment. This product was offered to the market in August, 1958. During the next fifteen months, TDC sold about forty-five of these torches, almost all of them to research and development laboratories. These laboratories used the torches for experiments in welding, cutting, and spraying as well as more basic research into the nature of plasma.

Sales of the company for 1958 and 1959 were as shown in Exhibit 1.

Exhibit 1

Year	General Purpose Torches	Research Contracts	Total
1958 (estimated)...............$ 20,000		$50,000	$ 70,000
1959 (estimated)............... 395,000		25,000	420,000

TDC's sponsored research had primarily been directed at gathering information relating to the particular applications of plasma technology—for example, learning the techniques to form titanium in particular shapes and thicknesses by plasma spraying. The terms of these contracts normally did not require TDC to surrender any proprietary rights, in that TDC could use the research findings as well as the sponsoring company.

TDC had never had either a separate sales force or manufacturing representatives. Management believed that the company did not have enough sales to support its own sales force. However, management also thought that whoever was representing TDC in a sales capacity should be well informed on the latest developments in plasma technology. In its opinion, manufacturing representatives would not have the technical background, the motivation, or the close association with the laboratory which would be necessary.

Therefore, in selling the general purpose torch, the first step in the sales procedure was to generate interest through articles in trade magazines and through papers presented at meetings of technical societies. (The way in which this was done is described in greater detail later.) Typically, each such article generated a considerable number of inquiries, mostly in the form of letters to TDC. The company then sent these prospective customers promotional literature describing the torch and invited them to visit the TDC plant to see a demonstration of the torch. In some cases a TDC engineer would visit several interested companies to answer questions about the plasma torch and to learn more about the prospective customers' specific interests in regard to plasma research.

Many prospective customers also visited the TDC plant; in 1958 and

1959, about 50 per cent of those who visited the TDC plant purchased general purpose torches.

A general purpose torch and the needed accessory equipment sold for about $7,500 to $12,000, depending chiefly on the capacity of the power supply. The accessories included a control console which automatically regulated the flows of electricity, stabilizing gas, and cooling water. There were also the pumps and heat exchanger for the cooling water, and the power supply which converted alternating current to the direct current required for the plasma torch; the power supply accounted for 50 to 75 per cent of the total cost of the plasma torch "package."

TDC's production activities were largely subcontracted. The company had seven or eight general purpose machine tools, on which were produced several components of the control console used with the general purpose torch. The power supplies were produced to TDC's specifications by a large manufacturer of electrical equipment; these were shipped directly from the manufacturer's plant to the customer. The torches were produced by another company, which shipped them to the TDC plant for assembling, adjusting, and testing. The control console was assembled in the TDC plant, from both purchased components and parts manufactured by TDC.

One problem associated with TDC's small sales volume, and mentioned several times by management, was the high cost incurred because many components could not be purchased in volume. Another cost problem, even more important in management's opinion, was the lack of production engineering in the general purpose torch. One executive estimated that the manufacturing cost of the torch could be cut by 75 per cent just by simplification and substitution of standard parts and less expensive materials.

TDC also offered a spraying service. In spraying, powder was fed into the high-velocity plasma stream, and then impacted in a molten state onto a part to be coated, forming a high-density, well-bonded coating. Almost any material could be sprayed, including tungsten, platinum, titanium, and various carbides and borides.

Use of plasma in spraying applications had been investigated by TDC on a contract-research basis for several years. In December, 1959, management was planning to offer a service, beginning in early 1960, in which TDC would spray materials on a contract basis. Management thought that such a service might enjoy a rapid growth in sales, perhaps becoming a significant part of the total business.

From its initial capitalization of $1,000 in January, 1958, the company's growth had been financed entirely from internally generated funds. The general purpose torch was a "high-margin" product, and all profits had been retained within the company. In 1959, profits before taxes were estimated at about $110,000. The company had not done any long-term borrowing, although management was not adverse to doing so if growth made it necessary.

Browning had served both as President and as Chairman of the Board until the fall of 1959, at which time he turned the presidency over to Merle Thorpe, an engineer in his early thirties who had joined the company in 1956 after working several years for a competitor. Thorpe had taken part of his engineering work under Professor Browning at the Thayer School. Browning said he was spending about 60 per cent of his own time on laboratory work, about 30 per cent on teaching, and about 10 per cent on administrative duties. Browning described himself as more an engineer than an administrator and seemed glad that he had been able to pass the administrative duties to Thorpe, who apparently was both a competent and an enthusiastic manager.

Browning owned 60 per cent of the outstanding stock, Thorpe owned 30 per cent, and two TDC technicians owned the remaining 10 per cent. In speaking of growth, Browning said: "We could stabilize at this point, concentrate on certain applications of plasma technology, and have a nice comfortable business. However, we do not choose to do this. We prefer to grow as fast as possible, consistent with minimizing risk."

Thorpe, the President, emphasized that an outstanding characteristic of the company was growth. He said: "We talk about how things used to be done, and we are referring only to six months ago."

TDC had had no difficulty in attracting competent engineers; in fact, a number of visiting sales engineers had asked management to consider them when additional engineers were hired. Management thought the company's location (in the heart of the New Hampshire ski country) was an incentive for many people, possibly with a special appeal for graduates of Dartmouth College or the Thayer School of Engineering. Another incentive was the broad scope of problems which a TDC engineer encountered; this apparently was the reason why two engineers had left more specialized jobs at Bell Laboratories to come to TDC.

Origination of the Idea for a Plasma Cutter

Browning had been interested in the problems of industrial cutting for a number of years. He had used the general purpose plasma torch for cutting experiments, but did not believe that it could be used as a commercially practical cutter, inasmuch as its power capacity was too low, its electrode usage was too high, and it lacked the reliability needed for sustained operation. TDC had conducted some sponsored research in the fall of 1959 to accumulate systematic data in regard to the cutting capabilities of the plasma torch. This information included cutting speeds, metal thicknesses, and operating costs. The sponsor of this research was a large processor of scrap who was interested in learning whether the application of plasma technology to its cutting problems would be more economical than the mechanical shears and oxyacetylene torches he was using.

This research, which was sponsored by the scrap processor on a cost-reimbursible basis, cost about $5,000. The findings confirmed Browning's opinion that the general purpose torch was not a commercially practical cutting tool. However, the data indicated that plasma cutting might be an economical way of cutting a great variety of materials. It was known that the cutting speed, cleanness of cut, and thickness of cut were all functions of the electrical power of the torch. The general purpose torch, with which the experiments were conducted, carried maximum power of 100 kilowatts. Extrapolating from the data gathered in the experiments, TDC engineers concluded that a torch with a power capacity of 200 kilowatts might be an economical cutting tool, one which would offer substantial cost savings over oxyacetylene cutting torches. Browning was not sure that a plasma cutting torch with the desired characteristics could be developed; however, if it could be achieved, he estimated that the resulting cutting costs might be less than 50 per cent of the equivalent costs using oxyacetylene equipment.

In December, 1959, Browning was considering whether to undertake the development of a plasma cutter. Browning devoted over half of his time to laboratory research. At that time, having finished certain other projects, he wondered whether he should concentrate his attention upon the development of a practical plasma cutter.

The chief technical objective which Browning thought necessary to achieve was a higher power capacity—200 kilowatts rather than the 100-kilowatt capacity of the general purpose torch. In doing this, he thought it might be possible to utilize the body of the general purpose torch (called the F–40 torch body); however, it would probably be necessary to change the basic kind of gas flow from linear flow to a whirling "vortex" flow. The life of the general purpose electrode was about 10 to 30 hours; since a new electrode cost about $22, Browning thought it highly desirable to experiment with various materials, cooling systems, and shapes in an attempt to increase this electrode life.

In speaking of the technical problems involved, Browning emphasized the empiricism of approaches to problems encountered in finding commercial applications for plasma technology. Minor changes in the dimensions, shape, or material of an interior component of the general purpose torch could markedly change the performance or reliability of the torch in an almost unpredictable manner. He said: "I made no estimate of the time it would take to develop a practical plasma cutter because I wasn't even sure it could be done." He added: "Invention and the investigation of new concepts do not lend themselves to planning."

A project to develop a practical plasma cutter, if undertaken, would probably occupy about 50 to 60 per cent of James Browning's time (which was about the maximum he thought he could devote to laboratory work). Probably, it would also require at least half the time of one laboratory technician and of a machinist who would produce the equipment for testing. If the initial investigations were successful, Browning thought it probable that additional company personnel would be added to the project to assist in testing, engineering design, and market development. As previously mentioned, Browning did not think it possible to predict the amount of time or effort it would take to achieve a practical plasma cutter.

Browning thought there was absolutely no doubt of the need for a practical plasma cutter. He cited the growing use of materials such as graphite, aluminum, copper, and stainless steel, none of which could be cut efficiently with oxyacetylene torches.[2] He considered the company's earlier research, sponsored by the scrap processor, which indicated that a plasma cutter might offer substantial savings in operating costs over oxyacetylene cutting methods. Browning had always been interested in industrial cutting problems, and his earlier consulting work had included investigations of gasoline and oxyacetylene torches. This experience, plus his conversations with the scrap processor, gave him what he considered a good "feel" for the market for industrial cutting equipment. He estimated that there were between 4,000 and 7,000 machine-driven oxyacetylene installations used for cutting in the country and that the number of hand-held oxyacetylene torches was probably in the hundreds of thousands. He did not estimate the potential market for a plasma cutter, although he felt it might run to thousands of units per year (with a total dollar value of several million). However, he was confident that TDC could sell at least several hundred plasma cutters yer year, and that that volume would be sufficient to make the product a successful addition to the line.

A Competitive Product

Several years earlier the Ajax Corporation, a division of a large chemical company, had developed a plasma cutting torch which it sold to companies wishing to cut materials such as aluminum, titanium, and tungsten, which could not be cut with oxyacetylene torches. Ajax did not promote the torch for ordinary cutting of mild steel, and only concentrated on those applications in which only plasma cutting could do the job. The price of the Ajax torch and associated equipment was about $5,000 to $6,000, with the purchaser paying a use royalty of about $2,000 at the time of purchase.

Technically, the Ajax cutting torch differed from the proposed TDC plasma cutter in several ways. Its maximum power capacity was slightly over 100 kilowatts, which, in the opinion of TDC's management, imposed severe restrictions on cutting speed, thickness, and quality of cut. The method of stabilization used in the Ajax torch was called "wall stabilization." According to the Ajax patents, in this method of stabilization "the plasma gas, rather than constricting the arc, becomes an integral part

---

[2] Copper and aluminum conducted heat away from the cutting area too rapidly to permit efficient cutting. Stainless steels formed chromium oxides with melting points above the 5,600 degree Fahrenheit maximum temperature of the oxyacetylene flame.

of the arc stream, filling the nozzle from wall to wall." The extent to which wall stabilization actually differed from gas-sheath stabilization and vortex stabilization, the methods used by TDC, was open to question, since there was a very limited scientific understanding of the actual mechanisms involved. According to the TDC management, the Ajax torch also was difficult to adjust, and involved a time-consuming and delicate process by which the electrode was centered.

The performance characteristics and operating costs of the Ajax cutting torch were estimated, very roughly, by the TDC management. The operating costs, which ranged up to 10 cents per foot for two-inch-thick mild steel, were, in the opinion of TDC's management, excessively high. This was primarily due to the fact that the Ajax torch used argon gas (cost, about 10 cents per cubic foot).

Browning estimated that Ajax had sold about two hundred torches over the last few years, almost all of them for cutting uses in which oxyacetylene torches were not suitable. TDC thought that Ajax looked upon its cutting torch mainly as a "gas user" and sold it primarily because it provided customers for Ajax's argon and hydrogen.

Ajax's sales of plasma cutting torches and the gases to be used with these torches appeared to be very small compared to its sales of oxyacetylene equipment and associated gases. Total sales of oxygen and acetylene for both welding and cutting uses were estimated at over $1 billion for 1959; it was estimated that Ajax accounted for a substantial part of these sales. TDC executives thought that Ajax's strong commitment to the oxyacetylene market was the reason Ajax had not promoted its plasma cutting torch for any uses in which it would compete with oxyacetylene torches. This was in direct contrast to James Browning's point of view; he thought it was entirely possible that the plasma cutter would eventually replace completely the use of oxyacetylene torches for cutting purposes. TDC had no established position in the oxyacetylene field which would be disrupted.

A Point of Decision

As Browning considered whether to undertake this development project, he also considered his own personal interests. He thought that the technical problems would be scientifically interesting. He said he had always taken pride in solving problems such as this, in which his scientific training could be brought to bear practical fruit.

He also thought it particularly important that any engineer within the company should be free to investigate problems he found particularly interesting. He applied this philosophy in managing the engineering effort of the firm; and he considered it important, of course, in his own choice of a project.

Another factor considered by Browning was the $100,000 in cash which TDC had in the bank. He did not think he could foresee the exact development costs of the new product, and he made no prediction as to the funds required to manufacture and market the new product. However, he knew that if his initial investigations were successful, TDC would have to make additional financial commitments in order to exploit his findings. He thought that the company's $100,000 in cash plus its continuing stream of income resulting from sales of the general purpose torch would permit TDC to take advantage of the information resulting from his initial investigations.

The decision would be made by James Browning. Despite the factors favoring such a project, he did not consider the decision an easy one. The company was growing rapidly, and there were other possible applications of his time. There was a need for improvement of the general purpose torch in order to decrease its manufacturing cost and improve its reliability. There was a need for adapting the torch to such specific applications as the testing of rocket nose cones, which would probably involve accumulation of test data and development of accessory equipment.

Apart from his work with TDC, Browning had developed another product, a sandblaster utilizing a rocket burner which appeared to be several times more effective in cleaning than conventional, compressed-air sandblasting equipment. Browning wondered whether he should spend some time investigating the prospects for this product. He knew that some additional development time would be needed to perfect the product.

Another alternative considered by Browning was to devote more time to administrative duties within the company, perhaps advising other TDC engineers and supervising the co-ordination of various projects. There was no one within the company who filled the position of chief engineer or research director, and this situation was reflected in the fact that there had been some duplication of projects.

These alternatives all appeared highly promising to James Browning, although it was difficult to estimate the relative value of his time if applied to the different alternatives.

In December, 1959, the proposed TDC plasma cutter was only an idea. As Browning considered the various factors pertinent to the decision, he wondered whether he should undertake the project, choose one of the other alternative uses of his time, or seek additional information before making a decision.

APPENDIX

Plasma Technology

Definition of Plasma. Plasma is a state of matter in which all or part of the atoms have broken down into ions and free electrons. It should be distinguished from blood plasma, which is a completely different substance. Plasma is sometimes referred to as a fourth state of matter.

True plasmas, in which all electrons are stripped from the atomic nuclei, exist only at extreme temperatures, far above the maximum temperature of 60,000 degrees Fahrenheit encountered with the plasma cutter. The plasma cutter, by achieving temperatures between 5,000 and 60,000 degrees Fahrenheit, produces a partial plasma, in which some of the atoms are caused to separate into free electrons and positive ions.

The Plasma Torch. A plasma torch (see sketch) is a device for producing plasma. Its operation involves having an electric arc jump from one electrode to another through a confining space. A plasma-forming gas is constricted to flow through the same passage. That portion of the gas which comes in contact with the arc is heated to a very high temperature. The gas, which is partially ionized and therefore a plasma, is then ejected from the nozzle of the torch.

The peripheral gas—that not touching the arc itself—is relatively cool and

SIMPLIFIED DRAWING OF
PLASMA CUTTER

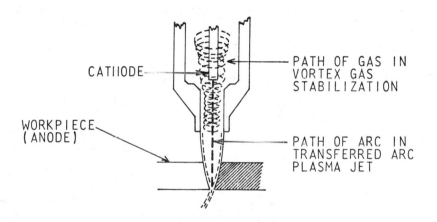

CATHODE

PATH OF GAS IN
VORTEX GAS
STABILIZATION

WORKPIECE
(ANODE)

PATH OF ARC IN
TRANSFERRED ARC
PLASMA JET

GENERAL PURPOSE
PLASMA TORCH

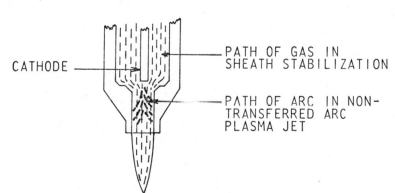

CATHODE

PATH OF GAS IN
SHEATH STABILIZATION

PATH OF ARC IN NON-
TRANSFERRED ARC
PLASMA JET

has a higher velocity than the ionized gas within the arc. In this way the walls of the torch are protected from the intense heat of the arc and plasma (although it is still necessary to cool the walls with water). The peripheral gas is less ionized than the gas within the arc; it therefore is less conductive. This phenomenon, coupled with the relatively higher speed of the peripheral gas, tends to constrict or "squeeze" the arc, further increasing the temperature of the plasma. The arc is therefore carried down the torch while being kept in the center of the chamber, away from the walls of the torch.

Plasma torches are either of the nontransferred-arc or transferred-arc type. In the former the arc begins and ends within the torch. The proposed Thermal Dynamics general purpose torch was to be of this sort. In this torch the cathode is the wall of the torch. After the arc has traveled some distance toward the nozzle, it breaks through the stabilizing gas to impinge upon the wall in an umbrella pattern. It does not damage the torch wall because it has already given up most of its energy to the gas and it strikes the wall over a broad area.

The transferred-arc type of plasma torch involves an arc which leaves the torch in order to impinge upon a workpiece; the workpiece must be a conducting material, since it serves as an electrode. Because of the longer contact with the arc, more gas heating occurs, and temperatures as high as 60,000 degrees Fahrenheit are possible. The plasma cutter utilizes a transferred arc. The cutting process occurs as the metal is melted at the point of contact with the arc and hot plasma. The molten metal is then blown away by the plasma and hot gases, which emerge from the torch at speeds of up to 40,000 feet per second.

There are various kinds of stabilization, including gas-sheath, vortex, wall, and magnetic. This report deals with gas-sheath stabilization which was to be used in the TDC general purpose torch, and with vortex stabilization, also to be used in the TDC plasma cutter.

In gas-sheath stabilization the injected gas moves in a parallel relationship to the arc within the torch. The arc is constricted by a sheath of gas, much thicker than the arc diameter. The high velocity of the gas prevents the arc from grounding on the nearest point of the nozzle; the arc is thus carried down the nozzle until the gases in the surrounding sheath become sufficiently heated and ionized to permit the arc to ground against the nozzle wall (assuming that it is a nontransferred-arc torch).

In vortex stabilization the stabilizing gas is swirled into the chamber to produce an intense vortex. The arc travels within the low-velocity core of this vortex out the nozzle to impinge upon the workpiece (assuming this is a transferred-arc torch). Vortex stabilization apparently permits a longer arc than other methods of stabilization and is more suitable for higher power inputs. Thermal Dynamics engineers considered it a less reliable method of stabilization because it was newer and had not been tested so extensively.

There are a number of other critical factors in plasma torch design which will only be mentioned. These include electrode shape, electrode positioning, kind of stabilizing gas, nozzle design, power requirements, and materials of construction.

Vitality in Research Organizations

I would suggest recognition of the following as important elements in maintaining the vitality of a research institution:

1. It is primarily a human problem, a problem in human selection, human relations and group spirit;
2. A well defined but broad technical objective furnishes a rallying point and sharpens decisions;
3. The freedom and dignity of the individual in the world of science is a paramount principle;
4. An orderly organizational structure with room for recognition of a variety of skills is helpful;
5. A program of successful work which is self-governing and which keeps moving dynamically forward into new ground is the purpose of the whole thing;
6. Just and adequate economic rewards, like good equipment, are a necessary but far from sufficient requirement.

RALPH BROWN, Vice-President, Research
Bell Telephone Laboratories

FROM: "Vitality in a Research Organization and How to Maintain It," *Proceedings,* Sixth Annual Conference on the Administration of Research, Georgia Institute of Technology, 1953.

EL PASO ELECTRONICS CORPORATION[1]

In the spring of 1959, Dr. Kane, the manager of the Research Services Laboratory at El Paso Electronics Corporation, was deep in thought when Bob Handy, a case writer from the Harvard Business School, entered his office. The Research Services Laboratory had been formed only three months ago, merging all the various service functions within El Paso's Research Center which required highly talented and educated personnel. Such services as electron microscopy, mathematical analysis, and computing, to name a few, had been growing increasingly important to El Paso's laboratories as work being done in basic research became more complex.

Dr. Kane looked up from a letter he was studying.

DR. KANE: I'm glad to see you received my message and could make it to this meeting. We have a very interesting problem, which I must admit has me baffled. This letter is the first symptom of the over-all problem, and I am anticipating several similar letters in the near future. It is from one of the men in the mathematical group, a top-notch analyst, who is resigning and going with another company. The letter is very interesting, as he seems to have thought this step through quite thoroughly, and it presents his reasons for leaving in detail. Here, take a look at it, and tell me what you think.

BOB HANDY: Perhaps before I read the letter, you could fill me in on the details and tell me something about the development of your organization.

DR. KANE: Certainly. As you probably know, we are a collection of all the service groups that do professional work. This includes mathematical analysis and computing; material analysis, which does X-ray spectrography, electron microscopy, and chemical wet analysis; and a technology group which builds prototype electronic devices and provides researchers with quantities of new materials to their specifications. In each of these groups, degree-holding professionals are a substantial percentage of our total staff.

BOB HANDY: How did this collection of divergent interests assemble under your supervision? What is their historical background?

DR. KANE: At one time or another, most of the services in this laboratory were located in the labs as a part of their research efforts. Originally, either a researcher had become interested personally in one of these fields, or the work he was doing, required one of these special services. There being no one to do this work for him, he obtained the equipment required and developed methods of his own. Usually, the man or men involved in the service had performed this work only as a side interest to his main research activity. However,

---

[1] All names are disguised.

once it is established that such a man has knowledge about a field or has done previous work in a field, all other researchers turn to him to get their specialized work done. He has the experience; usually, these requests start coming from the personnel in the man's own lab. The lab director approves of using this man as a specialist in a particular service area; soon the researcher has a service group established around him and is spending most of his time in service work. The next step has usually been a removal of this service section from the laboratory, either because administration of such activities absorbs too much of research management's time or because other labs start requesting these services; and to be fair to all, a service group should not be attached to any of its users. Situations such as this were the typical way these service groups were formed, and it was only three months ago that they were collected into one group with the status of a laboratory. Does this give you an adequate historical background?

BOB HANDY: I think so. Let me take a look at the letter you mentioned.

DR. KANE: By the way, this fellow informed me that he was leaving before I received his letter. He said that he wanted to transmit his feelings in writing both to me and to higher management.

The letter read:

DEAR DR. KANE:

As I have told you in our conversations on the eighth and ninth of June, I am resigning my position as senior analyst in the Research Services Laboratory. The purpose of this letter is to document and explain my reasons for resigning. As you know, prior to joining the service group, I was a member of the technical staff in the Basic Physics Laboratory. When that Laboratory purchased some computing equipment, I was assigned the responsibility of aiding the Laboratory members in the use of the equipment while maintaining my own research program. Eventually, the computing and analytical work took such a large amount of time that I dropped my own research. Subsequently, our group was removed from the Basic Physics Laboratory and joined Research Services.

With this as background, I would like to detail my reasons for leaving:

1. My training, ability, and interests lie in the field of research, not service. I do not see any possibility of my returning to research and very little hope of doing much real research in my present position; the demands for service are too great.

2. The status of my position both within and without the labs is much lower now than when I was doing research. I have even heard one laboratory director state: "The service groups are of secondary importance. The labs can get lower caliber people to do this work; and whenever a problem arises between them and the researchers, it should be resolved in favor of the creative people." This has become especially noticeable in the past year with the increased emphasis on basic work and "real creativity."

3. I am losing my position in my professional field, for I am not publishing. This is because I am not doing anything worthy of publishing. Acknowledgements are nice, but they are not articles written.

4. I find that there is a limit placed upon my salary level, for I am not as valuable now as I was as a researcher. This position also virtually excludes me from winning any of the yearly merit awards or the higher professional titles. In essence, my problem is a simple one: I have been removed from the lab's main line of activity, research. This shunting of my talents from the main line

may be more valuable to the company in the total picture; however, it has blocked enough of the important aspects in my development that I am unhappy. The only way I can remove these blocks is by my moving back to research, and I have found this easiest to do by moving to another company.

Thank you for allowing me to state my case.

Very truly yours,
DR. F. K. ROI

BOB HANDY: Well, he has certainly stated a strong case. What do you think about the arguments he presents?

DR. KANE: Unfortunately, most of the generalizations he makes are true. Of course, there are many people who are happy in service work, or who reached their limit in research and found this to be another avenue of growth. However, this letter, in my opinion, only represents the beginning of what may be a serious personnel problem. The sad thing is that we have recognized these complaints and tried to counteract them with various solutions but haven't yet succeeded. Let me tell you what we tried to do and where I now believe we went wrong.

We felt that the major complaint we were hearing was that the men were not doing research; so we initiated in most service groups a program of research, with the professional people setting minor portions of their time aside for research on the services they are performing. For example, the math group was doing services research, like writing new computer routines, working out some new analytical techniques, and keeping up with new activity in applied math and operations research. The comments we received on work like this were certainly interesting. They ranged from "Is this an appeasement project?" or "Which has priority on my time—research or service?" to "I can't do research in patches of time fitted among my service work." If I could pinpoint any one thing wrong with what we did, I would say that we didn't convince them that we *wanted* them to do research. They thought we were doing this as a consolation to them.

We tried other things as well. By consolidating these functions under a Research Services Lab, we put them on a par with the other labs, so they would not be treated as stepchildren when it came to budgeting funds, personnel, or space. We hoped to improve their status within the organization by granting them formal management recognition. Here again, we have run into problems; separating the groups from the labs in which they originated has drawn the lines of distinction sharper. At the same time, you probably recognize that scientific status in this organization is not determined by management as much as it is based upon the type of work you do, the papers you publish, and, in general, the contribution you make to science. In our hierarchy, service ranks lower than research, and management cannot do much about this without changing the jobs.

To answer the money problem is particularly difficult because we are so secretive about individuals' salaries; we can't show the men the records and let them see that the salaries are similar. The thing that really hurts us in this area is that the really top-notch men, who get the very high salaries and the awards and the titles, are all in research. Service personnel hear about these people and blame the difference in remuneration on the laboratory they are in rather than on differences in abilities. The final problem we have attacked is the inability to publish. We have talked with the various section heads within the labs to encourage their men to coauthor articles with service personnel when substantial service work was done on a project. Some groups are very good about this, while others don't care a bit. This has been a very spotty solution, depending upon which lab group the service is for.

Let's go to lunch. I promised Dr. Samuelson, Director of the Electronics Devices Laboratory, that we would have lunch with him.

During the luncheon with Dr. Samuelson, the topic of keeping good personnel in the service functions came up. Dr. Kane repeated the principles he had mentioned earlier, but Dr. Samuelson seemed to take violent exception to them.

DR. SAMUELSON: I think that you are working under a false impression when you assume that to get the abilities and talents required for our service work, we must use researchers and give them research to keep them happy. I don't think that you have considered whether or not service-oriented personnel exist with the talents we need. This is not your fault but is primarily due to our system of developing services within the research labs originally. Some of the problems you listed will still be important, but if you can remove the research orientation and motivation, you have taken a big step. The easiest way to do this is to hire persons with these qualities from outside; but if this is impossible, then we should consider breeding our own group of specialists from men with service orientation.

These two steps should be tried before we accept the fact that we need disgruntled researchers in these jobs; and to keep them, we must throw them the sop of some research to do. If we have to do research on some of these service areas, this is one thing, but doing it just to keep the personnel happy is quite another. I guess I sound pretty harsh, and I don't mean to be; but we have had trouble getting our service requests filled, and after all, this has been your primary job since this research-on-services program was launched.

Back in his office after lunch, Dr. Kane said: "You can see what type of problem I'm up against. I think that this is my most critical area—easing the professional personnel problems, both the immediate and the long range. I have to map out both a policy and a plan of action, sell it to top laboratory management, and hope that no more letters like this come across my desk."

UNION OIL COMPANY OF CALIFORNIA (B)

AFTER DISCUSSING the report given by the Shale Oil Committee and the recommendation made by W. L. Stewart, Jr., at the meeting on January 31, 1955, the Board of Directors voted to authorize the expenditure of $5 million over the next two to two and a half years for the purposes indicated by the Committee.[1] These were:

1. Develop and prove out a full-scale model of the oil shale retort designed by Union's Research Department.
2. Determine the optimum manufacturing method for producing marketable products from shale oil.
3. Obtain accurate estimates of capital and operating costs for a commercial shale oil operation.

As Chief Research Engineer, G. H. Hemmen would be directly responsible for the technical phase of the project. Hemmen reported to F. L. Hartley, General Manager of Research and a member or the Shale Oil Committee.

UNION OIL'S SHALE PROGRAM, FEBRUARY, 1955, TO JUNE, 1957

Design of the Retort

Since retorting was the major problem, work started immediately at the research laboratory at Brea, California, on the final retort design. By early summer, sufficient large-scale experimental work (with mock-ups and other test equipment) had been completed to demonstrate that the problem of moving shale uniformly up through a single large retort shell with the planned four-pump arrangement was more difficult than originally thought. After consideration of the money and time required to solve this problem satisfactorily, Hemmen and Hartley recommended to the Committee that the retort design be shifted from the four-pump conception to the largest possible retort fed by a single pump.[2] This recommendation was accepted by the Committee, though not without misgivings, for it meant (1) that about six months' research on the

---

[1] The "Union Oil Company of California (A)" case describes (p. 266–73) the Committee report and the recommendation. It also provides background information on the Union Oil Company, the West Coast petroleum industry, and shale oil developments prior to 1955.

[2] A description of the retort and its principles of operation are given in the "Union Oil Company of California (A)" case.

four-pump retort was now lost and (2) that the lower capacity, single-pump retort would probably not have as low an operating cost per barrel of oil produced as assumed in the earlier "paper study" economics.

The final design was based on a retort with a pump 5.5 feet in diameter. Its theoretical capacity was 360 tons per day. In commercial practice, it was thought that several of these units could be operated in a "nest" in order to utilize common auxiliary equipment. Only a single unit, however, was planned for the present program.

Preliminary Work in Colorado

Apart from detailed design work on the retort, a substantial amount of work was necessary to design and construct the over-all plant needed in Colorado to support the retorting research program. This work was placed under the direction of John Pownall, who was appointed Project Engineer, reporting to Hemmen. Since the aim of the Colorado work was proving out the retort under full-scale commercial conditions, Pownall had the job of building a plant as cheaply as possible that nevertheless contained all the essential features of a commercial operation. It was

Exhibit 1

THE OPEN-CUT MINE FACE AND THE PRIMARY CRUSHER

Primary crusher is directly beneath the truck. Structure to its left is the loading tower for the tramway. Mine site is 2,000 feet above the valley floor.

decided that, insofar as possible, the plant would be a hybrid: Mining would be done on a small strip-mining basis at minimum cost; crushing would be done in full-scale equipment to duplicate commercial rock size and distribution; retorting would be with one full-size retort; and testing following retorting would be at the research level.

The site selected for the plant was on Union's fee property about eleven miles north of Grand Valley, Colorado. The retort plant was located in a small valley at the base of the shale deposits. The mine site was about 2,000 feet above in the Mahogany Ledge outcroppings. See Exhibit 1. Mining was to be done by the stripping method (as contrasted to the room-and-pillar technique planned for a full-scale commercial plant). Mined rock would be crushed by a primary crusher at the mining elevation; it would then be moved by aerial tramway to the valley floor for further crushing and classification prior to being fed to the retort.

Construction of the Oil Shale Plant

In midsummer, 1955, the first construction contracts were awarded. The Isbell Construction Company of Reno, Nevada, was awarded the

Exhibit 2

THE AUXILIARY EQUIPMENT IN THE VALLEY

Tower for tramway, and secondary crusher and classifying screens. Conveyors move graded shale to a storage pile, and then to continuous sampler and retort in the background.

mining and road-building contract; the Stearns-Roger Manufacturing Company of Denver, Colorado, was named prime contractor for all other construction work in Colorado.

Much of the preliminary work in Colorado was done by the end of the first year. The road from the valley floor to the mine face had been converted to an all-weather road. Several core holes had been diamond-drilled along with the shale face to determine where "weathering" and overburden were at a minimum. The mine site had been selected, and the contractor had started to remove overburden. The retort site had been cleared, and two prefabricated buildings were erected. Foundation work for the major pieces of equipment had been started. Most of the auxiliary equipment had been selected and ordered.

Design and construction of the retort and related equipment continued during 1956. The design engineers, possibly because of the earlier setback on the "four-pump" conception, required extra time in preparing design specifications for the retort. Particularly troublesome were the rock pump and the sodium-cooled plow system. Because of its unusual dimensions, the rock pump was subcontracted for fabrication to the Allis-Chalmers plant in Milwaukee, Wisconsin, where it could be handled in their large boring mill.

Between October, 1956, and February, 1957, the retort was assembled at the plant and the crew trained for operation in a series of "dry" tests.

Exhibit 3

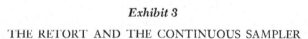

THE RETORT AND THE CONTINUOUS SAMPLER

The sampler is the light-colored structure to the right. The overhead crane and its supporting structure surrounding the retort are used for research purposes only.

Exhibit 4

OVER-ALL VIEW OF THE RETORT SITE

One of the prefabricated buildings is in the foreground, while the road to the mine site can be seen winding upward on the mountain to the right.

All auxiliary equipment was ready, and a substantial quantity of 30-gallon-per-ton shale had been mined, crushed, and stockpiled. Delays in design and construction of the retort had put the project about six months behind schedule. Exhibits 1–4 are from photographs of the completed plant.

Operation of the Retort Plant

The retort was "fired off" on March 11, 1957. To the relief of all concerned, operations went smoothly. Within a matter of days, Pownall (who had been moved from Project Engineer to Plant Superintendent) was able to report that "the retort had stopped running them, and they were now running it." Semiautomatic twenty-four-hour operations were achieved by the end of March. During April a variety of tests were made on various operating variables (e.g., rock-pump rate, plow speed, blower speed, gas-air mixtures, rock sizes, and richness).

During these tests, it became evident that the retort, as designed, could operate satisfactorily at about 400 tons per day—slightly above its design rate of 360 tons per day—but that further increases were unlikely. The main limiting feature appeared to be the plow system, which prevented the shale bed from rising any faster than at the 400-ton-per-day rate. On cold test the rock pump proved capable of operating at a rate considerably over 1,000 tons per day.

A brief failure of the blower system late in April caused the retort shell to overheat. After being shut down, the shell was found to have cracked along several critical weld joints and also to have deflected inward. It was evident that substantial rebuilding of the shell was necessary before the retort could safely be placed back in operation. The Research Department was particularly anxious to do this because of a new design idea developed jointly by some operating and design engineers: It was believed that the expensive and capacity-limiting plow system could be replaced by simple scrapers resembling windshield wipers. If true, this could mean that the retort would be both simpler and capable of substantially higher through-put. This could cut the retorting cost per barrel by as much as 50 per cent.

Research on the refining of raw shale oil was carried out during this period at the Company's California research laboratory. This work, which was essentially completed by June, 1957, had definitely established the fact that high-quality petroleum products could be produced from raw shale oil. Process studies had demonstrated that this could be done in conventional refining equipment and at about the same cost as was then being experienced in typical California refining operations.

The Shale Oil Committee met monthly during this period to review the program and problems (Hartley provided a detailed review to the Committee at each meeting.) When the plant was shut down because of the damage to the retort shell, the project's status was essentially as follows:

1. *Retorting.* The retorting principle had been shown to be sound. However, because of high capital cost and low capacity, retorting cost (on a commercial scale) was estimated to be about 50 cents a barrel higher than postulated in the earlier economic analyses. Additional work was needed to determine the durability of the retort and auxiliary equipment. Following the retort shutdown, Hartley formally requested that the Shale Oil Committee seek a one-year extension of the project in order to test the retort's capabilities and to experiment with various ways of boosting capacity. In particular, he stressed the possibility of replacing the plows by simple scrapers. If successful, this showed promise of boosting the capacity in excess of 1,000 tons per day. The one-year extension would require an estimated additional research appropriation of $3 million.

2. *Refining.* The refining work had gone essentially according to the original plan. High-quality products had been produced from raw shale oil in conventional equipment. Life tests in pilot plant equipment had demonstrated that a refinery operating on raw shale oil would experience no unusual operating difficulties.

3. *Economics.* Assuming the Bureau of Mines room-and-pillar mining cost estimates were accurate,[3] it now appeared that oil from oil shale could not be produced at a cost competitive with average domestic crude oil—at least using a retort operating as the Union retort did during March and

---

[3] See "Union Oil Company of California (A)," p. 258.

April. The cost differential was about 50 cents a barrel. The initial research appropriation of $5 million had been spent.

Other Shale Processes

During 1955 the Bureau of Mines closed its experimental shale oil plant in Colorado, since the Congress did not appropriate the funds necessary for further operation. The crude oil surplus and an "economy drive" in Congress were some of the considerations involved. The plant has not operated since, but has been maintained in stand-by condition.

During 1956 the Sinclair Oil Corporation stopped its experiments with the *in situ* burning process. The result of this work has not been published. Experiments with shale oil recovery by the "fluidization" process had also stopped.

In 1956 the Denver Research Institute began work on a method of shale

Exhibit 5

THE ASPECO PROCESS

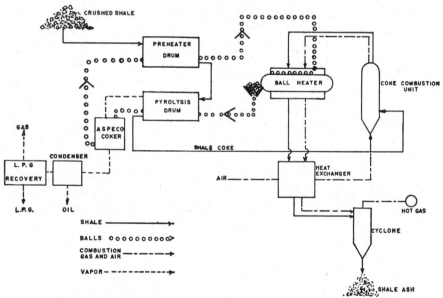

The main unit is the horizontal rotating kiln (pyrolysis drum), in which the hot metal balls are brought into contact with the crushed shale rock. As a result of this heating, vapors of shale oil are released and are withdrawn and condensed. The mixture of shale coke and the cooled balls is discharged from the kiln and separated on a screen.

The shale coke is then burned in the combustion unit, and the resulting flue gases are used to reheat the balls to retorting temperature. The spent shale is disposed of as waste.

Besides the shale oil, light petroleum gases (LPG) are also recovered. The remaining gas can either be burned or treated further and sold.

oil recovery known as the Aspeco process. This program was financed by a $250,000 contract with the Oil Shale Corporation (home office in Beverly Hills, California), which owned the western hemisphere rights to the process. The process was patented by and named after its Swedish inventor. A brief description of the process is given in Exhibit 5.

Related Technology

By mid-1957 the American Gilsonite Company, a joint venture of the Barber Oil Corporation and the Standard Oil Company of California, had under construction a small refinery at Grand Junction, Colorado, for the processing of gilsonite into petroleum products.[4]

American Gilsonite planned to mine the gilsonite hydraulically near Bonanza, Utah, crush it, and pump it as a slurry through a seventy-two-mile pipe line to the Grand Junction plant. This plant was designed to process 700 tons per day of gilsonite and yield 1,300 barrels per day of gasoline and 270 tons per day of calcined coke. It was estimated that the gilsonite reserve could supply a plant of this size for fifty years. The Company planned to market the liquid products locally and the coke in the Pacific Northwest.

CHANGES IN THE WEST COAST PETROLEUM INDUSTRY[5]

During the period from February, 1955, to June, 1957, several important changes occurred in the petroleum situation on the West Coast. The causes of the changes varied from local conditions to influences that were national and international in scope.

The West Coast Energy Supply

Although the total energy demand for the West Coast continued its postwar 4 per cent annual growth trend, the increase was not shared by all energy sources. Solid fuels and water power together supplied a relatively constant 10 per cent of the demand, with the gains of the latter offsetting the losses in the former. Natural gas had increased its share of the market from 20 per cent in 1950 to 30 per cent by mid-1957. Of the remaining 60 per cent, California crude supplied about 45 per cent, while imported oil supplied the remainder.

California crude production declined steadily from a peak of 1,000,000 barrels per day in 1953 to 932,000 barrels per day in mid-1957. Tankship

---

[4] Gilsonite is a solid hydrocarbon containing almost pure asphalt found in coal-like deposits in eastern Utah. It occurs in narrow beds in the western end of the Green River formation. (See "Union Oil Company of California [A]," p. 254.) Gilsonite differs from oil shale in that it can be converted to a liquid at low temperatures by a simple melting process, whereas oil shale must be heated sufficiently to induce a chemical change in the organic solid in the rock.

[5] "West Coast" refers to all operations of the petroleum industry in Arizona, California, Nevada, Oregon, and Washington.

Exhibit 6

MAJOR PIPE LINES TO THE WEST COAST

Name and/or Operator	Type	Estimated Capacity	Year Completed	Location
Trans Mountain Pipeline..................Crude		250,000 b/d*	1953	Edmonton, Canada, to Vancouver, Washington
Four Corners Pipeline Co. (Shell, Standard of California, Gulf, Continental, Richfield, and Superior)............Crude		70,000 b/d	1958	Aneth, Utah, to Los Angeles, California
Salt Lake Pipeline Co. (Standard of California)..........Product		60,000 b/d	1950 (looped in 1953) 1954	Salt Lake City, Utah, to Spokane, Washington
Yellowstone Pipeline Co. (Continental; Interstate; Union; H. Earl Clark, Inc.)....Product		30,000 b/d		Billings, Montana, to Spokane, Washington
Southern Pacific Pipeline, Inc...................Product		38,000 b/d	1955	El Paso, Texas, to Los Angeles, California (now both ends to Phoenix)
El Paso Natural Gas Co..................Natural gas		850,000 mcf/d†	1947	West Texas to Southern California border
El Paso Natural Gas Co..................Natural gas		1,355,000 mcf/d	1950	San Juan Basin to Topock, Arizona, tied in with:
Pacific Gas and Electric Co...................Natural gas			1950	Topock, Arizona, to Los Angeles and San Francisco, California
Pacific Northwest Pipeline Co..................Natural gas		650,000 mcf/d	1956	San Juan Basin to Sumas, Washington, tied in with Canadian line from Peace River field in California
West Coast Transmission Co. (Peace River area).........Natural gas		660,000 mcf/d	1957	San Juan Basin to Sumas, Washington, tied in with Canadian line from Peace River field in Canada (1957)

* Barrels per day.
† Thousand cubic feet per day.

movements of crude and partially finished products rose from essentially zero in 1952 to a rate of 150,000 barrels per day in 1956 and to 300,000 barrels per day in early 1957. Existing crude and products pipe lines were capable of adding another 340,000 barrels per day to the West Coast supply, though in the early part of 1957 they were not all being operated at full capacity.

Pipe Lines to the West Coast

Previous to 1955, there was a crude pipe line from Canada to the Pacific Northwest capable of supplying 250,000 barrels per day. In July, 1957, another crude pipe line with a capacity of 70,000 barrels per day was under construction from the Four Corners area (the junction of Colorado, Utah, Arizona, and New Mexico) to Los Angeles.

Two product pipe lines entering the West Coast area had a combined capacity of 90,000 barrels per day. A third line with a capacity of about 40,000 barrels per day was currently being used to transport finished products from the terminals at Los Angeles and El Paso to a midway terminal at Phoenix, Arizona. Flow in the western half of this line could be reversed, so that crude oil or finished products could be sent to Los Angeles from El Paso, Texas. There was no indication that such action was planned.

The third major natural gas pipe line to supply the West Coast area began operation in 1956. In 1957, this line tied in with a pipe line from Canada, thus allowing Canadian natural gas to reach West Coast markets for the first time.

Data on the major pipe lines to the West Coast are given in Exhibit 6.

California "Offshore" Oil

California's widely discussed offshore oil fields did not contribute to the oil supply during this period. Although the Tidelands Act of 1953 had given the states jurisdiction over offshore resources out to the three-mile limit, the California legislature had not yet passed a bill setting forth the terms of a lease. This was due to disagreement among the legislators with respect to many of the lease details. The amount of the royalty to be paid to the state was a particularly difficult issue.

National and International Influences

Even though crude oil production was restricted in many states,[6] both the supply of crude in storage and the price of crude rose during this period. Oil imports to the United States were at an all-time high in 1956, and many domestic producers (especially in Texas) were beginning to

[6] Production in Texas, for example, was limited by the state commission during much of this period to 10 to 15 days' production. California does not have a regulatory agency governing petroleum production. Production is limited by voluntary action policed by an industry group.

appeal to President Eisenhower to "do something" about the rising tide of imports.

The closing of the Suez Canal in December, 1956, brought about both a decrease in the amount of oil imported from the Middle East and an increase in the demand for American petroleum products by European countries. Although this lessened the problems of the domestic producers, the relief was of short duration. Shortly after the reopening of the Canal in March, 1957, Texas production was cut back even further, and the clamor for restrictions on oil imports became even greater. It was widely believed in the industry that some form of import restrictions would be imposed in the latter half of 1957.

The increase in domestic crude oil prices was attributed to the rising cost of finding and developing domestic crude oil. Though good statistics are lacking, it was estimated by the Chase Manhattan Bank that during 1957 the domestic petroleum industry invested, for each barrel produced, about $1.70 to find and develop new production, as compared to about 80 cents ten years previously. West Coast prices moved as follows: After remaining at $2.76 a barrel since the removal of price controls in February, 1953, the posted price of Signal Hill crude (27 degrees API)[7] rose to $2.92 in December, 1956. The following February the price rose to $3.17.

DEVELOPMENTS IN THE UNION OIL COMPANY

Exploration and Production

During the period from January, 1955, to June, 1957, the Union Oil Company was quite active in exploring for new crude reserves. Panama and Peru were added to the areas where exploration was going on. In fact, the sharp increase in exploration costs was one of the major reasons for the decline in earnings in 1955, despite an increase in physical and dollar volume of sales.

Although several important crude oil discoveries were made, reserves remained relatively constant in 1955 and 1956. Union became a substantial importer of crude oil for the first time in 1956. Imports averaged 12,400 barrels per day, but this amount was expected to rise in the future. Union contracted in 1956 for the construction of three 60,000-ton "super-tankers," each with a capacity of 450,000 barrels. Delivery was to begin in 1958.

Manufacturing and Marketing

In April, 1955, the Santa Maria refinery (a delayed coker) went on stream. The function of this plant was to supply the Oleum refinery with

---

[7] Twenty-seven degrees API gravity crude was often used as a reference point, since it represented a typical California crude oil. The measurement system is based on standards developed by the American Petroleum Institute.

Exhibit 7

STATISTICAL SUMMARY

Operations	1956	1955	1954
Exploration and production:			
Exploratory wells completed:			
Oil...	22	27	34
Gas..	13	6	6
Development wells completed:			
Oil...	237	240	206
Gas..	11	11	6
Dry holes..................................	94	121	140
Controlled gross oil reserves at year end (thousands of barrels)...............................	610,000	607,800	598,400
Company's equity in reserves at year end:			
Crude oil (thousands of barrels)..............	495,400	497,700	495,200
Natural gas liquids (thousands of barrels).......	37,500	40,000	42,300
Natural gas (million cubic feet)...............	2,182,600	1,987,900	864,200
Controlled gross crude oil production (thousands of barrels).................................	48,494	47,974	46,522
Company's equity in crude oil production (thousands of barrels)...........................	37,728	37,901	37,164
Company's equity in crude oil production as a per cent of refinery runs......................	61.4	65.9	69.4
Manufacturing:			
Refinery crude oil runs (thousands of barrels).....	61,453	57,471	53,552
Marketing:			
Petroleum product sales (thousands of barrels)....	57,912	57,058	55,755
Crude oil sales (thousands of barrels)...........	17,381	16,154	15,279
Total Sales (thousands of barrels)..........	75,293	73,212	71,034

Financial	1956	1955	1954
Assets at year end (thousands of dollars):			
Total assets..................................	650,705	546,480	511,238
Net investment in property, plant, and equipment..	400,766	379,742	358,837
Working capital..............................	158,527	88,305	80,250
Ratio of current assets to current liabilities........	3.5:1	2.7:1	2.7:1
Earnings and expenditures (thousands of dollars):			
Gross income................................	401,518	368,761	351,722
Net earnings.................................	34,241	30,523	35,888
Cash dividends declared (including preferred through 1955)...............................	18,261	16,273	15,766
Depreciation, depletion, and similar allowances....	61,410	61,284	50,044
Cash income.................................	95,651	91,807	85,932
Capital expenditures..........................	85,285	87,969	91,702
Net earnings* (dollars per common share)..........	4.45	3.93	4.78
Share owner's equity at year end* (dollars per common share).................................	50.78	48.25	46.40

* Based on common shares outstanding at end of each year, adjusted for subsequent common share dividends, and to reflect, where applicable, any common shares issued upon conversions of debentures.

Note: Form of summary changed in 1956 from previous method of reporting.

coker distillate obtained from processing low-grade Santa Maria Valley crude oils. This enabled the company to increase the yield of gasoline and decrease the yield of fuel oil.

Union also expanded its primary marketing area to include Central America. Some progress was made in marketing specialty products (particularly lubricating oil) to the east within the United States. Limited distribution of products also started in the countries bordering the West Coast of South America.

Statistical data on the Company's operations are given in Exhibit 7.

Personnel Changes

Five members of the Shale Oil Committee were promoted between January, 1955, and mid-1957. Max Lorimore was named Comptroller in April, 1955. In July, 1956, A. C. Rubel was elected President, and W. L. Stewart, Jr., was elected Vice Chairman of the Board. At the same time, F. L. Hartley was elected Vice President for Research. The following year, C. F. Parker was elected Vice President for Economics and Planning. In July, 1956, Rubel replaced Stewart as Chairman of the Shale Oil Committee.

THE SHALE OIL COMMITTEE REPORT, JUNE, 1957

In its report to the Executive Committee and to the Board of Directors, the Shale Oil Committee outlined the work that had been accomplished at the Colorado site and at the laboratory at Brea. The members of the Committee indicated that they believed the retort was capable of continuous operations at the design capacity of from 300 to 400 tons per day. The importance of the successful operation of the rock pump was stressed. The retorting cost was estimated to be about $1.00 a barrel, but the Committee stated that the cost would be greatly reduced if the changes proposed by the Research Department for increasing throughput worked out satisfactorily.

The Committee requested an additional $3 million appropriation in order to continue the project for one more year. A goal of determining the retort's durability and reducing retorting costs to about 50 cents a barrel was indicated. It was pointed out that unless this could be done, there was little possibility of producing oil from Colorado oil shale at a cost comparable to that of average domestic crude oil.

THERMAL DYNAMICS CORPORATION (B)

The Decision as to Whether to Undertake the Project

James Browning decided to undertake a project to develop a practical plasma cutting torch. He said he found the problems interesting; he thought the technical objectives could be achieved; and he was confident that a large and profitable market awaited the company which was successful in developing such a product and promoting it vigorously.

Initial Development of the New Product

Subsequently, Browning spent some 25 to 30 hours per week working on the project. Initially, his efforts were concentrated on trying to achieve a gas stabilization pattern in which the gas whirled at high speeds around the electric arc. This pattern differed from that of the TDC general purpose torch, in which the gas traveled in a straight path through the torch, parallel to the arc.[1] Browning had had very limited experience with swirl or "vortex" stabilization, but he thought it would be necessary in order to carry a high current through the torch and out to the workpiece without "shorting" against the wall of the torch. His approach to investigating vortex stabilization was largely empirical, since it was difficult to predict the results of varying the shape of the gas inlet slots, the diameter of the nozzle, or the amount of power.

Assisting Browning were two men who were putting in half time on the project—a technician who performed the laboratory work and a skilled machinist who built various parts to Browning's specifications. This machinist was a key man in the company's product development efforts. He could take rough drawings and convert them into finished parts; and because of his close familiarity with the laboratory problems of using plasma, he could interpret, make his own decisions as to details, and often contribute useful suggestions relating to product design. He worked exclusively with the company's engineers and did not construct any parts for production models. Often, he had parts ready for laboratory testing within a few hours after receiving the sketch.

In March, 1960, the project approached a second point of evaluation, in which a decision was necessary. Browning had been successful in achieving a form of vortex stabilization which promised to make possible a plasma cutter with a power capacity of 200 kilowatts. However, the

---

[1] See drawing in "Thermal Dynamics (A)," p. 289.

309

decision had not yet been made as to whether the new plasma cutter would make use of the torch body used with the general purpose torch or whether the plasma cutter would be incorporated into a completely redesigned torch body, one developed specifically for the new product.

The general purpose torch body was a cylindrical nylon tube which housed various components, including those which regulated the stabilizing gas flow, the electrode, and the nozzle which shaped the pattern of the plasma as it emerged from the torch. These components were the essential "heart" of a plasma torch and were to be considerably different in the plasma cutter than in the general purpose torch. Browning's investigations of vortex stabilization had been directed primarily at developing certain of these new components. It was technically possible for the plasma cutter to be housed in the body of the general purpose torch. This body was more than a cylindrical casting. It included the electrical leads and the inlets for stabilizing gas and cooling water. The dimensions of the body had been carefully developed by extensive testing in order to provide maximum product life and to minimize problems of heat transfer and electrical shorting. Browning thought the cutting performance of a plasma cutter (speed, thickness of metal cut, and quality of cut) would be about the same, regardless of which alternative was followed.

The general purpose torch was a research tool, and its body was bulky and expensive. It was too heavy to be used as a hand-held plasma cutter, which would limit its use to machine-driven installations. It was versatile and could be used with various attachments and components to do spraying, cutting, or welding; this was an important attribute for a laboratory tool, but was not a particularly useful characteristic (in management's opinion) for an industrial plasma cutter.

One significant factor pointing toward a completely new design was the high cost of the F–40 torch body. It had never been designed with production economies in mind, and management estimated that its manufacturing cost could be decreased from about $350 to about $75 just by the substitution of standard parts and simplification.

A factor favoring the use of the F–40 torch body was its reliability. It had been used for almost two years, and the "bugs" in it had been discovered and corrected through appropriate changes in dimensions and materials. Management felt that any new design would have reliability problems which would not be discovered except through extensive testing and perhaps not until the product was placed on the market—such things as corroding parts, leaking seals, and faulty electrical connections. Overcoming these problems would require scarce engineering time, would delay the introduction of the product to the market, and perhaps would result in dissatisfied customers who found "bugs" in the new product.

In regard to timing, Browning estimated that the choice of a new torch body design would delay introduction of the new product by six months to a year. Management did not consider speed of development to be of primary importance, since there were no specific customers clamoring for the new product. However, management desired to have the product on the market and contributing to the company's profits as soon as possible. TDC also feared that other companies, recognizing the need for a practical plasma cutter, might develop one and beat TDC to the market.

If the old F–40 torch body was chosen for the new product at this time, management anticipated that TDC would develop at some future time a "second generation" of plasma cutters. This second-generation product would incorporate various changes resulting from what TDC had learned in testing, producing, and marketing the first generation of plasma cutters. The second generation of the new product would also be incorporated in a lightweight, inexpensive torch body designed specifically for use in industrial cutting. A lightweight plasma cutter could be used as a hand-held tool, which, in management's opinion, would expand the potential market for the new product tremendously.

A Point of Decision

Browning believed that investigation of vortex stabilization had proceeded to the point at which a decision would have to be made as to whether the plasma cutter would be incorporated in the old F–40 torch body or in a new torch body specifically designed for the new product.

Wise Capitalists Avoid New Inventions

Fifteen years is about the average period of probation, and during that time the inventor, the promotor and investor, who see a great future for the invention, generally lose their shirts. Public demand even for a great invention is always slow in developing. That is why the wise capitalist keeps out of exploiting new inventions."

> OWEN D. YOUNG, Chairman of the Board
> General Electric Company
> Founder of Radio Corporation of America

FROM: G. Archer, *History of Radio to 1926* (New York: American Historical Co., 1938). Cited in MacLaurin, "The Process of Technological Innovation," *American Economic Review*, March, 1950.

PHOTON, INC. (E)

IN DECEMBER, 1961, after a long conference, Kurtz M. Hanson and Robert M. Campbell decided to start developing the tape-operated machine with separate keyboards, and also to bid on the General Electric contract. The new tape-operated design would be designated "the 540 model."[1] Even though the 540's development would further complicate operations in Photon, it broadened the company's product line; and the technological advance it represented would give Photon a greater lead over competitors, thus helping to increase sales. In agreeing to bid on the GE contract, Hanson and Campbell felt the action was almost a necessity, because it was the only way that development of the ZIP machine could be financed in the near future. Also, if another company won the contract, this competitor would have a distinct advantage over Photon in the field of computer read-out. Therefore the development engineers immediately began working on the 540 model, and the two managers drew up a bid proposal for the contract.

Throughout the spring of 1962, work continued on the 540 model, and negotiations were initiated with GE, although the contract had not yet been awarded. During this time, Hanson saw the need for a large amount of money to pay for development of the 540 model and plan for increased production. In March, $1,785,000 was raised through the sale of subordinate income debentures to the company's directors, officers, and stockholders. Of this amount, $1 million was used as working capital to sustain operations, and $785,000 was applied to reducing Photon's long-term debt. With the financial situation thus eased somewhat, Hanson and Campbell concentrated on improving the efficiency of the production operations. The main obstacle was that an efficient layout could not be accomplished in the old, four-story building. As a result, in April, Photon moved from its Charles Street plant to a modern, one-story building in Wilmington, Massachusetts (fifteen miles north of Boston). The new plant was a great improvement over the previous facilities, and the rent was about the same. The new plant gave Photon a prosperous look, and it also enabled the staff engineers to reduce inefficiencies in production with an improved one-level layout.

After the relocation, the work of the development engineers continued at a good pace; and by May of 1962 a reliable, operational model of the

---

[1] Necessary background can be found in "Photon, Inc. (A), (B), (C), and (D)."

540 was completed at a total cost of $100,000 spread over the six-month development period. Exhibit 1 gives a description of the 540 model.

Exhibit 1

DESCRIPTION OF PHOTON MODEL 540
PHOTOTYPESETTING MACHINE

The 540 model is basically the same idea as the original 200 model (illustrated on page 227) except that the keyboard is a separate unit which is connected to the photo unit with a special Photon tape. This design allows several keyboards to be used with a single photographic unit, so that the full capacity of the photo unit (ten characters per second) can be utilized.

The operational specifications of the machine are as follows:

Composing speed...............10 characters per second
Maximum line length.............42 picas (7 inches)
Point sizes......................4 to 72 points
Type face selection.............192 type fonts (12 sizes, 16 faces)

The 540 model offers all the typesetting features of the 200 model, in addition to multiple-keyboard input. The 540 model uses the same photo unit as the 200 model; however, the design of the rack and keyboard circuitry is modified. An electrical-type storage unit was designed for the 540 model instead of using the mechanical-type storage unit in the 200 model. This and other design changes were directed toward decreasing the cost of keyboards, so that customers would more readily purchase more than one.

An illustration of the 540 model is shown on the following page.

It was first seen by the public in May at a trade show in Germany. The next month, when it was shown in the United States, the new machine was very well received, and orders began coming in almost immediately. By the end of June a considerable backlog of orders had begun building up. To meet this unusual situation, Campbell temporarily took charge of the Production Department and immediately emphasized increased production with strict quality control. To meet the increased demand, some personnel were shifted from the Development Department into Production.

Meanwhile, in June of 1962, GE announced that Photon had won in the bidding for the development of a high-speed phototypesetting computer read-out machine. Photon's development engineers took the ZIP design off the shelf and began developing a prototype. They planned to complete an operational model by March of 1963.[2] (Exhibit 2 is a news article from the *Typographical Journal* concerning the GE contract being awarded to Photon.)

As the push for increasing production grew, so did the problems. About 20 per cent of the matrix discs had to be rejected after they were prepared because of faulty emulsions; suppliers failed to meet their

---

[2] The major physical differences between the final ZIP machine design and the other Photon models is that ZIP uses a static matrix (instead of the rotating matrix in other models) and has solid-state components.

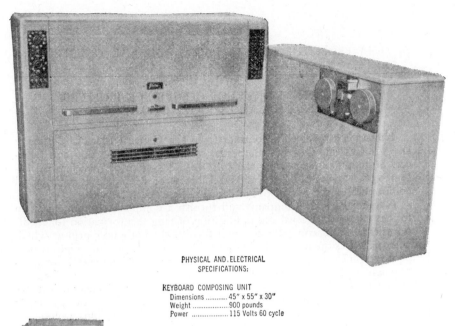

PHYSICAL AND ELECTRICAL
SPECIFICATIONS:

KEYBOARD COMPOSING UNIT
    Dimensions .... 45" x 55" x 30"
    Weight .... 900 pounds
    Power .... 115 Volts 60 cycle

PHOTO UNIT RACK
    Dimensions .... 15" x 55" x 38"
    Weight................... 500 pounds

PHOTO UNIT
    Dimensions .... 24" x 55" x 45"
    Weight................... 1,300 pounds
    Power................... 115 Volts 60 cycle

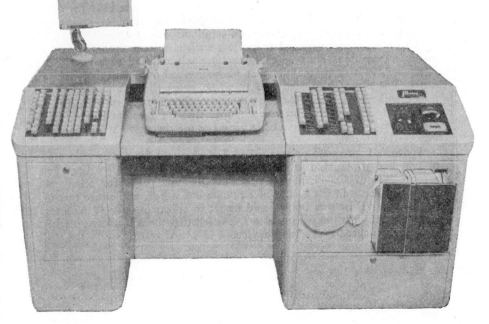

THE PHOTON MODEL 540

Exhibit 2

ARTICLE FROM THE TYPOGRAPHICAL JOURNAL, OCTOBER, 1962

PHOTON TO DEVELOP COMPUTER PRINTER FOR NATIONAL LIBRARY OF MEDICINE

Photon has received a contract from the General Electric Company Defense Systems Division, Bethesda, Md., to design, develop and fabricate a computer printer for the MEDLARS system of the National Library of Medicine. The National Library of Medicine is a principal component of the U.S. Government Public Health Service.

General Electric Company will furnish a complete computer system for the storage, retrieval and publication of tagged information for medical scientific literature. Photon will furnish the computer printer which will operate as the output device for this system and produce high-quality photographic composition on film, at a photocomposing speed not hitherto achieved.

The Photon computer will operate off-line from the magnetic tapes which form the output of the computer system. The magnetic tape input is read-out, decoded, sorted and temporarily stored in binary code by solid state electronic circuits. Width values of each character, or space, are placed in storage, as well as the particular style of character. The particular location of each letter within a line is placed in temporary memory. This information is then fed to the photographic section.

The photographic section consists of glass matrices, containing several hundred characters (upper case, lower case, numbers, punctuation and symbols, etc.). They are located directly in front of a multiple light source. The light sources are arranged so that there is one light for each individual character on the matrix. Any single character, or groups of characters, can thereby be illuminated simultaneously.

An optical system is used to project each character onto film, on a common base line. Thus, as characters are selected and successively illuminated, at high speeds, they are photographed onto sensitive film or paper. The film is contained in a magazine, or cartridge, and consists of a long roll which is indexed as soon as the photography of each line is completed. The output film or paper may then be developed by a rapid continuous process and is available for offset use through any of the conventional methods.

Photon's high speed printer called ZIP, operates from magnetic tape or punched paper tape at speeds ranging from three to five lines per second—300 to 500 characters per second. Type pages for telephone books can be set in the matter of a minute and a half, and entire text of the usual novel or text book could be set in approximately 45 minutes. With the growing use of computers, it is felt that there is a large market for this high-speed typesetting device.

delivery schedules; and bottlenecks appeared on the production line. By November the production problems had become serious; although the work force had increased by more than 40 men, output had not increased proportionally. By this time the backlog, consisting principally of orders for 540's, had grown to $1.75 million. In an attempt to improve Photon's production performance, Campbell assigned five men as expediters, with each responsible for all the problems in a particular section of the production line.

In December, output had improved to the point where Photon was able to produce twelve photo units and five keyboards for the month. Twelve more production employees were hired, bringing the manufacturing personnel up to a total of 90 men.

As a result of the improved sales and the tremendous push for increased production in the last half of the year, Photon showed a loss of only $12,393 in 1962. Thus the development of the Photon machine, which started in 1946, was finally on the verge of becoming a profitable operation. Exhibit 3 shows financial statements for 1962.

Hanson and Campbell were very optimistic about Photon's future. They felt that sales would double each year for the next three years and that profits would increase at an even greater rate. Much of this optimism was based on their appraisal of the competitive situation. Neither of Photon's competitors, Harris-Intertype and Mergenthaler Linotype, had made any significant changes in their photocomposition machines since 1960. (Exhibit 3 of "Photon, Inc. (C)," page 236, shows a comparison of the Photon 200 machine with Harris' Photosetter and Mergenthaler's Linofilm.) Furthermore, to the best of Photon's knowledge, neither Harris nor Mergenthaler had introduced any new phototypesetting equipment, although it was possible they had some in the prototype stage.

Exhibit 3

FINANCIAL STATEMENTS FOR YEAR ENDED DECEMBER 31, 1962

BALANCE SHEET

ASSETS

Current assets:

Cash		$ 216,492
Accounts receivable		951,471
Inventories—at lower of cost or market		871,654
Prepaid expenses		7,160
Total Current Assets		$2,046,777
Deposit with escrow agent		18,577
Accounts receivable—miscellaneous		5,565
Plant and equipment—at cost	$ 453,237	
Less: Accumulated depreciation	271,226	182,011
Patent license, at cost, less amortization		7,771
Unamortized debenture issue expenses		66,921
Development costs of new products—deferred		128,239
Rental deposit		23,940
		$2,479,801

Exhibit 3 (Continued)

LIABILITIES AND STOCKHOLDERS' EQUITY

Current liabilities:

Notes payable to bank.......................		$ 190,000
Accounts payable............................		270,065
Accrued payroll, taxes, and other expenses........		169,312
Advance payments by customers...............		42,120
Total Current Liabilities.....................		$ 671,497

Long-term debt:

Convertible subordinated 6% note payable........		206,000
5% convertible subordinated income debentures, due December 1, 1971.................		1,704,300

Commitments and Contingent Liabilities:

Stockholders' Equity:

Common stock

Outstanding, 412,815 shares..................	$ 412,815	
Capital surplus...........................	5,339,046	
	$5,751,861	
Deficit..	(5,853,857)	(101,996)
		$2,479,801

INCOME STATEMENT

Net sales......................................		$1,850,783
Other income, less sundry income deductions........		8,384
Total income..................................		$1,859,167

Less:

Cost of sales..............................	$ 986,686	
Engineering, research, and development expenses	178,204	
Selling expenses...........................	296,782	
General and administrative expenses..........	262,155	
Moving and relocation expenses...............	28,029	
Depreciation of plant and equipment..........	48,948	
Interest and amortization of debenture issue expense..............................	24,447	
Provision for state taxes....................	7,964	
Total costs and expenses..................		1,833,215

Income—before provision for contingent interest on income debentures.......................		$ 25,952
Less: Interest on 5% convertible subordinated income debentures.........................		38,345
Net loss for year.............................		($ 12,393)

Consequently, Photon's management felt that with the 200 model and the recently introduced 540 model, Photon was able to offer the customer more flexibility, greater reliability, and a lower price for comparable capabilities than any competitor. In addition, Photon's 510 and 520 models performed a function, i.e., compatability with Monotype or TTS keyboards, which was not performed by any other phototypesetting machine on the market.

As an indication that the printing industry was beginning to recognize the superiority of Photon equipment, Campbell said: "An increasing number of sales we make are based on the cancellation or conclusion of leases for competitive equipment which is being returned to the manufacturer." Exhibit 4 describes Photon's product line.

PHOTON'S PRODUCT LINE, DECEMBER, 1962

Model	Price	Speed	Maximum Size	Type Selection	Line Length	Separate Components	Input	Matrix	Automatic Features
200	$63,385	2–3 char./sec.*	72 points	16–19-character alphabets (17,280 characters)	54 picas	One (keyboard, computer, and photo unit combined in one)	Integral, or tape/card*	Disc	Centering, quadding, justification, variable justifying and interword space, runarounds, insertion of leaders, blanks, ruling†
510	$23,250 to $25,650 plus matrix†	10 char./sec.	18 points (special to 72)	1 size, 1–4 faces	42 picas	Two (photo and rack)	6-level TTS tape	Disc	Centering, quadding, justification, insertion of blanks (keyboard can still be used for hot type)
511	$25,450 to $28,700 plus matrix†	10 char./sec.	18 points (special to 72)	12 sizes, faces	42	Two (photo and rack)	6-level TTS tape	Disc	(Greater capability than 510 model)
512	$25,050 to $29,750 plus matrix†	10 char./sec.	18 points (special to 72)	1 size, 16 faces	42 picas	Two (photo and rack)	6-level TTS tape	Disc	(Greater capability than 511 model)
513	$27,250 to $33,800 plus matrix†	10 char./sec.	18 points (special to 72)	12 sizes, 16 faces	42 picas	Two (photo and rack)	6-level TTS tape	Disc	(About 80 per cent of 200 model's capability)
520	$21,150 to $22,200 plus matrix†	10 char./sec.	18 points (special to 72)	1 size, 1–4 faces (keyboard may limit)	42 picas	Two (photo and rack)	Monotype tape (31 channels)	Disc	(Approximately same as 510 model)

Exhibit 4 (*Continued*)

Model	Price	Speed	Maximum Size	Type Selection	Line Length	Separate Components	Input	Matrix	Automatic Features
521.........	$23,950 to $26,700 plus matrix‡	10 char./sec.	18 points (special to 72)	12 sizes, 1-4 faces (keyboard may limit)	42 picas	Two (photo and rack)	Monotype tape (31 channels)	Disc	(Approximately same as 511 model)
522.........	$23,550 to $24,600 plus matrix‡	10 char./sec.	18 points (special to 72)	1 size, 1-16 faces (keyboard may limit)	42 picas	Two (photo and rack)	Monotype tape (31 channels)	Disc	(Approximately same as 512 model)
523.........	$25,750 to $28,500 plus matrix‡	10 char./sec.	18 points (special to 72)	12 sizes, 1-16 faces (keyboard may limit)	42 picas	Two (photo and rack)	Monotype tape (31 channels)	Disc	(Approximately same as 513 model)
540.........	$76,950	10 char./sec.	72 points	16-19-character alphabets (17,280 characters)	42 picas	Three (keyboard, control rack with reader, photo unit)	Photon 1-inch tape (8 channels)	Disc	(Almost same flexibility and capability as 200 model; several keyboards can be used with one photo unit)
900 (ZIP)........	N.A.	300-500 char./sec.	N.A.	N.A.	N.A.	One	Magnetic or paper tape from computer	Static	N.A. (has solid-state components)

* Speed of the standard 200 model is limited to the speed of a single operator (203 characters per second); however, when it is specially equipped to accept tape input (Flexowriter's eight-level tape, Justawriter's seven-level tape, Teletypesetter's six-level tape), the full ten-character-per-second capacity of the photo unit can be utilized.

† For explanation of these features, see "Photon, Inc. (D)," Exhibit 1 (p. 276).

‡ Cost of the matrix disc varies according to the number of type faces included. The prices vary from $610 for two type faces to $2,800 for sixteen type faces.

Forecasting for the coming year, Campbell expected 1963 sales to consist of about 60 per cent 200 model machines and 40 per cent 540 model machines, with the 510 and the 520 making a negligible contribution.

In view of the profit and rapidly expanding sales, Hanson and Campbell decided it was time to formulate an explicit corporate strategy to use as a framework for operations in the future. In particular, they were interested in establishing some guidelines for growth, diversification, marketing, and the amount and direction of the research and development effort. They met once again to draft the strategy which would guide Photon to increased profits in the future.

The Decision as to Whether to Develop a New Torch Body

James Browning and Merle Thorpe decided to utilize the old F–40 torch body in developing the plasma cutter. They also decided to undertake development of an inexpensive, light, hand-held torch body at some undetermined time in the future. The primary reason for these decisions was the desire to avoid at this time the reliability problems which they thought would be associated with the development of a new torch body.

Further Development

Technical development continued under Browning's supervision. He concentrated his attention upon the internal geometry of the plasma cutter in order to perfect the pattern of gas stabilization flow and in order to increase electrode life. A major task at this stage of development was overcoming problems of reliability, associated with the fact that materials were forced to operate under extreme conditions. Substantial progress was being made in this area. In Browning's opinion, the project was approaching the point at which the major technical problems had been solved, and he felt subsequent development effort should be devoted more toward further improvements in reliability and toward gathering cost and performance information.

Browning was not too interested in that kind of work and did not think it was the best use of his talents, saying: "I'm more an inventor than an engineer." He felt that if the plasma cutter was to be carried to market introduction, it would be necessary to assign a competent man, with both engineering and executive capabilities, to have complete change of final development, market planning, and all activities connected with the new product. Those men in the TDC organization who had such capabilities were completely tied up with other responsibilities and, in the opinion of Browning and Thorpe, could not be freed to concentrate upon this project.

In addition, there was no one in the TDC organization who had experience in marketing a relatively large-volume product, as the plasma cutter was expected to be. Management also thought it desirable to add to the TDC organization someone with experience and contacts in the oxyacetylene equipment field. Thorpe recalled a man he had met several years earlier, George Klasson, who had extensive experience in sales and engineering in this field. Thorpe thought it might be possible to bring this man to TDC to supervise the plasma cutter program. Management did not investigate any other man for the job because Klasson seemed to meet the requirements so admirably.

These factors brought management to a re-evaluation of the outlook for the plasma cutter and resulted in what was later referred to by Browning as "the most significant decision" in the development of the plasma cutter.

The decision facing management was not just whether to hire an additional engineer-executive. As management saw it, it was a decision as to whether to devote a major percentage of the company's resources to the project. If the plasma cutter was to be introduced to the market within the next year, the level of effort devoted to the project would have to be increased. The nature of Browning's early development work on the plasma cutter had been such that he and his two part-time assistants could investigate the problem adequately; little would have been gained by putting additional personnel on the project. However, if Klasson was hired and the new product was carried to market introduction, there would be hundreds of minor problems to be solved. Different activities associated with the project could be carried on simultaneously, such as arranging for promotional literature, working with the subcontractors on production problems, and assembling detailed cost and performance data.

If the project was to be continued, management anticipated that Klasson might be hired to supervise the project. He would require the full time of the company's most competent research machinist, the full time of a laboratory technician, and the full time of a man to assist in engineering design. It was anticipated that experienced men would be placed on the project, and that additional men would be hired and trained to take over their duties. In addition, Browning did not plan to drop the project suddenly; he would assist Klasson until he was "on his feet," and he would continue to some extent his own laboratory investigations of certain technical problems associated with the plasma cutter, principally concerned with alternative approaches to electrode design. Therefore, Browning estimated that a decision to hire Klasson would involve a commitment to spend from $5,000 to $7,000 per month on the new product.

In evaluating the technical factors bearing upon the decision, Browning thought that the major technical uncertainties had been diminished to such a degree that there was no question that a practical plasma cutter could be achieved. He thought that the problem of electrode life merited additional attention, but that the plasma cutter could be introduced to the market without major advances in this area. Improvement of reliability and appearance, the development of accessory equipment, such as a control console and the mechanism which would guide the plasma cutter, and the gathering of cost and performance data appeared to be the principal technical tasks remaining. Because of his awareness of the multitude of technical "bugs" that might arise, Browning hesitated to estimate the time necessary to achieve these objectives.

Another factor bearing upon the decision was the company's financial position. In March, 1960, the company's cash balance in the bank was about $100,000, all accumulated from retained earnings of the previous two years. Sales of the general purpose torch were proceeding at the rate of about $80,000 per month. This product, which was TDC's chief revenue producer and which carried a high profit margin, was supporting the company's other development work. If sales stayed at the level of $80,000 per month, management estimated that the company could support development of the plasma cutter (even at the proposed rate of $5,000 to $7,000 per month) without drawing down the cash balance of $100,000.

In management's opinion, the greatest risk associated with a decision to expand development on the plasma cutter was whether the sales of the general purpose torch would hold up. In March, 1960, the short-term sales outlook was "shaky," primarily because of a general downturn in business, and management knew that "when business gets bad, expenditures for research equipment are among the first to suffer." If sales dropped drastically, perhaps to $30,000 per month, the drain on the company's cash balance would be rapid, and the $100,000 would be exhausted within a few months. Management was concerned that a "double-barreled" combination of added product development expenditures and a possible downturn in business might bring TDC to the point where it would not be able to complete development of the plasma cutter or where it might be forced to introduce it to the market before testing was completed.

TDC had not taken any specific steps during the three months preceding March, 1960, to gain additional information about the market. Nothing had happened to shake management's opinion that there was a large market for a practical plasma cutter.

A Point of Decision

Browning and Thorpe considered these factors in discussing whether to hire Klasson to supervise the plasma cutter project. Management realized that it did not have a great deal of information it would like to have, including studies of possible channels of distribution and methods of promotion, laboratory data on the economics of cutting with the new product, and a more thorough study of the patent picture. However, the gathering of this information would be one of the primary responsibilities of the new executive if he was hired.

If management decided to hire Klasson and to provide him with the assistance it thought he would need, this would mean a commitment of about 10 to 15 per cent of the company's total personnel to this one product development project. Management wondered: Should Klasson be hired? Should the present level of effort be continued under Browning's supervision? Should the project be dropped? Should the decision be delayed until more information was obtained?

TECHNICAL NOTE ON MICROELECTRONICS (Mid-1963)

MICROELECTRONICS IS a term used to refer to that current state of the art which produces the most compact electronic circuitry technically possible. Work on microelectronics is not supported merely for the purpose of the reduction of size. Small size is, however, inherent in the solid-state technology which is behind much of this work. The aim of this technology is the production of more sophisticated, more reliable, cheaper electronic systems. Presently, the term "microelectronics" is most frequently applied to the specific technologies of thin-film circuits and integrated semiconductor circuits.

The recent developments in microelectronics have been spurred by the growing complexity of modern electronic systems and the concurrent demands for size and weight limitation, increased switching speed, and greater reliability. What was a laboratory curiosity five years ago is today a technological way of doing business, and the effects on the electronics industry could be profound. Exhibit 1 shows what one major consulting firm projects will happen to the market for electronic circuits over the next decade. Exhibit 2 shows the market projections used by a major manufacturer of both components and microelectronic circuits.

The potential market can be broken down into three major product categories: military and space electronics, commercial digital circuits, and other (linear) commercial circuits. The latter two groups include consumer and industrial applications and the less sophisticated instrumentation applications of defense-oriented companies. Because of the reliability, size, and weight requirements of military systems and the government's willingness to pay, microcircuits are being incorporated into many new military and space electronic systems. All branches of the armed services have been supporting substantial research programs in this field, and NASA has already committed itself to semiconductor integrated circuitry for the Apollo guidance computer. Digital integrated semiconductor circuits are available for several applications from a number of manufacturers. While the manufacturers of digital computers are committed to using microelectronic circuits in future production models, there are differences of opinion about which of the four basic approaches is the current or the potential optimum. There is an even greater degree of uncertainty about the future role of microelectronic circuits for analogue and other linear circuits in commercial applications.

Exhibit 1

MARKET FORECAST*

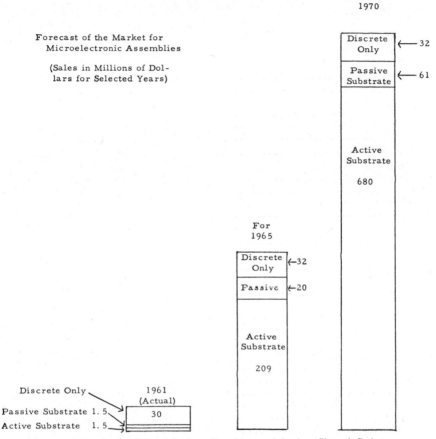

Forecast of the Market for
Microelectronic Assemblies

(Sales in Millions of Dollars for Selected Years)

For 1970

Discrete Only ←— 32
Passive Substrate ←— 61
Active Substrate 680

For 1965

Discrete Only ←32
Passive ←20
Active Substrate 209

Discrete Only
1961 (Actual)
Passive Substrate 1. 5
Active Substrate 1. 5
30

* Figure compiled by Stanford Research Institute. Quoted by permission from *Electronic Design.*

Basic Approaches

There are four basic technological routes to the microminiaturization of electronic circuits:

1. *Assemblies of Discrete Components.* Conventional circuits are assembled using discrete components which are connected together to form the circuit. Over the last decade a number of techniques have been adopted which have reduced the size and cost of assembled circuits. Special connectors and printed circuit boards have replaced wiring. Welding has been replacing soldering. Special modular approaches and smaller components with space-saving configurations have continued to yield substantial reductions in volume and weight. Several widely used packaging techniques, such as micromodules, "Swisscheese," and "cordwood," are defined in the appendix. Also see Exhibits 3, 5, 6 and 7. Exhibit

Exhibit 2

GROWTH OF ELECTRONIC COMPONENT SALES
(Millions of Dollars)

	1952	1957	1962	Projected, 1967	Projected, 1972
Discrete active:					
Tubes:					
Receiving....................	$ 259	$ 384	$ 302	$ 235	$ 150
Power and special................	174	185	325	415	480
Semiconductors:					
Transistors......................	2	70	290	375	470
Diodes and rectifiers..............	17	73	155	200	255
Others.........................	35	35	180	265	400
Total........................	$ 487	$ 747	$1,252	$1,490	$1,755
Discrete passive:					
Capacitors........................	$ 200	$ 214	$ 352	$ 483	$ 595
Resistors........................	125	171	315	435	525
Inductors:					
Coils...........................	78		81	87	92
Transformer reactors.............	112	110	149	200	243
Total.......................	$ 515	$ 570	$ 897	$1,205	$1,455
Circuit packages:					
Filters and networks................	$ 19	$ 22	$ 47	$ 95	$ 170
RCL modules.....................	6	10	16	23	30
Functional assemblies...............	5	15	37	125	200
Microelectronic circuits:					
Thin film........................	....		5	75	200
Semiconductor....................	....		10	225	800
Total........................	$ 30	$ 47	$ 115	$ 543	$1,400
Electrochemical and other:					
Connectors.......................	$ 64	$ 94	$ 197	$ 227	$ 270
Relays and switches................	110	179	273	393	515
Other...........................	200	414	606	812	1,050
TV picture tubes..................	171	183	175	205	265
Antennas, speakers, etc.............	153	197	195	235	290
Grand Total, Components.....	$1,730	$2,431	$3,710	$5,110	$7,000

Courtesy: Sprague Electric Co.

4 also illustrates a number of terms used to describe the processes involved in several different approaches.

2. *Thin-Film Circuits.*   The thin-film technique might be considered a logical extension of printed circuits. Layers of material a few thousandths of an inch thick are deposited on a base (substrate) to form passive electronic components (resistors, capacitors, and inductors), insulation, leads, and connectors. Exhibit 8 illustrates equipment developed for the U.S. Naval Avionics Facility, Indianapolis, by IBM. Exhibit 9 illustrates the process involved. The masks used for the laying-down of the thin films are manufactured by a number of techniques, the latest of which is the numerically controlled machining of graphite. Some investigators also hope to be able to build up active elements (transistors and diodes) as thin films to make completely integrated circuits. Passive thin-film circuits are

Exhibit 3
MICROMODULE RADIO CIRCUIT

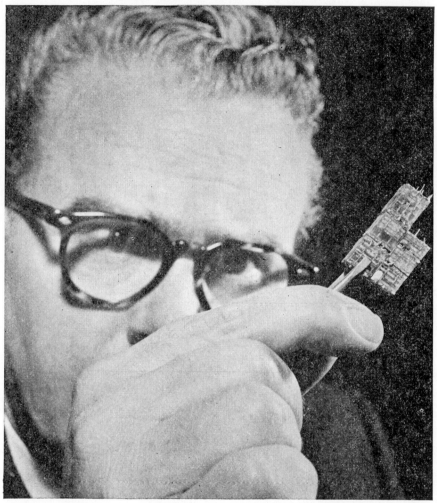

Courtesy: Radio Corporation of America

This photograph shows, encapsulated, "the works" of a military radio prepared by RCA for the U.S. Signal Research and Development Laboratory.
The tiny micromodules, circuit-building blocks, are a third of an inch on each
side and do the work of full-sized discrete components. The basic structure is
planned to allow the incorporation of thin-film and integrated circuits as
they become available.

currently combined with discrete active components in a number of
applications. The result is called a hybrid circuit.

3. *Semiconductor-Integrated Circuits.*   Integrated circuits, produced
by semiconductor manufacturing methods, contain not only the passive
components, but also active components such as transistors, all in a single

Exhibit 4

TYPICAL MANUFACTURING PROCESS

FABRICATION OF MOTOROLA INTEGRATED CIRCUITS

1   EPITAXIAL WAFER

A layer of N-type silicon is epitaxially grown on a P-type silicon substrate, becoming a single crystal extension of the substrate wafer. This provides a PN junction at the point where the layers join. The entire surface is then protected with a silicon dioxide (glass) layer. The epitaxial layer ultimately becomes the collector for transistors or an element for diodes or junction capacitors.

2   ISOLATION MASKING

"Windows" are selectively etched through the oxide coating to prepare for isolation diffusion. The surrounding oxide is masked against the etching process by microphotolithographic techniques. These advanced processes make possible uniform, precise placement of multiple integrated circuit patterns during Motorola's "batch" processing of many wafers at one time.

5   SECOND DIFFUSION

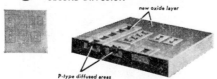

A P-type diffusion of much shorter duration than the previous isolation diffusion process forms the transistor base regions, resistors, and diode and capacitor anodes for the final circuit elements. Note that as the diffused material enters the wafer it also diffuses laterally, forming each junction on the surface at a protected location under the oxide coating.

6   EMITTER/CATHODE/CROSSOVER MASKING

Again the oxide coating is selectively etched (using microphotolithographic techniques) at locations precisely indexed to the partial components laid down during the previous diffusion procedure. In the case of resistors (which were deposited in the last diffusion process), no further formation is required. Hence, these areas will remain beneath the oxide during this masking step.

9   METALLIZATION

A thin, even coating of metal is evaporated over the entire surface of each wafer. Following another precise photo-masking step, the metal layer is selectively etched to leave a pattern of interconnections between transistors, resistors, diodes, and other circuit elements. Some layer areas of metal may be left to form silicon oxide dielectric capacitors in conjunction with the underlying substrate.

10   WAFER SCRIBING

At this point all components and interconnections of the circuits have been formed. Wafers are then scribed into individual circuits for mounting to the ten-lead headers. All preceding fabrication processes are applied to wafers containing many integrated circuits, and the simultaneous processing of a large number of wafers, makes possible large-volume, low-cost circuits with a high degree of uniformity.

Courtesy of Motorola Semiconductor Products, Inc.

Exhibit 4 (Continued)

Production processes used in fabricating Motorola's advanced integrated circuits are given here as a guide in understanding typical processing techniques. The methods outlined are not limited to any single Motorola circuit type, but are descriptive of the general approach used in custom and standard integrated circuits being produced by Motorola.

3 FIRST DIFFUSION

new oxide layer

P-diffused area

Diffusion of a P-type impurity into the exposed wafer areas pro-des isolation where needed in the final circuit by forming "chan-ls" through to the basic P-type substrate. The isolated "islands" N-type silicon thus formed make possible the deposition of mul-le elements on the same wafer without creating unwanted com-on connections between elements. A new oxide layer is formed er the exposed areas after isolation diffusion is completed.

4 RESISTOR/BASE/ANODE MASKING

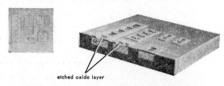

etched oxide layer

Windows are etched through the second oxide layer at locations suitable for positioning of transistor base regions, resistors, and the anode portions of diodes and junction capacitors which are to be used in the completed circuit. Precise masking and alignment techniques used at the various process points maintain exact placement of the multiple components to be used in each of hundreds of circuits.

7 THIRD DIFFUSION

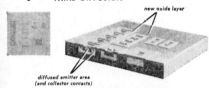

new oxide layer

*diffused emitter area
(and collector contacts)*

Diffusion of an N+ material forms transistor emitter areas, node regions for diodes and capacitors, degenerative layers for uit contacts, and crossovers. In some circuit types, low value stors are also formed at this time. The formation of a number ifferent circuit functions simultaneously, in this manner, lends f to close control of overall circuit performance.

8 INTERCONNECTION MASKING

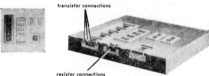

transistor connections

resistor connections

Patterns to form the connections between circuit components are etched on each wafer. This step exposes each circuit component at the proper point to allow for "wiring" of the circuit during metallization. Again as in all previous masking steps, precision masking protects any component junctions formed during foregoing diffusion processes. Tin oxide or other thin film resistors may be deposited on the silicon dioxide if needed for proper circuit performance. Additional photo-masking and etching steps produce the proper geometry.

11 DIE AND WIRE BONDING

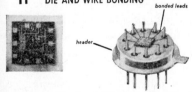

bonded leads

header

After separation into individual circuits, each chip is mounted on a ceramic wafer, then to a header by means of a very high temperature eutectic solder. Short wires, .001" in diameter, are bonded from the circuit to the proper header leads. This rugged mounting method and the advanced wire bonding techniques used make it possible for Motorola circuits to withstand severe centrifuge, shock and vibration conditions.

12 HERMETIC WELDING

completed unit

The addition of a welded cap, providing a hermetic seal for each Motorola integrated circuit, completes the fabrication process. Each unit then undergoes a 3-foot drop test on a maple block, stabilization baking, and 20,000 g centrifuge testing in accordance with military specifications to assure ruggedness and reliability.

Exhibit 5

CAPABILITIES OF MICROCIRCUITS*

	Circuit Type		
	Discrete Components	*Thin-Film Hybrid*	*Semiconductor Integrated*
Reliability per function (mean time to failure, hours).................	10^6	10^7	10^8
Price per function....................	$20	$20–$40	$20–$80
Resistance range (ohms)..............	$1–10^6$	$10^2–10^5$	$10^2–10^4$
Capacitance, maximum (farads)........	10^{-5}	10^{-7}	10^{-8}
Inductance, maximum (henries)........	10^{-2}	10^{-4}	Negligible
Speed (megocycles):			
Pulse repetition....................	20	20	5–10
Gain—band width..................	100–400	100–400	50
Temperature coefficient, parts per million/degrees centigrade.......	±50	±1,000	±1,000
Ability to breadboard................Excellent		Good	Poor
Design to production time.............	Days	Weeks	Months
Change flexibility....................Excellent		Medium	Poor
Packing density (parts/cubic feet).......	10^5	10^7	10^8

* Compiled from industry sources.

block. This approach is generally dependent upon the skills utilized in the manufacture of discrete semiconductors, such as diffusion, alloying, and masking. Exhibit 4 provides a detailed description of a typical process for manufacturing integrated circuits.

4. *Functional Blocks.* These are also referred to as molecular electronics. They are the theoretical ultimate in microelectronics. They would utilize electron and nuclear spins, force fields, and other physical properties of materials to perform a complete circuit function within a single piece of material. Despite the existence of similar-sounding trade names, most of the work in this area is still in the basic research stage.

These four approaches are not mutually exclusive, and many companies are using hybrid systems to get the most mileage out of the current state of the art. Because of the number of hybrid approaches available and the number of companies carrying on the research and development programs in this area, there can be and is considerable overlap in the way terms are used. In this note, and in the appropriate case, p. 354, the term "thin film" will refer to circuit sections which have only passive elements deposited on the substrate, and the term "integrated circuit" will mean semiconductor-based circuits, usually modified silicon blocks, on which other components are added by diffusion, alloying, or deposition. Hybrid thin-film circuits are those which have discrete active components attached to the passive thin-film circuit.

Technical Considerations

Although reduced size is the feature which most readily distinguishes the results of these technological advances, the success of each advance is

Exhibit 6

SIZE TRENDS IN ELECTRONIC SYSTEMS ILLUSTRATED

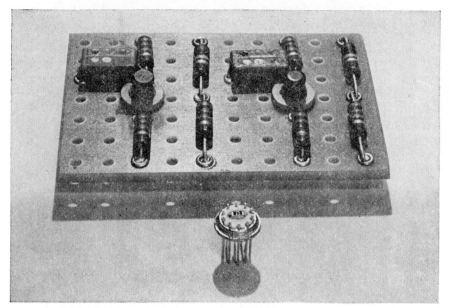

Courtesy: Motorola Semiconductor Products, Inc.

Integrated circuit amplifier in front of the breadboard of the same amplifier using discrete components. The integrated circuit mounting is typically 0.36 inches in diameter.

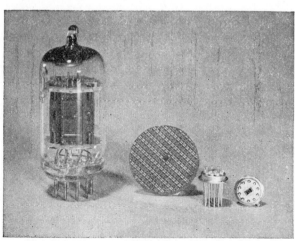

Courtesy: Motorola Semiconductor Products, Inc.

Comparison of size between a vacuum tube, an integrated circuit wafer containing a number of identical circuits, and two views of a two-stage, high-frequency amplifier utilizing an integrated circuit.

Exhibit 7

SIZE TRENDS IN ELECTRONIC SYSTEMS

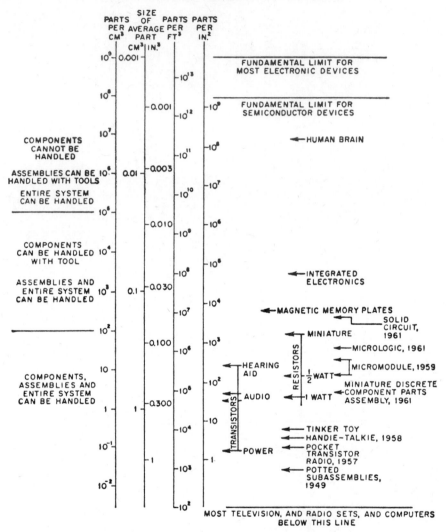

Packing density of electronic devices and circuits (from Edward Keonjian, *Microelectronics* (New York: McGraw-Hill Book Co., Inc., copyright 1963; used by permission).

determined by its ability to meet a number of important needs of electronic systems.

3. *Application or Functional Performance.* Within their limitations, microelectronic devices have provided performances at least equivalent to standard devices. For applications such as military computers and guidance systems and aerospace instrumentation, the advantages of increased re-

Exhibit 8

VACUUM DEPOSITION SYSTEM

Courtesy: U.S. Naval Avionics Facility, Indianapolis

A four-chamber vacuum deposition system built for the Bureau of Naval Weapons Industry Preparedness Measure conducted by the Naval Avionics Facility, Indianapolis, Indiana. The ultraclean air chambers at each end of the vacuum chambers complete the cleaning-deposition-photolithographic complex required to produce thin-film circuit panels at the rate of 480 square inches of four-layer circuitry per eight-hour day. The unit was built by IBM Federal Systems Division.

liability and reduced size and weight are extremely important. The major limitations on performance have been:

1. The devices are available only at low power levels and not for high-power circuits, electromechanical devices, and power supplies.
2. Serious heat-dissipation problems occur in high-density circuits which degrade performance. Although the ability to operate at low power reduces the magnitude of this problem, temperature sensitivity and differential thermal expansion are still serious problems in thin-film and integrated circuits.
3. High-frequency limitations still require the use of vacuum tubes in microwave systems.
4. Cost and manufacturing methods considerations favor simplified, standardized, high-unit-volume applications.

Reliability.   Unless systems based upon microelectronics are more reliable than conventional systems, they cannot find markets in military or commercial applications. Maintenance and repair of these circuits is out of the question. When a circuit fails, it must be replaced with a whole new

Exhibit 9

SCHEMA OF PROCESS FOR THIN-FILM CIRCUITS BASED ON EQUIPMENT IN EXHIBIT 8

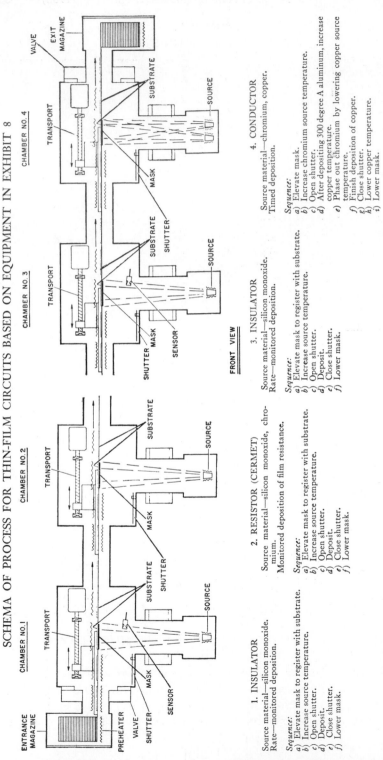

FRONT VIEW

1. INSULATOR

Source material—silicon monoxide.
Rate—monitored deposition.

Sequence:
a) Elevate mask to register with substrate.
b) Increase source temperature.
c) Open shutter.
d) Deposit.
e) Close shutter.
f) Lower mask.

2. RESISTOR (CERMET)

Source material—silicon monoxide, chromium.
Monitored deposition of film resistance.

Sequence:
a) Elevate mask to register with substrate.
b) Increase source temperature.
c) Open shutter.
d) Deposit.
e) Close shutter.
f) Lower mask.

3. INSULATOR

Source material—silicon monoxide.
Rate—monitored deposition.

Sequence:
a) Elevate mask to register with substrate.
b) Increase source temperature.
c) Open shutter.
d) Deposit.
e) Close shutter.
f) Lower mask.

4. CONDUCTOR

Source material—chromium, copper.
Timed deposition.

Sequence:
a) Elevate mask.
b) Increase chromium source temperature.
c) Open shutter.
d) After depositing 300 degree A aluminum, increase copper temperature.
e) Phase out chromium by lowering copper source temperature.
f) Finish deposition of copper.
g) Close shutter.
h) Lower copper temperature.
i) Lower mask.

By heating source materials, a vapor stream of particles rises through the source gate valve with the shutter open, then passes through the apertures of the graphite mask and condenses on the substrate, producing the desired pattern. When a new substrate is introduced into the system from the entrance magazine, all of the substrates index one place, and the substrate in No. 4 chamber stores in the exit magazine.

Source: Same as Exhibit 8.

unit. This increased cost of replacement must be offset by an order-of-magnitude increase in the mean time between failures (MTBF). Exponents of microelectronics are counting on an even greater reliability improvement. It has been this potential for greater over-all reliability which has led the government to underwrite the development of micro-electronic circuits.

The principal reasons for conventional circuit failures are:

1. Joint or connector failure.
2. Component failure.
3. Deterioration due to environmental conditions such as heat, vibration and shock.
4. Improper or marginal use due to poor design or fabrication.

Theoretically, integrated circuitry should contribute considerably to the solution of all four of these problems. As standard design practice moves from discrete components toward functional blocks, the number of external connections is reduced rapidly. The introduction of the mechanized production equipment needed to handle the process flow should produce greater product uniformity. Emphasis on the modular design concept should result in more careful design and a reduction in the number of components. The use of integrated circuits puts pressure on the designer to reduce the number of different circuits used in order to increase the yield of the manufacturing process. Redesign under the concept of integrated circuits has led to a 50 per cent reduction in the number of component equivalents in certain small computers.

The few independent tests performed so far indicate that integrated circuits can give a 10- to 100-time improvement in reliability. Actually, the problems of achieving a meaningful reliability measurement are quite serious. Circuits have become so reliable that millions of hours of expensive laboratory testing are needed to establish the standard measurements. Even then, these efforts are not true substitutes for millions of hours of field testing.

In some applications the reduction in system size and weight gained from microcircuits is sufficient to allow designers to consider the use of redundant circuits in order to enhance total system reliability.

Size and Weight. While reliability has been the principal focus of government-financed research and development, the size and weight reductions realized have been a real advantage in space-age applications. The limits of component density for the competing approaches are shown in Exhibits 5 and 7. One Navy program, which is now operational, has led to the replacement of the standard transistorized plug-in cards on Navy avionic digital navigation computers by silicon integrated circuits. This has yielded an 80 per cent weight reduction and a 5 to 10 per cent purchase cost reduction. In the redesigned system the Navy expects to realize a 95 per cent weight reduction and an 80 per cent volume reduction. A guidance system manufacturer reports a 100-to-one size reduction and a 50-to-one weight reduction in logic circuits.

Because of their small size, microelectronic circuits are produced in sheets, each of which may contain as many as a hundred individual circuits. Most operations in the process are chemical or vacuum-metallurgical in nature and are mechanized. Hand operations are avoided wherever possible.

Speed. In modern high-speed computers the speed of the memory and logic units is limited by the travel time between components and the waiting times for the circuits to switch. By reducing the number of components and the distance between them, microelectronic circuits improve the potential computer performance considerably. At present, it is possible to achieve slightly higher switching speeds with thin-film hybrids than with integrated circuits, but semiconductor manufacturers expect that they can eventually accomplish anything with integrated circuits that can be done with discrete semiconductor components.

Tolerances. This same argument applies to tolerances. Except for digital circuits which do not require close tolerances, the further wide-spread use of thin-film and integrated circuit techniques rests on the ability of the manufacturers to achieve the necessary tolerances at high yields. Thin-film deposition techniques can currently give capacitors and resistors with value tolerances of about 20 per cent. In addition, the values produced by a controlled process apparently change with the application because "component" values appear to be interdependent. Many companies, therefore, are using thin-film hybrids for digital circuits and waiting to see how the technology develops before going further.

Other Factors. Exhibit 5 shows the factors which industry experts have mentioned as being relevant to a management appraisal of the effects of microelectronics. Several of these are concerned with manufacturing methods as well as the performance of the end product.

Production Methods

Conventional assemblies utilize printed circuits to which small, carefully designed components are connected by soldered or welded leads. There are a number of ways of orienting the components and the support structures to conserve space and improve connection life. The resulting modules are frequently encapsulated in plastic resins to improve product reliability.

Thin-film manufacture deals primarily with the deposition of resistors, capacitors, and interconnections. In one process, an optically smooth substrate (glass, quartz, or glazed ceramic) is cleaned chemically and ultrasonically. The substrate is then undercoated with a layer of silicon monoxide. Then, successive layers of selected materials are vacuum-deposited through masks to build up in specific areas connectors, resistors, capacitor dielectrics, and insulators. The process takes place in a vacuum chamber in which the material is vaporized and deposits on the exposed surfaces (see Exhibit 9). Refractory metals such as tantalum and tungsten, which vaporize only at extremely high temperatures, are deposited by cathodic sputtering. In the sputtering process the circuit substrate is placed in a vacuum between two electrodes. The cathode, made of the material to be deposited, is bombarded by positively charged gas ions, usually argon. Atoms of the cathode are ejected and deposited on suitably exposed portions of the substrate. Other production methods under consideration include ion beam deposition. This is an experimental technique which has the potential advantage of allowing a number of materials to be deposited without masks, a molecule at a time. It is further possible that automatic programming could make possible the accurate and economical use of the ion beam to manufacture custom circuits.

Masks are usually prepared by photoengraving methods in which a light-sensitive emulsion or "resist" is applied over the mask material. The emulsion is then exposed through a contact negative of the circuit pattern. This polymerizes the resist, and the unpolymerized portion is dissolved off. The shape of the area to be coated is thus etched out of the mask. In the manufacturing of tantalum resistors the material is deposited over the whole surface of the circuit, and the resist is applied directly to the resulting surface. Completed circuit layers may be anodized or gold-coated to protect against corrosion. Exhibits 8 and 9 illustrate the manufacture of thin-film circuits. Circuits are usually prepared on six-inch-diameter wafers, which are then cut or scribed and broken into individual circuits. Final lead-wire attachment is performed by hand under a microscope.

The manufacture of integrated circuits requires semiconductor device techniques plus thin-film techniques. Exhibit 4 illustrates a typical process in detail. Exhibit 6 shows the size of a circuit wafer and a mounted circuit.

Functional blocks have not yet reached the manufacturing stage.

Costs

The available studies of manufacturing costs and selling prices indicate a market situation much like that which has affected transistors since 1959, except that the factory cost of integrated circuits may fall even more rapidly. One study indicates that the factory cost of integrated circuits produced at a rate of 75,000 per month is a little over a dollar each. At the rate of a million circuits per month, this could drop to 45 cents each. Germanium transistors made individually in large automated plants cost about 30 cents each. Thin-film circuits in like volume would cost between 30 and 55 cents each, plus the added cost of the discrete active components. These economics definitely favor the use of integrated circuits for high-volume applications.

Even the 75,000-units-per-month level, however, is currently unrealistic for anything other than a large digital computer manufacturer, whose systems use many similar circuits. The same potential for overcapacity exists in the area of thin films. A small production line such as that shown in Exhibit 8 can produce 5,000 to 10,000 four-layer circuits per shift. The system is automated so that a turntable, very similar to that found in a juke box, brings materials to the vaporizer in the proper sequence, while a changer simultaneously switches masks.

For a few years, at least, the relevant question will be how the costs compare for producing circuits in small quantities. Over the next several years, discrete component circuits will probably continue to have the cost and flexibility edge for small lots, although military reliability and size requirements may rule them out of many areas. For small lots, thin-film hybrid units are cheaper than custom-designed integrated circuits. This is due to the setup costs, which include the making of masks and the running-in and stabilizing of the production process. If one is starting from outside the semiconductor industry, thin-film hybrids require considerably less capital investment than integrated circuits. Presumably, a firm already engaged in the large-scale manufacture of semiconductors has a decided edge in investment cost, since much of the available equipment and facilities can be utilized for integrated circuit manufacture. Semiconductor manufacture is a capital-intensive operation. The amount of capital required will depend in large part on the kinds of yields which the manufacturers can achieve. At present, yields under 10 per cent are not at all unusual, even for proven processes of integrated circuit manufacture. Fifty per cent is perhaps the expected yield in the long run.

The cost-per-circuit figures cited above related to production costs in high volumes. Manufacturers state that prices will remain considerably above these levels for some time to come. They point out that this is likely because of low process yields, the high capital investment costs, and large investments for engineering and R & D. Nevertheless, prices will probably fall rapidly as more companies attempt to capture the market now held by Texas Instruments, Motorola Semiconductor, and Fairchild Semiconductors. One small producer has forecast a $40 per integrated circuit average industry selling price for 1963, $22 for 1964, and $14 for 1965. At the same time, he expects total dollar volume to triple. The price for commonly used digital circuits is considerably below this average price.

Market Potential

Exhibits 1 and 2 show estimates of the future market for microelectronic circuits. Whether these prove too optimistic or not depends on the speed with which costs can be reduced and capabilities improved. Exhibit 10 is one projection of what will happen to the costs of microcircuits over a ten-year period. Those who take a less optimistic viewpoint note that the diffusion cycles of new products in the electronics industry run five to seven years and also point out that microcircuits may offer advantages that are beyond the needs of most product lines. Present techniques produce reliability enough for most applications, and there is

Exhibit 10

PROJECTIONS OF COST AND RELIABILITY TRENDS
FOR EQUIVALENT CIRCUITS*

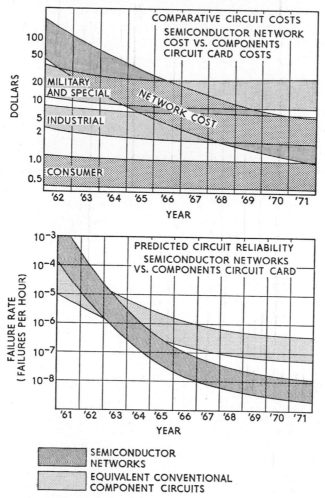

* Both projections are by courtesy of Texas Instruments, Inc. They were originally made public in October, 1961.

no use in reducing the size of industrial instruments and TV sets when we still have to see the output and read the setting on the control knobs.

No one is making any predictions about who is going to sell what to whom. Some 60 companies are currently engaged in the development and manufacture of thin-film or integrated circuits. Some 30 firms already have circuits on the market, or at least advertise them. Most large manufacturers of components or systems have some in-house capability, at least in the area of thin films. Many of these are holding or monitoring programs aimed at keeping current on the state of the art and at seeing what parts of the technology can be adapted to fill the particular needs of the firm.

The dollar volume of microelectronic circuit sales that will be achieved over the next five years depends in large part on the future activities of the Department of Defense, which is supporting the development of new techniques and hoping to see a 10 to 15 per cent reduction in electronic systems costs by 1973 due to this advance. Manufacturers report that contracting officers are pushing hard for the incorporation of integrated circuits into current procurements, and are pushing for standardization to reduce costs and allow for interchangeability of replacement parts. On the other hand, the Office of Electronics of the DOD has issued a policy statement which calls for the support of microelectronics, but urges that the users not press for standardization on the ground that the technical climate is too fluid and offers many opportunities for continuing and worthwhile-innovation.

Two leaders in the field of integrated circuits have adopted special product strategies designed to meet the demand for low-volume custom circuits at a reasonable price. Motorola Semiconductor Products has developed a "multiple chip" process in which the circuit is made of several different functional chips, instead of a single block (see Exhibit 11). Commonly used circuit portions are made in quantity and then assembled to form the desired special circuits. The Texas Instruments "master-slice" technique is based on the manufacture in large volume of standard silicon wafers containing many component equivalents, but no

Exhibit 11

ALTERNATIVES IN INTEGRATED CIRCUITS

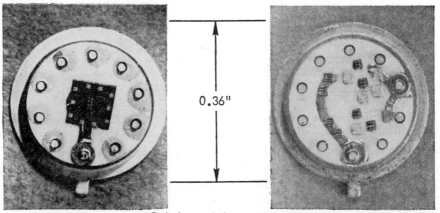

Both photographs by courtesy of Motorola Semiconductor Products, Inc.

Single-block integrated circuit   *Multiple-chip integrated circuit*

These two photographs show two methods of achieving the same circuit, a high-speed translator. Both circuits are mounted on the same size of transistor header and have essentially identical performance characteristics.

aluminum interconnections. These interconnections are then laid down through a special mask to complete the custom circuit.

Research and Development

While the industry wonders whether microelectronics will eventually obsolete a number of job and product classifications currently in use, there is an unprecedented demand for physicists, metallurgists, chemists, and semiconductor engineers to develop further and apply the state of the art. Even circuit engineers seem to be in increasing demand, although an important premium is being placed on experience or training in one or more of the above-mentioned sciences. The reason for this is the fact that integrated circuits designers must be familiar not only with electronic circuits per se, but also with the fabrication procedures and characteristics of semiconductor processes. The reduction of conventional circuits to integrated circuit form requires special knowledge about a new technical frontier. All manufacturers of integrated circuits offer design assistance, but one major manufacturer warns systems manufacturers that they will need a staff of specialists capable of correlating conventional circuit design with the unique requirements of integrated circuit technology, saying: "Retention of specific features of each manufacturer's equipment demands an in-house engineering effort."

Several manufacturers feel that the factor which will limit the future growth of integrated circuits is the shortage of personnel to design and evaluate these circuits. This shortage stems from the combination of an actual shortage of trained personnel and the apparent unwillingness of practicing designers to attempt to learn how to adjust their design and evaluation techniques to the requirements of this new technology. This problem has so concerned Motorola Semiconductor Products that this company is now offering an intensive program at its headquarters to train practicing engineers in integrated circuit design and fabrication. This is being done with full recognition that much of the company's know-how will thereby reach its competitors.

One group has estimated the cost of supporting several levels of research on integrated circuit and thin-film technology. If a company is desirous of gaining a major foothold in this field and in contributing to the advancement of the state of the art, they calculate that it should be prepared to spend over $2 million on capital equipment and an annual budget of about $1.4 million to support about 50 researchers. A more limited program, requiring about 22 men, an annual budget of $690,000, and $1 million in equipment, would produce only limited innovation but would maintain a competitive competence. If an electronics company wished to monitor developments and have a nucleus of personnel capable of applying know-how as it becomes known, they estimate that it should be prepared to invest about $0.5 million in equipment and pay the $275,000 annual budget of a 10-man group.

One major supplier of components has reported that its research and development program on integrated and thin film circuits utilized six Ph.D., eight Master, and eighteen Bachelor degree scientists and engineers, and 32 technicians. This did not include the large number of professionals working on components for discrete microelectronic circuits, nor did it include any production personnel. The equipment costs cited for this R & D effort were also high. One piece of analytical equipment cost $110,000, and a production line to build prototype integrated circuits for customer evaluation cost $250,000.

APPENDIX

GLOSSARY OF TERMS

Breadboard: A pilot circuit in which the various components are connected by detachable wires which can be changed easily for test purposes.

Cordwood: The technique of producing circuits by stacking discrete parts as close as possible and interconnecting them into circuits by welding or soldering leads together.

Micromodule: The technique of mounting components on small ceramic wafers. The wafers are then stacked and connected by wires rising through uniformly spaced notches to provide interconnections and structural rigidity. See Exhibit 3.

N-type material: An impure semiconductor material in which the predominant current-carrying charges are negative. This characteristic is produced in pure semiconductor materials by adding impurities such as phosphorus.

P-type material: An impure semiconductor material in which the predominant current-carrying charges are positive. This characteristic is produced in pure semiconductor materials by adding impurities such as boron.

Redundancy: The making of additional electrical paths available above and beyond the number functionally required.

Resist: A material such as ink, paint, polymer, or metallic plating used to protect portions of a surface from the action of coatings, etchants, or plating.

Sputtering: A process for making thin-film circuits in which atoms are ionized and set into motion by bombardment with gas molecules propelled by an electric field.

Substrate:	Thin metal, glass, or ceramic material on which thin-film circuits are deposited. Silicon crystals used as a base for integrated circuits also are referred to as substrates.
Swiss cheese:	The technique of producing circuits by inserting components into holes in printed circuit boards, and connecting them to the circuit by soldering, thermocompression, bonding, or conductive epoxyadhesives.
Thermo compression bonding:	The joining-together of two materials without an intermediate material by the application of heat and pressure, but not electric current as in welding.
Thin-film circuit:	A product in which conducting, insulating, or semiconducting materials are deposited as films on a single passive substrate to perform a circuit function.
Vacuum deposition:	A process for making thin films in which the material to be deposited is first evaporated in a high vacuum and then condensed on a thin metal or glass plate suspended directly above it.
Wafer:	See Substrate.

THERMAL DYNAMICS CORPORATION (D)

JAMES BROWNING and Merle Thorpe decided to hire George Klasson to supervise the plasma cutter project; the decision was made with the expectation that at least three other men would be assigned on a full-time basis to work on the project under Klasson's supervision. The Board of Directors approved the decision, with all members saying they realized this meant a major commitment. Management's chief reasons for this decision included confidence that the technical objectives could be achieved, belief in a large potential market, the personal interest of Browning, and the company's cash balance of $100,000, which would make it possible to support the project for some time even if sales declined.

Final Development

Klasson accepted the offer and joined TDC in April, 1960. Since he had no background in plasma technology, he initially worked very closely with Browning. As he learned more about plasma and the plasma cutter, he relied less upon Browning and assumed more responsibility for all phases of the plasma cutter project. This was in accordance with Thorpe's general policy of giving a man an area of responsibility and letting him "carry the ball."

Klasson assumed responsibility for the further technical development of the new product, and under his supervision a new concept of electrode design was developed which increased electrode life from about 10 to 30 hours to over 50 hours. The tungsten electrodes used in the old design cost about $22 each, while those used in the new design cost about $3.00 each.

Development work also involved what Klasson called a "thousand little problems," many of them involving slight changes in the internal geometry of the plasma cutter.

In June, 1960, Klasson drew up a schedule to assist in planning the various activities associated with the development of the new product. These included the following:

1. Design and manufacture of the handle.
2. Selection and ordering of the carriage for the torch.
3. Selection and ordering of the exhaust system.
4. Selection and ordering of the face shield and gloves.
5. Selection or design of a coolant circulator.
6. Design and manufacture of the control console.

7. Selection of a power supply.
8. Selection and ordering of packaging.
9. Consultation with public health officials in regard to possible health hazards.
10. Design and printing of promotional material.
11. Writing and printing of an instruction booklet.

For each activity, Klasson estimated the number of months needed and indicated on a graph the start and completion of each task, with particular attention to when each item would be ready for shipment. He had no desire to delay introduction because a particular activity, such as writing the instruction booklet, had not been started in time. The responsibility for all of these activities rested with Klasson, who had three men working full time with him on the project.

Machine-driven oxyacetylene installations included equipment for holding the cutting torch and moving it across the material to be cut. Often, there was also equipment (called a pantograph) which would permit a number of cutting torches to cut a particular shape simultaneously, reproducing a "master shape." TDC was designing the plasma cutter so that it could be installed on this existing equipment.

However, a problem was presented, in that existing equipment had been designed with the relatively slow cutting speeds of oxyacetylene torches in mind. The plasma cutter was able to cut mild steel much faster, but was limited to some extent by the speed of existing devices which moved a cutting torch across the material to be cut. TDC planned to approach manufacturers of this accessory equipment in order to persuade them to manufacture special high-speed equipment.

During the summer of 1960 the Ajax Corporation[1] (which had been selling a plasma torch for cutting purposes) offered to license TDC to use all Ajax patents which applied to plasma technology. Ajax indicated that it considered certain of its patents to be basic and implied that the TDC general purpose torch infringed upon these patents. Ajax asked for royalties which, in the opinion of TDC's management, were completely unreasonable.

Browning had known that Ajax had applied for over thirty patents pertaining to plasma technology. Most of these were still pending, so he had had no opportunity to become familiar with them. However, the patents which Ajax claimed to be basic had been issued several years earlier, and Browning was familiar with these. Both Browning and TDC's patent counsel had studied these Ajax patents at the time they were issued. They applied to what Ajax called "wall stabilization," which was similar to the "gas-sheath stabilization" and "vortex stabilization" that TDC utilized.

According to Browning, the essential question was whether gas-sheath stabilization was a form of wall stabilization. He said: "The patents are

---

[1] The name of this company has been disguised.

complex and can only be interpreted by one intimate with the field." TDC had applied for patents on gas-sheath stabilization, but these were still pending. The problem was further complicated by the fact that the theoretical understanding of the mechanism of gas stabilization was poor and was the continuing subject of investigation by various individuals interested in the field.

Browning and TDC's patent attorney jointly studied the patents for several days; they included in their study certain patents which had been recently issued to other companies active in the field. They concluded that TDC was not infringing upon the Ajax patents, and Browning made the decision to reject the Ajax offer and to proceed without interruption on the development of the plasma cutter. He was aware that Ajax might choose to involve TDC in long and costly legal proceedings, but he thought TDC's patent position was sound. Another factor, although one not heavily weighting his decision, involved the possible antitrust implications of a large company such as Ajax trying to stamp out a company with only forty-five personnel.

In November, 1960, TDC was issued a patent on gas-sheath stabilization. Management thought that the issuance of this patent reduced considerably the probability of patent infringement proceedings.

In August of 1960, Klasson and Thorpe "froze" the design of the plasma cutter. The decision had been postponed for some weeks while certain variables of electrode design were being investigated. Despite the fact that the continuing experimentation was leading to greater understanding of the electrode design, they finally decided upon a particular design so that components might be ordered and market introduction might take place several months hence without further delay.

During the fall of 1960, laboratory work with the plasma cutter centered upon the gathering of performance and cost data which could be used in promotional literature and in advising prospective customers as to how the plasma cutter could be used to solve their particular problems. Data on the performance and operating costs of the TDC plasma cutter, the Ajax torch, and oxyacetylene torches are given in Exhibit 1.

In early December, 1960, TDC made arrangements to sell plasma cutters to three different companies on a trial basis. If, after forty-five days' use in the field, the companies were satisfied with the performance of the new product, they would pay TDC for the machines. (TDC would have preferred outright sale of the plasma cutters, but the prospective customers insisted on trial purchases because the product was new and unproved.) TDC anticipated keeping in close touch with these customers in order to learn of any problems arising from the use of the product in the field.

Klasson was also taking steps to insure that health hazards or rumors of health hazards might not interfere with the development of the market for the new product. He knew that an operator would have to wear an apron, a mask, and protective gloves when operating the equipment. He knew there was a danger that toxic gases might be formed as a by-product, necessitating an exhaust system. He was not sure whether there was any danger of ear damage from the shrill screams of the equipment or of inhalation of suspended metal particles. Accordingly, Klasson had arranged for several representatives of the U.S. Department of Public

Exhibit 1

COMPARATIVE COST AND PERFORMANCE DATA—
CUTTING MILD STEEL PLATE

	TDC Plasma Cutter		Oxyacetylene Torch		Ajax Plasma Torch§	
Plate* Thickness (Inches)	Cutting Speed† (Inches/ Minute)	Cutting Cost‡ (Cents/Foot)	Cutting Speed (Inches/ Minute)	Cutting Cost (Cents/Foot)	Cutting Speed (Inches/ Minute)	Cutting Cost‡ (Cents/Foot)
¼	525	0.23¢/ft.	26	2.00¢/ft.	525	0.83¢/ft
½	200	0.65	22	2.60	...	...
¾	100	1.75	20	3.05	100	6.11
1...........	80	2.07	18	3.90	...	...
1½.........	50	...	16	...	...	...
2...........	40	3.10	13	5.15	40	10.93
3...........	20	...	10	...	...	...

* Material cut is ordinary mild steel.
† Cutting speeds given are not maximum but are limited by speed of traveling mechanism and available power.
‡ Cutting costs do not include overhead and amortization of equipment involved. Neither do they include replacement costs of electrode or nozzle for plasma torch.
  Assumed costs were the following: oxygen, 0.5 cents per cubic foot; natural gas, 0.08 cents per cubic foot; nitrogen, 1.38 cents per cubic foot; hydrogen, 2 cents per cubic foot; power, 1.05 cents per kilowatt-hour; labor, $2.00 per hour.
  § It is assumed that cutting speed, power consumption, and gas consumption are the same for the plasma torch as for the TDC plasma cutter. (In fact, cutting speed of the former is probably considerably less because of lower power capacity.) The plasma torch uses a mixture of 65 per cent argon and 35 per cent hydrogen for stabilizing gas.
  Assumed cost of argon: 10 cents per cubic foot.
  Investment costs might be as follows: oxyacetylene unit, $100; plasma cutter and associated equipment, $8,000; plasma torch and associated equipment, and "use" license, $8,000.
  Source: Thermal Dynamics Corporation.

Health to visit the TDC plant for several days, in order to test for possible health hazards and to make suggestions regarding such hazards.

Browning said that it would not be necessary for TDC to obtain any sort of underwriter's approval on the plasma cutter.

Management was not greatly concerned over promotion of the new product. Arrangements had been made for articles describing the product to appear in several technical journals in the late autumn of 1960; a picture of the plasma cutter in action would be the cover picture for two of these magazines. Securing this publicity had not been difficult, apparently due to the novelty of the product and the close relationship cultivated by management with the editors of various journals. Past experience had indicated that the publication of the articles would be followed by a deluge of letters inquiring about the new product.

TDC had prepared several pamphlets describing the company and the plasma cutter; these would be sent, along with a card requesting more information, to any prospective customer inquiring by mail about the plasma cutter. Subsequent follow-up would depend upon the method of distribution which TDC chose for the product.

This decision about channels of distribution was viewed by management as of particular importance in determining whether the "invention" became a significant "innovation." Management was considering five alternative methods of distribution:

1. To develop TDC's own sales force.
2. To establish an exclusive sales arrangement with a large company which produced and sold gases such as nitrogen and hydrogen.
3. To establish an exclusive sales arrangement with a large company which produced and sold electrical power supplies.
4. To establish nonexclusive arrangements with a large number of welding supply distributors.
5. To establish geographically exclusive sales arrangements with a number of manufacturers' representatives around the country.

One factor bearing upon this decision was the over-all size of the market. Management was particularly concerned that the demand for plasma cutters might grow so explosively that TDC would be unable to supply the market. Unsatisfied demand might cause other companies to enter the field; TDC might then find itself at a disadvantage in competing with large, well-financed companies having strong sales forces.

TDC was planning in terms of selling $1 million worth of plasma cutters (not including power supplies) in 1961. With the aid of extensive subcontracting, Browning thought it might be possible to supply several times that volume of plasma cutters to the market if needed. Management hesitated to estimate the total potential market for plasma cutters, but thought it might some day total many millions of dollars annually.

Plasma technology was developing rapidly, and Thermal Dynamics, Ajax,[2] and Western[2] were rapidly tying up a number of possible technical approaches to various problems through patent applications. Management thought that if potential competitors did not enter the field within the next year or so, they might never do so because of the lead that TDC would have built up in technical know-how and market acceptance.

This concern with meeting the demands of what might grow quickly into a very large market caused management to favor alternatives 2 and 3, in which established sales organizations could be enlisted to the TDC cause almost overnight.

A second factor, which management considered vital, was the importance of training salesmen in plasma technology and keeping them in touch with the anticipated rapid technical advance in the field. Management wondered whether a sales organization with other products to sell

---

[2] Names disguised.

would have the time or the interest to keep informed and to instruct potential customers in the use of the plasma cutters.

Producers of both gas and of electrical equipment would find the plasma cutter complementary to their lines. A TDC plasma cutter would use between $4.00 and $5.00 worth of hydrogen and nitrogen gas for each hour of operation. (However, there was some possibility that future technical development might result in practical air- or water-stabilized plasma cutters, both of which would offer large cost savings to users but little incentive for promotion by companies which sold industrial gases.) The plasma cutter would also be attractive to producers of electrical power supplies, inasmuch as about 50 to 75 per cent of the total price of a plasma cutter and accessory equipment ($7,500 to $12,000) was accounted for by the power supply.

Thermal Dynamics had been in contact with a large producer of electrical equipment which indicated a definite interest in handling the plasma cutter. This company's welding supply division had over a thousand salesmen. The firm produced the power supply which TDC offered with its general purpose torch.

The details of the proposed agreement had not been worked out, but would include the following features:

1. The electrical company would receive a discount from list price of about 35 per cent on the plasma cutter.
2. The agreement would be for three years and could be discontinued by either party on sixty days' notice.
3. List prices on the plasma cutter would be set by Thermal Dynamics.
4. TDC would have the responsibility for training the salesmen, although the electrical company would pay the salaries and expenses of the salesmen while they were attending whatever schools TDC might set up to instruct them.

Some of the alternative methods of distribution looked intriguing, but management had not had the time to investigate them fully. In addition, TDC did not want to "stir up the industry" by making inquiries among a number of possible channels of distribution.

A Point of Decision

Management considered this decision to be of paramount importance, not only in bringing about the widespread use of the new plasma cutter, but also its long-run implications for the distribution of other products the company might develop. Management wondered whether the proposed agreement with the electrical manufacturer should be accepted, or whether a decision should be deferred until additional information bearing upon alternative methods of distribution could be obtained.

APPENDIX

The Competitive Picture

Since the potential applications of plasma technology were so widespread, a number of organizations were engaged in research and development in this area. These included various agencies of the federal government, a number of universities, several nonprofit research institutes, and such companies as General Electric, General Dynamics, and Avco Corporation. Most of the effort had been directed toward research into the basic nature of plasma or toward development in regard to particular applications with which TDC had not been concerned, such as chemical synthesis or magnetohydrodynamics.

Besides TDC, there were two companies[3] offering plasma hardware to the market—the Ajax Corporation, a division of a large chemical company, and the Western Corporation, a small West Coast company.

Apparently, Ajax had been promoting its cutting torch only for the cutting of nonferrous materials. Browning estimated that Ajax had sold about 200 to 250 of these torches since the product was first introduced in 1958. Estimated cutting costs for this torch are given in Exhibit 1 (page 349). It had a considerably higher cutting cost than the TDC plasma cutter, and was not economically competitive with oxyacetylene torches for the cutting of mild steel. (The Ajax torch used relatively expensive argon gas and had a relatively slow cutting speed because its power capacity was only about 100 kilowatts.)

The Western Corporation offered a nontransferred-arch torch to the market. The product was not suitable for cutting, but had been used for spraying and as a general purpose research tool. Apparently, the company had sold the product through manufacturing representatives. Browning understood that this method had not been very successful, due to the fact that these representatives were not sufficiently knowledgeable in plasma technology.

Thermal Dynamics, in developing the plasma cutter, had moved into competition with a number of other cutting methods, including shearing, sawing, and oxyacetylene burning.

For ferrous material, oxyacetylene cutting was the most important of these methods by far. With this method, a preheat flame using oxygen and acetylene brought the edge of the steel up to a temperature of about 1,400 to 1,600 degrees Fahrenheit. When this temperature was reached, a stream of pure oxygen under pressure was directed upon the heated metal, producing a severing cut from the oxidation of the iron as well as the erosion of unoxidized molten metal.

Browning estimated that there were 4,000 to 7,000 machine-driven oxyacetylene cutting installations in the country and that the number of hand-held oxyacetylene torches was in the hundreds of thousands. Ajax was one of the numerous companies supplying gases and oxyacetylene cutting equipment to this industry.

In regard to mechanical cutting methods, Thermal Dynamics reported that a limited amount of testing had indicated that plasma cutting was considerably more economical than sawing for all thicknesses of material. However, for straight cuts, mechanical shearing was apparently less costly for thicknesses up to one-half inch; for thicker materials, plasma cutting had a cost advantage.

---

[3] The names of these companies have been disguised.

Age in the Research Group

Here is the administrative difficulty I mentioned: the maintenance of this talent and this atmosphere. Freedom, informality, and change are generally associated with youth. And an article by Dr. Alexander Kennedy ("Individual Reactions to Change," *The Lancet*, February, 1957) indicates that originality is also an attribute of young minds. Dr. Kennedy states:

"The human brain, in the most intelligent groups, is not mature until the age of 25, at which time there is still much more to be learnt. But after 25, there is a very slow decline in the speed of thought and the capacity for learning. Between 25 and 35 the seeds of a man's best ideas are laid down, even if they flourish much later. After 35, maturity and experience must compensate for the gradual but definite slowing of mental activity which is taking place.

"A few, with sound brains and well-trained habits of mind, can maintain their originality well into the senium; but in one whose ability has never been adequate, or whose decline has been more rapid than usual, the mental mechanisms by which he keeps up with his work and conceals the truth from himself and others are fully in operation by 40.

"The most powerful weapons protecting him are tradition and promotion by seniority. Too often the advice which should be given to a firm is: 'It would be economical to pension this man off generously—to pay him to stay away.' But by that time of life the currency acceptable to him is not so much cash as prestige."

I can only conclude, the management that wishes to obtain maximum effectiveness and originality in the solution of research problems from its R & D organization must constantly maintain a climate of youthfulness and challenge.

Dr. WARREN C. LOTHROP
Vice President
Arthur D. Little, Inc.

FROM: "What Top Management Must Know About Research and Development," *American Business*, August, 1958.

ELECTRONIC ASSOCIATES, INC.

IN LATE 1962 the management of Electronic Associates, Inc. (EAI), was watching carefully the developments taking place in the field of microelectronic circuits. When two of the firm's engineers, who were on educational leave, approached EAI management and requested permission to write a report on the company, the management suggested that the topic of microelectronic circuits was of considerable interest to it. This subject also interested the students, and on January 12, 1963, they submitted to Andrew Wollaston, Vice President of Corporate Planning, a technical report and specific recommendations. Exhibit 1 presents a

Exhibit 1

SUMMARY OF CONCLUSIONS AND RECOMMENDATIONS FROM THE REPORT ON MICROELECTRONICS

Two major facts point to the need for EAI to take immediate action with respect to microelectronics: (1) The innovation in microelectronics will have significant impact on EAI as well as the electronics industry; and (2) with EAI tending to move more and more into digital applications, the new microelectronic technology will affect EAI's product line sooner than it would if the company were producing only analogue equipment. It is apparent from industry information that digital components are well on the way in terms of research and development, and that many microelectronic processes are applicable to EAI digital circuitry.

Thus, as a first-action step, we recommend the establishment of a microelectronic study team, with an initial budget of $15,000 to $20,000. This budget is intended to cover, initially, a full-time administrative engineer to head the group for a six-month period. At the end of that time, it is expected that the company will be ready to decide on the next step. The innovation in microelectronics cuts across product lines and is not the type which would be introduced through one of the functional areas represented by product team members.

The study team should be composed of four members, besides the chairman, each working an average of less than one day a week on the project. The large team membership is recommended to permit effective communication with key departments, and to expedite the flow of information to the team chairman. Team membership should include a representative from Control Instrumentation, Computer Engineering, Marketing Services, and Production Engineering. The study team's functions should be:

1. To investigate applications of microelectronics to EAI's products.
2. To contact all companies knowledgeable in microelectronics technology and obtain all pertinent data available.
3. To become thoroughly familiar with the state of the art.

354

Exhibit 1 (Continued)

4. To set up information gathering, dissemination and retrieval systems.
5. To conduct a general program to inform all personnel of the need to gather information on microelectronics.
6. It is also recommended that EAI encourage and fully finance graduate study or outside courses in fields related to microelectronics, e.g., solid-state physics.

It is recommended that the group start as soon as possible with a detailed report on comparative costs, product-line and process applications, investment data, technical feasibility, and general progress due at the end of six months. It is also recommended that the Marketing Services representative begin to consider the feasibility of a marketing survey to determine the interest of EAI's customers in purchasing smaller analogue computers and other miniaturized equipment.

Assuming that the company will want the group's work to continue after the completion of the first phase, we recommend that EAI purchase representative component circuits and begin testing the applications in EAI products. This should lead to preliminary conclusions as to what technologies can be applied to various product lines.

The third recommendation is that relations be established with several different microelectronic circuit manufacturers. In addition to giving EAI access to different processes, this step will lessen the risks of loss of proprietary designs. If and when EAI should decide to purchase such circuits, different parts of a product could be contracted out to different manufacturers.

The knowledge gained by having a large number of contacts would also facilitate a transition into producing EAI's own microcircuits if management should decide to do so. EAI would be in a better position to know which process should be installed and perhaps how it should be operated.

The fourth recommendation concerns the gradual standardization and freezing of circuit designs. One of the advantages of microelectronic circuits is that a large number of identical circuits can be produced at low cost. To take fullest advantage of this fact, EAI will have to standardize and freeze the design on equipment manufactured by this method. Instead of small changes in design, EAI should plan a program of "saving up" many minor changes in design and then bring out a new-model system component incorporating all these changes. The timing of such circuit standardization would, to a large extent, depend on the cost savings realizable from using standardized microcircuits in large volumes.

The fifth recommendation is that EAI seek government-sponsored development projects in Production and Engineering for microelectronic components. Such projects would enable EAI personnel to gain firsthand familiarity with the technology; and in addition, EAI might be in a better position to obtain the information available to the government from efforts of other contractors in the field. EAI might be in a good position to obtain such contracts, since most of the research in microelectronics has been directed toward digital circuitry. EAI, with its design capabilities in analogue circuitry, might be in an excellent position to do research on the application of microelectronics to analogue circuits.

The sixth recommendation is that if trends toward digital circuit use continue, EAI should develop at least a partial in-house productive capability. Thin-film capability should exist by 1965–66. Thin films are currently thought to be the practical process for analog circuitry, and many digital integrated circuit processes utilize thin-film techniques in the latter stages of circuit-block

Exhibit 1 (*Concluded*)

construction. Thin films are the most technologically advanced technique at present and are a logical learning step forward from present skills in high-density packaging. If, in the long run, integrated circuit processes were chosen, it might be desirable to purchase partially completed wafers and use the technology acquired in thin films to complete a specific circuit. The process portion done by EAI would be consistent with acquired skills, and EAI would have retained the ability to custom-make circuit batches and also avoid releasing proprietary designs and circuit techniques to a supplier.

summary of their recommendations. The technical report was similar in content to the "Technical Note of Microelectronics (Mid-1963)" (page 326).

Background

In 1945, L. F. Christianson and ten associates, who had served together in the Army Signal Corps, founded EAI. They started out performing research and development for the government, mostly on X-Y plotters, computer plotters, and electronic systems. Early products included X-Y plotters and other data-plotting and -recording equipment.

By 1951, EAI management saw the need to manufacture proprietary products in order to generate sufficient profits for growth and began the development of a general purpose analog computer. Production of the first model started in 1952. By 1955, EAI had captured two thirds of the market for this product. See Exhibit 2 for a ten-year financial and statistical summary. By 1962, company sales had grown to $21.3 million, and over 1,400 people were employed. The corporate headquarters, main manufacturing plant, and development engineering laboratories were located at Long Branch, New Jersey; computational service centers at Princeton, New Jersey; Los Angeles, California; Brussels, Belgium; and Burgess Hill, England; and an engineering and manufacturing operation at Burgess Hill. Foreign sales accounted for 25 per cent of total revenues.

Profits had increased steadily, and EAI had achieved an excellent working capital position (see Exhibit 3). The company management felt that it had achieved a diversified product line. While the government, directly or indirectly, accounted for half of company sales, no single purchaser regularly accounted for as much as 10 per cent of total sales. On September 19, 1962, EAI was listed on the New York Stock Exchange.

Corporate Objectives

L. F. Christianson, President of EAI, had defined EAI's analog computer as a simulator, that is, an electronic device in which physical variables are represented by electrical voltage and which changes voltages in relation to each other in the same way that the variables in a problem change, thus simulating the conditions of the problem and yielding the same answers. Although the analog computer market was expected to continue to grow (from about $10 million at the beginning of 1957 to an

Exhibit 2

TEN-YEAR FINANCIAL AND STATISTICAL SUMMARY

	1953	1954	1955	1956	1957	1958	1959	1960	1961	1962
Orders received ($000)	1,700	4,016	7,081	11,002	10,536	14,542	14,013	15,171	18,637	22,574
Net sales (contracts completed) ($000)	4,274	4,060	5,484	8,817	12,248	10,216	14,482	15,105	18,684	21,306
Net income ($000) (after taxes)	130	246	493	973	979	314	803	828	1,112	1,821
Working capital ($000)	715	897	1,383	3,526	4,258	4,911	5,352	6,116	12,194	13,038
Long-term debt ($000)	34	35	28	1,612	1,543	1,531	484	566	3,550	3,446
Net property, plant, and equipment ($000)	208	441	504	956	1,243	1,322	1,936	2,233	2,541	3,088
Stockholders' equity ($000)	927	1,332	1,902	2,891	4,044	4,819	6,968	7,802	11,357	12,808
Capital shares outstanding*	593,557	655,617	721,046	735,006	744,381	767,374	836,640	837,542	924,314	907,719
Net income per share outstanding	$0.22	$0.38	$0.68	$1.32	$1.31	$0.41	$0.96	$0.99	$1.20	$2.01
Dividends per share†	$0.04	$0.05	$0.10	$0.10 + 5%	5%	2%	3%	5%	5%	5%
Number of associates‡	335	326	470	822	748	825	1,138	1,020	1,114	1,481

* Computed on number of shares outstanding at close of each period after giving retroactive effect to two-for-one splits in 1957 and 1955, and stock dividends as set forth above.
† Percentage figures refer to stock dividends issued in 1956, 1957, 1958, 1959, 1960, 1961, and 1962.
‡ Employees and principals in this firm are referred to as associates.

Exhibit 3

CONSOLIDATED BALANCE SHEET*

	December 31, 1962	December 31, 1961
ASSETS		
Current assets:		
Cash	$ 679,024	$ 1,104,092
Bank certificates of deposit and notes at cost, plus accrued interest	......	650,776
Receivables:		
Trade	5,662,552	4,998,280
Other	31,399	23,737
Prepaid expenses	51,031	48,722
	$ 6,424,006	$ 6,825,607
Inventories:		
Work in process	$ 5,638,560	$ 4,116,820
Less partial deliveries and progress billings	386,792	360,405
	$ 5,251,768	$ 3,756,415
Finished goods and components	2,137,472	1,405,121
Demonstration equipment	461,801	172,939
Raw materials and purchased parts	3,123,030	1,845,474
	$10,974,071	$ 7,179,949
Total Current Assets	$17,398,077	$14,005,556
Property, plant, and equipment:		
Land	$ 150,826	$ 145,613
Buildings	1,332,817	1,104,582
Machinery and equipment	2,464,184	2,025,093
Equipment for lease to others	1,204,291	812,570
Construction in progress	....	69,622
	$ 5,152,118	$ 4,157,480
Less accumulated depreciation	2,064,084	1,616,132
	$ 3,088,034	$ 2,541,348
Other assets:		
Patents and patent applications at cost, less amortization	131,422	139,726
Deferred charges	79,497	49,483
	$ 210,919	$ 189,209
Total	$20,697,030	$16,736,113
LIABILITIES		
Current liabilities:		
Notes payable—bank	$ 1,000,000	$ ......
Instalment on long-term debt, due within one year	100,000	......
Accounts payable	644,593	337,739
Accrued expenses	192,326	156,888
Accrued salaries and wages	408,753	234,032
United States and foreign income taxes	1,461,138	809,933
Other taxes	323,834	223,565
Dividends payable	70,460	29,636
Advances on sales contracts	129,332	......
Amounts received from employees under stock purchase plans	29,455	19,326
Total Current Liabilities	$ 4,359,891	$ 1,811,119
Long-term debt	3,446,261	3,549,509
Total Liabilities	$ 7,806,152	$ 5,360,628

Exhibit 3 (Continued)

	December 31, 1962	December 31, 1961
LIABILITIES		
Deferred United States and foreign income taxes....................	$ 83,354	$ 18,200
Stockholders' equity:		
Capital stock—par value $1.00............	$ 907,719	$ 880,299
Capital surplus........................	10,958,476	9,828,953
Retained earnings......................	941,329	648,033
Total Stockholders' Equity..........	$12,807,524	$11,357,285
Total........................	$20,697,030	$16,736,113

* Condensed from 1962 annual report.

estimated $20 million in 1960), and although EAI, during this period, would do about two thirds of the total business, the management wanted to avoid dependence on a single product and also to put the company's development competence to work in other fields. Thus, in 1959, EAI embarked on a five-year diversification program based on its strength in the development and production of electronic products requiring a high degree of technical competence.

The growth goal of this program was a doubling of the business in five years. It called for 50 per cent of the sales volume to come from products other than general purpose analog computers by 1967. In addition, satisfactory profits were to be maintained, while research and development expenditures were treated as expenses in the year in which they were incurred. The program called for EAI to supply proprietary products to three major markets—scientific laboratories, process industries, and educational institutions. EAI took steps to hasten its diversification into instruments and process control through acquisition and internal product development. Besides seeking new markets and products to supply to them, management also set out to bring more engineering, marketing, and production personnel into active product planning, to encourage them to report on potential customer needs and to initiate product proposals. Fifteen per cent of the firm's employees were trained engineers or mathematicians, and many others were skilled technicians. Once a new product had been developed, emphasis was placed on developing the market through advertising and sales promotion.

In order to hold its competitive advantage, the company followed a policy of producing all products to meet the highest quality, performance, and reliability standards, and maintained extensive quality control and quality assurance programs. A staff of field service engineers serviced equipment and assisted customers with applications problems.

EAI Product Lines

Analog computers accounted for two thirds to three quarters of total company sales. These were designed primarily as engineering and scientific tools, and were utilized by aeronautical, aerospace, chemical, nuclear, and education groups. It was in these technically advanced activities that simulation by analogue computers was most effective and saved the most time and money. These industries could provide the problems and the staff necessary to keep an all-analog computer busy. Also, these computers were suitable only for problems which could be formulated as differential equations which could be programmed into a computer.

As a rule, analog installations were not retired due to rapid obsolescence. New, more advanced computers were often added to existing installations to increase capacity and allow greater flexibility, but the older units often continued to do the problems for which they were designed initially. Older systems could be rebuilt, rewired, and refurbished; but over time, they became out of date for flexible, general use as the manufacturers continued to add features which increased ease of operation or allowed special applications.

Electronic Associates was improving its products continuously. Usually, larger computers were sold to meet the needs of a diverse group in the user company, including mathematicians, engineers, scientists, and representatives of top scientific management. All of these users influenced the vendor choice and often wanted the latest equipment on the market, whether they were sure they needed all of its capabilities or not.

Exhibit 4

A FULLY EXPANDED 231–R ANALOG COMPUTER

The company's largest capacity computer was the 231–R analog computer, which operated at high speeds with high accuracy (see Exhibit 4). It accounted for a large portion of the total sales revenue of the firm. One of its biggest uses was the solution of missile design and flight simulation problems. Customers often purchased systems including several 231–R consoles, expansion racks, and output equipment, such as an eight-channel recorder, table-top X-Y plotter, or large analog plotter. System prices ranged from approximately $100,000 to $1.5 million, depending on the capacity and accessory equipment ordered.

The systems were assembled from available modules on a made-to-order basis. Each 231–R system sold was at least slightly different in over-all capability, depending on customer needs. This was possible because the computer was designed on a building-block basis, using standardized modules of operational amplifiers, electronic and servomultipliers, resolvers, integrators, and function generators. Some wiring and special accessories were custom-engineered. These units were constructed using conventional vacuum tube, wiring, printed-circuit, semiconductor, resistor, electromechanical, and capacitor components (see Exhibit 5).

The latest addition to the large computer line was HYDAC (HYbrid Digital-Analog Computer), a fully integrated digital-analog computer. In HYDAC the digital computer's memory, logic, and mathematical

Exhibit 5

PRECISION COMPUTER NETWORK—A SYSTEM COMPONENT

The components at center right of exposed view marked EAI are encapsulated digital circuits. The size of the unit may be determined by observing the plug-in end of similar units on the computer in Exhibit 12.

resolution capabilities combined with the analog computer's principal strengths of great computational speed, flexibility, and large computing capability. It was developed because computional techniques for scientific problems had advanced in many areas to the point where the abilities of both approaches were needed (see Exhibit 12).

The TR–10 was a small desk-top analog computer, designed for use by individual engineers and small laboratories and for teaching computation techniques at educational institutions. It was the first transistorized analog computer put onto the market. System prices ranged from

Exhibit 6

THE TR–48 TRANSISTORIZED DESK-TOP ANALOG COMPUTER

$4,000 to $10,000. It had sold well and was expected to continue to add to over-all sales growth.

The TR–48 was designed to fill the gap between the 231–R and the TR–10 in accuracy, computational capability, and price. It was a fully transistorized computer selling between $7,500 and $30,000. Most sales were for slightly more than $20,000, and the product was developing a market which could be much greater than that currently experienced with the TR–10 (see Exhibit 6).

Process Control Computers

For the market for on-line process control computers, EAI had developed the PC–12 (see Exhibit 7). Its plug-in, all-solid-state units were similar to those in the TR–10 and the TR–48. A patching module

Exhibit 7

A PC-12 TRANSISTORIZED PROCESS CONTROL COMPUTER

allowed program flexibility such that the computer could be used for multiple purposes or in on-line simulation and control. It was specifically "ruggedized" for process control applications, and contained some different characteristics and special elements. In practice, most installations involved a considerable amount of applications and systems engineering.

EAI expected the market for process control computers to expand rapidly. The analog approach allowed the PC–12, often selling under $20,000, to do jobs which would be uneconomical on much larger and more expensive digital systems. As the companies gained more experience with larger applications, EAI expected the average price to climb over $20,000. Systems as large as $300,000 were anticipated.

Instruments

The 1962 sales of instruments, including digital voltmeters and X-Y plotters were about $2 million. The company was placing strong emphasis on the marketing of this product line. The major products were transistorized digital voltmeters, selling for $2,950 and $3,950, which were well received, and the Variplotter, a plotter line which would translate an analog voltage output into an easily understood graph or chart. The latest version of this product also used transistorized circuitry. Most of the

Exhibit 8

THE MODEL 1110—TRANSISTORIZED (11 × 17 INCHES)
X-Y PLOTTER

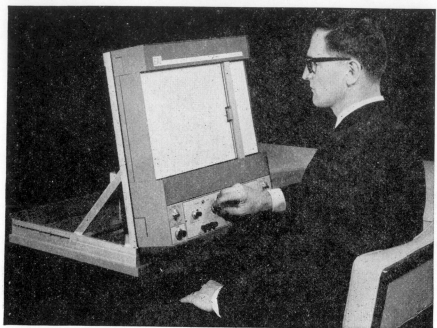

Source: EAI product brochure.

weight and size of these devices was in the display surface and the mechanical system which drew the curve (see Exhibit 8). These units sold for $1,850 and up. They were sold to engineering, research, and production men, who, as a rule, liked to purchase equipment which incorporated the latest technical features. At the same time, however, these men shied away from new technologies with which they had had unsatisfactory experiences. For example, the early problems with transistors in instruments left many a "transistor-shy" engineer.

Data-Processing Equipment

The company supplied users of digital computers with digital plotters and other similar accessories. EAI's 1962 digital plotter sales accounted for one third of the estimated market, and the company did not anticipate much of an increase in its share of the market, but it did expect the market to continue to expand.

The digital plotter consisted of a standard X-Y plotting board with a digital input and a digital-to-analog converter. It transformed data from punched cards, tape, or digital computer output signals into a continuous graph. These units were used for charting financial data, continuous quality control, graphing, meteorological maps, and other types of engineering plotting.

Computation Services

The company computation centers rented out time on EAI analog and hybrid computers to users with or without the services of EAI programming personnel. They worked to find new applications for EAI products, educated potential customers, and enabled the company to sell computational services to companies which might not have been able to utilize a whole computer system. They also gave EAI practical experience as a computer user. The Princeton Computation Center was also the home of the company's Advanced Study Group and Systems Analysis Group which conducted research on computation methods and computer techniques. The Advanced Study Group developed and built the first HYDAC prototype and continued to work on programs, language, and the design and building of experimental units for new or expanded HYDAC systems.

Research and Development

EAI management considered research and development to be an important factor in its efforts to maintain its competitive position. EAI had been investing 9 per cent of sales in this function. It also supported its R & D capability by designing and developing special systems for the government and industrial concerns. EAI had developed and manufactured several guided missile range instrumentation systems, as well as systems for the photorectification of aerial photographs and the control of color-printing plate manufacture directly from scanned color transparencies.

The company's primary technical effort was engineering, oriented toward end products and selected to keep EAI abreast of the state of the art. Christianson had stated that EAI "makes a profit on our engineering talent by converting this research into salable products. To put it another way, we believe how well you spend your research dollars is more important than how many you spend."

Most of the formal research activity was done at the Princeton Computation Center, where fifteen scientists in the Advanced Study Group and the Systems Analysis Group worked on the problems involving computer logic, computation methods, special applications, and new systems.

Development work took place within the various engineering groups, each of which was responsible for a product line. Because there was a close technical relationship between the products, considerable mutual interchange between the different engineering groups occurred. Most items had been and still were made for use with analog equipment. The total staff of ninety engineers and scientists in these groups had had many years of experience in the design of analog and digital circuitry. In

Exhibit 9

MANUFACTURING PROCESS FLOW FOR ANALOG COMPUTERS*

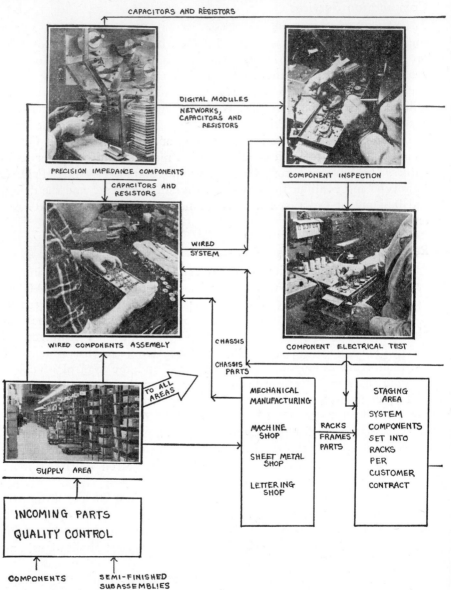

CAPACITORS AND RESISTORS

PRECISION IMPEDANCE COMPONENTS

DIGITAL MODULES
NETWORKS,
CAPACITORS AND
RESISTORS

COMPONENT INSPECTION

CAPACITORS AND
RESISTORS

WIRED
SYSTEM

WIRED COMPONENTS ASSEMBLY

COMPONENT ELECTRICAL TEST

CHASSIS

CHASSIS
PARTS

TO ALL
AREAS

SUPPLY AREA

MECHANICAL
MANUFACTURING

MACHINE
SHOP

RACKS
FRAMES
PARTS

SHEET METAL
SHOP

LETTERING
SHOP

STAGING
AREA

SYSTEM
COMPONENTS
SET INTO
RACKS
PER
CUSTOMER
CONTRACT

INCOMING PARTS
QUALITY CONTROL

COMPONENTS

SEMI-FINISHED
SUBASSEMBLIES

* This drawing does not reflect the plant layout.

Exhibit 9 (Continued)

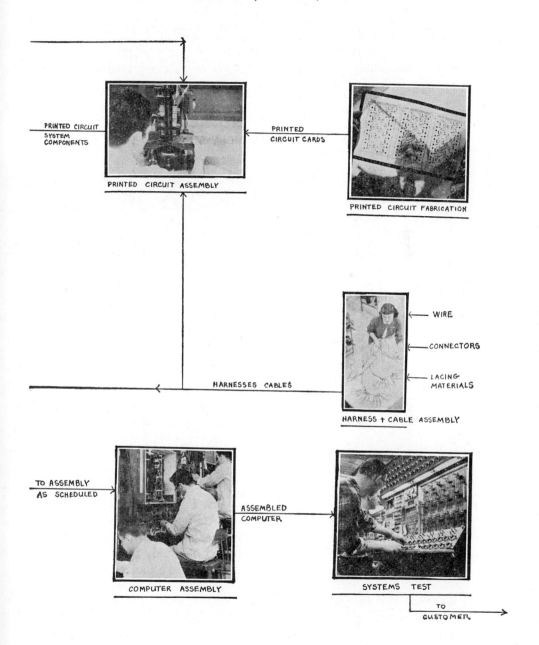

PRINTED CIRCUIT SYSTEM COMPONENTS

PRINTED CIRCUIT ASSEMBLY

PRINTED CIRCUIT CARDS

PRINTED CIRCUIT FABRICATION

WIRE

CONNECTORS

LACING MATERIALS

HARNESSES CABLES

HARNESS + CABLE ASSEMBLY

TO ASSEMBLY AS SCHEDULED

COMPUTER ASSEMBLY

ASSEMBLED COMPUTER

SYSTEMS TEST

TO CUSTOMER

addition, EAI had developed successfully new products and techniques in the area of precision components. The company produced for internal use precision capacitors, sine-cosine potentiometers, and special wire-wound resistors. Some precision capacitors were sold to other users.

Engineering activity was of two types: specific product development projects and study projects. The former were conducted to meet a customer or company need. Most were company-sponsored, although

Exhibit 10

CORDWOOD ASSEMBLY MODULE

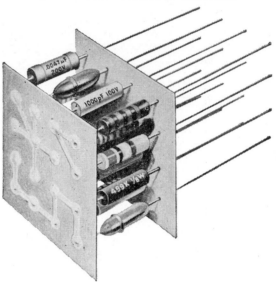

Courtesy: Sprague Electric Co.

NOTE: This exhibit does not necessarily imply that Electronic Associates, Inc., uses Sprague Electric Co. components or techniques.

some were undertaken for specific customers. The study project was used to investigate areas involving several products or functional groups. The members were assigned by their group managers to spend a portion of their time working with the other members of the study team. As a group, the team would be asked to take as open and broad a look at the assigned problem as was possible with the time allotted and to submit a report which included recommendations for further action. The costs of such studies were charged to the R & D budget rather than the product lines.

Manufacturing

Production.   Most of EAI's operating supervisors described the plant as a "big job shop." There were usually over a thousand job orders on the floor at any one time. The emphasis was placed on quality and meeting customer specifications at every decision or testing point. Purchased parts were a major cost item, and considerable effort went into the selection and purchase of materials to achieve economy and maintain quality.

Manufacturing operations required hand labor, not only for the assembly and welding of circuits and the manufacture of precision components, but also for the fabrication, painting, and assembly of cabinets and racks, and final assembling, wiring, and test. About one third of the manufacturing work force was involved in the assembly of wiring units (harnesses and cables), and in the final assembly of component modules and the wiring of interconnections to customer specifications, which was done by skilled technicians (see Exhibits 13 and 14).

Manufacturing operations were essentially project-controlled, with each computer built up and tested individually. The manufacture of precision components and digital circuits was done in a "white room" under controlled conditions. A modified "cordwood" circuit building technique was used for the digital circuits, which were then encapsulated. Circuit connections were welded, using techniques developed by EAI.

Production Engineering. Production Engineering processed design changes and specified production methods and processes for all product lines in the factory. It also handled procurement liaison, working with Purchasing on the use of new materials and on "make or buy" decisions. New parts and materials were usually tested and evaluated by Production Engineering, and pilot production runs were made in order to evaluate a proposed process change. Production Engineering was usually the coordinator for changes in process and standard product design between Marketing, Purchasing, Engineering, Scheduling and Control, and Quality Control.

Discussions with Executives

Wollaston also knew that several executives were keeping watch on microelectronics, and he had discussed developments with a number of them.

Jim Palmer, Manager of Production Engineering, was taking steps to educate himself and his employees by attending conferences and lectures on integrated circuits. In addition, he was going ahead with plans to use, where suitable, other new product and process developments such as multilayered wiring and mechanized construction and soldering of circuit boards. This would eliminate hand wiring on many assemblies. In the long run, he felt that integrated circuits would revolutionize electronics, but not the analog business, because EAI's accuracy requirements were "'way beyond" anything available in integrated circuits. Unlike several other executives, Palmer was not too concerned about allowing circuit manufacturers to have access to EAI circuit designs. He felt that they did not really have any problem in getting this information, anyway, and that

Exhibit 11

"TEASPOONFUL OF RADIO"

Courtesy: Radio Corporation of America

Teaspoonful of Radio. All the micromodule electronics of a military radio receiver equal to a six-transistor commercial type fit into a teaspoon with room to spare at Signal Corps and RCA demonstration of progress in the Army micromodule program. The tiny works of the radio—equivalent to an entire chassis of an ordinary receiver—was one of items displayed today to show progress in the Signal Corps–RCA program to reduce size and weight of space age electronic equipment. Cubical micromodules, measuring a third of an inch on each side, are made of microelements stacked to form modules which perform complete circuit functions. The program, expected to produce electronic equipment size reductions of 10 to one or more, is conducted by U.S. Army Signal Research and Development Laboratory at Fort Monmouth, N.J., with RCA as prime contractor. (Press release, August 28, 1962.)

they would still have many problems in getting into the analog business, just as EAI would have problems in making a market for any new and different product line.

EAL was using the cordwood technique in the manufacture of digital modules (Exhibit 10), and was using welding and encapsulation techniques for these and for the precision impedance components. Palmer felt that welding was not the final answer for EAI and that one EAI goal for the next five to ten years should be the use of discrete microelectronic assembly methods and controlled module sizes for stacking and mechanization. The extent of this move would depend on how much digital circuitry EAI was going to use for hybrid computers and for other new products. If the trend toward digital components was likely to continue, then Manufacturing would have to be ready for repetitive processes, a drastic change from the present job-shop operation based on skilled wiring technicians. He anticipated that the two types of operations would have to be managed separately.

Palmer felt personally that management should now look into the new materials technologies and make more widely known to the employees the impact of product trends and microelectronics on EAI operations. He thought that the original technical effort would have to be made by the product engineering groups. At this point, he did not see exactly where production engineers could contribute to this effort. He expected that the pressure from military purchasers would force EAI to produce assembled modules on a standard-size "wafer" or substrate, which could then be stacked to produce circuits (see Exhibit 11). The mechanical equipment for such a process would cost $35,000 to $50,000 and would handle component assembly, soldering of wafers, and encapsulation. Manufacturing the wafers would be a new business to EAI, but "so were precision capacitors." (EAI had recently purchased a going precision capacitor manufacturer in order to get and maintain a supply of components with the required accuracy. A recent cost study had indicated that this move had resulted in a 50 to 70 per cent saving over outside purchasing costs.) Palmer also remarked that EAI probably used enough semiconductors to operate its own semiconductor plant.

Harry Trask, Production Superintendent, had stated that he expected EAI to be in the microminiaturization business before too long. He felt that Production had to take a strong interest in microelectronics. He favored a "make" policy in this area, and said: "We develop, then find a need for it—most successful things are like that around here." He felt that the innovative pressure was now coming from the process end of electronic technology, and that EAI would have to acquire new skills in production in order to remain competitive. To accomplish this, he wanted Production Engineering to "get ahead of the game in integrated circuits" and interest Design Engineering in them before the impact became too great and threatened EAI's competitive position in design and production technology.

He thought that one way to do this might be to take on production development work for the Army Signal Corps Laboratories at nearby Fort Monmouth. He also noted that EAI was already well on the way toward microminiaturization, and cited the solid-state designs used in the TR–10 and TR–48 computers as examples. To some extent, he saw analog computers as being limited in the amount of size reduction which was actually useful, because of the need for large patch panels for

Exhibit 12

THE HYDAC 2000 WITH OPERATOR

At left is a 231–R analogue computer and at right a HYDAC 350 digital operations system.

programming and because the electromechnanical devices which drove the pen arms were not being reduced. On the other hand, there had been some interest in—but not much work done on—an automatic patching system for analog computers.

While Trask doubted that integrated circuits were reliable enough yet for analog units, he expected a vast improvement in the future and expected to see EAI in that business in about five years. He anticipated that EAI engineers would acquire the know-how in the same manner that they acquired their successful printed-circuit capability. They would go around the industry, ask questions, acquire knowledge, begin on a small pilot scale, and then expand production.

He did not foresee a day when EAI would run long conveyor lines, because the standardized mounting racks and the module system for computers were as far as the company was interested in going with standardization. He cited as one of the company's major strengths its flexibility in serving the customer, but he did feel that the resulting nonstandard operations had increased production costs because of the "learning curve" and production inefficiencies.

Harold Martin, Vice President of Engineering and Manufacturing, did not feel that EAI would have to manufacture its own microelectronic

Exhibit 13

ASSEMBLY AND TEST OF ONE OF THE LARGEST ANALOG COMPUTER
SYSTEMS EVER BUILT

It consisted of five fully expanded 231–R computers and was delivered to NASA at Langley Field, Virginia.

circuits. He expected that EAI would be a follower, rather than a leader, in applying this innovation. As he saw it, integrated circuits would not be technically useful for another three to five years, and the company which pioneered in introducing such a new circuit-manufacturing system usually experienced high costs and had process reliability problems to overcome. The net result of such innovations had often been dissatisfied customers, so that EAI, as the "Cadillac maker" of analog computers, preferred to be a "fast follower." In addition, analog computers were costly; and historically, they had been quite large. He thought that it might prove difficult to convince the customer that he was getting what he paid for if the size of the new units was reduced further.

Several individuals in Engineering were also trying to monitor developments in integrated circuits, but the almost daily reports of new products and the continuation of technical advances (and claims) made the job of keeping up a very difficult one. Christianson had expressed concern with regard to integrated circuits. In his opinion, the present activities of microelectronic circuit manufacturers seemed to be taking them in the direction of circuit design as well as manufacture. This could mean that EAI would have to give future design work to subcontractors who had integrated circuit production capability. If this were the case, the company might lose its design capability, and perhaps eventually its market, to the microelectronic circuit manufacturers. The main problem, in Christianson's opinion, was how to protect the company's proprietary circuit designs, if EAI was no longer manufacturing the circuits, but was designing them and sending the plans to outside manufacturers.

Wollaston also knew that the cost of materials was the largest single direct manufacturing expense, or about 30 per cent of net sales. Component purchases accounted for more than half of this. If EAI were to begin purchasing microelectronic circuits in quantity, this would not only affect over-all costs considerably one way or the other, but it would also change the nature of the company's production operations. Current transistor purchases included a large number of different types and values, and totaled less than a million units.

Organizing for Technical Change

Wollaston was concerned about the effectiveness of the organization as a whole in keeping track of new technologies and felt that it was his responsibility to recommend ways of organizing to monitor new developments. His discussions with his associates about integrated circuits had shown that there were individuals in the firm who possessed packets of information, but there did not seem to be a reliable way of making sure that this information was collected and compiled for dissemination to the people who might make full use of it.

The report which he had just read (Exhibit 1) had recommended that EAI utilize the Study Group Procedure to study microelectronics. The effort recommended, however, was somewhat larger in scale than normal. He knew that $10,000 could be made available within the existing R & D budget, but if $20,000 was allocated to this effort, it might have to be at the cost of some reduced effort on product development. In addition, he was considering the possibility of accomplishing the same results with the company's product planning concept, which was the usual process for dealing with the over-all problem of technological innovation. A third alternative, which he did not think should be ruled out, was the assignment of one experienced, imaginative engineer to the task of evaluating microelectronics.

Exhibit 14

THE SYSTEM TEST AREA OF THE MAIN MANUFACTURING PLANT
AT WEST LONG BRANCH, NEW JERSEY

The Product-Planning Concept

As a diversified, multiproduct company, EAI required some means of planning and controlling the development of its product lines. In order to meet this need, the product-planning concept was developed and implemented in 1962.

For each of the firm's major product lines, there was a product-planning team consisting of the product manager (Marketing), a production engineer, and a design engineer. The Advanced Study Group from Princeton had representatives on certain teams, especially those connected with computation. The team members always had a major responsibility for the product line in their functional department. The major task of a product team was to investigate product-line problems and opportunities. The teams reported to the Product Planning Committee on the results of the past year's efforts and prepared two product plans: a five-year plan which was updated annually and a one-year plan which described activities for the following calendar year. The data provided in the plan proposals covered not only data on marketing, manufacturing, and profitability, but also development programs and capital expenditure requirements.

The Product Programming Committee was headed by the vice president of corporate planning and included the president, the vice president of manufacturing and engineering, the vice president of marketing, the vice president of research and computation, the vice president of international operations, the chief engineer, and a product programmer. The product programmer was a staff man, who served as a Committee secretary, monitored the development program, and administratively approved product expenditures and production releases. The Committee determined the R & D funds to be provided for each of the product lines and, to some extent, the allocation of these funds.

New Products and Ideas

When individuals in production or engineering groups had ideas for new products or production methods, they first used resources available in their departments to test the idea in a limited way. If the idea merited further effort, the individuals worked with their supervisors to present it to the product teams and the Product Planning Committee for approval and development funds. Historically, ideas for most new products or product innovations had come up from Engineering or Marketing, and manufacturing techniques from Production or Engineering. Major industry innovations, such as transistors or printed circuits, were brought to the fore through any and all areas.

R & D expenditures ran about 9 per cent of sales, and the Product Planning Committee had been willing to distribute these funds on the basis of the future potential of the product line, rather than the current product volume. The product team submitting a proposal was expected to show how much money was needed and give reasons why this development should receive a high priority. R & D requests aimed at maintaining the company's competitive position in the analog computer market seemed to carry the most weight.

SECTION III

Finding and Evaluating Significant Technological Opportunities

ON SOURCES OF TECHNOLOGICAL INNOVATIONS

It is vital for management to realize that its own research and development department does not necessarily assure it of technological security. The notion that any group of industrial researchers, no matter how brilliant, will have every important idea impinging upon the firm's business (and have it before anyone else in the world!) is patently ridiculous. Yet, by attitude and action, this is what management often seems to expect of the R & D group. By omission of technological scouting and searching roles for R & D (or other groups), the firm acts as though all necessary innovations and significant technological progress will emerge from its own laboratories, or at least from within its own industry. Is this a certainty? Exhibit 1 presents some examples.

This list could be extended many pages. Space will not permit us to provide background data, but we refer the student to the fifty case histories in *The Sources of Invention* by Jewkes, Sawers, and Stillerman. Although there are notable errors in some of these studies, the cases still suggest with overwhelming conviction that management must do something more than trust in the R & D department for technological salvation. These cases, items covered in the reading references, and items in this book (such as the Du Pont story, page 383), suggest the same phenomenon: that *radical* technological advances spring from unlikely sources, and often from outside the industry most seriously affected.

Why should this be so? We suggest these contributing factors:

A successful commercial enterprise has little stimulus to change present practice. Its energies pour into filling its current needs. Problems of refining present practice, of increasing efficiency, of applications just a short technological step away, occupy its energies and attention. *Development* is the technological skill needed every day. *Research* is a distinct diversion from the presently necessary work. Neither executives nor technological people have much pressure on them to abandon the technological *status quo*. There is little motivation for radical change or strenuous efforts.

Training, education, and experience of a firm's personnel generally are rooted in present practice. It is unlikely that a firm will have technical skills or technical knowledge in other fields. A textile firm, for instance, normally would not have in-house capability in paper or plastics; yet, here are its two strongest technical competitors. A coal-hauling railroad would not be likely to have competence in atomic energy power plant

Exhibit 1

Concept	*"Logical" Concept Source*	*Actual Concept Source*	*Initial Commercial Support*
Synthetic fiber (nylon)......Textile industry		Chemical industry	Du Pont
Diesel locomotive..........Railroad equipment industry		Automobile industry	General Motors
Numerical control for machine tools............Machine-tool industry		Small control manufacturer	U.S. Air Force
Ball-point pen..............Fountain pen manufacturer		Hungarian sculptor and chemist (Biro brothers)	Individual
Polaroid film..............Photographic industry		Independent scientist (Dr. Land)	Independently financed
Color film................Photographic industry		Two musicians (Godowsky and Mannes)	Eastman Kodak
DDT insecticide...........Insecticide or argicultural chemicals manufacturer		Synthetic dye manufacturer	Same as source
Computer................Business machine manufacturer		Universities	U.S. Government
Hydrofoil boats...........Major shipbuilder or U.S. Navy		Inventor of the telephone	Italian businessman

progress, or in extra-high-voltage power transmission research. Thus, neither chance nor normal technical work will necessarily expose a firm to potential technological competition that crosses traditional industry product or process lines.

There is an emotional and social attachment around present practice, which inhibits the unbiased exploration of new possibilities. "A Case Study of Innovation," page 100, points out how an innovation that changes the relationships and values within its society is naturally regarded with indifference or hostility.

Maclaurin's study of innovation in the radio industry and Bright's study of the electric lamp industry (see the Bibliography) both concluded that innovation was largely the product of small firms or of individuals who were struggling for a foothold. In other words, big firms do not tend to originate radical technological advances that invalidate their present success and wipe out the value of their present investments —an understandable corporate response! There is, however, evidence that this has been changing in some firms and industries in recent years.

Historical experience and these comments must not be interpreted as a reflection on R & D men and activities. However, the record of history and current experiences suggest to management students that:

The major (and generally proper) function of most R & D departments appears to be development and product improvement, rather than basic research; of seeking the certain short-term gain, rather than the uncertain, long-term revolution.

A research program is no assurance that all the important technical concepts impinging on a firm will be found, recognized, or mastered; or that if recognized by one function or group in the company—say, R & D —they will be accepted by all others, such as marketing or top management.

The search for radical new technological concepts is a special task beyond the conventional R & D responsibilities. It involves "search" as much or more than "research." Sources of ideas are not necessarily found in the logical places. This means that an explicit recognition-appraisal effort or system is needed to find these new ideas and to give them an open-minded consideration.

A basic research program may come up with ideas of tremendous value in fields other than that of the firm's traditional business.

Management must so structure its organization and its efforts that it identifies technological concepts of importance to its business no matter where they may occur. This implies proper evaluation—imaginative, thoughtful exploration that is unbiased by the firm's experience and present competence.

QUESTIONS

1. Examine the history of any major technological advance (e.g., jet engine, FM radio, xerography, radar, frozen foods, etc.). What is the relationship of the source of the concept to the industry to which the idea has major value or significance? What was the initial response of that industry? How could management in that industry have identified this concept earlier? How could it have responded more wisely?

2. Study the origins of the major innovations in any one industry since 1945. What conclusions can be drawn?

3. Examine any ten of the case histories in the back of *The Sources of Invention*, by Jewkes, Sawers, and Stillerman (New York: St. Martin's Press, 1959). What are your conclusions? What management posture seems to be desirable?

4. Prepare a plan for a given firm (or a firm covered in this case book) to identify innovations that are of potential importance to it as early as possible.

Is the Independent Inventor Through?

A benign Providence . . . has made the modern industry of a few large firms an almost perfect instrument for inducing technical change. . . . There is no more pleasant fiction than that technical change is the product of the matchless ingenuity of the small man forced by competition to employ his wits to better his neighbor. Unhappily, it is a fiction. Technical development has long since become the preserve of the scientist and the engineer. Most of the cheap and simple inventions have, to put it bluntly, been made.

J. K. GALBRAITH

FROM: *American Capitalism.*

In addition, there is the independent inventor, whose day is not past by any means, and who has a much wider scope of ideas and who often does produce out of thin air a striking new device of combination which is useful and which might be lost were it not for his keenness. . . . New ideas are coming forward with as great frequency today as they ever have, and while a great research laboratory is a very important factor in this country in advancing science and producing new industrial combinations, it cannot by any means fulfill the entire need. The independent, the small group, the individual who grasps a situation, by reason of his detachment is oftentimes an exceedingly important factor in bringing to a head things that might otherwise not appear for a long time.

DR. VANNEVAR BUSH

FROM: U. S. Temporary National Economic Committee, Parts I–IV, pp. 871–72.

ORIGINS OF DU PONT'S MAJOR INNOVATIONS,

1920-1950[1]

By Willard F. Mueller[2]

E. I. du Pont de Nemours & Company is cited most often as the leading and most successful practitioner of basic and applied research. In truth, its success as an innovator has made it a symbol of the deterministic doctrine which makes firm bigness prerequisite to inventive capacity and success.

Its officials characterize Du Pont both as a firm grown big because of inventive superiority, and of inventive superiority made possible by firm bigness. Du Pont President Crawford Greenwalt pointed this out when he said: "For the Du Pont Company and I believe this is also true for the chemical industry, I can say categorically that our present size and success have come about through the new products and new processes that have been developed in our laboratories." Greenwalt further contended that not only is Du Pont's present size explained by its inventive superiority but that this superiority itself is based on Du Pont's size. As he puts it, the tasks confronting us a hundred years ago "were not very big, and a relatively small pool of talents and abilities could accomplish them. Today the tasks are correspondingly larger, and they require a larger pool of talent to accomplish them."

Du Pont, of course, has been an innovator in many fields. But what were the sources of the basic inventions underlying its many important innovations? Are these innovations rooted, as President Greenwalt contends, on "the new products and processes that have been developed in [its] laboratories"? It is the purpose of this paper to attempt to answer this question. Perhaps doing so for Du Pont will provide some additional

---

[1] "The Origins of the Basic Inventions Underlying Du Pont's Major Product and Process Innovations, 1920 to 1950," by Willard F. Mueller, from *The Rate and Direction of Inventive Activity*—A Conference (National Bureau of Economic Research, Princeton University Press, Princeton, 1962), pp. 323–46 (footnotes omitted). Reprinted by permission of Princeton University Press. Copyright, 1962, by the National Bureau of Economic Research. All rights reserved.

[2] Professor Mueller, now at the University of Wisconsin, has carefully supported every statement in this paper by references to published sources. The bulk of his 127 footnotes are drawn from testimony in antitrust cases and Du Pont publications and speeches. They have been omitted here to save space, but can be consulted in the book *The Rate and Direction of Inventive Activity*. The reader must realize that events since 1950 may or may not lead to different conclusions. What is the origin, for example, of Delrin and Corfam?

empirical content for our scantily filled economic boxes labeled "sources of inventive activity."

To answer this question for Du Pont, I shall restrict my analysis to Du Pont's experience during the period 1920–50. For nearly all of its over one hundred years of growth prior to 1920, Du Pont was solely an explosives and related products manufacturer. But shortly after the turn of the century, it began diversifying into various fields not directly related to explosives; and by 1920, it had taken great strides toward becoming a diversified chemical firm.

The definition of what constitutes important inventive activity at first sight seems beyond workable construction. It is impossible to define categorically where *unimportant* inventions end and *important* ones

Exhibit 1

DU PONT'S TWENTY-FOUR MOST IMPORTANT PRODUCT
AND PROCESS INNOVATIONS BETWEEN 1920 AND 1950,
RATED FROM 1 TO 5 ON THE BASIS OF THEIR
RELATIVE COMMERCIAL AND
TECHNOLOGICAL IMPORTANCE*

Year Introduced	Product and Process Innovations	Relative Importance (5 Denotes Greatest Importance)
1920	Viscose rayon	4†
1923	Duco lacquers	3
1923	Tetraethyl lead (bromide process)	3†
1924	Tetraethyl lead (chloride process)	2†
1924	Cellophane	4†
1926	Synthetic ammonia	1
1927	Moistureproof cellophane	3
1927	Methanol and higher alcohols	1
1928	Dulux finishes	2
1929	Acetate rayon	3†
1931	Freon	2
1931	Neoprene	2
1931	Titanium pigments	2†
1934	Cordura high-tenacity rayon	2
1936	Lucite acrylic resin	1
1939	Nylon	5
1940	Polyvinyl acetate and alcohols	1
1941	Rutile titanium dioxide	1
1942	Fermate fungicides	1
1943	Teflon	1
1944	Alathon polyethylene plastic	1
1948	Orlon acrylic fiber	3
1948	Titanium metal	3†
1949	Polymeric color film	1
1949	Fiber V (Dacron)	3†

* Based on *Fortune*, October, 1950, p. 114, except for viscose rayon, tetraethyl lead (chloride process), plain cellophane, acetate rayon, and titanium pigments. These were added by the author.
† This is the author's estimate of the relative importance of these products and processes. In all other cases the relative importance is that given each product in *Fortune*.

begin. All scientific inquiry and progress involve a continuing accretion of knowledge, with each piece of knowledge seemingly inseparably related to prior accumulations of knowledge.

But in reality, we generally can identify *inventions* as being distinct from mere additional accumulations of scientific knowledge, because they *result* in something of unique economic importance. Thus, my definition of an important invention is based on its economic result. If a product or process resulting from a unique organization of scientific knowledge is of significant economic importance to Du Pont's growth, I have considered it as being based on an important invention. I shall further avoid problems over definiton of what constitutes a really important Du Pont product or process by limiting the analysis to products and processes which were of obvious economic significance.

Exhibit 1 lists twenty-five of Du Pont's most important product and process innovations from 1920 to 1950, and is based largely upon such a list appearing in the October, 1950, issue of *Fortune*. All of the products and processes listed have contributed significantly to Du Pont's growth (in every case, Du Pont was the first or one of the first American concerns manufacturing the product), and most are likely to continue to do so for some time. In 1948, these products and their closely related derivatives made up about 45 per cent of Du Pont's total sales. The circumstances surrounding the acquisition or development of these products and processes, and their importance to Du Pont's growth, are set forth below.

Viscose Rayon, 1920

Du Pont first became interested in rayon during its World War I diversification program. It conducted research to develop a nitrocellulose process for making artifical silk (later called rayon), but it failed. It also negotiated to purchase the highly profitable American Viscose Company, the country's sole viscose rayon producer, but it considered the price asked excessive. Failing to develop its own rayon process and to buy the only concern operating in America, Du Pont turned to Europe. In 1919, it executed an agreement with the Comptoir des Textiles Artificials whereby the Comptoir gave exclusive rights to its viscose rayon technology to the newly created Du Pont Fibersilk Company. This Company was owned jointly by Du Pont (60 per cent) and the Comptoir (40 per cent). Only one other American concern (American Viscose) was in the field at the time Du Pont received access to patents protecting this valuable new product.

Viscose rayon has continued to be one of Du Pont's major products since 1920. As late as 1948, its sales amounted to $102 million, or about 10 per cent of its total sales.

Duco Lacquers, 1923

According to Irenee du Pont, Du Pont accidentally discovered Duco lacquer in 1920 while conducting research on photographic films. As he described it, on July 4, 1920, the power house was shut down shortly after a barrel of nitrocellulose solution had been prepared in connection with research on photographic films. This shutdown prevented experimentation with the solution for forty-eight hours. When the experimenters resumed their work, "to their amazement the contents of the drum had become so limpid and so fluid that you couldn't cast it on a wheel." This suggested to them that they might "put some pigments into [it] and make lacquers with very heavy pigment carrying power. . . . and they found it would work, and that was 'Duco.' " This nitrocellulose lacquer was a great improvement over existing nitrocellulose finishes. It was of special commercial significance because it reduced the time required to finish a car from days to hours. Although accurate estimates of Du Pont's "Duco" sales are not available from published sources, they have doubtless run into millions of dollars annually since the mid-20's.

Tetraethyl Lead (Bromide Process), 1923

Dr. Thomas Midgeley, Jr., of General Motors, discovered the ethyl bromide process of making tetraethyl lead. Since, at the time of this discovery, Pierre S. du Pont was not only Chairman of the Du Pont Board of Directors, but President of General Motors, it is not surprising that General Motors selected Du Pont to manufacture tetraethyl lead by this process. Du Pont and General Motors made an agreement on October 6, 1922, whereby Du Pont was to build a tetraethyl lead plant with a daily capacity of 1,300 pounds. The agreement set the initial price of tetraethyl lead made by Du Pont at $2.00 a pound, which the parties felt was adequate, to enable Du Pont to amortize the cost of its plant in one year. A Du Pont report on the "Origins and Early History of Tetraethyl Lead Business" stated that "the intent was plainly . . . to be that the contract should be 'a continuing one,' the du Pont Company undertaking to produce exclusively for General Motors, and General Motors agreeing to take its full requirements from the du Pont Company, except in the event of the latter's inability or unwillingness to produce the entire quantities required." The first Du Pont-made tetraethyl lead was sold in February, 1923; and by the middle of the year, it had gained public acceptance.

Tetraethyl Lead (Ethyl Chloride Process), 1924

Du Pont had just succeeded in getting tetraethyl lead production under way when Standard Oil of New Jersey discovered a superior manufacturing process—the ethyl chloride process. President Irenee du Pont, recognizing the superiority of Standard's process, wrote to Alfred Sloan of GM in June, 1924, that "the ethyl chloride method will be found cheaper both as to construction cost and operating cost than the ethyl bromide method." Had Standard manufactured and sold its own tetraethyl lead, Du Pont would have been in an unfortunate competitive position. Fortunately for Du Pont, however, it was able to make an agreement with

Standard which gave Du Pont the right to this new process. Between 1926 and 1948, Du Pont manufactured all of the country's tetraethyl lead. Its importance to Du Pont in recent years is indicated by Du Pont's 1948 sales, which amounted to $30 million, or about 3 per cent of its total sales.

Cellophane, 1924

Du Pont's association in rayon with the Comptoir des Textiles Artificials was directly responsible for Du Pont's entrance into cellophane. During Du Pont's negotiations with the Comptoir on viscose rayon in 1919, a Comptoir official also introduced Du Pont to a "transparent viscose film, known as cellophane." Cellophane was being manufactured by one of the Comptoir's associated companies, La Cellophane Societe Anonyme. La Cellophane had made cellophane since 1917, utilizing a process developed by Jacques E. Brandenberger, who in 1912 had begun producing a thin flexible cellulose film of the general type still manufactured today. On January 6, 1923, Du Pont received an option from La Cellophane to acquire its rights to manufacture cellophane in North and Central America.

Cellophane has been one of Du Pont's most spectacular and profitable success stories. By 1948, Du Pont's sales had grown to $74 million, or about 7.4 per cent of its total sales.

Synthetic Ammonia, 1926

Du Pont got its first technology in this field in 1916 when it acquired the American rights to the Birkeland-Eyde arc process of fixing nitrogen, which had been discovered in Norway. Du Pont never used this process and took no further steps toward entering this industry until 1924. In that year, it acquired the American rights to the Claude process from the Societe Anonyme l'Aire Liquide of France, for $2.8 million. Using this process, it built its first plant at Belle, West Virginia, in 1925. At about the same time, it also acquired four American ammonia concerns—three distributors and one manufacturer. Although Du Pont expanded its position in the market through these acquisitions, its technology remained inferior to that of some of its rivals—notably Allied Chemical and Dye Corporation. After having tried and failed to get the German technology on synthetic ammonia, it obtained the American rights to the important Casale process by purchasing the Niagara Ammonia Company in 1927. This process was superior to the Claude process. Du Pont constructed an entirely new plant to exploit it. Beginning in 1929, Du Pont further buttressed its technical position in synthetic ammonia as a result of its patents and processes agreement with Imperial Chemical Industries, Ltd., England's leading chemical firm. With technology from these various sources, Du Pont developed a modified Claude-Casale process, subsequently known as the "Du Pont process."

Getting the above technology and the various ammonia manufacturing and distributing concerns cost Du Pont a considerable amount. A Du Pont source states that "27 million dollars were invested—over a 10 year period—before the cumulative yearly net operating results showed a dollar of profit." No breakdown is available of the amount spent by Du Pont in developing its modified process and for plant investment.

Moistureproof Cellophane, 1927

Shortly after beginning production in 1924, Du Pont recognized as cellophane's greatest defect its imperfect moisture-proofness. In October, 1924, Du Pont made its initial appropriation authorizing research aimed at developing a moistureproof process. This authorization provided for hiring one researcher and the expenditure of between $5,000 and $10,000. By 1927, Du Pont had found a satisfactory moistureproofing process and began commercial production. In 1929, it received its basic patents covering this development. The importance of this process is indicated by the fact that in recent years the bulk of its cellophane sales (80 per cent in 1948) have been of the moistureproof variety.

Uncertain that its initial moistureproof patent could be enforced against potential cellophane entrants, Du Pont took steps to strengthen its moistureproof patent position. By 1930, it had patented "various modifications of moistureproof cellophane." A Du Pont employee explained that these patents were taken out "not only to strengthen the company's patent position, but also in an endeavor to prevent competition by a similar article."

Between 1930 and 1934, Du Pont took additional steps to bolster its patent position when it authorized a research project for this specific purpose. In 1934, President Yerkes of Du Pont Cellophane reported on the success of this project:

This work was undertaken as a defensive program in connection with protecting broadly by patents the field of moistureproofing agents other than waxes which were the only class of material disclosed in our original cellophane patents.

The investigation on this subject did in fact lead to the discovery of a number of classes of materials which could serve equally well for moisture-proofing agents, whether in lacquers or in other vehicles. Each of these classes has been made the subject of a patent. . . . Altogether 13 patent applications are being written as a result of the work done under this project, all in view of strengthening our Moistureproof Cellophane patent situation.

The $19,503 spent on this research project was very likely more than was spent for the total research in developing the initial methods of moistureproofing cellophane used by Du Pont. As noted above, the initial authorization for this research was made in October, 1924, and the appropriation was for between $5,000 and $10,000. That total expenditures for developing the initial process were not great is indicated by the fact that total "technical activities expenses," which included all types of technical work designed to improve production and process, came to only $32,048 during 1925 and 1926.

Although Du Pont did not incur any expenses involved in the basic research leading to the invention of cellophane, and only modest sums in developing its moistureproof process, it did spend large amounts in subsequent years in "research" aimed at cutting manufacturing costs and improving quality. Du Pont estimates that between 1924 and 1950, it spent $24,361,065 on cellophane research and technical development. Of this, almost 99 per cent was spent after 1929 and 75 per cent since 1939. Although no breakdown is given of how all of this money was spent, in 1935 it spent about 26 per cent of its cellophane research budget of $588,372 on chemical control, 66 per cent for product and process improvements, and 7 per cent for the development of additions to established lines of products. None of this cellophane budget went for fundamental research.

Methanol and Higher Alcohols, 1927

Methanol was first synthesized by the great French chemist Sabatier in 1905. After the Germans developed synthetic ammonia shortly before World War I, another French scientist concluded that the principles employed in ammonia synthesis might be applied to synthesize methanol as well. His speculations proved correct, and he was granted his first patent in 1921.

The Germans simultaneously developed a method for synthesizing methanol. In February, 1925, the first German-produced synthetic methanol arrived in the United States; by May, total American imports exceeded a quarter of a million gallons.

Shortly after Du Pont learned of the French and German success in synthesizing methanol, it began work on a production process of its own. The close relationship between synthetic methanol and synthetic ammonia no doubt made Du Pont's know-how in the latter field helpful in developing a synthetic methanol process. After two years' concentrated work, its efforts paid off in 1926, when it (accompanied almost simultaneously by Commercial Solvents) began producing the first American synthetic methanol. When Du Pont acquired Roessler and Hasslacher in 1930, it added somewhat to its methanol technology by getting access to the Starch patents covering copper catalysts for the conversion of CO and H_2O to methanol.

Du Pont soon discovered that in making synthetic methanol, it was possible to regulate conditions so that not only methanol but also other higher alcohols could be obtained, e.g., propanol, izobutanol, active amyl alcohol, and di-isoprohyl carbinol. No estimate is available of the expenditures Du Pont made to develop methanol and the higher alcohols. Presumably, they are included in the above-mentioned $27 million Du Pont invested in its ammonia enterprise over a ten-year period.

Dulux Enamels, 1928

Dulux enamels represented a substantial improvement in resin-base finishes. William S. Dutton, in his biography of the Du Pont Company, reported that the basic resin essential for making Dulux was discovered by General Electric scientists. Du Pont acquired the rights to General Electric's discovery and carried it into commercial production.

These finishes have been used most extensively in refinishing automobiles and as original finishes for refrigerators. No estimates are available of the relative importance of Dulux sales; but apparently, they have contributed significantly to Du Pont's finish business for many years.

Acetate Rayon, 1929

Acetate rayon is fundamentally different from, and in many respects superior to, viscose rayon. Before 1929 the Celanese Corporation was the only American concern manufacturing this product. Since Celanese was selling its acetate rayon at twice the price of viscose, profits probably were very high. At any rate, Du Pont began looking about for a means of entering this industry during the mid-20's. It again turned to France. In 1927, it acquired the manufacturing and sales rights to acetate flake from the Societe Chimique Usines du Rhone; and in 1928, it obtained similar rights to the cellulose acetate yarn process from the Societe Rhodiaceta. By 1948, Du Pont's total acetate rayon sales amounted to $32 million, about 3 per cent of its sales.

Freon, 1931

Thomas Midgeley, Jr., of General Motors, who had discovered tetraethyl lead about a decade earlier, discovered a revolutionary refrigerant in the late 1920's. This refrigerant was subsequently called Freon. Although General Motors had initially considered manufacturing this product itself, Du Pont's close kinship with General Motors apparently paid off again. In August, 1927, General Motors and Du Pont formed a jointly owned subsidiary, Kinetic Chemicals, Inc., in which Du Pont received a 51 per cent interest. The importance of Freon refrigerants is demonstrated by the fact that it has become the "almost universal refrigerant." By 1944, Kinetic's sales amounted to $12 million.

Neoprene, 1931

Neoprene, the first general purpose synthetic rubber made in this country, is another Du Pont original. Dr. Elmer K. Bolton developed neoprene on the basis of the fundamental researches of Father Julius A. Nieuwald of Notre Dame University. However, since Dr. Nieuwald was "not even casually interested in the search for a satisfactory synthetic rubber," but in acetylene gas, the credit for applying his basic discoveries to synthetic rubber goes to Du Pont's brilliant chemist, Dr. Bolton. Du Pont reports that it spent "three years and almost a million dollars on research" to develop neoprene. Although no information is available of Du Pont's neoprene sales, they undoubtedly have been substantial.

Titanium Pigments, 1931

Shortly before 1920, American, Norwegian, and French researchers made the basic discoveries underlying commercial titanium compounds. But it was not until the late 1920's that titanium pigments—used chiefly in paints—became commercially important. In 1930, Du Pont recognized that titanium pigments were likely to replace lithopone to a large extent. To take immediate advantage of this new and growing field, in 1931 Du Pont acquired control of Commercial Pigments Corporation, one of the country's two producers. Du Pont's subsequent growth in this field was rapid. By 1940, sales reached about $16 million. No information is available of its more recent sales in this field.

Cordura High-Tenacity Rayon, 1934

William H. Bradshaw, Research Director of the Du Pont Rayon Company, developed a stretched and twisted viscose fiber of exceptional strength. Du Pont introduced this fiber, which it called Cordura yarn, for cord tire fabrics. Du Pont classifies this development as an important product "improvement" rather than the development of a new product. Du Pont rayon tire yarn sales in 1948 amounted to $40 million, or about 4 per cent of its sales.

Lucite, 1936

Du Pont received its vital technology for methyl methacrylate plastics, which Du Pont introduced as "Lucite," from Imperial Chemical Industries, Ltd., of England. Beginning in the early 1930's, Du Pont received seven methyl methacrylate patents from ICI. These covered methacrylate monomers; "Lucite" molding powder; "Lucite" dentures; "Lucite" molder sheets; lacquers; finishes; and adhesives and cements. Du Pont paid ICI only $121,680 for these vital product and process patents. The importance of this product to Du Pont is illustrated by its post–World War II sales, which amounted to between $20 million and $40 million a year.

Nylon, 1939

Nylon was solely a Du Pont invention, and doubtless ranks as one of the most outstanding accomplishments of modern industrial chemistry and private-industry-sponsored research.

Du Pont research that ultimately led to nylon began about 1928. The year before, under the direction of Dr. C. M. A. Stine, Du Pont initiated a program of fundamental research. In accordance with the primary objective of this program, which was to discover scientific knowledge regardless of immediate commercial value, Du Pont began a number of chemical explorations. One of these projects was headed by Dr. Wallace H.

Carothers. Carothers continued work he had begun at Harvard University on condensation polymers.

His early work at Du Pont yielded considerable fundamental knowledge of polymerization (how and why small molecules unite to form "giant" molecules), which initially was only of "academic value." Then, "quite by accident," one of his assistants made a fortunate discovery. President Greenwalt explained what happened as follows: "Well, one day one of Carothers' associates was cleaning out a reaction vessel in which he had been making one of those polymers, and he discovered in pulling a stirring rod out of the reaction vessel that he pulled out a fiber; and he discovered its unusual flexibility, strength, and the remarkable ability of these polymers to cold draw."

This discovery had obvious commercial implications for Du Pont, which already was in the textile business as a rayon maker. Although this particular fiber was not very strong or elastic, and was softened by hot water, its discovery suggested that some related compound might produce a product possessing characteristics suitable for commercial fibers.

Du Pont followed up this discovery with "a concentrated effort in the laboratory to synthesize a polyamide which might form the basis for a commercial textile fiber." Carothers and his associates tried time and again to synthesize a new superpolymer possessing suitable textile qualities. At one time, prospects were so dark that Carothers discontinued his investigations. Fortunately, however, he resumed his search; and on February 28, 1935, he synthesized the superpolymer used in manufacturing the first nylon.

The original nylon, initially referred to as Polymer 66, was made in the laboratory by extruding a synthetic fiber through a spinneret improvised from a hypodermic needle. Du Pont scientists and engineers next tackled the job of bringing this laboratory-made fiber into commercial production. During the following two years the Company's efforts involved "the development on a laboratory scale of the manufacturing processes for the intermediates, the polymer and nylon yarn, and the development on a semi-works scale of the chemical engineering data for the erection and operation of a large-scale plant." Upon completing its semi-works plant, and after pronouncing nylon commercially feasible, Du Pont announced on October 27, 1938, its intention of building a new commercial plant at Seaford, Delaware, with an annual capacity of three million pounds. Before the first unit of this plant began operating, late in 1939, Du Pont decided to increase its capacity to four million pounds; and before the plant was completed, its capacity was increased to eight million pounds. Early in 1940, Du Pont announced plans to construct a second plant at Martinsville, Virginia; and in July, 1948, it opened a third plant at Chattanooga, Tennessee. By 1948, Du Pont's nylon sales had grown to $120 million; and Du Pont estimated its 1948 earnings before taxes at $37.9 million, on an operating investment of $83.9 million.

Public statements on the costs and risks in bringing nylon to the commercial stage are, at best, misleading, and most commonly entirely inaccurate. But a Du Pont document made public in a recent antitrust case sheds considerable light on this question. In 1938 a representative from Imperial Chemical Industries, Du Pont's leading international patents and process partner, made two visits to Du Pont for the specific purpose of studying the discovery and development of nylon. This representative reported to ICI that Du Pont's research expenditures in the early years of nylon research "were relatively modest, but as promising indications evolved the pace was quickened." According to this source, by the time Du Pont had reached the point where it could build a pilot plant, expenditures amounted to $787,000. The pilot plant, which was completed in 1938, was designed and built at a cost of $391,000. Another "development" cost cited by this source was approximately $782,000 (about the same as that spent on all pre-pilot-plant research) for sales development. ICI's representative concluded that "the total cost of research and development can thus be taken at [$1.96 million]."

In 1938, after completing its pilot plant, Du Pont authorized the expenditure of $8.6 million to build a three-million-pound-per-year nylon yarn plant. Apparently this plant did not represent much of a gamble or require great additional development expenditures. Dr. E. K. Bolton, Du Pont Chemical Director, later said of this plant: "Except in size, the Seaford plant was practically a duplication of the semi-works plant in all details. Each step of the process and the equipment for it had been worked out throughly on a semi-works scale, and it was unnecessary to gamble with untried methods and equipment on a full-scale." Moreover, the market development expenditure apparently indicated a satisfactory demand for nylon before work began on the full-scale plant. According to Du Pont's Dr. Bolton: "Hosiery manufacturers had evaluated the yarn and pronounced the stockings to be of commercial utility."

Polyvinyl Acetate, 1940

Polyvinyl acetate is used in manufacturing what is popularly known as safety glass. The resin formed from polyvinyl acetate is used as an interlayer in glass to prevent shattering.

Du Pont received its basic patents for polyvinyl acetate from ICI, and has been manufacturing it since 1941. Although available sources do not cite production figures, a Du Pont official claims it was one of the most important products Du Pont received as a result of its patents and processes agreements with Imperial Chemical Industries of England.

Rutile Titanium Dioxide, 1941

Because of its superior "hiding power and more concentrated capacity," this product represented an important improvement over previous titanium pigments. Although hiding power had been increased consistently since titanium pigments were introduced, Du Pont's rutile titanium dioxide represented the first time it had "been appreciably increased." This important product improvement was the result of Du Pont's own research efforts in this field. However, almost simultaneously with the introduction of rutile titanium by Du Pont, National Lead (its only significant rival at the time) introduced a similar product as a result of independent research. No information is available of the research and development costs of this product, nor of its commercial importance.

Fermate Fungicides, 1942

"Fermate," named after the first and last syllable of its chemical name, ferric dimethyl dithiocarbonate, is a new fungicide and beetle repellant. It can be used to protect many fruits, vegetables, and flowers against certain diseases. Du Pont presumably developed this new fungicide in its own laboratories. No information is available as to its development costs or sales.

Teflon, 1943

This remarkable plastic is resistant to the attack of chemicals that would destroy gold or platinum, and "it is a highly efficient electrical insulation, even at high temperatures, and particularly at the high frequencies of television and other electrical equipment." *Fortune* described Teflon's discovery as a "research accident" growing out of Du Pont's systematic research efforts. According to this account, Dr. Roy J. Plunkett was working with tetrafluoroethylene in the hope that it might have useful refrigerating properties. After synthesizing some tetrafluoroethylene, he stored it in a cylinder for a few weeks. When he opened the cylinder, he discovered that some of the compound had polymerized. Thus, accidentally, "Dr. Plunkett had turned up the most heat-resistant plastic and the most inert organic compound ever discovered." No information is available as to the subsequent development cost, except that *Fortune* said that once it discovered that tetrafluoroethylene would polymerize, Du Pont "had no difficulty devising a commercial process."

Alathon Polyethylene Plastic, 1944

Polyethylene is one of the lightest and most versatile of modern plastics. Its uses are numerous, and *Fortune* refers to it as "the fastest growing plastic on the market." Among its best-known uses today are ice-cube trays, food boxes, flexible refrigerator bowls, cosmetic containers, and plastic bags.

Imperial Chemical Industries invented and developed polyethylene shortly before World War II. It disclosed this invention to Du Pont under their patent and processes agreement. After learning of the great military importance of this plastic (it was used as an insulator in radar units), Du Pont immediately sent a technical mission to England to obtain the necessary technical information. Shortly thereafter, Du Pont began manufacturing polyethylene "entirely at the request of the United States Government and solely for war purposes." ICI waived all claims for royalties on polyethylene manufactured for war purposes. After the war, Du Pont received a formal license to manufacture polyethylene for commercial purposes. Up to May 31, 1950, it paid ICI royalties of $272,200 under this agreement.

Although Du Pont had conducted some independent work along these lines, President Greenwalt pointed out that it could not have manufactured polyethylene without obtaining a license from ICI. In 1948, Du Pont's polyethylene sales amounted to $1.3 million.

"Orlon" Acrylic Fiber, 1948

"Orlon" is the second important discovery resulting from Du Pont's basic research in synthetic fibers. This new synthetic fiber has outstanding resistance to sunlight, is quick-drying, holds its shape, and is more resistant to outdoor exposure than any other fiber. Du Pont initiated its Orlon research in 1941, when its rayon pioneering research section decided that acrylonitrile might polymerize into a good yarn. Its expectations proved well founded, and before the war ended, it had turned out in a pilot plant some of the new fiber for limited use in the war effort. By 1947, after Orlon's development had reached a point where full-scale production seemed warranted, Du Pont drew up plans for its first plant. This plant, costing about $17 million, was located at Camden, South Carolina, and had an estimated annual capacity of about seven million pounds. Even before the plant began operations in October, 1950, Du Pont completed plans to build a second plant across the street from the original one. The second plant cost about $25 million and had an estimated capacity of about 30 million pounds.

No detailed breakdown of the research and development costs of Orlon are available. President Greenwalt mentioned $25 million as the total cost of research, development, and initial investment. He said that $5 million of this amount was spent on bringing Orlon from the research through the pilot plant and market development stage, and that the other $20 million involved the initial plant investment. Another Du Pont source stated that "Du Pont has invested more than eight years of intensive research and development work, and an estimated $22 million in 'Orlon.' "

Titanium Metal, 1948

The discovery and introduction of titanium metal may well rank with that of aluminum. This remarkable metal is almost as strong as steel, although weighing 40 per cent less.

In 1943 the United States Bureau of Mines obtained access to a German-owned titanium metal process seized by the Alien Property Custodian. Shortly thereafter, the originator of this process, Dr. Wilhelm

Kroll, who had fled the Nazis in 1940, joined the Bureau of Mines, where he continued his work. Under Kroll's direction, this process was improved, and by 1946 the Bureau of Mines had a titanium metal pilot plant in operation. After the Bureau of Mines published its report, "Metallic Titanium and Its Alloys," in 1946, a number of American manufacturers manifested immediate interest. Du Pont and National Lead, the country's two dominant titanium dioxide manufacturing concerns, began working on commercial processes immediately. By September, 1948, Du Pont announced that it had a pilot plant in operation. And by 1950, its capacity had grown to 55 tons and accounted for the bulk of the country's production of 75 tons in that year. In 1951, Du Pont completed its first semicommercial plant, thereby pushing production to 700 tons during 1952.

Dr. E. A. Gee, of Du Pont's Pigment Department, testified that the Company had spent more than $4 million on titanium research up to November, 1953, and that at the time, it was continuing its research at the cost of about $1 million a year. Du Pont's total investment for research and initial production reportedly approximated $9 million as of that time.

Polymeric Color Film, 1949

Du Pont developed this film to compete with other color films used in the important colored motion-picture film field. Du Pont's colored film replaces a gelatin emulsion, used in all other color films except Technicolor, with a synthetic polymer. Instead of dyeing the film, its process builds the color directly into the polymer. This product is another "first" for Du Pont growing out of its pioneer work in polymers begun in 1928 by Dr. Carothers. However, although included in *Fortune's* list of important product discoveries, Du Pont still had not begun commercial production of it as of August 3, 1954.

"Dacron" Polyester Fiber, 1949

"Dacron" fiber (initially called Fiber V by Du Pont) possesses many qualities superior to any other fiber; for example, it is wrinkle-resistant, even when wet, and has high resistance to stretch. Du Pont introduced this new synthetic fiber commercially in the American market in the spring of 1953. Much of the basic chemistry underlying Dacron goes back to Dr. Carothers' work on high polymers. Whereas Carothers first experimented with *polyesters* in his efforts to build "giant" molecules, he soon concluded that *polyamides* offered greater promise. As noted above, his work in polyamides led to the discovery of nylon.

But while Du Pont concentrated on *polyamides*, English scientists made further investigations of *polyesters*. About 1940, Calico Printers' Association, Ltd., began research on polyesters in an effort to develop a synthetic fiber. By 1941, it had prepared laboratory-scale quantities of polyethylene terephthalate polymer which could be used in making fibers. However, World War II delayed further work on this fiber, which the Association called "Terylene." In 1947, Imperial Chemical Industries acquired Calico and began pilot plant production during 1948.

When Du Pont learned about this new fiber from ICI, it "negotiated for the purchase of patent rights then owned by Calico Printers' Association, Ltd." Du Pont subsequently received eight different patent and process items relating to Dacron from ICI under its patents and processes agreement. After receiving the basic patents permitting it to manufacture Dacron in the United States, Du Pont developed the processes necessary for its production.

Dacron has proven of even greater commercial importance than Orlon. Du Pont reports its total research, development, and initial plant investment in Dacron at about $65 million. Of this amount, it reports that it spent between $6 and $7 million before it was able to begin building its first commercial plant. This presumably includes the costs of its original research, development, and pilot plant.

SUMMARY OF DU PONT'S PRODUCT AND PROCESS INNOVATIONS

Of the 25 important product and process innovations discussed above (they constituted about 45 per cent of Du Pont's total sales in 1948), 10 were based on the inventions of Du Pont scientists and engineers. If we break down these 25 innovations into *new products* and *product and process improvements*, we find that of the 18 *new products*, Du Pont discovered five and shared in the discovery of another (see Exhibit 2). Of its seven most important *product and process improvements*, Du Pont was responsible for five.

Of Du Pont's five new-product discoveries, only neoprene, nylon, and Orlon have achieved substantial commercial significance to date. On the other hand, most of the new products developed by others but introduced into the American market by Du Pont have been very important in Du Pont's growth. Especially important have been viscose rayon, tetraethyl lead, cellophane, synthetic ammonia, acetate rayon, Freon, titanium pigments, Lucite, polyethylene, and titanium metal. Many of these were big money-makers before and during World War II, and practically all seem likely to continue to be important for some time. Du Pont enjoyed large innovator's profits in rayon during the 1920's and grew rapidly in this field up to 1948. Its earning record in cellophane has been phenomenal over a twenty-five-year period. Without any competitors between 1923 and 1948, tetraethyl lead also must have been a profitable field. Freon, which had become the almost "universal refrigerant" by 1948, similarly must have been a profitable field. By 1948, Lucite sales already exceeded $20

Exhibit 2

SUMMARY OF NEW PRODUCTS AND PRODUCT AND PROCESS
IMPROVEMENTS INTRODUCED BY DU PONT AND THEIR
SOURCE, 1920 TO 1949*

New Products	Year of Initial Production	Original Source of Basic Invention	Relative Importance of Invention (5 Denotes Greatest Importance)
Viscose rayon	1920	Other	4
Tetraethyl lead (bromide process)	1923	Other	3
Cellophane	1924	Other	4
Synthetic ammonia	1926	Other	1
Synthetic methanol	1927	Other and Du Pont†	1
Acetate rayon	1929	Other	3
Freon refrigerants	1931	Other	2
Neoprene	1931	Du Pont	2
Titanium pigments	1931	Other	2
Lucite	1936	Other	2
Nylon	1939	Du Pont	5
Polyvinyl acetate	1940	Other	1
Teflon	1943	Du Pont	1
Alathon polyethylene	1944	Other	1
Orlon	1948	Du Pont	3
Titanium metal	1948	Other	3
Polymeric color film	1949	Du Pont	1
Fiber V (Dacron)	1949	Other	3

Product and Process Improvements	Year of Initial Production	Original Source of Basic Invention	Relative Importance of Invention (5 Denotes Greatest Importance)
Duco lacquers	1923	Du Pont	3
Tetraethyl lead (chloride process)	1924	Other	2
Moistureproof cellophane	1927	Du Pont	3
Dulux finishes	1928	Other	2
Cordura high-tenacity rayon	1934	Du Pont	2
Rutile titanium dioxide	1941	Du Pont	1
Fermate fungicides	1942	Du Pont	1

* These products and processes are classified on the basis of discussion appearing in text.
† Du Pont shared this discovery with others.

million a year; and in polyethylene, Du Pont had a stake in the "fastest growing plastic on the market." Titanium metal and Dacron will doubtless be important factors in Du Pont's growth for years to come.

Of Du Pont's seven most important *product and process improvements*, five were Du Pont originals. Especially important were Duco, moisture-proof cellophane, and Cordura fiber. Duco has been an important seller ever since the mid-20's. Most of the cellophane sold today is of the moistureproof variety. Du Pont sales of rayon tire yarn in 1948 came to $40 million. Much of this presumably was Cordura.

The above sample strongly suggests that Du Pont has been more successful in making product and process improvements than in discovering new products. Except for nylon, Orlon, and neoprene, Du Pont's major product innovations have been based upon technology acquired from others.

SIGNIFICANCE OF THESE FINDINGS

What is the significance of these findings for the question: Has Du Pont's bigness, as is so often claimed, created a perfect environment to spawn inventive activity?

Its record during the period of this study does not support such a generalization. Although Du Pont expanded its research expenditures as it grew—from slightly under $1 million annually shortly before 1920 to $38 million in 1950—there has not been a proportional acceleration in the *important* inventions (as defined herein) coming from its laboratories. Nylon still remains its greatest success story. And neoprene, discovered in 1931, probably has been exceeded only by nylon and Orlon; and the latter was an outgrowth of its basic discoveries underlying nylon.

It is well to recall here that Du Pont's basic research leading to the invention of nylon and neoprene was done during the late 1920's and early 1930's, when Du Pont's total research and technical budgets averaged $5 million a year, about one sixteenth of its 1958 budget. Yes, the Du Pont that initiated the research leading to nylon and neoprene was truly a small firm by today's standards. Its sales in 1928 were only one seventeenth as large as they were in 1959. In truth, by 1950, its nylon sales alone were larger than its 1928 sales of all products.

Du Pont's success in making important product and process improvements did not increase proportionately to its increasing research expenditures during 1920–49. Its greatest achievements of this kind were Duco lacquers and moistureproof cellophane. Both of these were developed in the 1920's.

The above conclusions must be modified in several important respects.

First, because I have concentrated my analysis on only the inventions underlying Du Pont's most important innovations, I have left unmentioned many of Du Pont's successes. While I cannot quantify my judgment on this score, I believe that if I had been able to identify the technical sources of Du Pont's many less spectacular innovations, the quantity of such accomplishments would be more closely correlated to the size of Du Pont's research expenditures during 1920–49.

Second, it is possible that this analysis has treated too short a period in Du Pont's growth to permit generalizations. Perhaps since 1950, Du Pont's inventive achievements have accelerated. But unfortunately, it has not been possible to gain access to reliable information concerning its inventive activities since 1950.

No opprobrium is intended by the preceding analysis of the sources of inventions underlying Du Pont's most significant innovations. Du Pont management must be commended for its aggressive and farsighted search for new products and processes, and for continually looking outside as well as within Du Pont's laboratories for them. It recognized new opportunities when they arose and backed them with a tremendous push of money, of mass production, and of salesmanship.

But a fundamental question is raised by these findings: To what extent can we, as a nation, rely on, and become dependent upon, the fundamental research efforts of a relatively few large industrial firms? Although such firms may be perfect vehicles of applied research and innovation, they may not (1) have adequate economic incentives for sponsoring or (2) be able to create the ideal environment for conducting the basic research leading to the inventions underlying important innovations.

Apropos of the question of adequate incentives, Dr. Richard Nelson of the Rand Corporation concludes his excellent theoretical analysis of the economics of basic research by saying: "Though private profit motives may stimulate the firms of private industry to spend an amount on applied research reasonably close to the figure that is socially desirable, it is clear . . . that the social benefits of basic research are not adequately reflected in opportunities for private profit, given our present economic structure."

Apropos of the environment which big businesses create for conducting basic research, Dr. Clarence Cook Little, Director of Jackson Memorial Laboratory, and former President of the University of Michigan, put it this way: "Scientific research is an intensely personal effort. . . . Like the artist, the creative scientist must be permitted to pursue his own ideas unhampered by restrictions of organized groups. The large groups have made extremely important contributions only when an original discovery, made by a single individual, is already available for further technical development."

Obviously, case studies alone cannot prove or disprove theories. But I hope this one will contribute to the slowly growing empirical evidence useful in testing what are still largely unverified theories of the sources of inventive activity.

QUESTIONS

1. Examine the sources of Du Pont's major innovations. What conclusions can be drawn?
2. What role have Du Pont's laboratories played in Du Pont's innovations?
3. If Du Pont's experience is any guide, how should a firm design its innovative policy? Its innovative effort?
4. Does management have a responsibility in finding new inventions? How should this be exercised? How should it be co-ordinated with the research and development activity?

How Much Shall We Spend on Research?

I have heard one company executive say that fully 90 per cent of his research programs don't pan out, but the 10 per cent justifies the entire cost many times over.

This might lead someone to believe that if you pour more dollars into research, that 10 per cent will increase because it will be part of a larger total. However, "the law of diminishing returns" applies to research just as it does to economics. A substantial increase in the research budget may not bring any increase in research productivity at all. In fact, it may confuse the issue by directing the attention of the research organization on so many different goals that it never quite reaches any of them. Whether in research or anything else, more money isn't always the answer. To be sure, I have seen an estimate that Du Pont spent about $40 million to bring its Delrin plastic from the laboratory to market—and it is a very successful product. However, the Varian brothers out in California invented the klystron tube on a budget of $100, and the company they founded now derives sales of more than $30 million from that product and its related equipment. My point is simply that dollars are no guarantee of results—and the ingenious scientist in a modest laboratory that looks like a laboratory can frequently out-produce his brethren who do their research in one of those all-glass buildings with every gadget imaginable.

DONALD C. POWER, Chairman of the Board
General Telephone & Electronics Corporation

FROM: "Top Management Looks at Research & Development," an address at the Research Management Program, Battelle Memorial Institute, October, 1963.

SHORTLY AFTER he reported as financial assistant to Charles du Pree, President of Electro-Music, Martin Barrett was instructed to look into the matter of evaluating research proposals.

"We have no satisfactory way of evaluating research proposals," said Du Pree. "Surely there must be something better than the rough comparison of vague opinions and economic guesses which we now use."

Barrett pointed out that he was not a scientist or engineer and that he had no training in research management in his M.B.A. work. While willing to take on any job, he felt ignorant on this particular topic. He had joined Electro-Music as a member of the treasurer's staff, and had thought he would be dealing with relatively conventional financial problems having to do with the business of manufacturing and selling musical instruments.

Du Pree replied that he realized Barrett's position, and went on to say:

> None of us know much about research evaluation, Martin. What's more, I don't believe that there is very much understanding of the basic problem. But it is a fact that our experience with electronic organs has given us enough electronic competence to get a toehold in military research and development. We did do a satisfactory job on building 500 special Signal Corps radio sets for the Army, and I now have at least three military R & D proposals on my desk, and one suggestion that we develop an electronics research program in NASA's field. Also, our best electronics scientist urges us to get into research on lasers, and I don't even understand the principle of the things, let alone their market. We are going to have to learn to evaluate research and development based on new technologies and products, or return to the old business of guitars and electronic organs. Frankly, I'm interested in bigger things.

A few days later, Martin Barrett received a notice of a two-day conference on technological planning to be held at Harvard Business School. He called it to Du Pree's attention, and it was decided that both of them would attend.

After the conference, Du Pree discussed the papers with Barrett: "Ansoff's idea for evaluating research proposals was most interesting, but I don't see how we can estimate, in significant numerical relationship, all the factors he has identified.[1] Some things in his equation are so uncertain that it seems to me as though the final 'figure of merit' number is

[1] For the original paper, see H. I. Ansoff, "Evaluation of Applied Research in a Business Firm," p. 468.

meaningless. Isn't there a simple approach to the same idea? I want you to look into this next week."

Barrett searched through various bibliographies on research and development. He found that the chemical industry had given considerable attention to R & D problems. In *Chemical and Engineering News* magazine, April 17, 1961, pages 110–18, he came across a "product profile chart" approach that related to his problem. He then commenced a critical examination of this article (Exhibit 1) by John S. Harris, Director

Exhibit 1

NEW PRODUCT PROFILE CHART

A weighted, visual comparison of all the facts in product development can guide management toward the best decisions on commercializing the products

JOHN S. HARRIS
Monsanto Chemical Co.,
St. Louis, Mo.

If you have an effective research and development organization it should, and normally does, have more projects than it can handle with its available money and manpower. This is a healthy situation as it allows you to select the best projects—providing you have an effective and reasonably reliable method of evaluating the candidates. The stumbling block lies in the phrase "reasonably reliable method of evaluating," when there are so many factors to consider and so little data to go by in the early stages.

Let's define first just what, when, and whom we are talking about in the evaluation and selection of products and projects. After stressing the need for additions to a company's product coverage, Joel Dean, in his "Managerial Economics," puts development of new products into three stages:

Exhibit 1 (Continued)

PRODUCT COUNT-DOWN. Once the construction is under way and the fixed capital goes in, it's too late to recall the questions about the new product that should have been asked earlier. The time for the complete facts, clearly presented, is when the management team makes its decision to commercialize

• Scouting-out potential product additions.

• Appraising these proposals and making the product selection.

• Launching each new product venture in a way that gives it a maximum chance of success.

We are talking here about the second step—that of appraisal. In our discussion we will arrive at the most important aspects to be evaluated for any potential product, and we will develop a simple means of applying them as an aid in decision-making. A careful analysis of the key characteristics of any new product—and a continuing review of them during development—will assist you in two ways. First, it will help in choosing for development those chemicals with

the strongest commercial possibilities; and secondly, from among these you can distinguish the products which show the greatest potential profit for your company.

Now, when should the appraisal be used? It can be applied to a new chemical whose preliminary screening tests indicate promise for use in a certain field. The chemical may be a product manufactured by a competitor which you want to consider manufacturing yourself. It may be a product produced abroad for which there is no domestic manufacturer. With a little modification, you can even use this system to evaluate a new field for which you don't yet have a product. In the stages of a new product, the first appraisal should be made before any major research expenditure, and new appraisals should be made with

increasing accuracy until the final decision to commercialize is made.

Who will make the appraisal depends on your organization, as it should be done by whoever is responsible for selecting and developing new products. If you are unfortunate enough to have these functions split you can at least hope that both groups will agree on the same appraisal system.

At the beginning you will lack data on many factors that will be important when the time comes to ask management for a decision to manufacture and sell. Certainly one goal during the stages of research and development is to provide information on these factors.

Although the following statement

Text continued on page 116

Exhibit 1 (Continued)

NEW PRODUCT PROFILE CHART

Financial Aspects

The most important characteristics of a new product (and the ones to which all other aspects can ultimately be related) are, of course, financial. There are many different ways to evaluate the economics of a product, but a few criteria are commonly used to cover the basic considerations. Actual numerical values for these criteria will depend on your company's objectives and accounting methods.

The final test of a product, after we have deducted all the expenses of making and selling it, is the amount it earns compared to the money we had to invest in it. This, of course, is the RETURN ON INVESTMENT. Though, in a sense, this is the most critical of the financial aspects, there are two other values describing different char-

		MINUS		PLUS	
FINANCIAL ASPECTS		−2	−1	+1	+2
Return on investment (before taxes)					
Estimated annual sales					
New fixed capital payout time					
Time to reach est. sales vol.					
RESEARCH & DEVELOPMENT ASPECTS					
Res. investment payout time					
Dev. investment payout time					
Research know-how					
Patent status					
Market development requirements					
Promotional requirements					
Product competition					
Product advantage					
Length of product life					
Cyclical & seasonal demand					

Return on investment (before taxes):
−2 Less than 20%
−1 20% to 25%
+1 25% to 30%
+2 Greater than 30%

Estimated annual sales:
−2 Less than $100,000
−1 $100,000 to $1 million
+1 $1 to $5 million
+2 Greater than $5 million

New fixed capital payout time:
−2 More than 5 years
−1 3 to 5 years
+1 2 to 3 years
+2 Less than 2 years

Time to reach est. sales vol.:
−2 More than 5 years
−1 3 to 5 years
+1 1 to 3 years
+2 Less than 1 year

Res. investment payout time:
−2 More than 3 years
−1 2 to 3 years
+1 1 to 2 years
+2 Less than 1 year

Dev. investment payout time:
−2 More than 3 years
−1 2 to 3 years
+1 1 to 2 years
+2 Less than 1 year

Research know-how:
−2 No experience & no other applications
−1 Partly new with few other uses
+1 Some experience or new vistas
+2 Considerable experience or potential

Patent status:
−2 Unsettled patent situation
−1 Open field or many licenses
+1 Restricted to few licenses
+2 Patent or exclusive license

Market development requirements:
−2 Extensive educational program
−1 Appreciable customer education
+1 Moderate customer resistance
+2 Ready customer acceptance

Promotional requirements:
−2 Extensive advertising & promotion
−1 Appreciable requirements
+1 Moderate requirements
+2 Little promotion needed

Product competition:
−2 Several directly competitive products
−1 Several competitive to some extent
+1 One or two somewhat competitive
+2 No competitive product

Product advantage:
−2 Higher price, equivalent quality
−1 Competitive; or higher price and quality
+1 Competitive price but quality advantage
+2 Both price & quality advantage

Length of product life:
−2 Probably 1 to 3 years
−1 Probably 3 to 5 years
+1 Probably 5 to 10 years
+2 Probably more than 10 years

Cyclical & seasonal demand:
−2 Seasonal and subj. to business cycle
−1 Seasonal
+1 Subject to business cycle
+2 High stability

(*The ratings for this aspect will depend on the individual company's type of business, accounting methods, and financial objectives. The values shown above are estimated on the basis of various published information to bracket the averages for large chemical companies.)

Exhibit 1 (Continued)

acteristics that are also important when thinking of a new product.

ESTIMATED ANNUAL SALES is the gross number of dollars we expect the product to bring in. The sales are estimated at what we can reasonably expect at mature sales volume, in the uses we can now foresee. The TIME TO REACH ESTIMATED SALES VOLUME, however, varies widely between products, and this is an index of how long we may have to wait before recovering our investment. If you favor discounted cash flow as an investment tool, the previous criteria can be combined.

The most critical part of the investment we make in a new product is that which is tied up in new equipment. Unlike raw materials which can be returned or resold, or existing idle equipment which is borrowed, the larger part of investment in a new plant is likely to be lost if the new product fails. The NEW FIXED CAPITAL PAYOUT TIME measures how long it will take to recover this part of the total investment, where loss liability is greatest.

Three of the four aspects above are ratios, so comparisons can be made between projects of different sizes. Size itself is important, however, and this can be graded on the basis of annual sales. Beyond these there are two other financial values often used by management to establish the size of the manufacturing project and the capital requirement. They are ANNUAL EARNINGS and TOTAL CAPITAL INVESTMENT. Since there are times when capital is short and others when you may have excess capital to invest, Total Capital Investment cannot be used for comparison except at a given moment. This value and Annual Earnings, which establishes the actual magnitude of profitability, are necessary information and should accompany the analysis even though they are not used comparatively. On the profile chart they are shown in a separate box with the assumed volume and price.

PRODUCT:

Est. Annual Sales _____ lbs.

Price: $

Annual Earnings: $
(before taxes)

Total Capital Investment: $

PRODUCTION & ENGINEERING ASPECTS

Required corporate size
- −2 Can be made by any bucket operator
- −1 Most companies could compete
- +1 Average or larger sized companies
- +2 Only a very large company

Raw materials

Equipment
- −2 Limited supply or suppliers
- −1 Limited availability inside company
- +1 Readily available from outside sources
- +2 Readily available inside company

Process familiarity
- −2 New plant needed
- −1 Mostly new equipment
- +1 Some new equipment
- +2 Present idle plant usable

- −2 New process — no other application
- −1 Partly new — few other uses
- +1 Familiar process — some other uses
- +2 Routine process or promising other uses

MARKETING & PRODUCT ASPECTS

Similarity to present product lines
- −2 Entirely new type
- −1 Somewhat different
- +1 Only slightly different
- +2 Fits perfectly

Effect on present products

Marketability to present customers
- −2 Will replace directly
- −1 Decrease other sales somewhat
- +1 Slight effect
- +2 Increase other product sales

Number of potential customers

Suitability of present sales force
- −2 Entirely different customers
- −1 Some present customers
- +1 Mostly present customers
- +2 All present customers

Market stability

Market trend
- −2 More than 500
- −1 Less than 5; or 100 to 500
- +1 5 to 10; or 50 to 100
- +2 10 to 50

Technical service
- −2 Entire new group needed
- −1 Some additions necessary
- +1 Few additions necessary
- +2 No changes necessary

- −2 Volatile market, frequent price cuts
- −1 Unsteady market
- +1 Fairly firm market
- +2 Highly stable market

- −2 Decreasing market
- −1 Static, mature market
- +1 Growing market
- +2 New potential market

- −2 Extensive service required
- −1 Moderate service requirements
- +1 Slight service requirements
- +2 Negligible service required

Production and Engineering Aspects

Usually the smaller the company, the less it will cost to manufacture a given product, assuming the company has or can afford the required facilities. Thus a product that can be manufactured by companies appreciably smaller than ours will quite

Exhibit 1 (Continued)

NEW PRODUCT PROFILE CHART

likely be cheaper for them to make DDT formulations or floor cleaning compounds can be made in little more than a tub and at lower cost than we can achieve. On the other hand, production of ethylene or cortisone requires in one case the investment of a large amount of capital and in the other a large amount of research talent and diversified production equipment. For lack of a better term, this might be called REQUIRED CORPORATE SIZE; and from our point of view, the bigger the requirements for a given product, the safer it is from lower-cost competition. If your company is a smaller one, you may rate this aspect just the opposite.

Preferably the size of the companies that could manufacture a product should be defined quantitatively. Unfortunately, this aspect has not been used in the past nor has it been evaluated to any great extent. Though we have analyzed several possible criteria, none has shown adequate correlation so far; and unless you can quantify this factor, an intuitive judgment will be necessary.

RAW MATERIALS for a new product should be readily available, ideally from inside your company or from more than one supplier. A material in tight supply or controlled by a competitor would be a disadvantage.

Another aspect is EQUIPMENT. A plant represents not only the investment of money, but engineering time, construction, and other factors. It would be desirable if present idle plant equipment could be used in the manufacture of a new product. In this way, not only are idle-plant charges absorbed, but often a lower actual investment cost on the new product is possible—even if your accounting department doesn't figure it this way.

The final production consideration is PROCESS FAMILIARITY. It is hard to put a cash value on this, but a brand-new type of operation can usually be expected to give more trouble and require more time and effort in starting up production. A routine process in which you have considerable experience is commensurately easier to get under way. On the other hand, a new process might show promise of being widely applicable in other areas or of opening up new vistas. This would be a distinct advantage, offsetting to some degree the difficulties likely to be encountered.

Research and Development Aspects

The estimated cost of research and development should be compared to expected earnings of the product. There often is little or no relationship between the effort required in research and in development if you have them organized separately. If you wish to manufacture an established intermediate like adipic acid or phenol, comparatively little development expense is involved. On the other hand we have found that a synthetic hydraulic fluid takes far more development than research time. As with some of the financial aspects, numerical ratings for RESEARCH AND DEVELOPMENT PAYOUT TIME will depend on your accounting methods and your company's objectives.

When looking at a new product from the research point of view, a major consideration is RESEARCH KNOW-HOW. If it involves a synthesis similar to others in which you are practiced, much less work will be required. Thus, it is likely that the process will be relatively more efficient. But, like the previously mentioned Process Familiarity, the advantages may outweigh the short term problems if the necessary research work shows considerable promise beyond the immediate product being considered.

The final Research and Development aspect is PATENT STATUS, although this is equally important from any other point of view. The last 15 years have left very few products or chemical fields that a single company can claim as its own. A patent or an exclusive license is a strong advantage for a new product. In fact, chemicals or applications covered by patents afford about the only available protection for a margin of profit sufficient to underwrite major projects.

Marketing and Product Aspects

From the perspective of marketing, a number of characteristics of a potential new product should be considered. An important one is SIMILARITY TO PRESENT PRODUCT LINES, which is a measure of how a new product will fit in and, to a large extent, how much training of your present sales force will be required. The EFFECT ON PRESENT PRODUCTS measures whether the new product will replace one that you now have or might increase the sales of another product. For example, sales of a new solvent-resistant elastomer to packing manufacturers might help the sales of your synthetic lubricant. MARKETABILITY TO PRESENT CUSTOMERS means that the salesman, without additional calls, can increase his product line and the chances of higher sales to present customers. For us, NUMBER OF POTENTIAL CUSTOMERS ideally would be "more than a few but less than many." When sales depend on one or two or three customers, the loss of even one of these can be serious. On the other hand, when customers are numbered in the hundreds it becomes a difficult and expensive sales problem to contact them. The choice of the ideal number will depend on your company and its products.

SUITABILITY OF THE PRESENT SALES FORCE is important because there will be times when a new product would mean addition of an entire new group. This might be because of complexities in selling the product— for example, rubber and petroleum additives; or it might be because an entire new market is involved, as in the case of a consumer product to be distributed by an industrial sales organization.

Various markets show quite different degrees of MARKET STABILITY. The market for weed killers is subject to extensive price-cutting in that small formulators can drive the price down to where no one can sell them very profitably. Plasticizers are highly competitive, yet until recent years the market was considerably more stable. Other products such as rubber chemicals, because of some characteristic of the market, can be comparatively stable.

It is most desirable to find products for sale in consuming industries where the MARKET TREND is strongly upward. Some industries, for example synthetic dyes, have stabilized and will probably grow little more. Others —the desirable ones like synthetic fibers and certain plastics—are new and growing.

Product lines vary greatly in their TECHNICAL SERVICE REQUIREMENTS. Intermediates, for example, do not require customer education. Unfortunately, this is not true in the case of a new transformer fluid or a paper chemical, and the expense should be considered.

MARKET DEVELOPMENT REQUIREMENTS vary considerably in different fields. It becomes less and less necessary to educate the farmer in the use of agricultural chemicals, providing he can see an economic advantage. On the other hand, it will require a long educational period for wood preservatives to reach their ultimate level. Ready customer acceptance of new products is a big advantage.

Another marketing aspect is PROMOTIONAL REQUIREMENTS. Some product lines require very little adver-

Exhibit 1 (Continued)

tising promotion. There is a wide difference in the amount of advertising and promotion needed for an established pharmaceutical like aspirin as opposed to a new line of formulated agricultural chemicals or antifreeze. Such promotion is expensive and should be considered in advance along with other important sales characteristics.

With regard to the new product itself and its characteristics, there are four major considerations. First is PRODUCT COMPETITION. The fewer the competitive products or producers, of course, the better. Although this factor may at first seem similar to the Required Corporate Size described earlier, there is an important difference. While Required Corporate Size reflects quality of the competition and the likelihood that you can compete on an even cost basis, Product Competition establishes the present amount of competition from other products or producers. If imports are already or likely to be a problem, they should be considered as well.

PRODUCT ADVANTAGE, sometimes difficult to assess objectively, has a large bearing on ease of introduction and ultimate success of a new product. A me-too chemical that is equivalent in price and quality to those already available is much less desirable than one with either a price or quality advantage, or both.

An estimate of LENGTH OF PRODUCT LIFE can, at best, be little more than a guess. Yet there are some fairly consistent differences between product groups; and the rate of obsolescence of agricultural pesticides is generally much higher than that of, say, resin intermediates or rubber chemicals. It is instructive to compare the estimated Product Life to the pay-out times on new capital, research, and development investments. You should certainly expect a remaining period of real net profit.

Finally, many products are subject to CYCLICAL AND SEASONAL DEMAND. Agricultural chemicals come to mind, of course, because of their seasonal nature, which means carrying heavy inventories or having idle plant equipment. Products going into certain markets are much less subject to the business cycle than others. Aspirin sales don't drop very much when business is bad—though winter colds do insert a seasonal factor—and other pharmaceuticals hold up about as well. But chemicals that go into products that the consumer can get along without or postpone using—such as resins for paint—drop markedly during a business down-turn. Such a characteristic is a disadvantage.

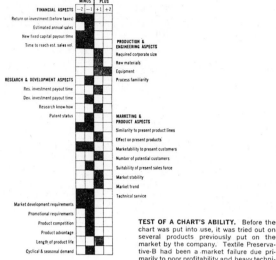

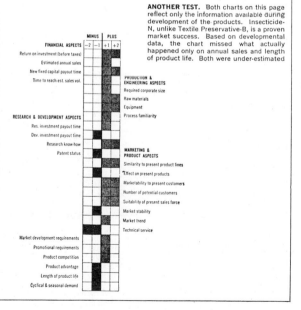

TEST OF A CHART'S ABILITY. Before the chart was put into use, it was tried out on several products previously put on the market by the company. Textile Preservative-B had been a market failure due primarily to poor profitability and heavy technical service and marketing demands. The chart would have emphasized these, and it could have saved much time and expense

ANOTHER TEST. Both charts on this page reflect only the information available during development of the products. Insecticide-N, unlike Textile Preservative-B, is a proven market success. Based on developmental data, the chart missed what actually happened only on annual sales and length of product life. Both were under-estimated

Exhibit 1 (Continued)

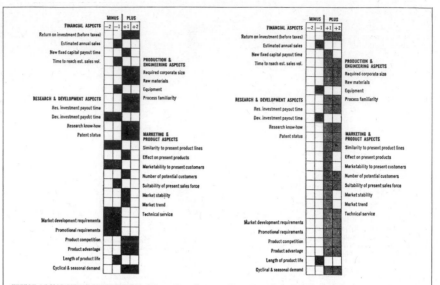

EFFECT OF MARKETING ALTERNATIVES. Where alternatives are available, such as in marketing methods, the profile chart provides comparison of which is better. Drilling Additive-R could have been marketed in either of two ways. Case I (left) shows the effect of direct sales to the many drilling mud companies. Case II shows what happens when the product is sold through a distributor specializing in additives to drilling mud companies. Clearly, marketing is a controlling factor

Continued from page 111

can easily start a wide and lingering debate, it will be said flatly that no mathematical formula can be employed consistently to place an intrinsic, numerical value on a product or project in its early stages. Invariably, weighting factors for the different aspects of a new product are required; and, also invariably, a case can be found where any one of the aspects will override all the others. The possibility of moving a troublesome by-product without financial loss could be more important than many other considerations; or the production of a critical intermediate in another case could offset many less favorable aspects.

After evaluating several such decision-by-formula systems, we have concluded that the weight given different aspects of a new product must be variable and a matter of personal judgment. With both the weighting factors and the values dependent on the feelings of the appraiser, we would be deluding ourselves in thinking we had a consistent and even semi-exact method of selection.

What we need, then, is more than a means of appraising new products, projects, or applications at successive stages of research and development. The method should also consider and report all important aspects of a new product and make them apparent to experienced management. It should not mask any important considerations by lumping good and bad aspects together to arrive at an average.

The Product's Profile

Many check-lists and articles have been published on the important aspects of a new product over the last 20 years, and we have drawn freely on these. The basic problem is to arrive at the smallest number of criteria that will include all aspects of importance to successful commercialization of a new product. These criteria should be mutually exclusive—that is, no more than one should describe the same basic consideration.

Suppose you have analyzed your company and its objectives, and you now have a list of basic criteria—those things that should be evaluated for any new product. How should you present them? There are many ways, but one very effective means is to use a profile chart. This is a graphical technique employed in geology, psychology, and other fields where a visual means of indicating saliencies, particularly by area, is needed.

A profile view, whether of an artist's model or the Rocky Mountains, calls attention to outstanding features without bothering with details. A profile of a potential new product should do the same thing. It should allow a quick look at the product's merits and

Exhibit 1 (Continued)

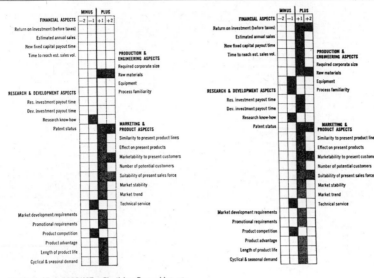

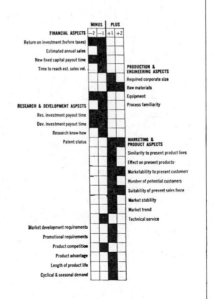

HISTORY OF A PRODUCT. Plasticizer-D provides an example of how the profile chart of a product can change during its development. At Stage I (above left) it has shown promise in screening tests. Process work hasn't yet been started thus, neither the process nor economics is known. Several months later, during process research, the chart at Stage II (above right) still rates the product high. Economics look good. An unavoidable by-product has been found, but it is expected to sell at a profit. But Stage III (lower right) shows a much different picture. More work has shown the by-product won't sell. This depresses financial aspects, and necessary pricing lengthens the time to reach volume sales; process research shows the need for new plant. At this point Plasticizer-D was dropped

shortcomings, calling particular attention to those that justify further attention.

This can be done in several ways, but suppose we set up a simple scoring system for each of the important criteria with a range, say, from −2 to +2, giving four levels of desirability. The levels could be fewer or greater in number, but remember that we do not want to place any great emphasis on numerical values. Rather, we are seeking only a visual indication of levels of desirability for each criterion —but not to be able to compare one criterion with another.

In the resultant New Product Profile Chart we have arrived at 26 aspects

Exhibit 1 (Concluded)

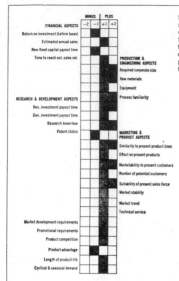

STILL UNDECIDED. Resin Intermediate-H, still in commercial development, shows less than joyful financial aspects. Why, then, try to commercialize? The reasons can be seen in the favorable production and marketing areas of the chart

aspects of a chemical have been evaluated.

• It calls attention to major strengths and weaknesses of the product.

What the profile chart should not be expected to do is grade your projects in any quantitative sense. The pluses and minuses cannot be totaled to give a figure with any real meaning, nor is there likely to be any minimum number of unfavorable aspects that will rule out a new product.

The chart will not substitute for judgment. But it does present the important criteria in a simple and graphic way that facilitates appraisal and final decision by management.

This article is based on a paper presented before the Division of Chemical Marketing and Economics at the 139th National Meeting, American Chemical Society, held in St. Louis, Mo., March 21 to 30, 1961.

JOHN S. HARRIS *is presently director of economic planning for Monsanto Chemical's organic division. In 1943, to escape after a year in the analytical laboratory, then Monsanto's training and staging ground for both chemists and engineers, Mr. Harris took the first transfer offered: to the organic division's development department. But, in spite of a hasty entrance, he spent the next 17 years, except for a two-year stint in sales, in commercial development ranging from application chemist to administrative assistant, from steroidal hormones to solid fuel rockets, and from technical service to market research. His publications have similarly varied from a chapter in an ACS monograph ("Phosphoric Acid, Phosphates, and Phosphatic Fertilizers") to articles in Agricultural Chemicals, Precision Metal Molding, and Product Engineering. Holder of "a few unprofitable patents," he studied at CalTech, received his B.S. in chemical engineering from Missouri School of Mines, and his M.S. in engineering administration from Washington University (St. Louis).*

of a new product that should be examined in our particular business before proceeding with active development. There is nothing sacrosanct about the number of criteria; 26 simply seemed to be the minimum number that would describe our products and the business we are in, as well as our objectives. We have added and changed a few criteria when using the chart for inorganic chemicals instead of organic, or for overseas sales instead of domestic. If yours is a small company, certain aspects may be reversed in your ratings as compared to ours.

The Product Profile Chart in Use

Our use of the Product Profile Chart has gone through a number of stages since it was first tried in 1955. For a time we used it experimentally on new products. It was applied to earlier projects that had either succeeded or failed, to see how well it would have described them and whether it would have called attention to the strong and weak areas.

This procedure uncovered several aspects that we had not included and sharpened up some of the ratings (but not all—we're still not sure of how to apply numerical values to certain of the criteria). In the latter part of 1956 we formalized the system by report and have used it where needed and applicable ever since.

Though the original criteria were based on experience with organic chemicals and domestic sales, the New Product Profile Chart was later adapted to other classes of chemicals and even to sales abroad. The latter provides a good example of the need to adapt new product criteria to the market. Sales in the United States are not dependent on such aspects as convertibility of monies and stability of governments. But these can be very important in overseas sales.

The Product Profile Chart is intended to serve as a tool in appraising new, potential products for commercial promise and profitability. If you revise the criteria to suit your company and its objectives, you will find that the chart can assist in two ways:

• It assures that the more important

Exhibit 2

NEWS-PRODUCT PROFILE CHART

PRODUCT: _____

Est. Annual Sales _____ lbs.

Price: $ _____

Annual Earnings: $ _____ (before taxes)

Total Capital Investment: $ _____

	MINUS		PLUS	
	-2	-1	+1	+2

FINANCIAL ASPECTS

Return on investment (before taxes)
- -2 Less than 20%
- -1 20% to 25%
- +1 25% to 30%
- +2 Greater than 30%

Estimated annual sales

New fixed capital payout time
- -2 Less than $100,000
- -1 $100,000 to $1 million
- +1 $1 to $5 million
- +2 Greater than $5 million

Time to reach est. sales vol.
- -2 More than 5 years
- -1 3 to 5 years
- +1 2 to 3 years
- +2 Less than 2 years

RESEARCH & DEVELOPMENT ASPECTS

Research know-how
- -2 No experience & no other applications
- -1 Partly new with few other uses
- +1 Some experience or new vistas
- +2 Considerable experience or potential

Res. investment payout time
- -2 More than 5 years
- -1 3 to 5 years
- +1 1 to 3 years
- +2 Less than 1 year

Dev. investment payout time
- -2 More than 3 years
- -1 2 to 3 years
- +1 1 to 2 years
- +2 Less than 1 year

Patent status
- -2 Unsettled patent situation
- -1 Open field or many licenses
- +1 Restricted to few licenses
- +2 Patent or exclusive license

PRODUCTION & ENGINEERING ASPECTS

Required corporate size
- -2 Can be made by any bucket operator
- -1 Most companies could compete
- +1 Average or larger sized companies
- +2 Only a very large company

Raw materials
- -2 Limited supply or suppliers
- -1 Limited availability inside company
- +1 Readily available from outside sources
- +2 Readily available inside company

Equipment
- -2 New plant needed
- -1 Mostly new equipment
- +1 Some new equipment
- +2 Present idle plant useable

Process familiarity
- -2 New process—no other application
- -1 Partly new—few other uses
- +1 Familiar process—some other uses
- +2 Routine process or promising other uses

MARKETING & PRODUCT ASPECTS

Similarity to present product lines
- -2 Entirely new type
- -1 Somewhat different
- +1 Only slightly different
- +2 Fits perfectly

Effect on present products
- -2 Will replace directly
- -1 Decrease other sales somewhat
- +1 Slight effect
- +2 Increase other product sales

Marketability to present customers
- -2 Entirely different customers
- -1 Some present customers
- +1 Mostly present customers
- +2 All present customers

Number of potential customers
- -2 More than 500
- -1 Less than 5, or 100 to 500
- +1 5 to 10, or 50 to 100
- +2 10 to 50

Suitability of present sales force
- -2 Entire new group needed
- -1 Some additions necessary
- +1 Few additions necessary
- +2 No changes necessary

Market stability
- -2 Volatile market, frequent price cuts
- -1 Unsteady market
- +1 Fairly firm market
- +2 Highly stable market

Market trend
- -2 Decreasing market
- -1 Static, mature market
- +1 Growing market
- +2 New potential market

Technical service
- -2 Extensive service required
- -1 Moderate service requirements
- +1 Slight service requirements
- +2 Negligible service required

Additional market/product factors

Market development requirements
- -2 Extensive educational program
- -1 Appreciable customer education
- +1 Moderate customer resistance
- +2 Ready customer acceptance

Promotional requirements
- -2 Extensive advertising & promotion
- -1 Appreciable requirements
- +1 Moderate requirements
- +2 Little promotion needed

Product competition
- -2 Several directly competitive products
- -1 Several competitive to some extent
- +1 One or two somewhat competitive
- +2 No competitive product

Product advantage
- -2 Higher price, equivalent quality
- -1 Competitive; or higher price and quality
- +1 Competitive price but quality advantage
- +2 Both price & quality advantage

Length of product life
- -2 Probably 1 to 3 years
- -1 Probably 3 to 5 years
- +1 Probably 5 to 10 years
- +2 Probably more than 10 years

Cyclical & seasonal demand
- -2 Seasonal and subj. to business cycle
- -1 Seasonal
- +1 Subject to business cycle
- +2 High stability

* The ratings for this aspect will depend on the individual company's type of business, accounting methods, and financial objectives. The values shown above are estimated on the basis of various published information to bracket the averages for large chemical companies.

JRH/1/61

of Economic Planning for Monsanto Chemical's organic division. Barrett's goal was to determine whether the procedure seemed appropriate for his firm's potential research activities, and how the scheme needed to be modified, if at all, for projects in the electronics field.

(Note: Exhibit 2 is provided as a work sheet.)

Choosing between Development Projects

[W]hile it is true that even $100,000 put into each of all the various un-
orthodox engines proposed between the wars would have been a serious
drain on the total funds available for all development, the number of innovations which could show real promise even on paper was not so great.
There was, in fact, a great difference between the turbojet and all the
other unorthodox engines proposed between the wars, and this difference could have been seen even at the time. The turbojet promised enormous improvement in airplane performance on the basis of assumptions
which were reasonable, even if they were not certain. All the other
engines mentioned above, on the contrary, promised at the most very
limited gains, and in most cases experience had already shown that the
practical obstacles to the attainment of these limited gains were very
great.

The real trouble with the various unorthodox engines on which public
funds were spent with no result in the United States between the wars
was that even granting that they were perfectly practical technically,
they did not promise enough superiority over existing engines to make
it worth while to spend enough money to make them work. As a result
only small amounts were spent, and these amounts were a total loss.

ROBERT SCHLAIFER

FROM: *The Development of Aircraft Engines and Fuels* (Boston: Harvard Business
School, 1950).

PARSONS & AKRON

In 1960, J. B. Torn, then Director of Research for Parsons & Akron, participated in an intercompany study on the evaluation of research and development proposals. The study was inspired by the collective dissatisfaction of many directors of R & D departments and some of their top managements with evaluation procedures. The review of the variety of approaches, ranging from simple check lists to elaborate "figures of merit," confirmed in Torn's mind the need to improve his own firm's procedures. The lack of consistency and completeness in relating research project objectives to corporate objectives disturbed him; and the choice of projects, their initiation, reporting, and the co-ordination of division and corporate research efforts were haphazard. He felt that the lack of method might be contributing to what, in his eyes, was a less than vigorous effort to commercialize the research and development output available to the operating divisions.

When Torn was promoted to Vice President of Research and Engineering in 1962, establishment of a uniform research and development evaluation procedure had high priority on his list. Over the next year, he pushed the effort to come up with procedure that was sound, and that was acceptable to managers of the operating divisions, as well as to marketing, corporate planning, the controller, and top management. One of his first steps was to ask the executive vice president of marketing administration to assign a man with marketing experience to work with the corporate research staff. Roger Jett from marketing was assigned to work with the research staff, and he assisted Torn's group to develop the new evaluation procedure. By mid-1962 a tentative document was completed and distributed for review.

When Torn finished a draft that seemed reasonably good, he passed copies on to industrial friends and a few college professors and consultants. (Major portions of this draft comprise Exhibit 1.) He asked them to give him their frank opinions on the usefulness of this procedure. Meanwhile, he received internal reactions from Parsons & Akron division managers and top executives during early 1963.

The corporate marketing staff was enthusiastic about the attempt at systematic appraisal and the implied encouragement of a more aggressive new-product effort. However, the staff members had reservations about the amount of detail required. They wondered if the procedure would be carefully followed by the research and marketing people in the operating divisions. Would the tendency be merely to fill in the blanks and get the report done? Torn agreed that this was an open question. However, he decided to review the appraisals of outsiders before taking any action.

Exhibit 1

PROPOSAL FOR EVALUATION AND REPORTING OF RESEARCH
AND DEVELOPMENT ACTIVITIES IN PARSONS & AKRON

Introduction

The following is a presentation of research and development in Parsons & Akron and an attempt to relate logically the corporate research and development objectives to a method of project selection, initiation, and reporting.

Objectives

The corporate objectives of Parsons & Akron indicate a concentration of activities on those business areas where the corporation is strong in marketing know-how or technology, or both.

The corporation in the future will engage in new business derived from or closely related to the basic materials of our current products, but only after thorough technical and market research indicates that such new business can be conducted at satisfactory earnings returns on the required capital investment.

Within the scope of these areas, research, development, and engineering have the following specific purpose: to lead in basic and applied research and engineering in all areas of science relating to the business outlined above to insure a constant flow of ideas and information related to new or improved products, processes, services, and methods designed to advance the company's progress.

Meeting the Objectives

To contribute to the objectives, maximize profits, and conserve resources, the research and development activities will continue to be directed toward developing a technological base which can be used by management in adding new market profitability by developing new ideas for existing products, adapting existing products as required, and creating new products, new processes, and improvements to present processes. Therefore, before committing significant funds to any of these types of technical work, it is necessary that reasonable precautions be taken to ascertain the practicability of entering the field, the commercial possibilities, and the probable investment involved. The earlier the evaluation is made, the greater the probability of meeting the objectives in an efficient manner. The following is a detailed discussion of an evaluation procedure which will permit the ranking of projects and the selection of those which most completely fulfill our objectives. Since not all activities lend themselves to the same method of evaluation for purposes of discussion, they will be classified as either research or development in nature. The use of these terms creates some problems in semantics. However, the following terminology will be used for this purpose.

Research Projects

Fundamental Research. Fundamental research projects cover those activities directed toward an understanding of the technological base of a com-

Exhibit 1 (Continued)

mercial endeavor. Such research is not directed toward a specific end product or development, but rather toward the understanding of an area of knowledge. Fundamental research is normally directed toward the "seeding" of ideas which should have later application in the development of new or improved products or processes.

Applied Research. Applied research projects are those activities which are directed toward building a technological store of detailed information which will act as a base for specific product and process developments or as a base toward solving day-to-day problems within the limits of day-to-day business activity.

Development Projects

Development efforts are those which are directed toward a specific new or improved product or process. A project of this nature is tangible, and it results upon successful conclusion in a workable commercial process. Characteristically, these projects have:

1. A specific end point or result.
2. A time objective or target date for completion—this can and should be established.
3. A fairly clear pattern. Although the development projects as a whole are nonrepetitive, the pattern of steps—either all or in part—usually is repetitive.
4. Steps which are largely mechanical, as in drafting, model making, or pilot operations and testing.
5. Comparisons with similar steps in preceding projects.

Appropriations for work in either of these three areas will require review by management based on marketing and technical considerations, with the following exception: Research and development personnel can "self-generate" ideas without individual management approval, and without review by marketing as long as the work is done within the budgetary limitations for exploratory projects. All exploratory works of a promising nature on which further work calls for large-scale appropriations will require management authorization.

In order to fulfill the stated requirements of our corporate objectives, it is therefore necessary that, as early as possible, estimates be made not only as to research or development feasibility but also marketing potential and estimated profits. These estimates in the very early stages may be wide of the mark; however, critical areas will be highlighted which can be carefully appraised during the subsequent evaluations. It is vital, however, that economic evaluations be made before the pilot stage is reached.

RESEARCH PROJECTS

Projects of this type generally continue over a period of several years, although the information obtained will have both short- and long-term impacts on profit. Generally, when the profit impact is short-term, such projects will be part of a specific development project. While the purpose of such research usually is to gain technological advancement, it may be also used to

Exhibit 1 (Continued)

Form A

RESEARCH PROJECT AUTHORIZATION REQUEST

Date_____

_____Division

Original Request ( )
Reappraisal   ( )

Authorization No.	Function	Title	Annual Cost

Project Scope and Objective:

Relation to Corporate Marketing and/or Operating Objectives:

Additional Research and Development Opportunities Created:

Utilization of Parsons & Akron Skills:

Availability of Personnel:

Availability of Facilities:

If Work Is to Be Done, Who Will Do It?

Signed: Approved: Date
   Project Engineer_____ Division Research Committee_____ _____
   Division Engineer_____ Administrative Research Committee_____ _____

---

create a favorable image with the public, our employees, and our customers. As mentioned previously, all such activities must have primary direction in the fields of Parsons & Akron's business interest.

Initiation

Requests for funds for this purpose should be accompanied by comments covering the following:

Exhibit 1 (Continued)

1. Title of project.
2. Annual cost.
3. Project scope and objective. (In statement, consider if the technological objectives seem feasible in light of present knowledge.)
4. Relation to corporate operating and/or marketing objectives. (In statement, consider if the project objectives could be met. Would the project be commercially attractive—to the desired degree?)
5. Additional research and development opportunities created.
6. Utilization of Parsons & Akron skills.
7. Availability of personnel.
8. Availability of facilities.
9. If work is to be done, who will do it?
10. Patent potential and problems.

The attached authorization request (Form A) is a means of providing this information and formally requesting funds for this purpose.

Project Reappraisal

Research projects should be reappraised at least once each year, and in addition to the ten factors above, the following should be examined:

1. In the light of the new knowledge, that is, at the time of asking the reevaluating question, are the technological objectives still feasible?
2. If the technological objectives were met, would the results *still* be commercially profitable (to the desired degree)?
3. Is the rate of progress toward the final objectives satisfactory?

In light of the answers above, one must decide whether to abandon the project, continue it at the same rate, or accelerate the activity.

DEVELOPMENTAL PROJECTS

Specific development projects are requested to accomplish a particular purpose, with funds being requested to cover both the exploratory and the development phases of the project. Since management must determine which projects will yield the greatest return on the investment of money and manpower, a measurement of anticipated profitability of these activities is required. Work of this kind, being tangible in nature, lends itself to analysis prior to the time the work is actually authorized.

The marketing and commercial, research and development, production, and financial implications should be estimated. It is vital, however, that economic evaluations be made before the pilot stage is reached. This is when expenditures become rapid. To generalize, it may be said that the closer the project is to commercialization, the more valuable the appraisal will become.

The authorization request (Form A) and profit work sheets are a means of providing this information and should, when summarized, permit the selection of those projects which offer the greatest potential. The actual cost of the project, as well as the technical progress, should be reappraised from time to time. The timing of commercialization may be of equal if not greater importance than cost. The questionnaire and request form will also provide a convenient method for project reappraisal. This should be accomplished at least

Exhibit 1 (Continued)

once each year and in the calendar quarter preceding entry into the piloting of the commercial phase. An additional review may also be expedient when cost approaches 90 per cent of the authorized amount.

PREPARATION OF
DEVELOPMENTAL PROJECT AUTHORIZATION REQUEST

The request form (Form B) should indicate the division submitting the request, date, and identification as to whether it is an original request or a reappraisal of a previously approved authorization. Requests should be made to cover the sum total of more than one project should the group of individual projects be so related that the accomplishment of the desired objective depends upon the successful completion of one or all of the projects in the group.

The project profile analysis (Form C) is divided into four major sections covering the areas of marketing and commercial, technical, production, and financial. All factors are related in general terms as to whether they are favorable or unfavorable to Parsons & Akron. They are coded into five grades indicating a very good, good, average, poor, or very poor position. The factors in many cases will represent the summarization of detailed investigation and planning. The amount of detail to which the investigation is subject will depend upon the relative size of the project as well as the stage at which the estimate is made; i.e., the reappraisal just prior to development of a new product or a new process will generally require detailed investigation of all of the four factors.

It is intended that each of the four main factors should be appraised by members of the organization who are familiar with the aspects of each; i.e., the marketing and commercial factors should be appraised by marketing personnel, and financial factors should be evaluated by a member of the comptroller's staff.

The rating of a particular factor from very good to very poor should be an expression of opinion as to the relative effect of the proposed undertaking. The factors are generally self-explanatory; but it should be noted that the profitability rate calculation is based on use of the forms and theories which are now generally used in the evaluation of proposals for capital expenditures. However, it should be noted that Form C limits the economic life to ten years. In most cases, this will permit the calculation of a meaningful profitability rate. Some projects may have a delayed earnings impact, and for these cases the economic life should be extended over a longer period. Also, the cost of development is included as part of the required investment in addition to the usual items of preoperating and market development expense.

An explanation of individual Forms B, C, and 3,000 follows, and their use in a hypothetical example is shown.

Exhibit 1 (Continued)

Form B

DEVELOPMENTAL PROJECT AUTHORIZATION REQUEST

Date___12/31/60___

___ADMINISTRATIVE___ Division

Original Request: ( )
Reappraisal: (×)

Auth. No.	Function	Title	
AP 954	3	Foamed Polystyrene Widget Development	Gross Cost $ 652,000
			Credits $ 147,000
			Net Cost $ 505,000

PROJECT OBJECTIVES

Develop foamed polystyrene widget to be sold in the market now dominated by paper. New widget to be competitive in cost and offer savings in weight and insulation from shock.

PROFILE SUMMARY   VG   G   A   P   VP

    A. Marketing & Commercial
    B. R. & D.
    C. Production
    D. Financial

TIME TABLE

Technical & Commercial:

Code:
    Original_____ Current Est._____

Development Expense:

Original Est.	$ 20M	$ 140M	$ 100M	$	$
Actual & Current Est.	$ 35M	$ 191M	$ 221M	$ 45M	$ 13M

COMMENTS

Signed: Approved: Date
  Project Eng. __J.C. Smith__   Div. Research Com. __J.H.P.__   __11/30/60__
  Div. Eng. __R.F. Jones__   Adm. Research Com. _____   _____

EXPLANATION OF DEVELOPMENTAL PROJECT AUTHORIZATION REQUEST (FORM B)

Authorization Number

This should indicate the authorization number assigned by the divisional research committee. For example, Container Division project number 100 would be designated as C–100.

Exhibit 1 (Continued)

Function

Indicate the classification of research, development, and engineering expense as follows:

Function 3—Corporate new-product development
Function 4—Divisional new-product development
Function 5—Divisional new-process development, present product
Function 6—Divisional present process improvement

Title

The title of the project should be stated in as clear and concise terms as possible.

Project Objectives

Clearly state exactly what it is intended the project will accomplish. For example, "reduce container weight on Parsons machines by 20 per cent."

Profile Summary

The various factors are connected with a line which will form a profile or graph of the project. It will indicate whether the project generally is desirable or undesirable in view of the information available. Each of the four major factors are summarized from the project profile work sheet. A project the summary of which indicates a poor or very poor rating in any of the five factors indicates a questionable risk.

Timetable

Technical and Commercial. This portion of the form requests by quarter an estimate of time required for development, sales, and production to put the product on the market or the process into production. The time required should be indicated as a bar graph drawn through appropriate sections designating the calendar quarters. In the case of a reappraisal the original estimate should be shown as well as the current estimate. This will provide a means of determining if technological progress is developing in accordance with the original plan.

Development Expense. This details the cost, programmed by year, for the development phases. In the case of reappraisal the latest estimate should be provided, as well as the original.

Exhibit 1 (Continued)

Form C
PROJECT PROFILE WORKSHEET
(Circle appropriate rating and connect circles.)

A. MARKETING & COMMERCIAL FACTORS

1. Size of Total Annual Opportunity: VG (G) A   P   VP
    1st 5 Yrs.   10 Yrs.
    Units   4,000,000   4,000,000
    Dollars 16,000,000   16,000,000
2. Size of Annual P-A Market Opportunity: VG (G) A   P   VP
    1st 5 Yrs.   10 Yrs.
    Units   1,000,000   1,000,000
    Dollars 4,000,000   4,000,000
3. Adaptability to Marketing--distribution resources. VG (G) A   P   VP
4. Compatibility with current and long-range
    marketing objectives.   VG   G (A) P   VP
5. Volume/price effects on present P-A products. (VG) G   A   P   VP
6. Effect of probable government legislation. (VG) G   A   P   VP
7. Relationship to adversely owned patents.   VG (G) A   P   VP
8. Patent licensing possibility.   VG   G (A) P   VP
    Prepared by _____E.D.S._____

B. TECHNICAL FACTORS

1. Utilization of present P-A skills.   (VG) G   A   P   VP
2. Availability of personnel.   (VG) G   A   P   VP
3. Availability of facilities.   (VG) G   A   P   VP
4. Years to reach readiness for commercialization. 3.5 VG G (A) P   VP
5. Opens door to additional R. & D. opportunities. VG (G) A   P   VP
6. Timing compared to competition.   VG (G) A   P   VP
    Prepared by _____D.T.M._____

C. PRODUCTION FACTORS

1. Utilization of familiar processes.   VG (G) A   P   VP
2. Availability of raw materials and products. (VG) G   A   P   VP
3. Utilization of existing facilities.   (VG) G   A   P   VP
4. Freedom from hazards.   (VG) G   A   P   VP
5. Value added by in-company processing. 25% VG   G (A) P   VP
6. % of value added comprised of payroll. 40% VG (G) A   P   VP
    Prepared by _____B.E.R._____

D. FINANCIAL FACTORS

1. Increase in pretax profits--annual $ 200M . VG   G (A) P   VP
2. Anticipated capital outlay $ 350M .   VG (G) A   P   VP
3. Capital equipment obsolete as % of new capital
    equipment _____0_____ %.   (VG) G   A   P   VP
4. Cash recovery of capital investment 1.7 yrs. (VG) G   A   P   VP
5. Cash recovery of R. & D. and Capital
    Investment 3.7 yrs.   VG (G) A   P   VP
6. Profitability Rate 19.3 %.   VG   G (A) P   VP
    Prepared by _____J.M.P._____

AREAS OF UNCERTAINTY:

VG = Very Good;   G = Good;   A = Average;   P = Poor;   VP = Very Poor

EXPLANATION OF PROJECT PROFILE WORK SHEET FACTORS (FORM C)

A. Marketing and Commercial Factors

1. *Size of Total Annual Opportunity.* To take into account the measurement of the effect on size of a total opportunity such as the packaging of baby foods if we were to introduce a new, improved, or substitute product or new

Exhibit 1 (Continued)

or improved process. The indication of size, of course, is a measurement in units of current totals.

2. *Size of Annual Parsons & Akron Market Opportunity.* In the case of baby food, this would relate to our own current size and basically the effect of the new product or process on our own market opportunity.

3. *Adaptability to Marketing—Distribution Resources.* Would cover both domestic and international possibilities, in relation to our personnel, branch offices, and marketing facilities, including customers, of additional marketing resources needed.

4. *Compatibility with Current and Long-Range Marketing Objectives.* Calls for a relationship to our current stated marketing objectives and an indication of deviation or enlargement of them as it be needed.

5. *Volume/Price Effects on Present Parsons & Akron Products.* Indicates contemplated effects on both volume and pricing of present products and, of course, would indicate the direction of replacement or addition projected.

6. *Effect of Probable Government Legislation.* Consider either current legislation or areas of possible future legislation, such as trends in Pure Food and Drug Act.

7. *Relationship to Adversely Owned Patents.* Consider if patents owned by competitors could curtail or make more difficult utilization of the development activities.

8. *Patent-Licensing Possibility.* Consider if the development has potential income from licensing of patent rights to others.

B. Technical Factors

1. *Utilization of Present Parsons & Akron Skills.* Does research in this area require that Parsons & Akron seek skills which are not currently available within the organization?

2. *Availability of Personnel.* Are people presently available within the organization to perform this research?

3. *Availability of Facilities.* Are our present facilities adequate to conduct this research?

4. *Years to Reach Readiness for Commercialization.* Estimate the time required to complete the research and have process or product ready for manufacture.

5. *Opens Door to Additional R & D Opportunities.* Does this research aid in research in other current or proposed activities?

6. *Timing Compared to Competition.* Is Parsons & Akron following competition, or does it appear to be in the lead?

C. Production Factors

1. *Utilization of Familiar Processes.* Is the manufacture of this product or use of this process similar to other methods now in use?

2. *Availability of Raw Materials and Products.* Are raw materials and products readily available from either captive or outside sources?

3. *Utilization of Existing Facilities.* Can either idle or excess equipment or factories be used?

4. *Freedom from Hazards.* Does the manufacture of this product or the use of this process involve any hazards to our employees, the public, etc.?

5. *Value Added by In-Company Processing.* The per cent by which the raw material is increased in value by the proposed processing.

6. *Per cent of Value Added Comprised of Payroll.* Indicate the proportion of (5) above, i.e., labor. This will indicate the nature of the proposed product or process.

D. Financial Factors

1. *Increase in Pretax Profits—Annual.* Indicate the average annual pretax profits based on the opportunity estimate contained in the marketing and commercial factors.

2. *Anticipated Capital Outlay.* Indicate the estimated cost of capital equipment and facilities required to manufacture the units under marketing and commercial factors.

3. *Capital Equipment Obsolete as per cent of New Capital Equipment.* Estimate and relate the capital equipment to be obsoleted compared to the capital outlay in (2) above.

4. *Cash Recovery of Capital Investment.* Indicates the cash flow required to recover the proposed capital portion of a new facility.

5. *Cash Recovery of R & D and Capital Investment.* Indicates the cash flow required to cover (4) above and the proposed developments costs.

6. *Profitability Rate.* Average return earned on the amount of investment outstanding over the entire life of the project.

The ratings from very poor to very good should indicate the anticipated effect as it relates to the particular division involved. In others words, an annual market opportunity of 500,000 units might be rated very good in one division; however, in another, it might warrant only a poor rating.

Exhibit 1 (*Continued*)

Form 3000

DEVELOPMENTAL PROJECT EVALUATION

Auth. No.   AP 954   Est. Date of Commercialization July 1962   Date   12/31/60
Project Title   Foamed Polystyrene Widget Development

INVESTMENT

Fiscal Year Annual Period	1958	1959	1960	1961	1962	1963	1964	1965	
EXPENSE									
1. Development	35,000	104,000	87,000						226,000
2. Engineering		87,000	134,000	45,000	13,000				279,000
3. Mkt. Dev.				9,000	6,000	16,000	21,000	6,000	58,000
4. Pre-Operating					3,000				3,000
5. Other			13,000						13,000
Total Expense	35,000	191,000	234,000	54,000	22,000	16,000	21,000	6,000	579,000
CAPITAL									
6. Land				11,000					11,000
7. Buildings				74,000	100,000				174,000
8. Mfg. Equip.					147,000				147,000
9. Mobile Equip.					10,000				10,000
10. Other					5,000				5,000
Total Capital				85,000	262,000				347,000
WORKING FUNDS									
11. Accts. Rec.						45,000	16,000	7,000	68,000
12. Raw Mat'ls. Inv.					40,000				40,000
13. W.I.P. Inv.									
14. Fin. Goods Inv.						36,000	24,000	7,000	67,000
15. Other					12,000				12,000
Total Working Funds					52,000	81,000	40,000	14,000	187,000
TOTAL INVESTMENT	35,000	191,000	234,000	139,000	336,000	97,000	61,000	20,000	1,113,000

RECEIPTS

(1)	(2)	(3)	(4)	(5)	(6)	(7)	(8)
			PRE-TAX PROFIT			CASH FLOW BACK	
Annual Period At End	Total Dollar Revenue	All Costs Before Depr.	Before Depr.	After Depr.	On Profit After 50% Tax	Depreciation and Depletion	Total
-5th							
-4th				(35,000)	(17,500)	35,000	17,500
-3rd				(191,000)	(95,500)	191,000	95,500
-2nd				(234,000)	(117,000)	234,000	117,000
-1st				(54,000)	(27,000)	54,000	27,000
0				(22,000)	(11,000)	22,000	11,000
1st	2,900,000	2,610,000	290,000	187,500	93,750	102,500	196,250
2nd	3,420,000	3,100,000	320,000	225,000	112,500	95,000	207,500
3rd	4,080,000	3,600,000	480,000	412,000	206,000	68,000	274,000
4th	4,080,000	3,660,000	420,000	370,500	185,250	49,500	234,750
5th	4,080,000	3,650,000	430,000	392,500	196,250	37,500	233,750
6th	4,080,000	3,640,000	440,000	415,000	207,500	25,000	232,500
7th	4,080,000	3,640,000	440,000	427,500	203,750	210,500	414,250
8th							
9th							
10th							
TOTAL RECEIPTS							2,061,000

Years for Cash Recovery (Form 3403)   3.7
Profitability Rate (Form 3404)   19.3   %

EXPLANATION OF TIME SCHEDULE OF EXPENDITURES AND RECEIPTS (FORM 3000)

Form 3000 provides for the complete tabulation of all anticipated expenditures and receipts during the economic life of the project.

The *Investment* section classifies the expenditures by capital, expensed items, and working funds. The schedule provides for timing the investment.

Exhibit 1 (Continued)

It allows for spending during five years prior to the zero point (the end of the "0" period) and for three years after the zero point or start-up date.

The *Receipts* section allows for cash flowback for five years prior to the zero point (start-up). (The cash flowback during these periods will result from the tax benefit from expensed items in the investment.) The schedule also allows for receipts for ten annual periods after the zero point. The following columns are to be completed as follows:

Total Dollar Revenue

Dollar sales value of annual unit volume.

All Costs before Depreciation

Total cost of sales, i.e., plant costs, delivery, and sales and administrative expenses. These costs are before depreciation and federal income tax. Do not include in these costs the expensed items already included in the Investment section.

Pretax Profit—before Depreciation

Obtained by subtracting the amount in column 3 from the amount in column 2.

Pretax Profit—after Depreciation

Obtained by subtracting the depreciation and depletion for the year from column 4. The amount of depreciation and depletion is found in column 7.

Cash Flowback—on Profit after 50 per cent Tax

There are four types of items which should be included as entries in this column when and if they occur: (1) After-tax profit from operations, which is the usual entry, is obtained by multiplying the amount in column 5 by 50 per cent. (2) The book value of land and working funds at the end of the project's economic life. Land and working funds are not reduced by the federal income tax rate. (3) Include the cash benefit received from the residual values of depreciable assets at the end of the project's economic life. Generally, this situation will come as a result of assets in the investment having at this time some remaining book life. If it is assumed the assets are sold as usable units (the sale price is never to exceed the remaining book value computed on a straight-line basis), the profit (or loss) is taxed at the 25 per cent capital gains rate. If the assets are abandoned or sold as scrap, the applicable tax rate of the profit or loss is 50 per cent. (4) Also include the after-tax cash effects of the sale or abandonment of existing assets as a result of this project, using the procedure described on page 9 of the company manual on Instructions for the Preparation of Investment Analyses by the Discounted Cash Flow Method.

Cash Flowback—Depreciation and Depletion

The annual period charges for depreciation and depletion.

Exhibit 1 (Continued)

Cash Flowback—Total

Total of column 6 plus column 7.

EXAMPLE—REAPPRAISAL,
DEVELOPMENTAL AUTHORIZATION REQUEST

The Administrative Division has been in the process of developing a foam polystyrene "widget" for about sixteen months. It is believed appropriate at this time to reappraise the project in the light of present market conditions, of completion date, and of current estimates of the development costs. Marketing has advised that the total annual opportunity for the first five years amounts to four million units, valued at $16 million per year. In the tenth year, it is believed the opportunity will amount to four million units and $16 million. In view of this total opportunity, it is anticipated that Parson & Akron would be able to market annually, during the first five years, one million units at a value of $4 million and, in the tenth year, also to market one million units valued at $4 million.

Marketing people also appraised the other factors and rated them from average to very good as indicated on the profile work sheet. The research people considered the factors and rated the project generally very good. However, research has estimated that considering the progress made to date and the actual rate of spending, the development will now cost $505,000 rather than $260,000 as originally estimated. This is programmed as follows:

```
1958..........................$ 35,000
1959..........................  191,000
1960..........................  221,000
1961..........................   45,000
1962..........................   13,000
```

The new time estimates have been incorporated in the time table on the form, and indicate technological progress slower than originally contemplated. Production factors were also reappraised and rated and found to be satisfactory.

The financial factors were appraised, and the profitability rate was computed. In addition to the programmed expenditures for research and engineering mentioned previously, it was determined that market development would be required in the amount of $58,000, with spending to begin in the year 1961. Certain preoperating expenses were also anticipated. On completion of the development, it is believed that a plant should be situated in the Midwest and would require land valued at $11,000, buildings at $174,000, manufacturing equipment at $147,000, mobile equipment at $10,000, and miscellaneous equipment of $5,000. It is also expected that working funds would have to be provided for such items as accounts receivables and inventories.

The receipts were estimated, as well as costs of manufacturing and cash flows from investment and depreciation. From these basic data, it was determined that the cash recovery was 3 7/10 years and the profitability rate 19.3 per cent.

Exhibit 1 (Continued)

AUTHORIZATION OF RESEARCH AND DEVELOPMENT EXPENDITURES

Function of Administrative Research Committee

The Administrative Research Committee has been established to assist the president in the appraisal of our present and future research and development activities. The review by this Committee will not alter the basic responsibility of the Operating Division. This Committee will examine the allocation of research funds, and in this connection the annual budgets and plans of the divisions will be reviewed.

The Administrative Research Committee may from time to time suggest and direct new research projects to the divisions and may request review of minor as well as major projects in addition to its regular review of expenditures in excess of $50,000.

Authorization Procedures

Expenditures up to $10,000 for a research or development project or a group of related projects may be delegated to the chief engineer by the manager of the division or, in the case of the Administrative Division, by the vice president of research and engineering. Expenditures for research or development in excess of $10,000 shall be referred to the divisional research committee. The divisional committees are primarily responsible for research and development effort within their divisions and, in this capacity, approve all expenditures between $10,000 and $50,000. All actual or anticipated expenditures in excess of $50,000 ($10,000 for Administrative Division projects) shall be forwarded by the divisional committees to the Administrative Research Committee for review.

In determining projects to be submitted to the committees, it will be necessary to include not only single projects, but also families of projects which are for the development of a common over-all objective and which should be considered as one project by the committee.

All project requests in excess of $10,000 shall be submitted for committee consideration through the use of either the research or the development authorization request form. The chief divisional engineer or other personnel requesting project approval will originate the authorization request form. Sufficient copies will be prepared and submitted to the divisional engineer, who will recommend approval, if warranted, and forward the data to the secretary of the divisional research committee for inclusion in the next meeting docket. Requests for expenditures in excess of $50,000 submitted to the Administrative Research Committee shall be accompanied by the authorization request form and other pertinent information, as well as the recommendation of the divisional committees.

Approvals granted by the divisional research committees will be recorded in the committee meeting minutes. The approval will indicate the project title, the committee authorization number assigned, and the amount approved, together with identification as to whether it is of a specific or continuing nature. This information is necessary inasmuch as continuing projects are normally approved on an annual basis from year to year. This also applies to projects of $50,000 and over which are approved by the Administrative Research Committee.

Exhibit 1 (Continued)

The estimated costs submitted on the authorization request form should include all phases of cost in connection with the project, including direct labor, material, and overhead, as well as the cost of capital items which must be purchased for use in the project. In addition, all developmental requests submitted to the Administrative Research Committee should include recommendations for approval based on an evaluation, where applicable, of the marketing, technical, production, and financial factors. These factors apply primarily to new-product and new or improved process development. Funds for nonspecific research or other information-gathering projects shall be requested on an annual basis. Original as well as annual requests should be supported by an authorization request form, indicating the reason for the proposed investigation, the information to be acquired, cost, and possible future applications.

TERMINOLOGY

Classification of Research, Development, and Engineering Expense

Function 1: Fundamental Research. Research directed toward an increase of scientific knowledge in general fields related to the company's business (Administrative Division responsibility).

Function 2: Applied Research. Scientific investigation to obtain accurate information concerning materials, processes, and chemical and physical phenomena, which information is deemed necessary for a specific new product or process development, product or process improvement, or to answer some specific question in the field of technical services (Administrative Division and Operating Division responsibility).

Function 3: Corporate Product and Process Development. Development to provide new products and processes for making them where such products fall beyond the scope of the present operating division's objectives (Administrative Division responsibility).

Function 4: Divisional—New-Product and Process Development. Development effort having as its objective the manufacture and sale of new products related to the announced scope of the Operating Division's current business. This also encompasses the development of the processes for making such new products if such are required (Operating Division responsibility).

Function 5: Divisional—New Processes for Manufacture of Present Products. This is development work, the objeective of which is more economical manufacturing processes for an existing product line (divisional responsibility).

Function 6: Divisional—Improvements of Present Products or Processes. Engineering development, the objectives of which are to attain a better quality product or a cost reduction in the manufacture of a present product by modification of an existing process (divisional responsibility).

Function 7: Technical services. Engineering effort, using existing technology covering all the activities heretofore referred to in this company as "operating engineering." A partial list of such activities is as follows:

1. Plant layout and construction.
2. All engineering activities necessary in the provision of systems necessary for production purposes.
3. Maintenance and repair of structures and mechanisms.

Exhibit 1 (Concluded)

4. Investigation of equipment developed by others for possible purchase and use by our company for production purposes.
5. Installation and setting-up of operational features for production equipment, even though the equipment may not have been used previously by this company.
6. Standardization work, as on machines, molds, operating manuals, etc., for production activities.
7. Redesign and change of machines or other equipment for reduction of maintenance or operating costs.
8. Technical work necessary to make minor design and construction changes on production equipment to correct operational troubles.
9. Technical work necessary in making shape or other improvement factors in production which involves only the application of features previously proven in related items.
10. Investigations requiring technical assistance concerned with quality complaints. (Note: Such investigations may lead to research projects.)
11. Technical assistance to production or sales personnel in current problems.
12. Quality and performance testing of competitive products versus our own.

Exhibit 2 shows the technical management organization which Torn adopted, and its relation to top management. In 1963, corporate sales were well over $0.5 billion annually, but the divisions were in highly competitive markets. Since 1955, there had been an intense technological struggle between improved traditional and new synthetic materials for the markets served by all divisions. One of Parson & Akron's major competitors had done an outstanding job of developing major break-throughs in improved characteristics of a traditional container material. There was strong evidence of more to come from other firms as well.

Exhibit 2

TECHNICAL MANAGEMENT AND ITS RELATIONSHIP TO THE
MANAGEMENT ORGANIZATION

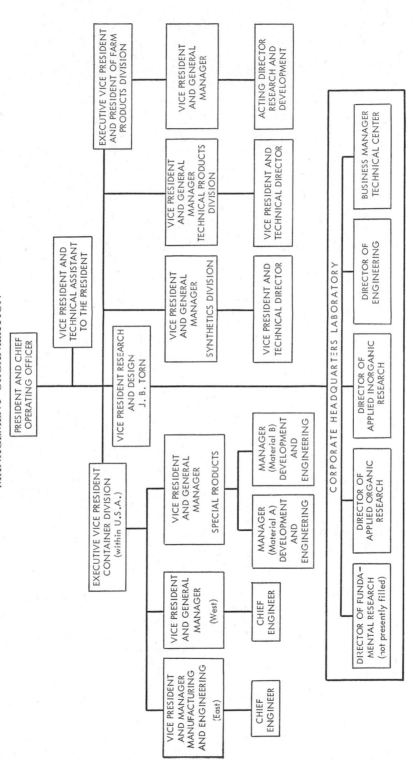

On the Feasibility of Intercontinental Missiles

Let me say this: There has been a great deal said about a 3,000-mile high-angle rocket. In my opinion such a thing is impossible and will be impossible for many years. The people who have been writing these things that annoy me have been talking about a 3,000-mile high-angle rocket shot from one continent to another carrying an atomic bomb, and so directed as to be a precise weapon which would land on a certain target such as this city. I say technically I don't think anybody in the world knows how to do such a thing and I feel confident it will not be done for a very long period of time to come. I think we can leave that out of our thinking. I wish the American public would leave that out of their thinking.

> Dr. VANNEVAR BUSH, Director of the Office
> of Scientific Research and Development
> and Chairman, Joint Committe on
> New Weapons of the Joint Chief of
> Staff (1942–1946)

FROM: Comments before the Special Senate Committee on Atomic Energy, December, 1945, cited in *Inquiry into Satellite and Missile Programs*, Part I, Preparedness Investigating Subcommittee on Armed Services, 85th Congress, November, 1957–January, 1958.

ON APPRAISING THE POTENTIAL SIGNIFICANCE
OF RADICAL TECHNOLOGICAL INNOVATIONS

APPRAISALS of the business potential of technological proposals must begin by recognizing that such proposals fall throughout a spectrum of uncertainty. The problem is to relate the time and cost (and probability) of the research and development effort to the time and financial returns (and probability) of commercial adoption. Where these elements are quite predictable and controllable, appraisal is a straightforward problem of economic evaluation. But many R & D activities do not fit this category. Then increasing degrees of time, technological, and economic uncertainties enter the picture. With radical technological proposals, it becomes increasingly difficult to pin down the business significance of the innovation.

Technological innovations can be identified, for business appraisal purposes, as falling into one of four categories:

1. *Routine Improvements.* These are minor engineering changes in which the technical knowledge for design, implementation, and application are known and predictable. No research is required; nor is exploratory development needed. Generally, the degree of advance or improvement is a minor percentage of present capability.

2. *Major Advances.* These are substantial changes in which the technological direction and needs are within the "state of the art," although not previously performed (at least by the firm in question). The necessary technology is identifiable and seems to be achievable. The technical program can be designed and planned with some certainty. Little new scientific knowledge is required, although engineering development will be needed to resolve the design details. Generally, the resulting advance will yield a major percentage improvement in an existing device.

3. *Technical Breakthrough.* This kind of advance involves a radical change or improvement that requires new scientific knowledge and consequent development work. Applied and, possibly, basic research is necessary. The technological answers seem to be feasible, but are, for the moment, unconfirmed or unknown. The supporting production requirements are therefore highly uncertain. The marketing implications also may be uncertain. Substantial improvement in capability is generally promised.

4. *"Blue-sky" Projects.* These are technological proposals in which the means of accomplishment or the end results are largely unknown. Substantial new scientific knowledge and consequent engineering knowledge is required. Basic research and applied research is indicated. There generally is a compounding of many technological uncertainties in knowledge, equipment needs, and results. Therefore, predictability is very low.

There is an inference that such projects will provide multiple of improvement in present capability and order of magnitude advances. It also follows that present devices may be largely eliminated, and even a present function may be eliminated. (For example, the development of extra-high-voltage power and transmission systems may eliminate the need for much physical movement of coal by "shipping" electricity over longer distances.)

This paper is intended to assist management in decision making on projects that fall toward the latter end of this spectrum. The student should be careful not to misinterpret the remarks that follow. For instance, the suggested procedure does not mean that evaluation by technical experts should be neglected. It does *not* mean that the non-technologist can make a sound evaluation of technical matters. What it does do is to provide a framework for business appraisal. To get proper answers to these questions, scientists, engineers, market analysts, and even industrial geographers and economists may be needed. Thus this paper does state that *the technologist, alone, may not necessarily and assuredly give a sound appraisal of the business significance of radical technological innovations.*

The appraisal and championship of technological innovations and radical technological proposals is theoretically the business of vice presidents and directors of research, development, and engineering. Two factors reduce their effectiveness in this role in many firms. First, some of these men focus their efforts (by assignment or by their own choice) to innovations internal to their firms and their own industries. They are not charged with what I shall call technological scouting, surveying, and forecasting in the search for those concepts of great potential, but which lie outside affairs of relatively immediate relationship to their firms' current technical interests. For example, have the railroads' technical staffs been studying extra-high-voltage electrical power transmission, atomic energy, and petrochemical progress as developments that may affect coal haulage? When did the steel companies detect plastics and laminated, foil-lined containers as a threat to the tin can? Are air lines considering new communications techniques and systems as alternate means of serving the functions implied by business travel? Would leather producers keenly follow plastics progress? Do book publishers do R & D work on recording systems? Do electric power utilities originate fuel cell research? There is so much to do within the firm that only the most imaginative or explicit effort would lead a firm's technological thinking to frontiers like these. Furthermore, additional man-hours and financial support are needed for such efforts, and small- and medium-sized firms cannot afford them. It is simply not reasonable for any firm to explore and even follow all the technological progress that might impinge, someday, on their firm's activities.

The second and by far the most serious reason why R & D men may not be effective in guiding the firm to far-out technological opportunity and threat is that top management and/or marketing management is unable to grasp or accept the significance of radical ideas that R & D brings to them. Production and financial top management may be unable or unwilling to grapple with the technological and economic feasibility questions. "Routine" product advances with relatively predictable problems and impacts cause no trouble; but assessing the significance of radical technological ideas is historically difficult.

As technological changes become more frequent and powerful, or require more of a commitment of resources or abandonment of present practice, they often are accompanied by economic, social, and political consequences of deepest sorts. Emotional obstacles to factual examination arise. Yet, successful innovation also depends upon interrelationships among these factors. Adequate assessment of technological innovations is important not only to managers and to military planners, engineers, and designers; but it is vital to financial and investment institutions, to administrators of social and political institutions, and to the owners, processors, and transporters of raw materials on both private and national levels.

History also demonstrates that judgments about technological proposals are colored by one's experience, vested interests (including intellectual), one's association with an involved institution, political attitude, social values, and, apparently, by one's age. These judgments may be quite apart from technological merit.

The notion that scientists and engineers have unique perception on the business potential of technological innovations deserves careful qualification. These technologists often see possibilities sooner and more clearly than others because they can visualize and accept technological feasibility and interactions. Since they are working on the frontiers of knowledge and in a climate of new findings, their thinking is (theoretically) not blocked by inability to consider a phenomenon, device, or system not in existence. Now, having acknowledged their special sources and strengths, we must recognize that they are subject to exactly the same foibles and forces that color the judgment of other men. Thus, Edison steadily advised against the use of A.C. electric power, and Lord Kelvin backed this judgment with a scientist's endorsement. Scientific opinion on the H-bomb development was widely split, apparently for reasons ranging from technological to moral. We could describe literally dozens of other situations in which technical experts' opinions were wrong for different reasons. Management, therefore, must reach its decisions with the help of technical specialists, but it is dangerous to assume that these specialists will assuredly provide an adequate appraisal of the business implications.

The corporation theoretically is well equipped to make wise decisions on technological innovations. Yet is is very easy to identify major corporate errors, even since World War II, in which firms with fine records of technological accomplishment rejected technological ideas that subsequently led to extraordinary businesses. As puzzling examples: Westinghouse's abandonment of its position in axial flow gas turbines, Eastman Kodak's rejection of Polaroid, and IBM's rejection of xerography. Similarly, we see industries virtually destroyed by their inability to respond to technological competition. The steam locomotive business versus the diesel locomotive, and the movie industry as disrupted by TV, are two examples. Thus the management challenge is clear: Anyone who aspires to the role of manager in this world of technological ferment must learn how to make sound assessments of radical technological advances and proposals.

This note attempts to help management identify those areas that need detailed consideration, even though that consideration cannot lead to certain, quantified answers. This identification is *preliminary* to the careful economic and technical analysis, market research, and matching of means and ends, resources and risks, which must be included. We are concerned here in singling out all aspects which should be explored. We must be sure that we shall not overlook an area of significance. Our goal is twofold: first, to explore without prejudice; second, to consider all the vital dimensions of the innovation. Some redundancy will be evident because we shall try to look at the same problem through the eyes of different affected parties and business functions.

OBSERVATIONS ON APPRAISAL

Certain phenomena have repeated themselves so often that we suggest some "rules" that help avoid common errors. Here are six such observations:

1. To grasp the significance of the innovation, we must set aside, *temporarily only*, the matter of technical feasibility. History repeatedly demonstrates that financial support and encouragement have been cut off or misdirected because the decision makers allowed opinions and knowledge of current technical feasibility to dominate their thinking. It is all too easy to allow *opinion* of technical feasibility to control support and adoption. Yet history shows that more often than not, technical obstacles are surmounted. Both technical progress and the associated economic and social impact seem to proceed on an exponential growth curve.

If the potential significance of some technological concepts was adequately appreciated, great efforts would be applied to overcome technological bottlenecks, and thus to make those technological visions come true. In many instances, they would come true much sooner.

Let me emphasize that I am not urging that the study of technological feasibility be ignored. My conclusion is that it belongs later in the appraisal process. Prejudgment on lack of technical feasibility fails to allow adequately for the power of determination, imagination, the exponential growth of knowledge and technological skill, and the happy results of serendipity.

2. We must be very cautious about judgments made when viewing early demonstrations of new comcepts or their application. Usually, at this stage the physical device is crudely constructed. The technical elements are not adequately refined and integrated, and may be understrength or underpowered. The inventor or builder may not understand all the technical problems encountered in operation. The failure of a single item, having nothing to do with the soundness of the technical concept, may give the appearance of failure to the whole system. It is then especially important to segregate the difference between failure in a principle from failure in a detail. We must try to determine without bias the requirements for technical success.

But the "successful" demonstration holds other pitfalls. The conditions and the supporting environment may be so specialized and favorable as to misrepresent the true situation. The demonstration may be vastly oversimplified or deliberately deceptive. An extremely limited capability may be made to appear as exceptionally powerful or effective.

Also, the mere demonstration of operation may cause one to overlook the actual efficiency and other factors that must be improved in order to have a commercially useful product. And even though we also may recognize the shortcomings, the "successful" demonstration may lead us to underestimate the time and cost of improving technical features.

I know of no sure way to resolve a proper answer. But if we are conscious of the sources of bias and error in demonstrations, we may be able to walk the tightrope between optimism and pessimism a little more securely.

3. It is foolhardy not to consider action of other possible technological competitors, even though they are not yet on the scene. There is a great and natural compulsion of inventors and innovators to compare their technological approach to the status quo, but this is rarely the only alternative.

4. An important variation of rule 3 is that refinement of the existing system may provide the most serious technological competition to the innovation. Upgrading the performance of present techniques may invalidate the economic, if not the technological advantages of the proposed approach. Cancellation of the coal pipe line as a competitor to the coal-hauling railroad is a 1963 example of this type of competition.

5. In examining innovations under the specific areas of consideration that follow, it is suggested that we look for "differences," "increases," and "reductions" in many parameters and effects of the innovation. Then the key question becomes "How much of a difference is significant?" Here is a tentative hypothesis: *If there is an order-of-magnitude improvement in some parameter such as speed, cost reduction, user input, etc., we probably have a potentially significant innovation.* This is not intended to imply that a mere doubling of improvement or, say, a 10 per cent gain may not result in a highly significant advance. But history suggests that *if* an order of magnitude improvement (or better) is obtained, *the consequences are almost surely tremendous.* Consider the atom bomb versus gun powder (power), the electronic computer versus the mechanical computation device (speed and size), the transistor versus the vacuum tube (size, life, and ruggedness).

No doubt the threshhold of business significance will vary in different fields, technologies, and times. The breaking of a technological barrier, such as plane speeds of Mach 1 in the mid-1940's or Mach 3 today, are instances where a slight increase over the status quo has great significance. However, I suggest that if an order-of-magnitude increase is detected, that fact usually means we have something potentially important, and which should not be lightly dismissed.

6. A caution must be applied to the foregoing concept. The law of diminishing returns applies to technological advances also. This obviously occurs when the advance has little additional economic or social value. For instance, air freight in 1963 offers overnight service coast to coast. Shippers want to have shipments leave in the evening and be on the other coast by the next morning. However, would they really welcome delivery in eight hours, instead of twelve, if a cost increase were involved? Similarly, a Mach 2 air transport that offers service from New York to London in three hours will be gladly adopted by most travelers over the present six to eight hours. But will Mach 3 transport offering two-hour instead of three-hour service be a valuable improvement to most travelers? If so, will a one-hour service be worth much over two-hour service? Clearly there is some point where the incremental improvement has no economic value to the user.

7. Diminishing returns points have another value to the manager. They may suggest that it is time to take a look at the technological bottlenecks or economic bottlenecks in the process. Thus, they may identify the next opportunity. For instance, the speed of aircraft for commercial transport work is approaching the point where further gains are of little practical interest in shorter runs (say, from New York to Boston). But these points of diminishing returns signal that baggage handling, ticketing, and travel from city to airport terminal are the real bottlenecks in air travel. Herein lie attractive, desirable opportunities for innovation.

MANAGEMENT'S ROLE

The manager's need is to identify those potential technological advances that will have economic value in widespread use within a time frame significant to the firm. We assert that there are necessary conditions to achieving this value. The concept must eventually prove to be:

1. Technically feasible.

2. Economically feasible.

3. Of economic interest to the user society. The criteria are:
   a) Better than the *status quo*.
   b) Better than any technological competitor.
   c) Nothing in sight to invalidate its fundamental purpose.
   d) Significant volume will be available.
   e) The cost does not exceed the user's means.

4. Timely. This implies timeliness with respect to need, to the availability of necessary supporting services, and to *acceptance* by the potential users.

AREAS OF CONSIDERATION

Effects on Product Performance

1. Will it extend capability of the system, procedure, or function?

2. Will it reduce the time, cost, space, materials, or skill required to execute or achieve its performance goal?

3. Will it produce new side effects or by-products deserving or requiring attention?

4. Does it offer opportunity for significantly different product characteristics?

5. Are there developments under way, technological *or other*, that may eliminate the basic need for the function performed?

Effect on the Inputs Required to Produce or Support the Innovation

1. Does it require new—or more—materials, components, or energy?

2. Does it take a significantly different order of capital or have a different cost structure?

3. Does it require a change in skill on the part of the work force making the innovation?

4. Does it change the productivity of labor, materials, or energy used?

5. Is the supporting technologial environment generally readily available, such as tools, instruments, and related equipment?

6. Does it take a significantly different order of time?

7. Does it require the co-operation or co-ordination of groups and institutions in a new way or degree for successful installation or operation?

8. Does the organization have an individual with the requisite skill, determination, and obsession to carry out this innovation?

Effect on Users

1. Does it simplify or eliminate duties and responsibilities of the user?

2. Does it change the user's cost significantly?

3. Does it provide the user with superior service?

4. Does it require individual buyers or users to alter their patterns of behavior?

5. Does it alter the operation of institutions or affect their motives, needs, or traditions?

6. Does it alter national posture or capability in a significant way?

Effect on Economic Society

1. Will it replace or reduce the demand for existing products or services?

2. Does it create or demand a new activity?

3. Does it require significant auxiliary and supporting activities and are they readily available?

4. What product or service demands will be increased as a primary or secondary result?

5. Will the application of this innovation on a widespread scale result in a demand for supporting technological exploration and development?

6. Does the technological base in this innovation provide potential for many new fields?

7. If the innovation is adopted, how rapidly will it spread?

8. Who will be adversely affected, and how rapidly?

A FINAL THOUGHT

Hindsight suggests that errors in technological-economic appraisal are made because of four failures:[1]

1. The failure of assumptions—incorrect interpretation of technology.

2. The failure of imagination—inability to translate technological advances into material consequences.

3. The failure of vision—inability to see interaction between various technologies and between them and social, political, and economic developments.

---

[1] I am indebted to Arthur C. Clarke for suggesting the idea of these "failures" and identifying three of them in his challenging book, *Profiles of the Future* (New York: Harper and Row, 1962).

4. The failure of nerve—unwillingness to adopt the action consequences implied by our appraisals.

While a sure method of appraisal seems impossible, hopefully an examination with this background and understanding will help.

QUESTIONS

1. Apply the suggested approach to a technological concept of some years ago. Suggestions: The railroads versus the canals; the missile versus the bomber; Kleenex versus the cotton handkerchief; the dishwasher versus manual drying of dishes; radar versus aural sound detection of aircraft; television versus the motion-picture theater; electronic computers versus mechanical and manual computation systems.

2. Apply the approach to current innovation concepts. Suggestions: Fuel cells versus gas turbines versus internal-combustion engines for automobiles; paper underwear to replace men's cotton underwear; Freeze-dried foods versus frozen foods and canned foods; contrast between freeze-drying and irradiated foods; foil-lined, laminated containers for beer versus aluminum versus tin cans; the Hovercraft and hydrofoil boats versus conventional vessels.

Note: You will have to track down usable data from industrial and professional technical printed sources and personnel.

3. Apply the approach to a case in this book. Photon, Clark Equipment Co., and Load-Glide are good candidates.

On the Conservatism of Technical Experts

In years gone by, studies aplenty have been made foretelling the future trends of speed and size of aircraft, powers and weights of engines, range and capabilities of radars, and so on. Occasionally, some devilish individual takes the trouble to go back and compare past predictions with later reality. Invariably, he finds that engineers and scientists are a conservative lot in their predictions. The immediate problems that confront them appear so formidable that they flinch from predicting ever-accelerating progress and conjure up visions of a natural barrier ahead which will cause the curve of progress to flatten off much as a biological population comes into equilibrium with its environment.

F. H. CLAUSER

FROM: "Magnetohydrodynamics: A Prophecy," an informal paper. NAS-ARDC Special Study Group, National Academy of Sciences, 1957.

MODERN PACKAGING MACHINERY CORPORATION

ON MAY 18, 1961, Seymour J. Burke, President of Modern Packaging Machinery Corporation of Chicago, Illinois, received a memorandum from Richard S. Phillips, his assistant. Phillips had graduated from a well-known eastern business school in June, 1960, and had started work as Burke's assistant the following month. During his first year with Modern Packaging Machinery, he had been given a number of projects to work on by Burke, with the intention that this activity would give him some detailed knowledge of a number of the company's problems. The projects that Phillips had been given were all matters which Burke had intended to look into himself, but which he had had to postpone because of the pressure of his current operating responsibilities. Starting in March, 1961, Phillips had been investigating the problem of rating the company research projects (details below). Burke had told him that he felt that the company's practices were sadly lacking in this area, and that it was essential that the company develop a more systematic way of evaluating its research activities. Phillips' memorandum contained the results of his investigation and concluded with the following paragraph:

> Personally, I feel that the project-rating system which I have come up with would be of considerable assistance to you and other company executives in refining your thinking about our research activity. However, as you are probably aware, there are varying degrees of opposition to this type of approach on the part of different members of our research staff. Their opposition can be traced to a number of factors; I believe the major factor is that they suspect that my proposed system will significantly or perhaps even completely downgrade the discretion they now have in making decisions on research projects.

Company Background

Modern Packaging Machinery Corporation had been started in 1948, when a group of administrative and engineering personnel left their employer, the International Chemical Corporation, to start their own business. International Chemical was a multibillion-dollar chemical and plastics manufacturer, with offices and plants throughout the United States. Among its facilities had been a research group located in Chicago, Illinois, specializing in the development of packaging machinery to utilize the new plastic packaging materials which International Chemical had started introducing toward the end of World War II. The group had expressed some dissatisfaction with International's policy of maintaining strict control over the avenues exploited by the Research Department, and had consequently decided to organize its own company in the same line of business (i.e., new packaging machinery developments). The men had pooled their own resources, obtained additional capital from a group of Chicago investors, and started business in an old warehouse building they had rented. The investors had sold their stock in the company to the founder group, in 1958, at a considerable profit.

By 1961, Modern Packaging Machinery Corporation had achieved recognition as one of the leading research organizations in packaging machinery. It worked closely with a number of plastics manufacturers, including International Chemical, to develop machinery capable of handling the continuing stream of new packaging materials for a great variety of specific different end uses. All the synthetic materials introduced in recent years had different physical characteristics, making them suitable for some and unsuitable for other end use applications. Modern Packaging Machinery Corporation made it its business to develop the specific equipment that would be required to use the various materials and to meet various product requirements.

After developing suitable machinery, Modern Packaging would produce its machines for sale, and worked closely with the chemical companies' salesmen in co-ordinating the sale of a Modern Packaging machine with contracts for the supply of packaging materials. However, Modern Packaging did not receive or pay any premiums or commissions in connection with the tie-in of its business with that of the packaging materials salesmen; both parties recognized that it was to their mutual advantage to work together in the marketing of their two related products. Over the course of the last decade, Modern Packaging had received several attractive acquisition offers from large chemical companies (including International Chemical); but the stockholders, who were all working members of the administrative or engineering staffs, had resolutely declined them all, mainly on the ground that they preferred to retain the independence which had been one of their main objectives in setting up the company in the first place.

Modern Packaging's sales amounted to almost $5 million in 1960. Net profit after taxes amounted to $200,000, and it was a common feeling among the stockholder-employees of the company that both their remuneration and their share of profits were very satisfactory.

Phillips' Memorandum

Extracts from Phillips' memorandum follow:

A Method for Rating Projects

Earlier this year, we began searching for a method which would allow us to be more selective in the machinery projects we undertake. Currently, we are working on more than 40 projects. Such a large number is not necessarily unhealthy; on the contrary, it is much healthier than having too few. But it does make the job of selecting the most important projects and assigning maximum manpower to those projects a very important function for our management group.

The fundamental theory behind the new method can be summed up as follows:

1. The project objective is set; and then, through management estimates, market research, and other methods, the market for the product to be developed is defined in terms of number of units to be sold and sales value. This is then converted into the gross profit (contribution) to be expected from such sales. This could be compared to the amount of money which is riding on a given horse in a horse race, or the value of the oil in a given oil well—assuming, in both cases, that either the horse wins or oil is struck. In other words, this is the stake for which the game is being played, without consideration as yet as to the odds for or against those stakes being attained.

2. With the "stake" known, it is now up to the proper executive or manager to set the probabilities of attaining the stake. To do this, we think that two factors ought to be considered, namely, the chances of technical success and the chances of commercial success. The probabilities associated with each of these factors are estimated for each project, using a series of subfactors with certain weights assigned to each, to arrive at a number from zero to 1.0 for each of the two probabilities. This technique cannot take the place of a competent manager with experience and good intuition, but should make the thought process more uniform and complete in evaluating the factors of commercial and technical success on each project.

Undoubtedly, there are people whose brains automatically work in the right fashion to arrive at the right decision, but there are many of us who will get the job done faster and more thoroughly if we have some standard to go by in addition to our own experience and judgment. A manager could always overrule a factor value which was derived from the weighted list if he felt intuitively that there was something big here which was being overlooked by the rating method being used.

3. If the stakes are now multiplied by the probabilities for technical success and commercial success, we arrive at what we call the "maximum expected value" (MEV) of the particular project under consideration. This represents the best estimate of the value of that project at the time you are evaluating it. In other words, it would be a fair selling price if you were to sell that project to some outsider or were to buy it from some outsider. Specifically again, referring to gambling, if the stakes on a given horse are $1,000 and the odds are one in ten that he will win, based on a sound appraisal of all the factors, then the value of a ticket on that horse is approximately $100 if you want to buy it or sell it.

4. We can then calculate another number called the PRN, or "project rating number," which defines the expected turnover of the development money over the life of a new product. The higher the number, the more times you will get back your development investment, and the more favorable, therefore, would be the project.

We believe that both these factors should be considered, that is, both the PRN and the MEV, and that, in addition, in some instances, the capital investment and the return on the capital investment will need to be reviewed. We therefore have provided some spaces on the suggested work sheets for capital investment, but have not yet worked out the basis by which one would calculate the return on investment, since there are so many ways in which this can be done.

Exhibit 1

CHANCES OF TECHNICAL SUCCESS OF EQUIPMENT—WORK SHEET

FACTOR	VARIANCE FROM ALREADY DEVELOPED EQUIPMENT	WGT.	Very Good (100%)	Good (75%)	Average (50%)	Poor (25%)	Very Poor (0)
1	Speed	24	Well below limits already attained - no problem	Same as those now in use	Faster, but still declared attainable by applying principles known to work for others or ourselves	Faster, but a solution is thought to be acceptable	Sufficiently fast to warrant an entirely new solution not now available
2	Versatility	24	Well below limits already attained	Same as those now in use	More versatile, but readily complied with	More versatile than that already attained, but a proposed solution is thought to work	Enough more versatile to warrant a new untried and unproven concept
3	Size	12	Required size results in a more simple and workable approach than other commercially acceptable equipment made by us or others	Simply a straight-forward application of existing sizes. No size problem	Minor alteration in size which can be readily attained with existing knowledge	Larger (or smaller) than this far reduced to practice but thought to be possible	Enough larger or smaller to warrant extensive development or design work to attain a solution
4	Product to be handled	16	More easily handled than normal or routine products	Simple application of existingly known and proven principles	Awkward, but not enough to handicap a solution in routine fashion	Awkward enough to warrant a new tack, but the proposed solution will work	Sufficiently awkward to warrant a novel approach which is untried and unproven
5	Packaging Material to be used	24	More machinable than any other material thus far encountered	Very machinable, no problem	Average machinability. Existing methods will work	Poor machinability characteristics necessitating special devices which, when tried, will work.	A new solution must be found to obtain the desired results
		100					

Exhibit 2

CHANCES OF COMMERCIAL SUCCESS—WORK SHEET

FACTOR		WT.	VERY GOOD (100%)	GOOD (75%)	AVERAGE (50%)	POOR (25%)	VERY POOR (0)
1	Relation to present distribution channels	4	Can reach major markets by distributing through present channels	Can reach major markets by distributing mostly through present channels and partly through new channels	Will have to distribute equally between new and present channels to reach major markets	Will have to distribute mostly through new channels to reach major markets	Will have to distribute entirely through new channels to reach major markets
2	Labor savings to customer	18	Very high labor savings in and of itself create a sizeable demand for equipment	Labor savings will be higher than normally realized for similar equipment	Labor will be equal to other types of corresponding equipment	Little or no labor savings will result	The added labor cost to customer will be appreciable
3	Pkg. material dollar savings to customer	15	Very significant savings to customer will justify cost of unit	Some savings over other methods	No change in the amount of pkg. material required	New concept adds slightly to the cost in materials	The added cost of materials over and above that of other methods will be a serious objection
4	Effect on quality of customer's product and/or package	14	A substantial improvement will attract appreciable interest in unit	Some improvement will result	No effect on quality	Quality will have to be lowered	A substantial sacrifice will have to be tolerated
5	Availability to customer	6	Equipment to be available in plenty of time to satisfy needs	Equipment to be available when needed	Delay in availability of equipment not expected to be harmful	Delay from time needed may be a problem	Delay from time needed will be a problem
6	Cost of plant changes to customer (beyond that of subject equipment) to utilize this concept	4	New equipment will conserve space and incur no expense and possible savings may result	Cost to utilize unit will be very low	The costs to utilize new approach are in line with those normally required	Cost to convert or utilize this equipment is objectionable, but will be tolerated	Extensive changes to plant and current methods will be a problem
7	Price	16	Priced below all competing equipment	Priced below most competing equipment	Same price as competing equipment	Priced above most competing products	Priced above all competing products
8	Exclusiveness to Modern Packaging (patents)	7	Can be protected by a patent with no loopholes	Can be patented, but the patent might be circumvented	Cannot be patented, but has certain salient characteristics that cannot be copied very well	Cannot be patented, and can be copied by larger, more knowledgeable companies	Cannot be patented, and can be copied by anyone or possibly, infringement may result
9	Place in the market	16	New type of product that will fill a need presently not being filled	Product that will substantially improve on products presently on the market	Product that will have certain new characteristics that will appeal to a substantial segment of the market	Product that will have minor improvements over products presently on the market	Product similar to those presently on the market and which adds nothing new
		100					

Exhibit 3

PROJECT-RATING AND PROFITABILITY STUDY

PROJECT TITLE: Semi-automatic Overwrap Machine

OBJECTIVE: To enable the wrapping and sealing of a wide variety of products in "X" film at 45/min.

EXISTING MARKETS: Poultry (smoke and fresh)

POTENTIAL MARKETS: Packers, Breakers, and Supermarkets

DATE: May 16, 1961
BY: R. S. Phillips
NO: 058 - 7030

DATE OF FIRST SALE: 1962

	1960 MIN.	1960 MAX.	1961 MIN.	1961 MAX.	1962 MIN.	1962 MAX.	1963 MIN.	1963 MAX.	TOTALS MIN.	TOTALS MAX.
1. MACHINERY SALES – UNITS	0	0	0	0	200	400	400	700	600	1100
2. MACHINERY SALES – $M @ 9 $M EACH	0	0	0	0	1800	3600	3600	6300	5400	9900
3. GROSS PROFITS (33 % of 2) – $M EACH	0	0	0	0	600	1200	1200	2100	1800	3300
4. DEVELOPMENT COSTS – $M	11	11	20	24	6	10	4	6	41	51
5. GROSS PROFITS AFTER DEVELOPMENT – $M	(11)	(11)	(20)	(24)	594	1190	1196	2094	1759	3249
6. CAPITAL INVESTMENT – $M										

SUMMARY

7. CHANCES OF TECHNICAL SUCCESS (0 TO 1) .25
8. CHANCES OF COMMERCIAL SUCCESS (0 TO 1) .60
9. TOTAL AVG. GROSS PROFIT EXCL. DEVEL. $M 2550
10. TOTAL AVG. DEVEL. COSTS $M 46
11. MEV (MAX. EXPECTED VALUE) $[7\times8(9-10)]$ $ 493 M
12. AVERAGE YEARLY RETURN %
13. PRN (PROJECT RATING NUMBER) $[(7\times8\times9)\div10]$ 11.1

CHANCES OF TECHNICAL SUCCESS

FACTOR	VG	G	A	P	VP	SUB TOTAL
1	24	18	12	✓6	0	6
2	24	18	12	✓6	0	6
3	12	9	6	✓3	0	3
4	16	12	8	✓4	0	4
5	24	18	12	✓6	0	6
TOTAL						.25

CHANCES OF COMMERCIAL SUCCESS

FACTOR	VG	G	A	P	VP	SUB TOTAL
1	✓4	3	2	1	0	4
2	18	✓14	9	4	0	14
3	✓15	11	7	3	0	15
4	✓14	10	7	4	0	10
5	6	✓5	3	1	0	5
6	4	3	✓2	1	0	2
7	16	✓12	8	2	0	12
8	7	✓6	4	2	0	6
9	16	✓12	8	4	0	12

PROJECT-RATING AND PROFITABILITY STUDY

PROJECT TITLE: Automated Line for Stemware Packaging
OBJECTIVE: To increase the productivity of the present manual operation.
EXISTING MARKETS: Produce   Bottle + canned items
POTENTIAL MARKETS: Terminal Distributor   Specialty Packaging

DATE: May 1, 1961
BY: R. L. Phillips
NO: 056 - 7040

DATE OF FIRST SALE *After 1962*	1959-60		1961		1962		1963-1967		TOTALS	
	MIN.	MAX.	MIN.	MAX.	MIN.	MAX.	MIN.	MAX.	MIN.	MAX.
1. MACHINERY SALES – UNITS	0	0	0	0	0	0	100	200	100	200
2. MACHINERY SALES – $M @ 30 $M EACH	0	0	0	0	0	0	3000	6000	3000	6000
3. GROSS PROFITS (33 % OF 2) – $M EACH	0	0	0	0	0	0	1000	2000	1000	1000
4. DEVELOPMENT COSTS – $M	12.5	12.5	9	15	16	30	5	15	45.5	72.5
5. GROSS PROFITS AFTER DEVELOPMENT – $M	(12.5)	(12.5)	(9)	(15)	(16)	(30)	992	1985	954.5	1927.5
6. CAPITAL INVESTMENT – $M										

7. CHANCES OF TECHNICAL SUCCESS   (0 TO 1) .59
8. CHANCES OF COMMERCIAL SUCCESS   (0 TO 1) .66
9. TOTAL AVG. GROSS PROFIT EXCL. DEVEL. $M 1500
10. TOTAL AVG. DEVEL. COSTS $M 59

SUMMARY

11. MEV (MAX. EXPECTED VALUE) [7x8(9·10)] $ 561 M
12. AVERAGE YEARLY RETURN   %
13. PRN (PROJECT RATING NUMBER) [(7x8x9)÷10]   9.9

CHANCES OF TECHNICAL SUCCESS

FACTOR	VG	G	A	P	VP	SUB TOTAL
1	24	18 ✓	12	6	0	18
2	24	18	✓12	6	0	12
3	12	9 ✓	6	3	0	9
4	16	12	✓8	4	0	8
5	24	18	✓12	6	0	12
TOTAL						.59

CHANCES OF COMMERCIAL SUCCESS

FACTOR	VG	G	A	P	VP	SUB TOTAL
1	4	✓3	2	1	0	3
2	18	✓14	9	4	0	14
3	15	11	7	3	✓0	0
4	✓14	10	7	4	0	14
5	6	5	✓3	1	0	3
6	4	3	✓2	1	0	2
7	16	12	✓8	4	0	8
8	7	✓6	4	2	0	6
9	✓16	12	8	4	0	16
TOTAL						.66

Exhibit 5

PROJECT-RATING AND PROFITABILITY STUDY

PROJECT TITLE: "X" Film Lapping Machine 50/min. with auto. Snipman.

OBJECTIVE: To apply as cover to tubes and trays.

EXISTING MARKETS: Produce   Hard Goods

POTENTIAL MARKETS:

DATE: May 1, 1961
BY: R. S. Phillips
NO: 057-7038

DATE OF FIRST SALE November 1961	1960 MIN	1960 MAX	1961 MIN	1961 MAX	1962 MIN	1962 MAX	1963-1964 MIN	1963-1964 MAX	TOTALS MIN	TOTALS MAX
1. MACHINERY SALES – UNITS	0	0	0	0	13	40	266	666	279	706
2. MACHINERY SALES – $M @ 7.5 $M EACH	0	0	0	0	100	300	2000	5000	2100	5300
3. GROSS PROFITS (33 % OF 2) – $M EACH	0	0	0	0	33	100	666	1666	700	1765
4. DEVELOPMENT COSTS – $M	1.3	1.3	15	20	10	15	2	6	28.3	42.3
5. GROSS PROFITS AFTER DEVELOPMENT – $M	(1.3)	(1.3)	(15)	(20)	23	85	664	1660	671.7	1722.7
6. CAPITAL INVESTMENT – $M										

7. CHANCES OF TECHNICAL SUCCESS (0 TO 1)   .45
8. CHANCES OF COMMERCIAL SUCCESS (0 TO 1)   .67
9. TOTAL AVG. GROSS PROFIT EXCL. DEVEL. $M   1233
10. TOTAL AVG. DEVEL. COSTS $M   35

SUMMARY

11. MEV (MAX. EXPECTED VALUE) [7x8(9-10)] $ 366 M
12. AVERAGE YEARLY RETURN   %
13. PRN (PROJECT RATING NUMBER) [(7x8x9)÷10]   10.8

CHANCES OF TECHNICAL SUCCESS

FACTOR	VG	G	A	P	VP	SUB TOTAL
1	24	18	12	✓6	0	6
2	24	18	12	✓6	0	6
3	12	✓9	6	3	0	9
4	16	✓12	8	4	0	12
5	24	18	✓12	6	0	12
TOTAL						.45

CHANCES OF COMMERCIAL SUCCESS

FACTOR	VG	G	A	P	VP	SUB TOTAL
1	4	✓3	2	1	0	3
2	✓18	14	9	4	0	18
3	15	✓11	7	3	0	11
4	14	✓10	7	4	0	10
5	6	5	✓3	1	0	3
6	✓4	3	2	1	0	4
7	16	✓12	8	4	✓0	0
8	7	✓6	4	2	0	6

PROJECT TITLE: Medium Sized Bread Wrapper
OBJECTIVE: A low cost machine to utilize plastic or glassine "X"
EXISTING MARKETS: firm: Bakeries Industrial cities Vending concerns
POTENTIAL MARKETS:

DATE: May 1, 1961
BY: R. L. Phillips
NO: 077-7051

DATE OF FIRST SALE: July 1961

	1960		1961		1962		1963-1965		TOTALS	
	MIN.	MAX.	MIN.	MAX.	MIN.	MAX.	MIN.	MAX.	MIN.	MAX.
1. MACHINERY SALES – UNITS	0	0	20	50	50	150	450	2250	520	2450
2. MACHINERY SALES – $M @ 1 $M EACH	0	0	20	50	50	150	450	2250	520	2450
3. GROSS PROFITS (33 % OF 2) – $M EACH	0	0	6.6	16.6	16.6	50	150	750	173	816
4. DEVELOPMENT COSTS – $M	0	0	4	15	2	6	2	10	8	31
5. GROSS PROFITS AFTER DEVELOPMENT – $M	0	0	2.6	1.6	14.6	44	148	740	165	785
6. CAPITAL INVESTMENT – $M	0									

7. CHANCES OF TECHNICAL SUCCESS (0 TO 1) .72
8. CHANCES OF COMMERCIAL SUCCESS (0 TO 1) .67
9. TOTAL AVG. GROSS PROFIT EXCL. DEVEL. $M 495
10. TOTAL AVG. DEVEL. COSTS $M 19.5

SUMMARY
11. MEV (MAX. EXPECTED VALUE) [7 x 8 (9-10)] $ 230 M
12. AVERAGE YEARLY RETURN %
13. PRN (PROJECT RATING NUMBER) [(7x8x9)÷10] 12.25

CHANCES OF TECHNICAL SUCCESS

FACTOR	VG	G	A	P	VP	SUB TOTAL
1	✓24	18	12	6	0	24
2	24	18	✓12	8	0	12
3	✓12	9	6	3	0	12
4	16	✓12	8	4	0	12
5	24	18	✓12	6	0	12
TOTAL						.72

CHANCES OF COMMERCIAL SUCCESS

FACTOR	VG	G	A	P	VP	SUB TOTAL
1	4	3	2	✓1	0	1
2	18	14	✓9	4	0	9
3	15	11	7	✓3	0	3
4	✓14	10	7	1	0	14
5	6	5	✓3	1	0	3
6	4	✓3	2	1	0	3
7	16	12	8	✓4	0	12
8	7	✓6	4	2	0	6
9	✓16	12	8	4	0	16
TOTAL						.67

Exhibit 7

PROJECT-RATING AND PROFITABILITY STUDY

PROJECT TITLE: Automatic Equipment to Produce touch form Package   DATE: May 1, 1961

OBJECTIVE: A 40/min. wrapping machine   BY: R. S. Phillips

EXISTING MARKETS: Phonograph/records, paper goods, books, games   NO: 038-7046

POTENTIAL MARKETS: Textiles

DATE OF FIRST SALE 1962	1961 MIN.	1961 MAX.	1962 MIN.	1962 MAX.	1963 MIN.	1963 MAX.	1964-1965 MIN.	1964-1965 MAX.	TOTALS MIN.	TOTALS MAX.
1. MACHINERY SALES – UNITS	0	0	10	30	50	100	200	700	260	830
2. MACHINERY SALES – $M @ 10 $M EACH	0	0	100	300	500	1000	2000	7000	2600	8300
3. GROSS PROFITS (33 % OF 2) – $M EACH	0	0	33	100	166	333	666	2333	866	2760
4. DEVELOPMENT COSTS – $M	69	106	25	33	6	15	5	10	105	164
5. GROSS PROFITS AFTER DEVELOPMENT – $M	(69)	(106)	8	67	160	318	661	2323	761	2596
6. CAPITAL INVESTMENT – $M										

7. CHANCES OF TECHNICAL SUCCESS (0 TO 1)	.70
8. CHANCES OF COMMERCIAL SUCCESS (0 TO 1)	.80
9. TOTAL AVG. GROSS PROFIT EXCL. DEVEL. $M	1818
10. TOTAL AVG. DEVEL. COSTS $M	135

SUMMARY

11.	MEV (MAX. EXPECTED VALUE) [7x8(9-10)]	$ 942 M
12.	AVERAGE YEARLY RETURN	%
13.	PRN (PROJECT RATING NUMBER) [(7x8x9)÷10]	7.55

CHANCES OF TECHNICAL SUCCESS

FACTOR	VG	G	A	P	VP	SUB TOTAL
1	24	18 ✓	12	6	0	18
2	24	18	12	6 ✓	0	6
3	12	9	6 ✓	3	0	6
4	16	12	8	4 ✓	0	16
5	24 ✓	18	12	6	0	24
TOTAL						.70

CHANCES OF COMMERCIAL SUCCESS

FACTOR	VG	G	A	P	VP	SUB TOTAL
1	4	3	2	1 ✓	0	1
2	18 ✓	14	9	4	0	18
3	15 ✓	11	7	3	0	15
4	14 ✓	10	7	4	0	14
5	6	5	3 ✓	1	0	3
6	4	3 ✓	2	1	0	3
7	16	12 ✓	8	4	0	8
8	7	6 ✓	4	2	0	6
9	16	12 ✓	8	4	0	12

PROJECT-RATING AND PROFITABILITY STUDY

PROJECT TITLE: Semi-automatic Raw Wrapper (Model 41)

OBJECTIVE: To market a unit to accommodate a wide range of package sizes.

EXISTING MARKETS: Bakery goods, Vending concerns, Caterers, etc.

POTENTIAL MARKETS: Frozen foods, Poultry, Meats

DATE: March 24, 1961
BY: R. S. Phillips
NO: 077-7051

DATE OF FIRST SALE	1959-1960 MIN	MAX	1961 MIN	MAX	1962 MIN	MAX	1963-1964 MIN	MAX	TOTALS MIN	MAX
1. MACHINERY SALES - UNITS	0	0	30	40	50	150	800	2000	880	2200
2. MACHINERY SALES - $M @ 5 $M EACH	0	0	150	200	250	750	4000	10000	4400	10950
3. GROSS PROFITS (33 % OF 2) - $M EACH	0	0	50	67	83	250	1333	3333	1466	3650
4. DEVELOPMENT COSTS - $M	23	23	12	16	4	6	0	4	39	49
5. GROSS PROFITS AFTER DEVELOPMENT - $M	(23)	(23)	38	51	79	244	1333	3329	1427	3601
6. CAPITAL INVESTMENT - $M										

7. CHANCES OF TECHNICAL SUCCESS (0 TO 1) .87
8. CHANCES OF COMMERCIAL SUCCESS (0 TO 1) .79
9. TOTAL AVG. GROSS PROFIT EXCL. DEVEL. $M 2558
10. TOTAL AVG. DEVEL. COSTS $M 44

SUMMARY

11. MEV (MAX. EXPECTED VALUE) [7 x 8 (9-10)] $1730 M
12. AVERAGE YEARLY RETURN %
13. PRN (PROJECT RATING NUMBER) [(7x8x9)÷10] 44

CHANCES OF TECHNICAL SUCCESS

FACTOR	VG	G	A	P	VP	SUB TOTAL
1	24 ✓	18	12	6	0	24
2	24	18 ✓	12	6	0	18
3	12	9 ✓	6	3	0	9
4	16	12 ✓	8	4	0	12
5	24 ✓	18	12	6	0	24
TOTAL						.87

CHANCES OF COMMERCIAL SUCCESS

FACTOR	VG	G	A	P	VP	SUB TOTAL
1	4	3 ✓	2	1	0	3
2	18	14 ✓	9	4	0	14
3	15 ✓	11	7	3	0	15
4	14	10 ✓	7	4	0	10
5	6	5	3 ✓	1	0	3
6	4 ✓	3	2	1	0	4
7	16	12 ✓	8	4	0	12
8	7	6 ✓	4	2	0	6
9	16	12 ✓	8	4	0	12
TOTAL						.79

We feel that it is necessary to achieve some standardization in the subfactors used to determine the probabilities of technical or commercial success if the new method is to have any consistency or meaning. Accordingly, the examples which are attached have all been worked out on the basis of the schedules of weighted subfactors, included as Exhibits 1 and 2. Exhibit 1 indicates the subfactors to be considered in arriving at the probability of technical success, and Exhibit 2 lists the subfactors to be considered in evaluating the chances of commercial success.

Exhibits 3 to 8 are six examples of project evaluations based on the suggested evaluation system, which were included with Phillips' memorandum as examples of how the method would be used. As explained in his memorandum, the figures for sales, prices, and probabilities were made as educated guesses by company experts. The percentage for "gross profit" was based on company experience.

Discussion of the Memorandum

After reading the memorandum, Burke sent it to the office of Robert C. Davey, a senior research engineer, with a request that he return it, with his comments, as soon as possible. Burke indicated that he wished the senior management of the company to arrive at a consensus on the problem with as little delay as possible, and that he hoped it would be possible to institute a system in the very near future, if not exactly along the lines proposed by Phillips, then based upon the methodology he had employed.

Davey had been one of the founders of the company. He was one of the oldest men employed by the company, and one of the most experienced. It was common knowledge within the company that Davey was not particularly receptive to experimentation with what he referred to as "quasi-scientific techniques which attempt to do the impossible, i.e., replace informed and experienced managerial judgment." However, Davey's opinions carried great weight within the company, at least in part because of his reputation of being an extremely creative machinery designer.

Davey's reply to Burke was on the latter's desk within three days. Its tone and wording made it clear that Davey was strongly opposed to the rating method suggested by Phillips. His opinions were summarized as follows at the end of his reply:

1. The schedules for determining "probabilities" of commercial and technical success are no more than check lists. They certainly are one way of seeing that all the factors that have to be looked into have been analyzed. But merely adding up the numbers you take off these schedules is no substitute for experienced judgment in determining what the meaning of the various factors is. It is unclear why some of the numbers are added together, and then their totals multiplied by each other.
2. It follows that the mumbo jumbo with formulas based on highly subjective numbers developed by this method of analysis is worthless.

The figures can be arranged in just about any way desired. PRN's and MEV's cannot make decisions.

3. The only way in which a research project can be evaluated is for an experienced man to make a "go" or "no go" decision. Experience and a feel for the situation are the only sound bases for making such a decision.

4. Even if there were any merit in the different weights assigned to the various factors on the schedules, in effect what is being asked is: "How long would it be before engineer X comes up with a way of solving this particular problem?" It is manifestly impossible to make a prediction in answer to this question. In my opinion, given sufficient time, *all* engineering problems are capable of solution. It only requires sufficient inputs of effort and/or capital, and time, to overcome any and all problems involved in any project. The question that judgment has to answer is: "How can we balance the cost of development against the likelihood of sale?"

5. While it might perhaps be argued that the use of probabilities would average out estimating errors over time, in this context the averaging concept is being misapplied. Averages are useful in estimating the time required for preparing engineering drawings or for estimating the cost of purchased parts in a given machine. Averages are not meaningful when expressed as a 0.8 probability of success, since this does not mean that each of five projects will be four fifths successful, but that four of five projects with this probability will be successful. In each individual case there can be only two outcomes—100 per cent success or 0 per cent success—never 80 per cent success.

Burke was disturbed by the vehemence of Davey's opposition to the rating system. His first reaction was to call both Davey and Phillips into his office the next day to discuss the proposal. After an exchange of rather cool pleasantries, the conversation turned to the matter at hand. Davey gave an example of what he objected to.

Mr. DAVEY: Look, Sey, I can show you exactly what's "bugging" me about this formula that young Rich has come up with. Take a look at the first two examples he's got in that report of his [see Exhibits 3 and 4]. You see how he shows his MEV to be $493,000 for the Overwrap project and $561,000 for the Automated Sleevewrap line? As I understand what he's driving at, this means that we ought to push ahead with the Sleevewrap project rather than the Overwrapper. He says there's $68,000 to be gained that way. I don't agree. If you look at the really *meaningful* line, total average gross profit, you see that it's just the other way round, and more so. The Overwrapper will pay off more than $1 million better in gross profits than the Sleevewrapper, if we concentrate on it. Now, how does this square with your estimate of only $68,000, the other way, young man?

Mr. PHILLIPS: Bob, you've unintentionally pointed out *exactly* what this new system will do. It will prevent us from being swayed by an apparent million-dollar excess one way when, in fact, the actual state of affairs is entirely different. You see, my figures are adjusted for the probabilities of each of the two projects actually being successful on two fronts: technically and commercially. Right there on the work sheets, you can see that I've quantified the various estimates I've received, and that they boil down to the Sleevewrap project having a 59 per cent chance technically and a 66 per cent chance commercially. Now the Overwrap project looks much better from the commercial point of view, with an 80 per cent chance. There's a big "if" there, however, and that is whether we can get it to market. It only ranked poor on each of the five criteria for technical success, and that comes out to only a 25 per cent chance. So you see, although I'll agree that the *stakes* are bigger for the Overwrap project, the chances are so much smaller, overall, that the *value* of pushing ahead with it is less than the value of the Sleevewrap project.

MR. DAVEY: Rich, has it occurred to you that there might be differing opinions about these probabilities, as you call them? Why, we'd only need to get that figure for "chances of technical success" up to, uh, say, 30 per cent, and the Overwrap project comes out on top. I'll tell you that I can concoct ninety-seven different reasons to make that 30 per cent, if I want to, and you'd never be able to challenge me. So if we had this crazy scheme of yours in operation, and I had that intuitive feeling, which I do, that the Overwrap project is bigger than the Sleevewrap project, why I'd be just a little bit tempted to make those numbers come out the way I'd need them. Can't you see that the only way that you *can* make these decisions is by bringing experience to bear on the problem?

Numbers! Even your own numbers don't back you up. What's this PRN that you've got there? The way I read it, that says that the Overwrapper is better, after all, and that contradicts your other numbers. Sey, I don't give a damn about what this young fellow's numbers show. I say that the Overwrap project is better for us than the Sleevewrap project; and I'm an engineer, and I *know*.

After his talk with Davey and Phillips, Burke decided to call a meeting of top company executives at which Phillips would have an opportunity to defend the system. In Burke's opinion, two topics could usefully be discussed at such a meeting: (1) Should Modern Packaging use some type of project-rating formula, rather than relying solely on executive intuition, in selecting research projects? (2) If so, what type of rating formula should be used?

The Judgment of Experts

Up to his death Rutherford believed that the use of nuclear energy on a large scale was unlikely (A. H. Compton, *Atomic Quest*, p. 279). Robert A. Millikan, "There is no appreciable energy available to man through atomic disintegration" (*Science and the New Civilization*, 1930, p. 163). Hertz did not think that the wireless waves he had discovered would have any practical application. (W. R. Maclaurin, *Invention and Innovation in the Radio Industry*, p. 15.)

Even Sir Winston Churchill, whose prescience has been as outstanding as his distrust of long-range prediction, said of atomic energy in August, 1939: "It might be as good as our present-day explosives, but it is unlikely to produce anything very much more dangerous" (*The Second World War*, vol. I, p. 301).

JEWKES, SAWERS, AND STILLERMAN

FROM: A footnote in *The Sources of Invention* (New York: St. Martin's Press, 1959)

ON THE APPRAISAL OF RISKS IN
TECHNOLOGICAL INNOVATION

DECISION MAKING on radical technological proposals is not a rigorous or consistent procedure. Judging from historical and known current practice (1) the aspects considered vary widely from case to case; (2) the depth of consideration given to each aspect is uneven; (3) the decision is based upon combinations of "faith," "hunch," opinion, incomplete quantification, and limited assumptions; (4) often, weight is given only to those aspects on which "good" information exists; and (5) significant social and political influences are frequently overlooked.

One questionable aspect of decision making on such problems is the manner in which a number of uncertainties are, consciously or unconsciously, lumped together and treated as one. Then the decision that follows is an intuitive appraisal of an unknown matrix of considerations.

History seems to demonstrate that unless there is identification of the critical areas, and systematic consideration of them, the innovation may founder upon some rocks that could have been revealed by careful inspection. Sometimes, it is almost startling to see the obviousness of the cause of the difficulties. We must grant that hindsight is much more perceptive than foresight; still, there are strong indications that careful review of risks can help to surmount troublesome problems, or at least help one to anticipate them.

Such a review will not guarantee that sound answers can be provided to all the questions raised. Risks will be identified that cannot be surmounted or circumvented. Indeed, the major drawback of a careful scrutiny is that it exposes so many uncertainties that their cumulative impact tends to deter the innovator. Despite this danger, an understanding of the areas of risk seems desirable. We should, I believe, review the uncertainties of technological innovations in terms of the predictability of component factors. These factors fall into identifiable areas.

Risks in Technical Areas

Scientific Risks. These are the uncertainties arising out of lack of complete theory or knowledge of needed scientific principles:

1. The principles or phenomena are unknown or unsuspected.
2. The principles have a significance that is unsuspected or beyond anticipated proportions.

460

3. The principles are discovered, but they are not mastered by the persons concerned.
4. The principles cannot be isolated or established because scientific equipment and/or test materials are not available or are inadequate.

Engineering Risks. These are associated with the inability (including excessive delays) to translate known scientific principles into practical developments. They include such things as:

1. Inability to design or develop the necessary mechanisms and controls.
2. Inability to design or develop the necessary manufacturing processes.
3. Inability to develop suitable materials.
4. Inability to provide adequate power.
5. Inability to integrate complex systems involving any or all of the items above.
6. Wrong information or assumptions on the operating environment or consumer requirements, thus leading to a product with inappropriate specifications.
7. Changes in external conditions *during* the development period (thus altering the design requirements), without a corresponding response by the designers.

Production Risks. These arise out of inability to translate a working model into a full-scale production operation:

1. Within the time and cost limitations, inability to obtain materials of desired quality, suitable equipment and power, technical personnel, or adequate trained labor. Lack of working capital also has frustrated many technological innovations in the production phase.
2. Learning-time delays (*a*) for labor to develop skill in performing individual tasks and (*b*) for the organization to be assembled, and to learn to grapple successfully with the manufacturing problems as an integrated team.

Risks in Marketing Areas

Technological innovations are characterized by special emphasis on certain adoption problems, due often to the novelty of the device or concept:

1. *Demand shortcomings,* which may be of a different character or slower in building up than anticipated.
2. *Customer response of a negative nature*—causes may be due to prejudice, changing tastes, preference, or an anticipated preference for a new alternative; the self-interest of the customer group; and sometimes by unanticipated usage that brings negative effects or reactions.
3. *Competitive actions* that alter relative attractiveness of the innovation. These include price cuts, product improvement, and provision of additional services to enhance attractiveness of the old device.

Interference Risks

Although the innovation may in itself be sound and find a ready market, external forces outside the supplier-customer sequence may delay the innovation through interference tactics. Historically, we see both systematic and sporadic interference with radical innovations.

Assessment of interference requires us to consider "who" and "how." Resistance may be *generated* by competitors, labor, government agencies, professional institutions, trade associations, religious organizations, special pressure groups, or individuals who are financially or emotionally involved. The "how" of resistance may be *through* many of the above, and using many different techniques. See "On Resistance to Technological Innovations," page 130.

Timing Risks

The sound innovation may fail because it is launched in an unauspicious time. Causes of poor timing include:

1. The general business cycle.
2. A special event impinging upon the industry to which the innovation is to be applied.
3. Conditions limiting the availability of the power, the materials, and the services required to support the innovation.
4. The international situation, or an international political or economic event affecting support or acceptance.
5. An unfortunate occurrence to the manufacturing firm or key individual.

Obsolescence Risks

These are uncertainties arising from technological or style changes, or changes in the technical means of accomplishing a portion of the task.

1. Technological competition through the development of superior approach.
2. The elimination of the basic need for the innovation by technological progress or innovation in another field. For instance, the development of the coal-burning steam turbine locomotive in 1939–40 was dropped because of the rapid progress and acceptance of the diesel locomotive.

Risk and the Individual[1]

We must also recognize that managers involved in risk situations influence both the decision and the outcome of action by their human qualities. Thus the "risk" in an innovation does not lie solely in the technical environment and those influential external events. It also depends upon the individuals who appraise, plan, and execute the effort. For example:

1. Men differ in their capacity to perceive and infer the factors affecting a future course of events. Also, they differ in their evaluation of the conduct of other men in responding to these future events.
2. Men differ in the relative weights given to those factors that they believe apply to a given situation.

---

[1] These concepts are drawn in part from Frank H. Knight, *Risk, Uncertainty and Profit* (Boston: Houghton Mifflin Co., 1921).

3. There is a difference in individual knowledge, imagination, and skill in perceiving and constructing action responses to assumed future events.
4. There are significant degrees of capability in personnel, resources, and managerial skill in achieving a given action response once it has been selected.
5. Conduct in situations involving uncertainty also differs with the degree of confidence that men place on the factors they evaluate, and in the validity of their judgments and their own ability to execute the desired program. This "confidence attitude" will affect the decision and course of action, quite apart from the correctness of the judgments.
6. The attitude, philosophy, and personality of the individual will affect his willingness to accept risks.
7. People may respond in quite different manners to the uncertainty situation, depending upon the relative seriousness of an adverse conclusion. This assessment of "seriousness" will vary with both the affairs of the organization concerned and the individual at the time of response.
8. There is also the strange but frequent occurrence in which an individual appraises a situation and then acts quite at odds with his own appraisal. Presumably, this is the result of subconscious evaluation imposed upon his conscious evaluation. Or perhaps it lies in subconscious inability to accept the conclusions he has consciously reached.

Some Conclusions

Careful analysis of the risk elements of an innovation seems essential, yet it is very likely to encourage skepticism. The trouble is that such a review is essentially negative. It is a search for problems rather than benefits, for failure rather than success. Somehow the innovation manager must shake faith in negative analysis, must be willing to recognize and accept "risks"; he must have "faith," must trust in serendipity, and yet not act to destroy opportunity for his institution or waste forces he directs. How can this be done?

One suggestion is that mathematical techniques may help us to evaluate a sequence of uncertainties more accurately. Will they also help us to evaluate more optimistically? Do present mathematical techniques of decision theory recognize the role of serendipity?

Another approach is that we should recognize risk as does the wise investor. He does not plunge all his resources on a gamble. Instead, he distributes his resources across a portfolio embracing projects with different degrees of risk. Note, however, that such an approach is not an appraisal procedure. Rather, it is a strategy deemed useful because accurate appraisal is impossible.

The process of research and development can be studied through cases and current observations. History and economics can teach us something about the interplay of men, institutions, and economic forces. Human relations research and organizational behavior studies should teach us something about the administration of change. Is this enough without a philosophy?

Does history show that great ideas emerged out of cautious appraisal?

We are compelled, I believe, to say "no." Technological innovation successes (and failures) are characterized by curiosity, persistence, determination, downright stubbornness, discontent, antagonism toward and resentment of the *status quo,* passionate enthusiasm, and blind belief. They are heavily indebted at times to luck. Often, serendipity—the happy faculty of finding something worth while other than what was sought— has been the source of benefit. We should not forget one of Maclaurin's major conclusions after studying the radio industry: that the important use of a technological innovation rarely is that for which it was conceived. To the extent that this conclusion is universally true, rigid decisions made on early appraisal are probably wrong.[2]

We are left in a dilemma: The risks and resource commitments require us to be careful in our appraisal of technological advances. However, our ability to conceive of benefits, applications, the proliferation of technical discoveries, and their interaction with future events, technological and otherwise, is highly inadequate.

Faith and the courage to take risks must become an accepted part of technological decision making. The wise manager will recognize that the techniques and thoroughness of analysis, so useful and necessary to most business problems, may be useful in cases of technological innovation, but they are insufficient. Sometimes, they are downright misleading. There is, I believe, a definite need for faith, hope, and cautious but optimistic investment in the unknown.

We must operate also with the distinct understanding that *some of our projects will fail.* We can be "sure" or "precise" only in areas of technological certainty. When we deal with "far-out" concepts, we must accept some degree of failure.

These factors call for a different attitude and philosophy of appraisal than conventional business education provides. Rejecting proposals that do not lead to assured pay-backs in clearly defined times is bound to lead to missed opportunities, some of which may have dire results for the firm. Of course, it may protect and conserve capital that would have been lost. And present value theory, which so heavily discounts the long-run future, may be spiritually at odds with proper response to technological opportunities.

QUESTIONS

1. Examine some historic technological decisions to identify the risks and the appraisal that was made of risk. How good was the appraisal? How was the decision reached?

---

[2] We must recognize that the innovation process from "idea" to "widespread commercial adoption" seems to involve a time span of over 10 years, at least, in most (but not all!) cases. Mansfield's studies on some twenty innovations show that from first adoption until half the leading firms adopted the innovation, the average time was 7.8 years. If our innovation is in the R & D stages, this period will be much longer.

2. Examine questions 1 and 2, page 443, from the viewpoint of "risk."
3. Examine current decision theory to consider whether "risk" is adequately introduced. How can analysis be improved?
4. Prepare a brief memorandum on appraisal for the president of Parsons & Akron to distribute as an appropriate supplement to the proposed research evaluation procedure.
5. Should consideration of the eight points under "Risk and the Individual" be introduced into top management's decision on a radical, major technological proposal? How can this be done?
6. How can the negative atmosphere created by careful identification of "risks" be offset properly, so as to arrive at a balanced judgment?

The Need for Skepticism

The synthesis of xenon tetrafluoride and related compounds described in the current issue . . . makes necessary the revision of many chemistry textbooks. For about 50 years, students taking elementary courses in the subject have been taught that the noble gases are nonreactive. Millions of pupils have absorbed this dogma and faithfully parroted it back at examination time.

The first evidence that xenon might participate in chemical combination was obtained by Neil Bartlett, who suggested that compounds of the type $XePtF_6$ could be made. This discovery has been followed up by a team of scientists at Argonne National Laboratory. The work they present is clear-cut and convincing. Xenon reacts with fluorine to form more than one relatively stable compound. A variety of different procedures independently confirm the chemical constitution of the new product. Indeed, the ease with which XeF_4 is made and its properties are explored is almost shocking. One can introduce the two gases into a simple system, heat the mixture for 1 hour at 400° C, and observe the formation of crystals. The experiment can be performed readily by any chemist and by many other scientists, even though they may have had only elementary training in chemistry. Some caution must be employed, for fluorine is poisonous and reactive, and the xenon fluorides may be dangerous. However, xenon and fluorine are available commercially in safe containers. Thus the essential ingredient in discovering XeF_4 was not money or equipment, but an idea. Even the choice of fluorine as a reactant seems obvious since it is the most reactive of all the elements.

There is a sobering lesson here, as well as an exciting prospect. For perhaps 15 years, at least a million scientists all over the world have been blind to a potential opportunity to make this important discovery. All that was required to overthrow a respectable and entrenched dogma was a few hours of effort and a germ of skepticism. Our intuition tells us that this is

FROM: An editorial reproduced by permission from *Science*, October 12, 1962.

just one of countless opportunities in all areas of inquiry. The imaginative and original mind need not be overawed by the imposing body of present knowledge or by the complex and costly paraphernalia which today surround much of scientific activity. The great shortage in science now is not opportunity, manpower, money, or laboratory space. What is really needed is more of that healthy skepticism which generates the key idea—the liberating concept.

P. H. ABELSON

EVALUATION OF APPLIED RESEARCH IN A BUSINESS FIRM

By I. H. Ansoff

Applied Research as a Phase of the Product Development Cycle

This paper is concerned with a framework for evaluation of applied research inside a business firm. One aim of such a framework is to provide a planning tool—a means for selecting from a list of competing research proposals those which will contribute most to the firm's profitability.

A second aim is to provide a control tool—a means by which accomplishment of selected projects can be monitored and controlled during their execution. The initial promise of the project must be continually re-evaluated against research results and other pertinent information which may develop. The project is then accelerated, decelerated, changed in direction or emphasis, or canceled altogether, depending on the outcome of the evaluation. Thus the contribution to the eventual profitability is optimized during the applied research phase.

Our concern is with applied research in business in contrast to other social institutions such as a government, a university, or a nonprofit foundation. It must, therefore, be viewed against the background of business objectives and strategy. Two basic business objectives are essential parts of this background. The first of these postulates that a business firm is a *perpetual enterprise;* its basic aim is to survive forever. The second states that the central objective is to *maximize profitability over the long run.*[1]

A firm's product-market strategy is implemented through a series of sequential activities, usually referred to as the product development cycle. Applied research is only one phase of this series of activities. In order to assess its contribution, therefore, it is necessary first to define the role of applied research in the development cycle and to relate it to the phases which precede and follow. With that accomplished, a framework for evaluation of applied research will follow naturally.

---

[1] Conceptually, the first postulate defines the "long run" as infinity. In all practical situations the long run is the foreseeable business horizon—the maximum time period for which forecasts can be made.

Definitions

The phase which occurs earliest in the development cycle is pure or basic research. Its result is creation of new knowledge, which, in the physical sciences, is concerned with structural and dynamic properties of matter. It is the process of creating mathematical equations and/or experimental procedures which explain observable (man-made or nature-made) phenomena.

Applied research, which follows, is the application of knowledge to the solution of previously unsolved (usually generic) problems. It can either be device-oriented, such as a breadboard which demonstrates that optical diffractive properties of matter (knowledge) can be used to compress electromagnetic pulses (problem), or it can be technique-oriented, such as a procedure for growing semiconductor crystals.

Applied research is sometimes defined as application of knowledge to "useful" purposes. Such a definition begs the central question of this paper, i.e., how to distinguish between "useful" and "useless" applied research projects. As we shall see, the word "useful" would rob the definition of its generic character, since what is useful to a business firm is not necessarily useful to a university.

Relation of Applied Research to the Development Cycle

The key characteristic implied in our definitions of applied research is the uncertainty of the outcome of a proposed project. Since the problem has not been solved before, the main object is to demonstrate that existing knowledge can be used to produce a solution.

The fact that the *degree* of uncertainty can vary over a wide spectrum gives rise to a major difficulty in defining clear-cut separation between applied research and activities which precede and follow it. At one extreme, it is not uncommon to find applied research proposals whose outcome is so uncertain as to require, in fact, creation of new knowledge and which should, therefore, be recognized as basic research. The problem is not simply one of proper classification. Rather, it is one of determining the proper approach and proper talents to be employed. Failure to recognize the principal bottlenecks may lead to wasteful effort by engineers and modelmakers where mathematicians and theoretical physicists are called for. It may also lead to grossly overrun projects and badly missed schedules.

Confusion as to the true nature of applied research occurs most frequently at the other end of the spectrum of uncertainty, where it may be confused with a later stage in the product development cycle, which is called product development. Product development is the application of a known problem solution to the construction of a device or the development of a procedure to specific performance characteristics. It is the process of reduction to practice of results of applied research.

It is not infrequent to find a product development project mistakenly classified as applied research. As in the previous case, such confusion can result in much misplaced effort and in even further-reaching consequences. The major problem arises from the fact that although applied research and product development activities are very similar (involving, usually, construction of a working device), their purposes are entirely different. The former is merely to show that a particular problem can be solved; the latter is to start a chain of steps which eventually lead to offering a product to potential customers. Whereas applied research may sometimes be justifiable if it merely holds a promise of substantial improvement in the state of the art, product development is *never* justifiable unless it holds a promise of making a profit for the company. Unless, prior to undertaking product development, an effort is made to determine the potential profitability, the result will be very high product mortality and hence a waste of research and development funds.

When an applied research project is successfully completed, it yields only one essential part of the information required for determining potential profitability. Applied research merely tells us that a particular *type* of device can be built or a fabrication technique used to produce a particular type of product. Missing at this point are the following essential pieces of information: Does a demand exist for this type of device (or product)? What *specific* performance characteristics are desired? How does performance relate to the price the customers are willing to pay? How is performance related to our costs to make the device? What competing devices are already available? How does our device compare with them? What will it cost us to put the product on the market?

If these additional questions can be answered satisfactorily, the results must be integrated into an over-all estimate of two central factors in product development decisions—the *potential return on investment* and the *associated risks* which will be incurred on the way to product commercialization.

Although central return-on-investment and risk estimates are not sufficient, for they measure the proposed product taken *by itself*, apart from the company's other products and markets. Further questions must be examined in order to determine the *strategic fit* of the proposed product: Does it fit the company's over-all product-market strategy, or will it necessitate a change in strategy? How does it relate to the present product-market position? What joint economies and diseconomies will result? How does the timing of its introduction fit in with introduction to or withdrawal from the market of the company's other products?

Thus, in addition to success in applied research, a host of other requirements, fully as important to future success, must be met before a product development effort is justified. It becomes apparent that applied research is only a part of a phase in the product development cycle which represents transition from basic research to product development. Other parts of the phase are:

1. *Applications analysis* (sometimes called systems analysis), which is concerned with the translation of customer needs into product performance specifications, as well as with studies of economic justification of the product from the point of view of the customer.
2. *Market research*, which analyzes the demand, the competitive factors, and the pricing structure as well as the marketing costs.
3. *Applications research* (sometimes called preliminary design), which translates the performance specification into a specific technical design and an estimate of the development and manufacturing costs.
4. *Business analysis*, which consolidates all the preceding factors into an analysis of profit potential, risks, and the strategic fit.

In a given project, any one of these factors may be equally as or even more important than applied research. The rate of mortality of development projects is directly related to the ability of the planning organization to isolate ingredients of the product research phase which are critical to success. For example, if the probability of success of applied research looms high, but it is not clear that there is an existing demand for the potential results, market research may be indicated as the primary activity.

The related activities described above are directed toward answering a central question, which is: Should the firm undertake development of a suggested product? Applied research is one of these aspects, dealing, as it does, with a question of whether existing knowledge can be used to produce the type of performance desired of the product. Other aspects inquire into economic and business factors involved. The entire complex of activities is then appropriately named *product research.*

The question of whether applied research should precede, follow, or be performed concurrently with other parts of the product research phase depends on the particular situation. In firms which have a long history of participation in a particular market, whose product technology is relatively stable, and whose growth is primarily through development of new products to supersede earlier models, applied research would normally come first. Pursuit of other parts may not be essential to success because, through long-time familiartiy with its products and markets, the firm has built up a large fund of product research information.

On the other hand, firms which are relatively new to their markets, which are participating in a dynamic technology, and which grow largely through product diversification need to give priority to other parts of product research. In such cases, successful applied research alone will not be sufficient to give indications of the profitability and strategic value of the proposed project.

Evaluation of Profitability

Since applied research is an integral part of product research, evaluation of proposed applied research projects should be subject to the same basic criteria which apply to the over-all phase. At the same time, the information usually available at the inception of an applied research project is sparse and uncertain, and not adequate for a definitive evaluation of potential profitability. For this reason, our approach to evaluation of applied research will be first to construct an over-all framework for evaluation of profitability and then to modify it to take account of the uncertainties in the information.

Figure 1–A represents a typical history of required investment in the course of a product development cycle for a specific product. The earliest phase is product research. It may or may not involve applied research

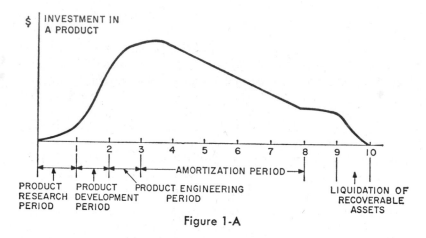

Figure 1-A

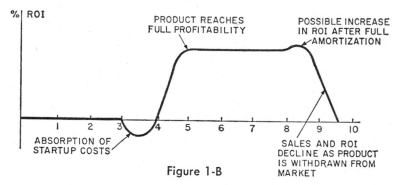

Figure 1-B

activity. At the termination of this phase, desirability of further development is evaluated, and the product development phase is initiated which terminates with successful construction of an engineering prototype. Following this, product engineering takes over. A production prototype is built, production drawings are prepared and proofed, manufacturing facilities are planned and installed, build-up of inventories begins, and a marketing plan is prepared and put into action.

As the curve suggests, the rate of investment into the new product progressively accelerates toward the end of the product engineering phase and then levels off as the product begins to show profit.

From that point on, investment recovery takes place in accordance with an amortization schedule, which is usually based on a conservative estimate of the useful life of the product. If it does turn out to be conservative, then, for a period, investment will level off at the value of the working capital and unamortized fixed assets which are required to support the product. Toward the end of the product's life, further investment recovery takes place through liquidation of inventories.

Figure 1–B shows the corresponding history of the return on investment. This remains at zero through the product engineering cycle and then usually turns negative for a time while the learning costs are absorbed. Then the return on investment builds up rapidly to a more or less steady-state level and declines to zero toward the end of the useful life of the product.

Figures 1–A and 1–B suggest that the following basic variables describe the value of the product to the sponsoring firm:

1. The average return on investment over the product lifetime. This is the basic measure of desirability.
2. The maximum investment that will have to be incurred, since this determines the drain on the company's resources.
3. The pay-out period, which is the time to full recovery of investment, on the assumption that all the product's earnings are used for this purpose, since this is an indication of how long the investment will be tied up.
4. The time to reach the maximum return on investment, since this indicates that the product enters its earning period.
5. The life span, since it indicates the duration of this period.
6. Last, but first in importance, the risks that will be incurred on the way to investment recovery.

A Framework for Evaluation of Applied Research

As mentioned earlier, the difficulty in evaluating profitability of applied research stems from the fact that the decision has to be made very near the beginning of the cycle, when the information available is at its worst. In a majority of cases the data are insufficient to attempt even an approximate computation of the return on investment. One way to get around this difficulty is to set up a number of individual criteria which are related to the basic elements of profitability, to evaluate the proposed applied research project in the light of each one of these, and then to combine the results into an over-all figure of merit which is generally proportional to the return on investment. A similar figure of merit is established for a measure of the risk.

The criteria shown below are broken down into two classes. The first is related to the numerator of the return on investment fraction, and hence to potential profit. The second is related to the denominator, and hence to the required investment.

CRITERIA RELATED TO POTENTIAL EARNINGS

I. Profit potential
 Estimate of total sales (earnings) over lifetime (E)
 Technological merit (M_t)
 Business merit (M_b)
II. Probability of success of project (P_s)
III. Probability of successful market penetration (P_p)
IV. Strategic fit of proposed project with other projects, products, and markets of the company (S)

CRITERIA RELATED TO INVESTMENT

I. Direct investment ($C_{ar} + C_{pr} + C_{pd} + C_{pe} + WC + F = C_d$)
 C_{ar} = Total cost of applied research effort
 C_{pr} = Total cost of product research effort (exclusive of applied research)
 C_{pd} = Total cost of product development effort
 C_{pe} = Total cost of product engineering effort
 WC = Working capital required
 F = Total cost of extra facilities required, such as staff, buildings, etc.
II. Joint cost effect (J)
 J = Savings factor in direct investment resulting from use or sharing of existing facilities and capabilities

Within the first class the first criterion is profit potential. The ideal measurement would be to estimate the earnings potential which will result from the proposed research. Since this may not be possible, the rating on this criterion is obtained from three estimates:

1. An approximate estimate of total sales (or earnings), which can be seen as the direct foreseeable result of the proposed research venture.
2. Technological merit, which ranks the project in terms of the contribution it can make to the state of the art.
3. Business merit, which estimates the breadth of business opportunity which will be opened up as a result of successful research.

All three of these factors are based on an estimate of the intrinsic merit of the proposed project, without reference to the performing organization and under the assumptions that the project will be successful and that a successful market penetration can be made.

The second major factor is to estimate the probability of success of the proposed applied research project. This is based on recognition of bottleneck technical problems which need to be overcome by research, on the clarity of the proposed approach to the solution, on past experience in similar types of research, and on availability and quality of technical skills available for the project.

The third major factor is another conditional probability. It is the probability that if the project is technically successful, a successful market penetration can be made. The estimate here is based on two major considerations. The first is the nature of the competitive environment: similar research efforts being performed elsewhere, their quality, and the strength of the companies behind them. Second is an estimate of the competitive capabilities of the sponsoring company. This includes existence of the required type of manufacturing, development, and sales competence.

The fourth factor which affects the estimated potential earnings is what we have previously referred to as strategic fit. It measures the contribution of the proposed project to the desired strategic direction of the company. It measures the joint economies and diseconomies which may result in conjunction with development of other products and performance of other research within the company. Finally, it determines the desirability of the timing of the product introduction with respect to the other products of the company.

The second class of criteria is related to the investment that will be incurred in the course of the complete life cycle. First is the investment required for the proposed applied research project. In addition, it is necessary to estimate the costs of the remainder of the product research cycle: product development, product engineering, capital investment, and working capital which will be required to sustain the product. In the early stages of the product development cycle, it may be extremely difficult to estimate most of these costs with any degree of precision. However, order-of-magnitude estimates can have a very significant influence on the decision to proceed with an applied research project.

For example, a firm which is contemplating research in the field of digital computer techniques must give serious consideration to the logical consequence of such work. Research on techniques will lead to development of computers. Successful entry into the computer field has traditionally required a multimillion-dollar investment. If the company does not have sufficient resources to provide for such expense, it may well choose to forgo research in this direction.

The second element of investment is a measure of the joint economies and diseconomies which may follow introduction of the product. This involves possible joint use of existing facilities, machinery, distribution channels, and so forth. On the negative side, the proposed project may call for the use of critical research skills which are in demand on other products.

The evaluation of the individual criteria can be performed by assigning an arbitrary scale to each and ranking competing projects on that scale. Following this, they are combined in an over-all figure of merit:

$$\text{Figure of merit (profit)} = FM_\text{p} = \frac{(M_\text{t} + M_\text{b}) \times E \times P_\text{s} \times P_\text{p}}{C_\text{d} \times J} \times S$$

This adds the rankings of the technical and business merits, and applies them as an adjustment to the estimate of the sales potential. These are then multiplied by the respective measures of probabilities of success of the project and probability of market penetration. The product is divided by the estimate of the investment which is adjusted by a factor estimating joint economies and diseconomies. This gives a figure of merit which approximates profitability of the proposed project taken by itself. To obtain the impact on other products and markets of the company, this fraction is multiplied by the strategic fit rating.

In addition to the figure of merit which is related to profitability, a comparably important yardstick is a measure of risk involved in undertaking the proposed research:

$$\text{Figure of merit (risk)} = FM_r = \frac{C_{ar}}{FM_p}$$

This is approximated by the ratio of the cost of the proposed research to the over-all figure of merit. Very roughly speaking, this is the dollar cost at risk in applied research per percentage of eventual return on investment.

The framework for evaluation of applied research described above has the obvious disadvantages of lack of precision and the dangers which stem from ordinal rankings. Furthermore, it is well known that use of fractions as a figure of merit without particular attention being paid to the behavior of the numerator and denominator can lead to erroneous conclusions.

Nevertheless, in view of the usual limitations on information available at the initiation of applied research, the proposed method has the following merits:

1. It provides a mechanism for anticipating costs and problems which can arise subsequent to research.
2. It permits a relative ranking of competing applied research projects.
3. It makes possible a comparison of applied research to other phases of product research.
4. It places applied research within the over-all business perspective of the firm.

· · · · · · ·

Discussion

Q. I want to know why you put S in that equation. After all, why do you care about the strategic fit? Isn't it true that you care because poor fit will force you into new areas of costs? Those are already reflected in C and D and perhaps in J. So, if you diagnose those right, where's the significance of strategic fit?

A. "Fit" is a central notion. I noticed that Mr. Smith talked about it . . . and so did Dr. Herwald. If, whenever a new business opportunity comes along, we were smart enough to investigate its complete ramifications, going back into the past and into the future of the company, there would be no need for strategy. All I'd need to do is have my profitability objective. The proposal that rings the bell highest in the scale would be the thing that I'd pick. The reason we are forced into strategy is essentially the uncertainty in whatever evaluations we make. Therefore, when I go through the exercise of strategic fit, in effect, I kind of make a lame duck allowance. It implicitly implies aspects of the J's, the C's, the D's that I may not be explicitly able to take care of in the equation. Another way of putting it, when we evaluate the rest of this formula, we are primarily concerned with the consequences of the product in question being taken by itself, as if the company had no other products on the market. The upward or downward adjustment in the return provided by S places this product into the over-all perspective of the product line.

Q. It's a reflection of your uncertainty relative to the proposal because the project is not a part of your traditional operating area.

A. I think not. I think it's a reflection of uncertainty relative to the fact that none of us know a hell of a lot about our businesses. We don't have a way of explaining business to ourselves. We don't have a way of computing the consequences of our actions.

Q. Could we name again the things you've considered under strategic fit?

A. Let me see what I have in the text and that will keep me from making a long-winded answer. No, I took care of it very nicely. I said that "to obtain the impact of other products and markets of the company, this fraction is multiplied by the strategic fit rate"! Seriously speaking, it has to stem, as Professor Quinn pointed out, from the definition of what a strategy is. To me a strategy is a very simple notion—it's a set of rules for selecting among investment opportunities that present themselves to you. It's the kind of rules that are going to optimize your company's objectives. Any of the definitions of Professor Quinn's strategy would fit, for example. If my company has made a success, strategically speaking, by being indispensable to the customer, then my measurement of whether this further contributes to my indispensability to the customer would give me an additional measure of confidence or lack thereof in the estimate of the various other factors in the formula, resulting in an upward or downward adjustment of the figure of merit. I'm sorry this reply is so long-winded, but it's because I don't understand it too well!

Q. We've been working in this field, too, and we've come up with equally vague mathematical expressions, containing equally vague parameters. Yours is about the same chart, as far as I can see.

A. You use them? Do you believe them?

Q. Yes.

Q. What's the advantage of putting all these things into a complex formula when you have the problem of the J factor going to zero or something like that, where your controls go out the window? Why not take into account these factors by listing them and thinking about them rigorously, and then coming up with what amounts to a present value analysis of the particular project?

A. This *is* a present value analysis.

Q. I just wondered, why go into the final formula? Why not simply rank proposals by the present value or rank by the return on present value?

A. This is a very relevant question. I think this is the kind of thing that makes some of us feel that we must strive toward a theory and some of us feel that we must go through business life by the case method. I'm not confusing you with a case method advocate entirely, but there are some of them in the vicinity.

One of the smartest mathematicians I know (I think he is a Harvard man) says that God has created all relations in only two shapes—either they're constants, or they are linear. He's obviously fibbing, but I think that the point he's making is that the human mind is very improperly constituted because it can't think of more than three things at any given time. Therefore, if you want to find any correlation between two human minds, it is important to reduce the thing that you are considering to some common understandable framework about which you can both argue and disagree. Essentially, this is why you attempt to reduce the expression to the over-all profitability figures. I don't know what you mean by present value analysis. . . . This *is* an attempt at present value analysis. This is also an attempt to combine factors into a kind of over-all judgment factor which goes up, in general, when profitability goes up; which goes down, in general, when profitability goes down. You get this kind of correlation. I think it's a matter of individual preference as to which way one likes to look at the universe.

Q. We're not really talking about the same thing. . . . I think present value adds a refinement on this general approach.

A. I think we'd better attempt to define precisely what we're talking about.

Q. You can do this by discounting the cash flows and profitability.

A. All you are doing is to apply some more correction factors to this analysis because what you discount is this equation.

Q. Isn't an element of judgment working all through here? The element of judgment is associated with each one of those subjects.

A. Oh, unquestionably. If I would call this science, my alma mater—Brown—would hear about it, and they'd take my sheepskin away. No, this is an attempt to set up some common grounds within which people can make judgments. You don't go out and hire a brand-new kid who's never been in a sales department or never done research and say: "All right, kiddo, here's the formula, and here's a bunch of research projects—now what are they worth?". . . This is for people of maturity and judgment. The only implied issue that we are raising here is whether you want to organize your universe in this manner so that, for a change, it would be almost comprehensible.

Q. Wouldn't your item, the estimate of total sales, be affected by what's in the back of your mind and all other factors in the numerator?

A. Don't you think this equation is terribly nonlinear?

Q. Yes, if you want to put it that way.

A. I don't want to put it that way. I just thought maybe we could communicate in the "right way." One tries to estimate the total demand situation independently of his participation in it. As the second step, one tries to deal with the probability of market penetration.

Q. Dr. Ansoff, you have the same thing written down, in a sense. How can you estimate the total sales figures unless you have something in the back of your mind as to its technological merit figure? So what I'm trying to say is that when you break this down, you can't help being influenced by both of these factors unless you combine them explicitly. So you may want to put the equation in a simpler fashion.

A. Yes, I'll put it in a simpler fashion. This is a well-known peril, and we're all subject to it. There are two issues here, I think. One is the awkward way in which I answered the earlier question. The answer to that is "yes" or "no," depending on what you define by these various terms. The other is the issue of practical application of this equation, and of getting yourself into the frame of mind so that when you're working on E, you're not worrying about P_t. My personal experience in this kind of thing has been that this is a difficult problem. As a result, what you find yourself doing is going through each item three or four times over because you catch yourself allowing judgment that you've already exercised to influence the judgment on another factor. There's no question about this. One of the things one tries to do when a group operates trying to solve a problem like this is to define as explicitly as one can, on a piece of paper, what we shall mean by E, and what we shall mean by P_s. That helps some, I think, but you're absolutely right about the interacting effect of judgments.

Q. What about the relative weighting of these different factors? It seems to me that it may be impossible to do anything with this or that factor. One has to know whether M_t is more important than P_s or vice versa. This is the essence of business judgment.

A. I'm not sure I understand the question.

Q. Of these different factors that are listed, what weights does the user give to these different factors? Which ones are relatively more important and which ones less? This would seem of great importance.

A. Yes, indeed. Whenever you try to do this analysis, it comes up almost automatically. It has come up in some of the exercises we've gone through here. I think it's perfectly obvious that when you set up the ordinal scales, you may assign ranges from one to 10 to this number and from one to 100 to that number. The manner in which you assign them is going to lean very heavily upon where you happen to find yourself in the business situation. I agree with you there. A great many more things could be done in ranking.

Q. Have you checked this retroactively in a couple of successful ventures?

A. I can claim one.

Q. How did it come out?

A. Very well. I must confess also that it was a real honey, and even if it didn't apply any R & M formulas to it, we probably never will be sorry.

Q. We've mentioned a figure of merit on this program. How do you use it? . . . There are many people who immediately assign fact to a number. . . .

A. I think that it's further-reaching than this. I think there's a tendency to be fascinated with the sound of your own ratings.

Q. Do you have a time factor specified in your equation?

A. It's implied by an attempt to estimate the total return over the life cycle of the product. This can be written in three or four different ways, depending on how crude or how fancy you want to get. You can compress this expression, you can expand that expression, having essentially the same form. You can, for example, go for simple exercises in the use of this equation by studying a relationship as a function of the position in the life cycle of the product. So our figure of merit becomes a variable. You can actually plot some graphs and see when this or that factor is going to do something for you and when it is going to hurt you. This will determine the capital requirement planning.

Q. This is an approach which, under certain circumstances, is very appealing to me. I've developed such an equation, but there are some limitations to it that I think you haven't used. In trying to evaluate the relative merits of roughly 20 different projects, we set up a limited *ad hoc* group. The results then were *ad hoc* results, and were only relatively true at that period of time for that particular project. A few years later a different group runs the same exercise with the same definition of the variability and the quantitative development of each factor before the rating takes place. They then review these 20 projects. The value judgments they set up on the order of magnitude between one project and the next were consistent with the original effort. As far as we know, we missed only one. For relative rating of these projects, I thought this was excellent.

A. We're doing a thing like this in one of our units and presenting it to intermediate management. This was when I was in the fortunate business of being in staff and looking up. Another way of putting it is that an approach like this has to be interpreted and a judgment framework established before it's brought up for decision.

QUESTIONS

1. Contrast the significant differences between the approaches of Ansoff and those in "Martin Barrett" (page 403), "Parsons & Akron" (page 416), "Modern Packaging Machinery" (page 445), and the note, "On the Appraisal of Risks in Technological Innovation" (page 460).

2. Devise an appropriate procedure for appraising research proposals for a firm in any of the cases in this book.

3. Obtain the research evaluation procedure for a local firm with a view to analyzing and improving it.

What Advantage Does the Independent Inventor Have?

When in 1937 I set out alone with my rather limited means to solve the big problem of finding a cheap process of production for ductile titanium, I was a visionary, and I was considered as such by the outstanding metallurgists of the United States. . . . It was the enjoyment of discovery, the curiosity to know what is around the corner, which motivated my action and let me get over hardships and relative poverty, until final success was achieved. This example should refute all those who claim that today individual research—as was done by Pasteur or Fleming—is dead, and that it has been replaced by the collectivist planned work of teams of groups of salaried men, who operate the scientific machinery in private and government laboratories in hopes of discovering something under the command of a director who, although usually removed from the observation of the experiments, is supposed to do the thinking. I do not agree with this claim. The free individual who accepts risks and years of sacrifice and who is driven by religious devotion to his task and by the spiritual joy which invention procures, in much the same way as is the artist by aesthetic achievements, can still today defy and outsmart the captive salaried research performed at extravagant cost in palatial laboratories where frequently nothing else is wanting but ideas. Money alone does not create or invent and the free individual still has great chances of success because his ideas originate in that same mind that commands the activity of his hands, while his thoughtful eyes watch the things that happen.

W. J. Kroll

from: "How Commercial Titanium and Zirconium Were Born," *Journal of The Franklin Institute*, September, 1955.

LOAD GLIDE[1]

In November, 1960, Bruce Rogers boarded a plane for Chicago. In his brief case were five copies of a report, "Aero-Lift: Breakthrough in Materials Handling." This was the title of the novel project he was about to put before the top management of Clark Equipment Company. Rogers, as Manager of Clark's young Development Division, was responsible for all research and product concepts that lay outside the normal development activities of Clark's major manufacturing divisions. These divisions included the Industrial Truck Division, for materials-handling work; the Construction Machinery Division, for mobile cranes, tractor shovels, and so forth; the Brown Trailer Division, which made motor truck trailers and large shipping containers; and the Automotive Division, which made heavy, automotive-type power train parts. Aggressive and imaginative management had raised Clark's sales from the $15-million range before World War II to about $185 million by 1960. Clark was the largest producer of rider-type materials-handling equipment (see "Clark Equipment Company" for corporate backround and product illustrations [page 173–176]).

The Development Division also included Glen Johnson, Marketing Manager, eight engineers, and two secretaries. It had been established by the President, George Spatta, and the Vice President of the Industrial Truck Division, R. H. Davies, in 1958. They felt that they needed a corporate agency to screen product concepts coming in through top management levels, as well as to generate and explore unusual ideas on its own.

Spatta was nationally known for leading Clark's aggressive growth program. Both Rogers and Johnson had over five years of experience in the Industrial Truck Division, and were thoroughly familiar with materials-handling vehicles and their applications. "Aero-Lift" was the first radically different concept that the Development Division had generated.

The Origin of "Aero-Lift"

The project began in midsummer of 1959, when Bruce Rogers was intrigued by the amount of publicity and technical activity given to ground effects machines (GEM). Was there a possibility that air could become the basis of an economic handling system, Rogers wondered? He

---

[1] Clark Equipment Company registered trade-mark.

recalled that in the late 1950's, someone had offered a home vacuum cleaner that "floated" on its own exhaust air. It wasn't until mid-January, 1960, that an engineer was free for an exploratory study. Then Rogers assigned Frank Dobbertien to the job, saying: "Let's make a study of ways to move material with air, other than pneumatic tube carrier systems or air movement of bulk materials."

Rogers and Dobbertien agreed that conventional GEM vehicles, helicopters, and airplanes were not suitable for Clark's type of industrial materials handling. They would start strictly from curiosity, and with no known need or application; there just might be a use for a new concept.

Dobbertien's first step was to trace technical literature on GEM. He attended symposiums and searched the literature of many technical societies, and university and government programs. Exhibit 1 shows some sources studied. Simultaneously, the development group built a small air-lift pallet with skirt to "seal" the air supplied from a shop compressor. The pallet lifted 9,000 pounds, but was not regarded as successful. To

Exhibit 1

SOME TECHNICAL LITERATURE SOURCES EXPLORED IN THE
AERO-LIFT PROJECT[1]

Symposium on Ground Effect Phenomena

October 21–23, 1959, the Princeton University Conference and the Department of Aeronautical Engineering in cooperation with U.S. Army Transportation Corps (Research & Development Command) as part of the ALART Program.

PAPERS AND AUTHORS

Study of a Current Plan for a Ground Effect Platform, P. Poisson-Quinton
Research Related to Ground Effect Machines, Richard E. Kuhn and Arthur W. Carter
A Review of the Princeton Ground Effect Program, W. B. Nixon and T. E. Sweeney
Ground Cushion Research at the David Taylor Model Basin—A Brief Summary of Progress to Date and a Preliminary Design Technique for Annular Jet GEM'S, Harvey R. Chaplin
Flow Phenomena of the Focused Annular Jet, J. C. M. Frost and T. D. Earl
Two-Dimensional Study of a Low Pressure Annular Jet GEM at Forward Speed, Jeffery Tucker
Labyrinth Seals, Carl Weiland
On the Vertical Motions of Edge Jet Vehicles, Marshall P. Tulin
Development of a Unique GEM Concept with Potential for Achieving Efficient Forward Flight, M. F. Gates and E. R. Sargent
Test Results of an Annular Jet Ground Effect Vehicle, Stephen Silverman
Forward Flight Characteristics of Annular Jets, Gabriel D. Boehler

---
[1] Title pages of these two symposiums *Proceedings* are included to show the range and character of papers.

Exhibit 1 (Continued)

Experience with Several Man-carrying Ground Effect Machines, William R. Bertelsel

Development of the Saunders-Roe Hovercraft SR–N1, R. Stanton-Jones

Some Remarks on the English Channel Crossing of the Hovercraft-Annular Jets with Deflectors, C. S. Cockerell

The Helicopter as a Ground Effect Machine, Evan A. Fradenburgh

Some Tests of a 7-Foot GEM Dyanamic Model over Uneven Surfaces, J. Norman Fresh

First International Symposium on Gas-Lubricated Bearings

Sponsored by the Office of Naval Research in cooperation with Air Force Office of Scientific Research, Army Engineer Research and Development Laboratories, Atomic Energy Commission, Bureau of Aeronautics, Bureau of Ordnance, Bureau of Ships, Maritime Administration, National Aeronautics and Space Administration, Wright Air Development Center, conducted by the Franklin Institute, October 26–28, 1959, Washington, D.C.

PAPERS AND AUTHORS

General Review of Gas-Bearing Technology, Dudley D. Fuller

Review of Research on Gas Bearings in the United Kingdom Atomic Energy Authority, S. Whitley

Air Bearings—Research and Applications at National Engineering Laboratory, Scotland, M. Graneek and J. Kerr

Refinements of the Theory of the Infinitely-Long, Self-Acting Gas Lubricated Journal Bearing, Harold G. Elrod, Jr., and Albert Borgdorfer

Dynamic Stability Aspects of Cylindrical Journal Bearings Using Compressible and Imcompressible Fluids, B. Sternlicht, H. Poritsky, and E. Arwas

Theory and Design of Self-Acting Gas-Lubricated Journal Bearings Including Misalignment Effects, J. S. Ausman

Numerical Analysis of Gas-Lubricating Films, W. A. Gross

On High-Speed Self-Acting Gas Bearings, N. Tipei and V. N. Constantinescu

Radial Flow of a Compressible Viscous Fluid between Parallel Plates: Theoretical Study and Experimental Research on the Thurst Bearing, R. Comolet

The Theory of the Externally-Pressurized Bearing with Compressible Lubricant, G. Heinrich

Survey of Gas-Lubricated Bearing Research in Japan with Recent Developments in the Study of Externally-Pressurized Bearings, Tokio Sasaki and Haruo Mori

A Few Individual Papers of Special Usefulness

The Propulsion Aspects of Ground Effect Machines, Robert W. Pinnes, Bureau of Naval Weapons, presented at the Institute of the Aeronautical Sciences twenty-eighth Annual Meeting, New York, January 25–27, 1960

An Analog Study of Levapad Stability, David J. Jay, Ford Motor Company, Dearborn, Michigan; and Harlan W. Peithman, Ford Motor Company, Dearborn, Michigan. Presented at the annual meeting of the American Society of Mechanical Engineers, New York City, November 30–December 5, 1958.

The Ground-Cushion Phenomenon, Hearings before the Committee on Science and Astronautics, House of Representatives, Eighty-sixth Congress, First Session, April 13, 14, and 15, 1959, No. 8 (Washington, D.C.: U.S. Government Printing Office, 1959).

support the weight, a high volume of air was needed, and this meant high horsepower, which was uneconomical. Efficiency was only 3 to 4 per cent.

In his literature search, Frank Dobbertien saw the *Journal of the American Helicopter Society*. Here, he came across mention of "Glideair," a project of Dr. Andrew A. Kucher, Vice President of Engineering and Research for Ford Motor Company. Dobbertien promptly visited Ford. He found that Dr. Kucher had advanced the idea that a vehicle could glide along the ground using a film of air in place of

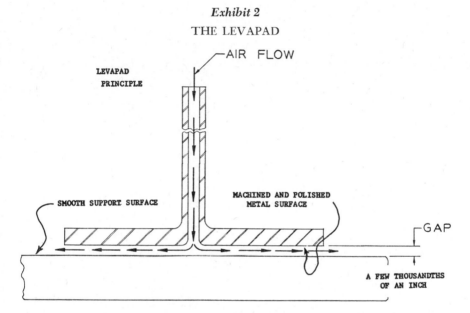

Exhibit 2

THE LEVAPAD

wheels, thus eliminating virtually all friction between vehicle and ground. This idea of "air levitation" had been put into working form through the use of the "levapad." This was merely a round plate with a hole in the middle, through which air was pumped. Air pressure raised the plate a few thousandths of an inch off the ground (see Exhibit 2). Ford people had simulated the application of levapads to road and rail vehicles through considerable research and test stand work. Dr. Kucher provided some data and technical information leads to Clark engineers.

Rogers and Dobbertien concluded that, instead of a ground effects machine, they had better look into air bearings, and their search moved into an intensive study of literature on gas-lubricated bearings.

A newspaper clipping sent to Rogers by a consulting firm on Clark's retainer described another "Glide-Aire." This was a Douglas Aircraft Company development intended to simplify the loading of cargo aircraft. It was based on both an air-in-floor (Exhibit 4) and an air-in-pad (Exhibit 3) concept, utilizing a flexible lower surface on both the load-carrying pallet and the pad. Douglas proposed that a low-pressure chamber be built

Exhibit 3

THE AIR CASTER

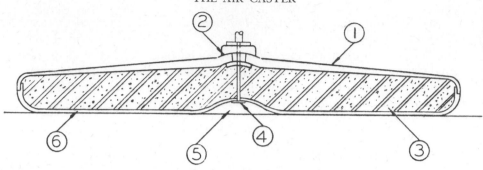

Principle of the air caster. Essentially, the air film suspension disc consists of a sheet metal stamping (1) to which is bonded a flexible planar material (6). The filler material is a cellular, flexible sponge (3) that will permit the disc face to conform to the surface over which it travels. The entire disc pivots about a point on the surface by means of a spherical bearing (2). The air supply is fed into the plenum chamber (5) through an orifice (4). Air bleeding out to the periphery provides a low pressure film which supports the disc and permits it to slide over the surface.

into the aircraft floor. Spring-loaded ball check valves in this floor would depress under the weight of a pallet load. The escaping air would become a lubricating film that would enable a man to push cargo into place in the hold of the plane without any other mechanical aids.

Obviously, this was the same "air-bearing" principle as the levapad, except that the air film or lubricant was held between a rigid supporting surface and a flexible moving surface, rather than between two rigid surfaces.

Contact with Douglas and its inventor, T. K. Peterson, established that the air-in-floor principle would work, and that Douglas held the basic patents. However, the aircraft industry did not seem to be interested in this cargo-handling concept. An important technical need was revealed: There must be a resilient surface around the area of air emission, so that the air film could conform to irregularities in the facing surface.

Exhibit 4

THE AIR-IN-FLOOR CONCEPT

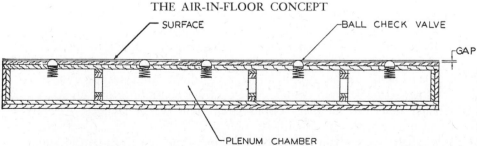

The air-in-floor concept. Air supplied to the plenum chamber flows through the nozzle when the ball check valve is depressed. The escaping air provides a thin fluid film which literally floats the load.

Exhibit 5

HOW THE AIR-IN-PALLET IDEA MIGHT BE APPLIED BY A SELF-
CONTAINED COMPRESSOR TO A WAREHOUSING OR SHIPPING
OPERATION (TOP) AND TO A SUPERMARKET RESTOCKING (BOTTOM)

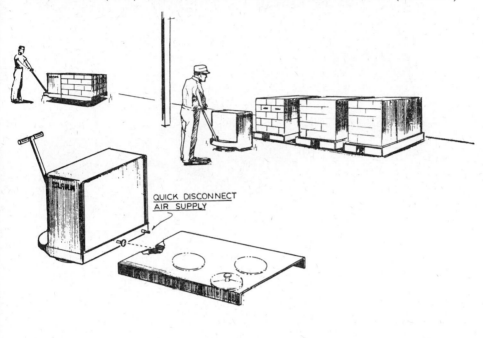

QUICK DISCONNECT
AIR SUPPLY

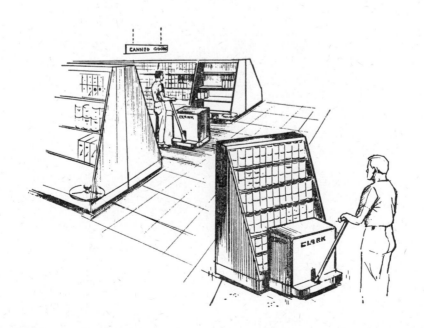

Exhibit 6

HOW THE AIR-IN-FLOOR IDEA MIGHT BE APPLIED TO TRUCKING (TOP)
AND AIRCRAFT LOADING (BOTTOM)

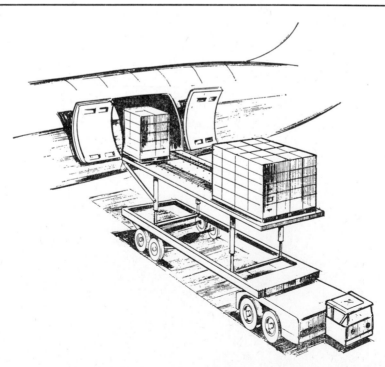

Exhibit 7

AUTOMATIC WAREHOUSING BASED ON AIR IN FLOOR

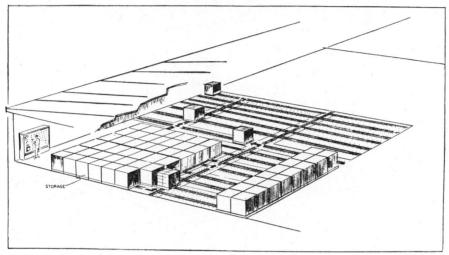

STORAGE

By Activating the Air Pressure in Successive Floor Sections and Using an Electromagnetic Propulsion System, the Storage and Retrieval of Pallet Loads Could Be Done Automatically

Meanwhile, Glen Johnson spent four months looking into markets. He described the concept to potential users—wholesale grocers, truckers, glass manufacturers, etc.—and tried to explore the significance of the idea to their operations. The reaction was quite favorable. Exhibits 5 through 8 are the types of material discussed with potential users. Exhibit 8 shows concepts for applying the principle to Clark's industrial trucks.

By January 31, 1961, approximately one thousand hours had been spent on the project. Rogers and his group believed that they had a promising idea. Using some "air casters" purchased from Douglas Aircraft Company, they experimented with air-in-pallet systems (see Exhibit 9). They were startled to see the slight effort needed to move a load. A push of less than five-pound force would move a load of over a thousand pounds.

Literature study was continued, and especially focused on air bearings. Some typical papers of interest were: "Wind Tunnel Tests of a Circular Wing with an Annular Nozzle in Proximity to the Ground" (NASA); "The Performance of Externally Pressurized Bearings Using Simple Orifice Restrictors," by Allen, Stokes, and Whitley of the United Kingdom Atomic Energy Authority (presented before the American Society of Lubrication Engineers); and "Pneumostatic Bearings," by V. H. McNeilly of Du Pont, as published in *Product Engineering*.

In January, 1960, the annual meeting of the Society of Automotive Engineers included a paper by Gerald Boehler of the Catholic University of America entitled "Basic Principles of Ground Cushion Devices." Exhibit 10 (from this paper) showed the range of effort going into GEM vehicles.

Exhibit 8

HOW THE AIR-IN-VEHICLE PRINCIPLE MIGHT BE APPLIED TO
INDUSTRIAL TRUCKS

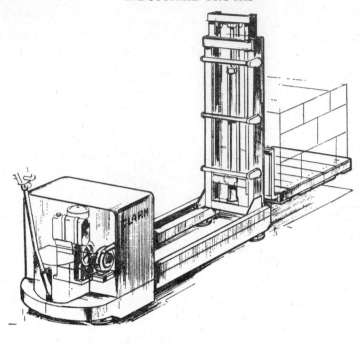

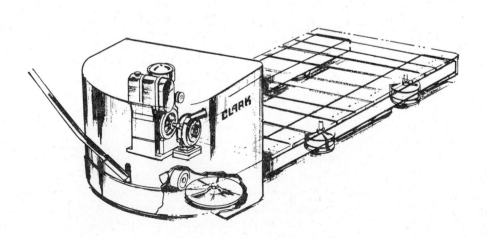

Exhibit 9

AN EXPERIMENTAL AIR-IN-PALLET SYSTEM, USING A SHOP COMPRESSOR
FOR AIR SUPPLY (RIGHT), AND THE PALLET ARRANGEMENT (LEFT)

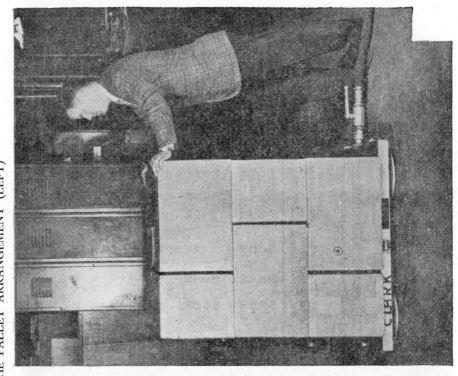

Exhibit 10

DESIGN DETAILS OF SOME EXISTING GEMS, PLANS, AND MODELS*

Company	Model No.	Type of Seal	Platform Length (Ft.)	Platform Width (Ft.)	Platform Height (Ft.)	Empty Wt. (Lb.)	Installed Bhp	Hoover Height (In.)	Max. Speed (Knots)	Per Cent Grade	Payload (Including Fuel) (Lb.)	Remarks
1. Aerophysics............GEM II		Peripheral jet	35.3	29.7	12.6	15,000	740	8	50	9	10,000	Design information, not yet demonstrated
2. A.M.F.		Peripheral jet	3.5 ft. dia. units joined			390	9	1	..	..	195	Weights and hp. approximate
3. Anti-Friction Hull........Hydrokeel		Plenum	24	8	5	3,500	185	..	33	..	1,000	
4. Avro, Canada............Avrocar		Peripheral jet	18 ft. dia.		5	3,426	3,000	36	250	..	2,174	GETOL; max. speed is design free-flight speed; vehicle not yet flown out of ground effect
5. Bell Aerosystems.........2015		Plenum	18	8	4	1,500	65	2	..	1	500	
6. Bell Aerosystems.........2033		Peripheral jet	18	8	4	1,700	140	..	..	..	800	Water vehicle, sidewall skegs
7. Bell Helicopter..........Air Scooter		Plenum	7.1	4.6	3	190	16	2	24	10	170	
8. Bertelson Mfg..........Aeromobile 200		Peripheral jet	16	8	5.5	1,400	200	12	35	10	800	Design information, not yet demonstrated
9. Bertelson Mfg..........Aeromobile		Plenum	8.4	5.9	2.7	408	72	6	35	..	175	
10. Britten-Norman.........Cushioncraft		Peripheral jet	19 ft. dia.		10	2,000	170	15	35	..	1,000	Max. speed not yet demonstrated
11. Curtiss-Wright..........ACM 1-1		Plenum	16	11	6	1,050	85	1	20	4	450	
12. Curtiss-Wright..........ACM 2-1		Plenum	21	8	5	2,500	300	12	26	8	960	
13. Curtiss-Wright..........ACM 2-2		Peripheral jet	21	8	5	2,500	300	9	35	10	960	
14. Curtiss-Wright..........ACM 6-1		Peripheral jet	21	8	5	2,300	300	6	55	13	960	Variable-width peripheral jet
15. Fletch-Aire...........Glidemobile		Peripheral jet	14.2	5.5	3.3	287	72	4	37	4	184	Variable-area jet
16. Ford Motor Co..........Levacar		Levapad	7.8	4.5	4	450	16	0.015	13		175	High-pressure pads (5040 psf); 3 rails for guidance
17. Gyrodyne Co............55		Peripheral jet	9.2	6	5.4	535	65	6	..	..	260	
18. Saunders-Roe (Westland Aircraft)............SR-N1		Peripheral jet	30	25.5	10.7	10,200	450 +700lb. thrust	8	48	10	1,000	Uses double peripheral jet
19. Saunders-Roe (Westland Aircraft)............SR-N2		Peripheral jet	63	29.5	21	26,000	3,200	12	70	16	24,000	Design data, vehicle in construction stage

Exhibit 10 (Continued)

Company	Model No.	Type of Seal	Platform Length (Ft.)	Platform Width (Ft.)	Platform Height (Ft.)	Empty Wt. (Lb.)	Installed Bhp	Hover Height (In.)	Max. Speed (Knots)	Per Cent Grade	Payload (Including Fuel) (Lb.)	Remarks
20. Hughes Tool Co. ....STV		Water wall	22.6	10.5	8.1	3,402	240	24	22	..	1,760	Side skeg, trapped cushion, bow and stern water wall
21. Hughes Tool Co. ....DTV		Water wall	15.7	8.2	4.3	1,630	240	..	..	..	320	All-water curtain
22. Nat'l. Res. Assoc. ....GEM I		Peripheral	14.6	8.2	4.3	1,050	80	14	22	7	250	Max. power developed 66 hp.
23. Nat'l. Res. Assoc. ....GEM III		Peripheral	24	12	7.1	1,430	140	18	26	10	320	Design data, vehicle in construction stage
24. Princeton University X-3		Peripheral	20 ft. dia.		4	850	48	18	22	..	220	
25. Princeton University X-3B		Peripheral	20 ft. dia.		4	1,150	180	24	..	..	450	Four radial stabilizing slots
26. Princeton University X-4		Peripheral	9 ft. dia.		4	200	15	3	17	10	200	Flexible cloth skirt
27. Princeton University X-2		Peripheral	8 ft. dia.		4	120	5	5	10	0	180	Flexible cloth skirt
28. Spacetronics		Plenum	18	9	?	800	..	4	..	..	200	
29. Spacetronics ....Hydro-Aire		Plenum	30	24	5	4,500	270	14	47	..	4,000	Performance quoted but not demonstrated
30. Goodyear Aircraft.		Plenum	8	5	5	750	35	1	..	..	250	Flexible airmat understructure, no forward propulsion
31. Folland Aircraft..........GERM		Peripheral	15	8	4.5	1,300	95	..	42	..	300	Two concentric jets, max. speed not yet demonstrated
32. Vickers (So. Marsten).....3031		Peripheral	47.5	20.1	?	10,500	1,000	18	60	..	6,000	Design data, vehicle in construction
33. Valmet Corp...............KAAR10 V-8		Plenum	14	6	10	650	18	..	38	10	400	Speed not yet demonstrated, ram wing concept
34. D.T.M.B..................448		Peripheral	8.3	3.3	1.5	....	..	..	..	..	....	Wind tunnel model, propulsive vanes in jet
35. D.T.M.B..................463		Peripheral	15	6	2	240	10	8	20	..	..	Dynamic flight model, propulsive vanes in jet
36. D.T.M.B..................472		Peripheral	6	3	1.5	....	..	..	..	..	....	Wind tunnel model
37. Carl Weiland (Grogg's Inc.) ILEN		Peripheral	33	30	7	14,000	720	16	60	0	2,420	
38. Grumman..................		Peripheral	10	5	4	650	140	14	42	25	880	Stability model, design data, in construction stage

* From "Basic Principles of Ground Cushion Devices," by Gerald Boehler, presented before the annual meeting of the Society of Automotive Engineers, January, 1960.

By September, 1960, Bruce Rogers felt he was on sound ground. After a half-hour talk with Spatta, he was asked to present the full concept to Clark's top management in November.

The Presentation

Clark's top management, including legal counsel and vice presidents of several divisions, were present for Rogers' presentation. In the first half hour, Rogers described Aero-Lift and then answered questions about the brochure he distributed. Excerpts from the brochure are shown in Exhibit 11. The brochure also included technical descriptions of the propulsion systems and the illustrations shown in Exhibits 2 through 8. Charts indicated that a 5,300-pound load on a 60 × 90-inch pallet could be supported by four psi in the pneumatic floor, and that a 12-pound force would move the load. The horsepower needed to supply 251 cubic feet of air per minute was less than 13 bhp. Using six 10-inch-diameter Glide-Aire discs at 15 psi, a 6,300-pound load could be moved over plywood flooring by a 52-pound force, and by 63 pounds over concrete flooring.

Exhibit 11

EXCERPTS FROM PRESENTATION BROCHURE ON AERO-LIFT

SUMMARY

Aero-Lift—applying the principles of air bearings to the movement of loads provides movement at power costs of less than 0.20 cents per ton-mile.

Materials-handling equipment markets penetrated by Aero-Lift equipment will produce an estimated annual sales dollar volume of $21.8 million in five years.

Out-of-pocket costs require maximum funding of $1.39 million, of which $720,000 would be supplied by Clark Equipment Company and be fully recovered in fifty-three (53) months.[1]

Annual gross profits at the end of five years are estimated to be in excess of $2.18 million.

Test-marketing contacts with following organizations indicate a very satisfactory market exists. Potential applications in materials-handling activities were expressed enthusiastically as a major breakthrough. Requests for price and delivery quotations on Aero-Lift equipment have been received, as well as offers of funds to develop a system tailored to particular requirements.

COMPANIES CONTACTED ON AERO-LIFT

Western Electric Company, Kearney, New Jersey
Pan American World Airways, New York, New York
National American Wholesale Grocers Association, New York, New York
Trans World Airlines, Kansas City, Missouri
Armour & Company, Chicago, Illinois
Dow Chemical Company, Midland, Michigan

---

[1] It was hoped that Douglas Aircraft would be the participating firm.

Exhibit 11 (Continued)

Pacific Intermountain Express, Oakland, California
Safeway Stores Company, Oakland, California
Brockway Glass Company, Brockway, Pennsylvania
United States Naval Supply and Research Development Facility, Bayonne,
     New Jersey
United States Air Force, Wright Air Development Division, Dayton, Ohio
Convair, San Diego Division, San Diego, California
Flying Tiger Airlines, Burbank, California
Seaboard & Western Airlines, New York, New York

AERO-LIFT

Aero-lift is a breakthrough in the field of materials handling which applies the basic principle of the air bearing to the efficient and rapid movement of unit loads. A thin film of low-pressure air is introduced between the base of a loaded pallet and the surface over which it moves.

Air-film suspension reduces the resistance to motion below that of conventional systems by more than 80 per cent. The cost of power to move a load is reduced to an absolute minimum.

Air-film suspension distributes a load over a floor uniformly; no concentrated wheel loads, no high axle loads, no abrasion of high-quality surfaces.

Air-film suspension offers improved materials-handling practices to existing and new markets: unitized cargo loading of ships, trailers, planes; preloading of supermarket shelves; department store shelf restocking; pipe-line flow of packages and unitized loads.

Air-film suspension offers multidirectional movement of loads and equipment—inherently supplies optimum maneuverability.

TYPICAL APPLICATIONS

Products

Basically only two: (1) A pad—which can be installed in pallets, containers, or any of the objects to be moved, permanently or as a quickly connected and disconnected attachment—through which air is fed to form the thin film of air between the pad surface and the supporting surface. (2) A plenum chamber floor—which, as a building-block segment, can be placed on existing floors (or built in) as strips or complete surfaces; and can be used as lengths of conveyors, as decks in load racks, as sections of loading docks, as highway trailer floors, etc.—through which air can be fed by selective valving to provide the thin film of air between the bottom of the load and the floor surface. Adaptation of these basic products can take many forms in their application to profitable products.

EQUIPMENT APPLICATIONS

Industrial Trucks

Pallet hand trucks—air pads replace wheels and rollers
Air power head—compressor power unit on "air pad" to supply air power
     to air-in-base unit

Exhibit 11 (Continued)

Warehouse trucks—replace wheels with air pads or air in base

Warehouse dollies—replace casters with air in base

Warehouse floor crane—replace wheel mounts with air in base; greater capacity-to-weight and stability-to-weight ratios

Fork lift truck—air-in-base chamber on lift mechanism to accomplish lateral load transfer into storage racks; eliminate narrow-aisle trucks

Platform trucks—air in platform; load and unload longitudinally or transversely

Fork lift truck—air platform fork; load and unload laterally: no maneuvering

Conveyors

Gravity chute—package transfer, shallow slope

Belt, powered—air film to reduce belt-wearing friction; overcoming friction problem will permit storage of unit loads in depth on wide, powered belts; faster belt speeds on bulk-handling trough conveyors

Moving sidewalks—air film solves problems of capacity and service life

Work transfer bridge—air in table moves work in process from operation to operation

Unit Load-Handling Equipment

Pallets—air in base

Pallet containers—air in base

Cargo containers—air in base; transfer on ship dock and in hold

Van containers—air in base; transfer from truck to rail to ship

Transportation Equipment

Highway trailers—air in floor

Railroad boxcars—air in floor

Cargo airplanes—air in floor

High-speed railway train

High-speed subway train

In-plant personnel carriers

Highway vehicles—potential medium for programmed traffic control

Break-Bulk Terminals

Across-dock movement of preunitized loads

Across-terminal movement of load packages for preunitizing of loads

Storage Equipment

Pallet racks—air in base for unit-load storage

Tote-pan racks—air in base for pan storage

Warehousing Equipment

Towline—aerolift with electromagnetic programmed compulsion can replace towveyors and radio-controlled tow tractors

Order-accumulating conveyor

Floor scale—air in floor provides means of fast weighing of loads automatically

Elevators—air in floor; movement of materials on and off in any direction

Exhibit 11 (Continued)

Manufacturing Equipment

Die transfer—in and out of presses, racks, and tables
Work-in-process transfer tables
Vehicle assembly lines
Press-feed tables—tin plate, sheet metal, paperboards
Shear-feed tables—plate, channel, bar stock
Saw tables
Prestressed concrete continuous molds—move extruded beams
Concrete blocks—provides means of a continuous-process forming and
   drying line
Concrete pipe—continuous-process line
Plywood and finished lumber transfer
Bottle-filling machinery
Paper mill transfer tables
Jig and fixture movement and positioning

Military Equipment

Aerodunnage for cargo—Unites States Air Force
Track vehicles, air in pads—Unites States Army
Boats and pontoons
Rocket sled—experimental, high-speed tests
Highway transport sled for ICBM's
Personnel transport—underground tunnels at missle base sites
Cargo transfer

Miscellaneous Equipment

Amusement park ride
Automated parking garage
Self-positioning heavy-duty jacks
Machinery-moving pads
Dry-dock boat-launching pads

PROPULSION, CONTROL, AND GUIDANCE

Propulsion—Electromagnetic

The low resistance to motion, inherent in air-film suspension, makes possible the direct application of electromotive force to the propulsion of materials. The rotor and field magnets and coils of an induction three-phase electric motor are laid flat, the field coils along the surface of the floor and the rotor segments in the base of a pallet. Application of alternating three-phase, 60-cycle, 220-volt current to the field strip creates a moving magnetic field which pushes the pallet along in the direction of the moving electromagnetic field. Power reversal reverses the direction of motion of the pallet. Less than one-quarter horsepower will move 4,000 pounds at speeds up to eight miles per hour.

Propulsion power cost can be less than 0.20 cents per ton-mile. Conventional-drive mechanisms now commonly in use can be applied to power pallets, containers, vehicles, and conveyors. Where a hard, positive driving force is suited to the product use or application need, the inherent character-

Exhibit 11 (Continued)

istic of low resistance to motion makes remote power delivery through hydrostatic drives more attractive. The full braking capability available by simply stopping air flow reduces drive-line complexity and provides "dead-man" safety control not available in normal propulsion-drive lines.

Control is inherent in any vehicle utilizing air-film suspension by either supplying air to allow its movement or not supplying air, causing full braking effort. Electromagnetic propulsion limits the velocity of a moving load to the designed-in characteristics of the field coil strip. Speed variations can be obtained from varying the design of the strip or the current frequency applied to the strip. Directional control is obtained by current direction. Block signal systems will prevent collisions on a strip or at intersections. A simple "dead-man" safety valve, which shuts off the air supply, eliminates any possibility of an unmanned vehicle moving.

Guidance, manually by conventional mechanisms or by hand, provides minute, precise movement and positioning with efforts as low as four pounds per 1,000 pounds moved.

Guidance is secured automatically by preprogrammed punched card, punched tape, magnetic tape, or memory circuit through the use of electromagnetic propulsion, block signal systems, and a master control panel; or pallet-installed seeker units provide material flow in semiautomated or fully automated warehousing which cannot be equaled.

MARKET POTENTIAL

Aero-lift has many applications in operations now performed by existing mechanical equipment. Existing markets will be penetrated in varying degrees. In some markets, present equipment may be replaced completely by Aero-Lift. New markets and uses will develop.

Conservative estimates indicate potential sales of $43.6 million for Aero-Lift in existing selected materials handling, and transportation markets of $1,335 billion—a market penetration of less than 3.3 per cent. It is believed that one half of this sales level could be achieved within five years with proper distribution and sales promotion.

AERO-LIFT

Industry or Product Group	Present Annual Sales (Millions of Dollars)	Estimated Annual Sales, Aero-Lift (Millions of Dollars)	Per cent of Market
Highway trailers	$ 500	$ 5.0	1.00%
Floor trucks and casters	25	5.0	20.00
Package conveyors	120	6.0	5.00
Towline and overhead conveyors	300	9.0	3.00
Pallet storage racks	50	5.0	10.00
Pallets, wood	150	7.5	5.00
Powered hand trucks	13	2.6	20.00
Rider-type industrial trucks	177	3.5	2.00
Total	$1,335	$43.6	3.27%

Exhibit 11 (Continued)

INVESTMENT REQUIRED

Initial

Market surveys	$ 20,000
Customer promotion	10,000
Product development	450,000
Prototype, build and test	75,000
Organization, basic	60,000
Pilot installation and warranty	50,000
Product promotion—direct sales, advertising, customer contacts, trial installations, transportation, etc.	82,000
Facilities and equipment, initial	100,000
Inventory	30,000
	$877,000

Of this, the participating corporation has already invested approximately $250,000 during its three-and-a-half-year effort developing the art of air-film suspension. Therefore an additional initial funding of approximately $627,000 would be required through a 12- to 18-month period.

Growth

Additional financing would be required to support, promote, and expand the operation through the growth period necessary firmly to establish the product and the Company in the market place. It is anticipated that this would extend over a time period of 18 to 24 months, during which time profits from product sales would begin to appear and be ploughed back into the operation to accelerate growth.

Anticipated funding:	
Product improvement	$ 25,000
Product expansion	50,000
Product development, test and build	100,000
Product promotion—direct sales, advertising, displays, dealer organization warranty, transportation, etc.	110,000
Facilities and equipment, expansion	75,000
Organization, expansion	90,000
Inventory	300,000
	$750,000

Of this, an estimated $150,000 would be recovered as profits from sales, leaving a net required funding of $600,000 for the growth period.

Maximum estimated out-of-pocket costs of $1.39 million would accumulate at approximately 40 months of operation and be fully recovered from profits at approximately 53 months of operation. An estimated $670,000 of the out-of-pocket costs would be assumed by the participating corporation in its minority position, leaving required funding by Clark Equipment Company at $720,000.

INVESTMENT RECOVERY

Customer interest and requests for pilot installation quotations presently indicate first-year gross dollar sales of approximately $425,000, giving a gross profit of $42,500.

Exhibit 11 (Concluded)

Customer interest measured from market sampling is sufficient to support estimated second-year gross dollar sales approaching $1.5 million, giving a gross profit of $150,000.

Potential market total annual dollar sales and conservative estimates of market penetration, as shown, support a position of gross annual dollar sales of Aero-Lift products and installations of $21.8 million at the end of a five-year period, giving an annual gross profit of $2.18 million.

At this level of business, the full potential of this concept has not been thoroughly exploited. Application techniques will improve and expand as installations prove their merit and economy. State-of-the-art knowledge in design and concept will accumulate and open new and broader markets.

It is conservatively estimated that annual dollar sales volume will continue to improve to a value in excess of twice that targeted for the initial five-year growth period.

After hearing the presentation, Spatta was noncommittal. He first raised some questions, which Rogers answered:

1. How does it work? Is this another Curtiss Aerocar?
   A. The Aerocar floats on a bubble of low-pressure air (0.75 psi) requiring a very large air volume. This device operates on a thin film of air. Up to 35 psi can be used, but five to 20 psi is best. The volume of air needed is very low.
2. What must Clark build?
3. What market penetration can we expect?
4. Is it competitive with other handling concepts?
   A. Yes, on a cost per pound—mile or ton-mile—this device moves loads at 0.2 cents per ton-mile versus 1.5 cents per ton-mile on railroads versus 23 cents per ton-mile by lift truck. However, note that this comparison stresses the fact that the lift truck is not a transportation device, but a handling-lifting device. In contrast, the Aero-Glide system is *not* a handling device; it is a moving (transportation) device.

One of the executives pointed out that the device would compete with lift trucks. Rogers answered that it would compete only in a few markets. He stressed that it actually competes with conveyors (which Clark did not build), and in places where lift trucks tended to be misapplied.

Spatta commented that it was Clark's policy not to build anything that could not be guaranteed. After a general discussion, he gave his decision to the group.

Top Management Speaks

From a speech by Mr. Robert S. Binkerd, Vice President of the Baldwin Locomotive Works, before the New York Railroad Club in New York City on April 25, 1935:

"Tonight, I propose, as far as our human frailty will permit, to speak without prejudice. I think I am in a position to do so; and when I say this I say it not only on behalf of the Baldwin Locomotive Works, but on behalf of the three recognized locomotive builders in this country. Each of us has the engineering brains and the manufacturing ability to build any kind of a thing that moves on wheels. . . .

"Today, we are having quite a ballyhoo about stream-lined, light-weight trains and Diesel locomotives, and it is no wonder if the public feels that the steam locomotive is about to lay down and play dead. Yet over the years certain simple fundamental principles continue to operate. Sometime in the future, when all this is reviewed, we will not find our railroads any more dieselized than they are electrified.

. . . .

"Therefore, the field of probably profitable application of the Diesel locomotive is pretty generally indicated at work speeds not exceeding 10 miles an hour.

. . . .

And I do wish to say unequivocally that there is not one scintilla of evidence to justify the claim that a Diesel locomotive of equal weight on drivers can be maintained at a cost as low as that of a steam locomotive of the same age after the first year or so. Everything points to the probability of a substantially higher maintenance cost for Diesel locomotives than for equivalent steam locomotives of the same age."

. . . .

On April 25, 1938, Mr. W. C. Dickerman, President of the American Locomotive Company, made a speech before the Western Railway Club in Chicago, excerpts of which read as follows:

"For a century, as you know, steam has been the principal railroad motive power. It still is and, in my view, will continue to be.

. . . .

Nine years after Mr. Dickerman read Diesel out of the picture, a later president of Alco sadly announced that Alco has ceased steam locomotive production and one of his vice presidents gave a statement to the press that they were "not intentionally going out of the steam locomotive business. It is simply a matter of demand. All orders and inquiries for new motive power from domestic railroads are for Diesel-electrics."

FROM: A Statement by C. R. Osborn, Vice President, General Motors, before the Subcommittee on Antitrust and Monopoly of the U.S. Senate Committee on the Judiciary, Washington, D.C., December 9, 1955.

OCEANOGRAPHIC INSTRUMENTATION

SHOULD SMALL MANUFACTURING FIRMS BE INTERESTED IN MANUFACTURING HARDWARE FOR THE MARINE SCIENCES?

IN THE fall of 1961, many industry executives, members of the investment community, scientists, and government officials were talking about the field of oceanography in the same tone of voice they had used a decade earlier when speaking of aerospace technology.

The Declaration of Policy of Senate Bill S–901, the Marine Sciences and Research Act of 1961, stated in part:

The Congress hereby declares that systematic, scientific studies and surveys of the oceans and ocean floor, the collection, preparation, and dissemination of comprehensive data regarding the physics, biology, chemistry, and geology of the sea, and the education and training of oceanographic scientists through a sustained and effective program is vital to defense against attack from the oceans and to operation of our own surface and subsurface naval forces with maximum efficiency, to the rehabilitation of our commercial fisheries and the increased utilization of these and other ocean resources, to the expansion of commerce and navigation, and to the development of scientific knowledge and understanding of the waters which cover 71 per cent of the earth's surface, life and forces within these waters, and the interchange of energy and matter between the sea and atmosphere.

The Congress further declares that sound national policy requires that the United States not be excelled in the fields of oceanographic research, basic, military, or applied, by any nation which may presently or in the future threaten our general welfare, maritime commerce, security, access to and utilization of ocean fisheries, or contamination of adjacent seas by dumping therein radioactive waste or other harmful agents.

The Congress further declares that to meet the objectives outlined in the preceding paragraphs of this act there must be a coordinated, long-range program of oceanographic research and marine surveys similar or identical to that recommended as a minimal program by the Committee on Oceanography of the National Academy of Sciences and National Research Council.

If the amount of interest in the field could be taken as an indication of what the future would hold, oceanic technology would surely be one of the country's next glamour industries. A large part of this interest had been aroused because of the publicity given to S–901 and to a government-sponsored symposium on oceanographic instrumentation held in August, 1961. The brief newspaper stories had said, "$100 million to oceanography in 1962," and many trade publications had written short articles painting the opportunities of the field in glowing colors [7, 8, 9].[1] In late

---

[1] Numbers in brackets refer to publications listed in the Bibliography (pp. 766–777).

1961, many executives of manufacturing firms were considering an attempt to enter the oceanographic hardware business. As they considered what little substantive data were available on the future of the marine sciences, they wondered if a market really did exist for products they could make, how big it would be, and how and when their firms should attempt to enter it.

Oceanography

Oceanography, as the term is used in this country, is the study of the ocean and all of its boundaries. It includes aspects of marine meteorology, submarine geology, and the physical, chemical, and biological sciences associated with the oceans themselves. Closely related to oceanography is limnology—the study of fresh-water bodies. Neither is a single science; both represent the application of many different sciences to study in a broad field. Oceanography includes survey activities, the regular and continuous gathering of data to keep charts and other navigational material up to date, and research work, which itself varies from "pure" research, done by oceanographers to further their basic understanding of the ocean, to "applied" research such as that on underwater sound propagation conducted by the Navy in connection with development work on acoustic homing torpedoes, submarine detection devices, or underwater communications systems. Having much in common with oceanography are a number of other scientific and commercial activities. These include meteorology, underwater seismographic work, commercial fishing, water-desalting efforts, underwater and antisubmarine warfare, and all other activities carried on in or on the ocean or affected by the ocean.

Prior to World War II, oceanography in the United States was what had been referred to as a "pastoral science," pursued by a small number of dedicated individuals, many of whom entered the field from other careers rather than directly from graduate study. During the war, impetus was given the science by the Navy's need to know about underwater sound propagation in order to develop echo-ranging devices (e.g., sonar) for the detection of submarines and to help submarines elude enemy destroyers. During the late 1940's and the 1950's the Navy continued its support of oceanography, and support was added by other government agencies and by private industry.

In 1961, oceanographic research was being carried on by about seventy institutions and laboratories in the United States. These included both government-operated and privately endowed institutions, although about 70 per cent of the funds for projects being carried on by the latter group was provided by government agencies [1]. The largest private institutions were Woods Hole Oceanographic Institution (WHOI), located on Cape Cod in Massachusetts, and Scripps Institution of Oceanography in La Jolla, California. The major portion of the oceanographic work actually performed by government agencies was done by the United States Navy

Hydrographic Office, the Coast and Geodetic Survey, the Bureau of Commercial Fisheries, and the Navy's Bureau of Weapons and Bureau of Ships.

Projects at private institutions were financed by the above government agencies and by others such as the National Science Foundation and the Atomic Energy Commission (which is interested in what happens to radioactivity from fall-out dust or nuclear waste dropped in the ocean). Private firms such as oil companies also supported some oceanographic work. In general, the private oceanographic institutions did not have a level of endowment income sufficient to finance large-scale projects by themselves.

The actual amount of oceanographic activity in the country is extremely difficult to determine. Prior to 1960, no national oceanographic budget was prepared, and virtually no central planning was done in the field. Each agency interested in some aspect of the ocean financed its own research or supported private projects from its individual appropriations. Many unrelated activities also contributed some oceanographic data as a by-product of their major function. An example of this is the use by Navy destroyers of the Bathythermograph (BT), which plots temperature versus depth on a smoked slide when lowered in the water. The shape of this plot shows some of the acoustical properties of the water where the "BT drop" is made. Knowledge of these properties allows the destroyers to position themselves so that the capital ships with them are given maximum antisubmarine protection by their echo-ranging (sonar) gear. However, the BT slides are kept and sent to the Hydrographic office for oceanographic use.

The lack of central oceanographic planning and the fact that few oceanographic institutions had money to finance specific research activities has led to a project-by-project financing pattern which also makes it difficult to determine the expenditures for oceanographic work in any year. An oceanographer interested in a particular investigation has had to "sell" his project to someone who would finance it, usually a government agency. Then, if successful, he received his own appropriation, which was spent on his research project as needed.

However, it has been estimated that the combined budget of all oceanographic institutions and laboratories in 1958 was about $24 million, and that these activities collectively employed about 2,700 people. In that year, there were forty-five ocean-going (more than 300 tons displacement) research and/or survey ships in operation. It is thought that the real rate of growth of expenditures for oceanographic work in the decade of the 1950's amounted to somewhat less than 10 per cent per year [1].

Recent Developments

Notwithstanding the increased activity, a number of government officials and scientists began to feel during the latter part of the decade that United States oceanographic capability was far short of what it should be, and that the existing and projected oceanographic programs were seriously insufficient. A number of developments contributed to this thinking. The advent of the nuclear submarine and the Polaris missile, along with concern about the Russian submarine threat, increased the military significance of underwater environmental knowledge. The belief that Russia's oceanographic program was far ahead of this country's (Russia had about 150 oceanographic research survey ships in operation in 1960) reinforced the military interest in oceanographic activity [6]. Other factors included the desire to exploit the mineral, chemical, and food resources of the oceans, to understand the ocean's function in forming the earth's weather, and to evaluate the effect of nuclear fallout on the ocean and its inhabitants. It was felt not only that increased knowledge in each of these areas would yield great benefits but that this country would be at a significant disadvantage if Russia were allowed to build up an oceanographic "knowledge lead."

As a result of this concern, the National Academy of Sciences–National Research Council formed, in 1957, a Committee on Oceanography. In 1959, this Committee produced a report entitled *Oceanography: 1960 to 1970*, which attempted to assess the status of oceanography in this country and made specific recommendations designed to strengthen the marine sciences [1]. Exhibit 1 gives a synopsis of some of the minimum recommendations made by the Committee.

Exhibit 1
OCEANOGRAPHY: 1960 TO 1970

Selected tables from the report of the Committee on Oceanography, National Academy of Sciences–National Research Council. These tables summarize some of the Committee's recommendations for a "minimal" national oceanographic program. They also are substantially the provisions of Senate Bill S–901, the Marine Sciences and Research Act of 1961.

Table I*
TEN-YEAR PLAN FOR INCREASING THE U.S. FLEET OF OCEANOGRAPHIC SHIPS
Function of Ships

	Research	Military Research and Development	Survey	Resources and Fisheries	Total
Present fleet	11	9	18	7	45
To be replaced	5	9	9	7	30
Still operational in 1970	6	..	9	..	15
Additional new construction	11	11	11	7	40
Total construction	16	20	20	14	70
Total fleet in 1970	22	20	29	14	85

* Table numbers refer to tables in the report, *Oceanography: 1960 to 1970*.

Exhibit 1 (Continued)

Table 3

RECOMMENDED SPONSORS OF NEW SHIPS

	500 Tons	1,200– 1,500 Tons	Larger than 2,000 Tons	Total
Navy	12	18	8	38
Coast and Geodetic Survey	2	6	2	10
Bureau of Commercial Fisheries	12	2	..	14
National Science Foundation	3	..	1	4
Maritime Administration	2	2	..	4
Total	31	28	11	70

Table 4*

RECOMMENDED SCHEDULING OF NEW SHIPS

Year	Ships Put in Service
1960	4
1961	11
1962	13
1963	13
1964	11
1965	8
1966	7
1967	3

* Abbreviated.

Table 10

ESTIMATED ANNUAL BUDGET FOR ENGINEERING NEEDS FOR OCEAN EXPLORATION*
(Millions of 1958 Dollars)

	1960	1961	1962	1963	1964
Deep manned vehicles	$2.0	$2.0	$3.0	$ 4.0	$ 4.0
Large manned buoys	0.3	2.0	1.3	0.2	0.2
Unmanned buoys	0.8	0.8	0.9	1.0	1.0
Aircraft	0.6	1.3	1.0	2.0	1.2
Other specialized vehicles	2.0	1.0	1.0	1.0	1.0
Development of new instruments	0.6	1.2	1.2	1.5	1.8
Other	1.1	1.2	1.2	1.2	1.3
Total	$7.4	$9.5	$9.6	$10.9	$10.5

* Only five years were estimated in the report. This table represents recommended budgets for government-sponsored engineering activity in connection with design and development of new and/or improved hardware for research. This budget does not include the cost of devices needed for applied problems nor the cost of any "conventional" or previously developed hardware needed for actual research projects.

Exhibit 1 (*Continued*)

Table 17

SUMMARY OF BUDGETS FOR NEW OCEANOGRAPHIC ACTIVITY*
(Millions of 1958 Dollars)

Year	Education and Manpower	Ships	Shore Facilities (Research)	Shore Facilities (Surveys)	New Devices	Radio-activity† in Oceans	Resources	Total
1960	$0.80	$ 39.80	$ 1.50	$0.76	$ 7.40	$3.08	$ 5.02	$58.36
1961	0.80	40.45	2.70	1.52	9.50	2.95	6.71	64.63
1962	0.80	45.30	3.90	3.00	9.60	4.35	5.43	72.38
1963	0.80	35.95	6.60	4.50	10.90	2.95	8.52	70.22
1964	0.80	33.65	10.50	6.00	10.50	2.95	7.55	71.95
1965	0.80	29.00	12.60	7.50	10.50	2.95	10.58	73.93
1966	0.80	20.55	13.50	8.26	10.50	4.39	10.93	68.89
1967	0.80	10.45	13.20	8.26	10.50	2.95	10.75	56.91
1968	0.80	10.45	13.20	8.26	10.50	2.95	10.92	57.08
1969	0.80	10.45	13.20	8.26	10.50	2.95	10.90	57.06
Total	$8.00	$276.05	$90.90	$56.32	$100.40	$32.43	$87.31	$651.41

* Not including special funds for basic research projects involving extensive international co-operation such as the proposed year-long international expedition to the Indian Ocean (estimated cost, $2 million).
† Plus ship-time charges of $11.7 million, to be subtracted from other categories.

Table 18

SUMMARY OF BUDGET FOR NEW OCEANOGRAPHIC ACTIVITY
BY AGENCY*
(Millions of 1958 Dollars)

Year	Navy†	Coast and Geodetic Survey	Bureau of Commercial Fisheries	Maritime Administration	National Science Foundation	Office of Education	Atomic Energy Commission	Bureau of Mines	Total
1960	$ 28.78	$5.83	$ 7.97	$5.45	$ 6.40	$0.50	$3.08	$0.35	$ 58.36
1961	28.83	6.09	13.86	3.80	8.35	0.50	2.95	0.25	64.63
1962	30.40	9.75	12.83	1.65	12.65	0.50	4.35	0.25	72.38
1963	33.80	8.70	12.42	.....	11.60	0.50	2.95	0.25	70.62
1964	35.22	9.30	11.75	.....	11.98	0.50	2.95	0.25	71.95
1965	32.68	9.20	15.03	.....	13.32	0.50	2.95	0.25	73.93
1966	27.45	9.88	12.38	.....	14.08	0.50	4.35	0.25	68.89
1967	20.36	6.43	12.20	.....	14.22	0.50	2.95	0.25	56.91
1968	20.36	6.43	12.37	.....	14.22	0.50	2.95	0.25	57.08
1969	20.36	6.43	12.35	.....	14.22	0.50	2.95	0.25	57.06
Total	$278.24‡	$78.04‡	$123.16‡ §	$10.90	$121.04‡	$5.00	$32.43#	$2.60	$651.41

* Not including special funds for basic research projects involving extensive international co-operation, such as the proposed year-long international expedition to the Indian Ocean (estimated cost, $2 million).
† Not including military research and development operations.
‡ Less payments by the Atomic Energy Commission totaling $11.7 million for ship time.
§ Includes recommended expenditures by the International Cooperation Administration and the State Department for projects involving international co-operation and technical assistance to other countries.
# Plus $11.7 million for ship time, averaging $1.17 million per year.

In 1960, Senator Warren Magnuson, Chairman of the Senate Committee on Interstate and Foreign Commerce, introduced a bill based on the Committee on Oceanography's recommendations for a comprehensive ten-year program and providing for the appropriations needed to carry it out [5]. The 1960 Marine Sciences Bill and a substantially similar bill, S–901, which was introduced in the 1961 Congressional session, were passed by the Senate but allowed to die in the House after being referred to the Committee on Merchant Marine and Fisheries. In 1961 the House Committee itself initiated several bills to provide more money for oceanographic research which, although they also failed to reach the White House, apparently indicated that there was an increasing amount of interest in oceanography in both Congressional chambers [6].

However, even though no co-ordinated marine sciences program had been established by Congress as of October, 1961, the various services and agencies which had an interest in the ocean increased their spending on oceanographic research. President John F. Kennedy's expressed interest in the marine sciences may well have affected the amount budgeted by these departments for this work. Funds spent by the government for oceanography in 1960 and estimates for 1961–62 are shown in Exhibit 2.

Exhibit 2

NATIONAL OCEANOGRAPHIC PROGRAM BUDGET SUMMARIES

Amounts actually spent and budgeted for oceanographic research, hardware, and supporting activities by agencies and departments of the federal government. These funds were requested within the normal budgets of the agencies concerned and appropriated by the Congress as part of the individual budgets rather than as a truly co-ordinated national oceanographic program.

Table 1

SUMMARY BY FEDERAL AGENCY
(Thousands of Dollars)

	Actual Fiscal Year 1960	Estimated Fiscal Year 1961	Estimated Fiscal Year 1962
Defense	$23,003	$22,729	$32,837
Commerce	6,202	11,389	24,691
Interior	6,723	8,704	15,472
National Science Foundation	7,833	9,148	19,607
Atomic Energy Commission	1,708	2,207	3,610
Health, Education and Welfare	340	698	1,150
Treasury	134	134	134
Total	$45,943	$55,009	$97,501

Table 2

SUMMARY, BY FUNCTION

	Actual Fiscal Year 1960	Estimated Fiscal Year 1961	Estimated Fiscal Year 1962
Research	$26,577	$31,883	$40,794
Ship construction	13,533	13,975	37,050
Surveys	4,168	7,117	8,725
Facilities	1,370	1,768	10,422
Data Center*	295	266	510
Total	$45,943	$55,009	$97,501

* The Oceanographic Data Center was established in 1960 to collect, process, store, and provide to oceanographers any and all oceanographic data generated by government agencies and oceanographic research institutions in the United States, and any other oceanographic data which may be made available to it.

In addition to the increased commitments of funds, these departments, through the Federal Council for Science and Technology, established in January, 1960, the Interagency Committee on Oceanography (ICO) to take the responsibility for co-ordinating the United States national oceanographic program. Although the ICO had no administrative authority, its chairman said, in answer to a question asked in the August, 1961, symposium, that its recommendations were usually followed. At that time the ICO seemed to be acting more as a communications medium than as an actual policy-making body, although even the function of "letting the other fellow know" was of great value to the over-all progress of the national oceanographic program at that time.

In the summer of 1961 the ICO undertook the job of encouraging private industry to provide better research hardware for the oceanographic field. It recognized that without the proper tools, research could not move forward as rapidly as it believed necessary. Therefore, in August of 1961 the ICO sponsored a government-industry symposium on the instrumentation needs of oceanography in Washington D.C. The purpose of this meeting was to "acquaint industry with critical parts of the National Oceanographic Program which require new thinking and technique development. It [was] intended that representatives of industry be provided with the technical aspects of current [1961] instrumentation problems, and with general background information on oceanography . . . considered necessary for successful solution of these problems." More than seven hundred people attended this symposium, representing some four hundred firms, ranging from one-man companies to giants such as General Electric, General Motors, and General Dynamics, and about two hundred universities, research institutions, and government agencies.

Although the program lacked cohesion—it was a collection of individual speeches rather than a co-ordinated presentation of the subject—it did provide some background in the work of oceanographers and some information on their instrument needs. To companies which had been connected with the ocean in some way, such as making sonar or navigational equipment, and to companies which were already watching the increase in oceanographic activity, the symposium was a general review of the ideas and thoughts of leading oceanographers. To representatives of many other firms the symposium was a formal introduction to the background and needs of the marine sciences. For both, it provided perhaps the first detailed list of instrument needs of the oceanographic field and the first indication of the size of the market for these instruments.

The Ways of the Oceanographer

Even though, at the ICO symposium, the oceanographers, or at least those who financed the oceanographers, were in effect inviting industry to serve them, they made clear that their needs would not be easily satisfied. (This invitation was re-extended by the oceanographers themselves in instrument symposiums held in connection with two predominantly scientific meetings held in the late summer of 1961.) In 1959, there were still only 520 professionally trained oceanographers in the United States [1], and these men tended to be a closely knit and hardy breed bound together not only by their small number but by the special difficulties under which they worked. Many of them often had to conduct their research on meager budgets with "homemade" instruments from small ships in often rough midocean locations. The resulting collection of traditions and prejudices which surrounded the field seemed to be something with which any prospective oceanographic hardware manufacturer should reckon. "If you haven't been to sea, you can't really appreciate our needs," was a statement repeated again and again by oceanographers in talking to industry representatives.

The typical oceanographer cannot be just a scientist. When he gets an idea for a research project, he must first get the funds with which to carry it out. Most oceanographic institutions have their plant, capital equipment, and normal administrative overhead funded, either by private endowment and contributions (e.g., Woods Hole Oceanographic Institution) or by the government (e.g., the Navy Underwater Sound Laboratory in New London), or are directly connected with a university. However, they normally do not have funds to finance specific projects. The oceanographer cannot go to any central oceanographic agency or clearinghouse for financial support, but must approach each agency which might be interested in his project. These agencies include the Office of Naval Research; the Navy's Bureau of Weapons, the Bureau of Ships, and the Hydrographic Office; the Commerce Department's Coast and Geodetic Survey and Weather Bureau; the Department of the Interior's Bureau of Commercial Fisheries, Geological Survey, Bureau of Sport Fisheries and Wildlife, and Bureau of Mines; the National Science Foundation; the Atomic Energy Commission; the Department of Health, Education and Welfare's United States Public Health Service; the Treasury Department's United States Coast Guard; and even the Army and the Air Force. The oceanographer may also approach private companies which need oceanographic information, such as oil companies doing tidewater prospecting or drilling, companies owning and operating undersea cables, ship designers, and chemical, exotic metal, or other firms hoping to extract valuable material from the sea.

Once the oceanographer has been successful in getting funds for his project, he must turn instrument designer and manufacturer. Rarely can he find "off-the-shelf" instruments which satisfy his needs, and he usually cannot afford to pay to have instruments designed and built by others. Not only do few manufacturers (some oceanographers say *no* manufacturers) understand the requirements of oceanographic instrumentation; but also, each researcher is working on a different project, and his particular data needs are rarely the same as those of any other oceanographer.

Some men, especially those who are as interested in the methodology of oceanographic research as in the research itself, spend a large portion of their time on instrument design; others use the services of the staff engineers most of the larger institutions employ to assist them. However, there is probably no oceanographer who would not say that at times he has had to spend too much time on instrumentation, to the detriment of his actual research work. He also must often oversee the actual manufacture and/or assembly work on the instruments he has designed, which is usually performed by machine shops in the institutions. Oceanographers state that this is necessary because outside firms do not have the knowledge of the ocean necessary to make reliable instruments, and because outside firms charge prices which are too high. (Most institutions' shops charge only material and direct labor to the oceanographer's project, covering overhead from their endowment income.) Even when work is done by outside machine shops, the oceanographer must usually follow the job closely to make certain that it is done correctly.

The time the oceanographer spends on his instruments is not only a function of the fact that few or no firms make such instruments, but also that he needs a level of reliability far above that demanded from most instruments. The oceanographer usually collects his data from ships at sea. Ship time is extremely expensive. The three smaller WHOI research vessels, the *Atlantis* (143 feet, 560 tons), the *Crawford* (125 feet, 290 tons), and the *Bear* (103 feet, 240 tons), cost the oceanographer about $1,000 per day at sea. The large WHOI ship, the *Chain* (214 feet, 1,900 tons), costs $2,000 per day. Even though several concurrent projects usually share the cost of any cruise, no oceanographer can afford even a third or a quarter of the cost of steaming five or more days to an ocean location only to find that his equipment does not work.

The oceanographer rarely waits until he returns to his desk to begin analyzing the data he gathers. Typically, he will evaluate each observation as soon as it is made against the background of his knowledge about the ocean. He makes on-the-spot tactical decisions about where to go next, changing his data-gathering program on the basis of each incremental bit of information. If he notices a particularly interesting phenomenon, he tarries to inspect it further. He must work in this manner in order to make the most of his ship time, limited by the vessel's other commitments and by his own research funds. Finally, he returns to his desk to examine more completely the data he has gathered. Upon completion of his project, or an important part of it, he delivers to the agency or company which financed it the analysis or information it desires and often publishes a paper on his findings.

Until 1961 the highly specialized and limited characteristic of this market discouraged most companies from attempting to offer a line of products for the oceanographer. This lack of industrial interest in turn reinforced the oceanographer's belief that he had to design and sometimes even make his own equipment.

There were, of course, several firms manufacturing military equipment such as echo-ranging gear. There were also many companies making equipment of use to the oceanographer, such as navigational aids, which had a total market much broader than oceanography. Some firms, especially foreign companies, produced for the oceanographer items which were related to their other products. A manufacturer of thermometers, for example, might offer a variation of its standard instruments for ocean use. Although a few small firms offered limited lines of oceanographic instruments, these were often crude and inefficient. They were usually offered because the company had at some time in the past been asked to make a special instrument for an oceanographic project. Usually, oceanographers allowed firms to make such an item, without restriction, for any other researcher who wanted it. In this manner, some small companies built up a collection of special instruments which they offered to make. However, these were of limited value to other oceanographers because they were made for a special project with its particular data needs. As of 1960, there were virtually no firms in the United States doing active development work on a line of oceanographic instruments.

Oceanographic Hardware Needs

At the ICO symposium, at other meetings of oceanographers, and in several articles published in 1960 and 1961, the various needs and requirements of the oceanographer were presented. Although, even in the fall of 1961, different men placed different emphasis on various requirements, and no organization as yet could speak for the field as a whole, it was possible for a manufacturer to get a reasonable idea of what would be asked of a firm which sought to supply the field. The characteristics, or qualities, required of most oceanographic instruments seemed to be as listed below:

Reliability. Instruments for the oceanographer must be reliable. He cannot afford to spend several thousand dollars getting to an ocean position, and be committed to spendng the same amount to get back, only to find that his instruments do not work. Similarly, he cannot afford to put instruments out on buoys for a long period of time and later find that they failed to function.

Quality Control. In addition to knowing that his instruments are functioning, the oceanographer must know whether or not they are sensing and recording their data within the accuracy limits required. If any component or circuit in an instrument is not functioning perfectly, the data record it generates might not be accurate. It is impossible to watch an instrument put in the water, so all instruments should have built-in alarm systems to maintain a constant check on how each part is working. These alarms should not only indicate a malfunction at the time it occurs, but should record its existence on the data record so that "good" data can be separated from "bad."

Immediate and Recorded Read-Out. All instruments for shipboard use by an oceanographer should provide an immediate read-out to allow him to make "tactical" decisions, in addition to a permanent recording of the data.

Data Record Compatibility. Data recordings from all instruments should be such that they can be processed by existing equipment at a minimum of cost and will be compatible with existing data. For example, oceanographers measure depth in meters and want read-outs in the metric stystem.

Equipment Ruggedness. All hardware must be designed so as to withstand the rough treatment it will get on a tossing ship.

Weight. Instruments should be as light as possible to minimize problems of handling them at sea.

Size. Instruments should be as small as possible because of shipboard space limitations.

Simplicity. Instruments should be adjustable and repairable by men with limited technical experience and without special tools or equipment.

Environmental Factors. Instruments must be able to withstand, or be placed in cases which will withstand, pressures at the depths to which they are to be used. The deepest point in the oceans, the Philippine Trench, is about 35,000 feet in depth, with a pressure at the bottom of about 15,500 psi. Although most instruments would not be sent to this depth, 83 per cent of the ocean area is between 10,000 feet and 20,000 feet deep. Pressures at these depths would be about 4,400 psi and 8,800 psi, respectively.

All parts exposed to the ocean must also withstand corrosion and electrolytic action, and must be protected from excess fouling and actual damage by marine organisms. These problems are often much more complicated than they would seem at first. Great pressure changes the characteristics of many materials, especially some of the plastics. For some as yet unexplained reason, nylon-stainless steel junctions which have been used on some cables have corroded in sea water. A small organism living at great depths likes to crawl into tiny cracks in neoprene insulation, causing it to fail as a root will crack a rock. Many such environmental stumbling blocks wait to trip the would-be instrument maker, and more are being discovered continually.

Price. As of 1961, few oceanographers were working with budgets such that they could afford to pay a high price for any single instrument. Although there seemed to be a possibility that with increasing national oceanographic budgets more money for hardware might begin to become available in the future, prospective manufacturers were advised to keep their prices as low as possible. However, two special factors seemed worthy of consideration by interested firms.

For most oceanographers the gathering of data was only a means to an end—one step in a complete program designed to test a scientific hypothesis or add to the store of knowledge about the workings of the ocean. Therefore the instrument designer should consider how any instrument would be used and what would be done with the data generated by it. Since an oceanographer had to pay for his whole project out of his budget, part of the "cost" of any instrument would be the cost of operating it, the cost of ship time necessary to get data with it, and, after the raw data were gathered, the cost of processing those data to make them useful to the oceanographer's analysis. For example, the cost of a new instrument might be reduced by making it record its data in such a way that the job of collating or processing them would be lower than that required with data from other instruments.

The second factor was that, in most cases, oceanographers in 1961 still purchased or manufactured instruments for specific projects. Although ships and, occasionally, some other major hardware items such as winches, cables, etc., were owned or leased by the institutions and "rented" to the oceanographer for each project, this practice did not normally extend to individual instruments. In most cases, instruments such as current meters, temperature gauges, nets, etc., were charged to the particular project for which they were initially needed. If they were later used for other research activities, these subsequent projects were not generally charged for their use.

This tradition had probably been built up because of two factors mentioned previously: Most oceanographers built special and unique instruments for each new project, so subsequent use of such hardware was unlikely; and most research institutions worked on slim budgets, so they tried to charge the cost of all new hardware to the project which first needed it. This tradition obviously presented problems to the manufacturer of high-priced instruments of advanced design which could serve the needs of many projects for a number of years. In the fall of 1961, one oceanographic engineer stated that he detected the first signs of a trend away from this tradition. He said that some men connected with oceanography seemed to realize that unless the institutions or government agencies were willing to purchase the more expensive new hardware items needed and rent them to individual oceanographers, as was done with ships, technically advanced instruments would continue to be unavailable to most research projects.

In addition to these specific points, oceanographers stressed the fact that men working on research ships often get seasick. Even the mere gentle rolling of a ship in a calm ocean reduces human efficiency; a rough sea can drastically cut both a man's willingness and his ability to think and work. This factor increases the need for simplicity, reliability, small size, and light weight in instruments.

Oceanographers feel very strongly that executives and design engineers of firms thinking of serving them should take the opportunity to go to sea on a research cruise. The institutions have indicated their willingness to take these men to sea as working members of the research team (but not as "tourists"), and several small-company executives went on WHOI cruises in August and September of 1961. However, in the summer of 1961 a number of oceanographers indicated, both in speeches at the various symposiums and in private conversations, their growing impatience with the parade of salesmen continually arriving at their offices. Their complaints were not with the interest that these men showed but with the fact that most of them came knowing nothing about oceanography or of the oceanographers' general needs. These scientists resented the fact that the salesmen expected them to explain things which could be read in any number of books about the ocean and, apparently, expected to sell instruments for oceanographic research without doing such reading.

Basic Needs of Oceanography

At the Washington symposium and the following meetings, several basic or general needs of the oceanographic field were presented. These desires, of a more general nature than the specific instruments needed, are presented below:

Continuous Data.   Prior to 1961, continuous records of deep-water data over long time periods (weeks or months) were virtually nonexistent. Although such observations had been made in some inshore areas, the high cost of ship time had discouraged the gathering of them in the open ocean. There was a limit to the extent of understanding which could be gained from the "spot observations" usually made from ships. Continuous records of the major ocean characteristics for long periods of time were needed to map the oceans completely.

In the spring and summer of 1961, Dr. Richardson of WHOI placed 21 buoys in a line from Martha's Vineyard to Bermuda. These buoys, anchored to the bottom, looked like large doughnuts six to eight feet in diameter and were made of Fiberglas-reinforced plastic. Arranged along the mooring cable of each buoy were temperature sensors which recorded the temperature at about ten-minute intervals on small strip charts. The exact number of instruments, usually between eight and twelve, depended on the depth of the water. Small batteries powered the units, which were placed in pressure-tight cases. At three-month intervals, Dr. Richardson had to service each buoy, hauling the mooring cable, removing completed strip charts, and putting new charts, batteries, ink, etc., in each instrument. Dr. Richardson's project included plans for about 100 such buoys in several different lines and for additional instruments for measuring characteristics other than temperature.

Dr. Richardson's buoy-line project represents a pioneering attempt to get continuous data economically. Whereas deep-water data collected by research ships cost from $15 to $25 per observation, excluding the capital cost of the ships, Dr. Richardson's buoy line has produced data costing less than 50 cents per observation, excluding the capital costs of the ships which service the line, but including all other equipment costs. Although these two types of observations are not strictly comparable because Dr. Richardson's are almost continuous, the magnitude of the difference in costs seemed significant to him.

Dr. Richardson's concept may become a standard data-gathering method, or other concepts may be developed, but most oceanographers agree that many more series of continuous data over long time periods are vital for a thorough understanding of the ocean.

Total Environment Information. A second major need of the oceanographic field is for complete information about all the basic characteristics of the ocean at the same time in the same spot. In the past, data on each characteristic have often been obtained separately or in conjunction with only one or two others. The total environment (including the biological environment) must be considered if real insight is to be gained into the workings of the ocean. This need, however, does not mean that any single oceanographic instrument must measure all characteristics. The ICO, in fact, specifies modular construction in all instruments and systems to provide the advantages of interchangeability, selected use, selected improvement, etc.

Navigation. In addition to instruments for measuring the characteristics of the ocean, the oceanographer needs highly accurate navigational equipment, so that he will know where he was when he gathered his data. Several new systems, among them the transit satellite project, promise to give the $\pm$ one-half mile to one-mile accuracy he needs on the required all-weather, twenty-four-hour-a-day, interference-free basis, if and when they become practical from an economical standpoint.

Communication. In relation to the methods of communication used in the aerospace field, the oceanographers' ways often seem crude indeed. Dr. Richardson, for example, must haul the entire mooring cable of his buoys to get the data being recorded. To make many observations, oceanographers still bring water up from the depths. (This procedure is, incidentally, quite expensive. Dr. Richardson has stated that each liter of water brought up by the small WHOI research ship *Crawford* on one 1960 cruise is estimated to have cost $16.30.)

This communication problem is complicated, especially for sensors placed for long times in a deep-water location. The solution may lie in long-range underwater telemetry, or in a combination of underwater and atmospheric transmission. To solve this and many other problems of the oceanographer, it is probably not necessary to design entirely new hardware items but only to modify and encase the excellent hardware now available for other uses so that it will withstand the ocean environment.

Hardware Needs

In addition to the many general requirements of the oceanographic field, some specific hardware needs have been stated, both by the Interagency Committee on Oceanography in a document prepared for its symposium [3] and by individual oceanographers at various industry meetings and conventions.

The ICO-prepared documents list the hardware requirements of three "oceanographic instrument suits." The largest one of these, in terms of the variety of instruments required, is the suit of hardware for oceanographic research and survey vessels. A total of seventeen separate instruments and seven instrument systems are listed. Some of these are close to existing products of various instrument companies (e.g., echo sounders, or fathometers, and winches), while others will require substantial original design and development work.

The instruments, equipments, and systems of this suit are listed in Exhibit 3, with a short explanation of each item. The priorities were as-

Exhibit 3

OCEANOGRAPHIC INSTRUMENT SUIT FOR OCEANOGRAPHIC
SURVEY VESSELS[1]

A list of instruments and systems needed for oceanographic vessels prepared in 1961 by the Interagency Committee on Oceanography. The brief explanation of each item summarizes the ICO's more detailed explanation and specifications. The priorities were assigned by ICO as explained in the text of this note. The market estimates are quoted from the ICO document and were accumulated by ICO from reports of potential users. The priorities, market estimates, and specifications reflect the opinions of ICO members and the various oceanographers and agencies which assisted in the preparation of the document. The ICO intended that they be guides for industry to help "stimulate the needed and desired new thinking" on oceanographic instrumentation.

Individual Instruments/Equipment	Priority	Market[2]
Hydrographic precision scanning echo sounder.............. 1		33–48
Highly accurate, fully stabilized depth sounder, sweeping a distance of half the depth on each side of the ship's track, providing an automatically plotted contoured chart read-out. Depth read-out: zero to 6,500 fathoms ± one fathom.[3] Stabilization: up to 60 degrees ±1/2 degrees.		

---

[1] The ICO uses "survey" and "research" synonymously to indicate the entire range of these activities.
[2] Number of instruments or systems estimated by the ICO to be needed.
[3] One fathom equals six feet.

Exhibit 3 (Continued)

Individual Instruments/Equipment	Priority	Market

Current meter for conducting coastal and oceanic subsurface
current surveys...................................... 2   100–370

> To measure and record direction and speed of currents (see Exhibit 4).

Shipboard wave meter................................. 3   63–100

> To measure and record wave spectra from the ship. It should be fully operable
> without the need of having men topside on the ship, so that "rough water"
> measurements can be made. Accuracy: ±5 per cent.

Multipurpose, constant-tension, heavy-duty oceanographic
winch.. 4   33–67

> Controlled torque, constant-tension winch with "break-load" capacity of 20,-
> 000 pounds, and with both conducting and nonconducting wire reels.

Sub-sea-floor strata profiler............................ 5   45–75

> To provide by remote means (from a ship-mounted or towed transducer) a rec-
> ord of the types, characteristics, and discontinuities in the sea-floor sediments
> and the face of the basement rock structure. Must perform reliably in ocean
> areas varying in depth from zero to 6,500 fathoms and be capable of penetrat-
> ing sediments to at least 2,000 feet in depth.

Small-craft, shallow-water echo-sounding instrument.......... 6   65–140

> Accurate, fully portable, A.C.–D.C. "fathometer." Depth read-out, zero to
> 250 fathoms ±0.5 fathom.

Surface ship and submarine gravity meter for survey use....... 7   24–46

> To provide continuous measurement of gravity profiles. Gravity read-out
> range: 977 to 984 gals. ±2 milligals.

Marine electron resonance magnetometer................... 8   40–80

> To provide continuous profiles of the earth's total magnetic intensity. Two
> sensors, capable of being lowered to depths of 1,000 feet and 6,500 fathoms,
> respectively, with provision for measuring depth. Magnetic intensity read-out:
> 20,000–100,000 gammas ±0.01 gamma. Depth gauge accuracy: ± 1/4 per
> cent of full scale.

Self-contained, deep-diving, oceanographic sensing instrument.. 9   70–360

> This instrument to be designed for utilization from oceanographic survey ships
> to allow the measurement and recording of certain key oceanographic data
> simultaneously with other under-way or stopped operations of the ships. It
> should be capable of making "free" descents to, and ascents from, depths of
> 6,500 fathoms. Its rate of sinking and returning should be able to be pro-
> grammed as desired for any "drop," and it should automatically return on
> reaching the prespecified depth of any drop. It should make simultaneous and
> continuous analogue recordings on magnetic tape of temperature, salinity,
> sound velocity, dissolved oxygen content, and depth of the water.

Surface navigation and buoy location transponder.............11   52–114

> Buoy-mounted transceiver unit to be triggered by existing radars to aid in buoy
> location, and a shipboard/airborne transceiver unit to provide automatic refer-
> ence grids for multivehicle operations.

Shipboard dye detector probe for oceanographic investigations.

> Instrument with rhodamine-type dye sensitivity to aid in studies of diffusion,
> turbulence, and ocean circulation. Four depth modules capable of being

Exhibit 3 (Continued)

Individual Instruments/Equipment	Priority	Market

dropped to 600, 1,000, 6,000, and 39,000 feet, respectively, with depth gauges capable of recording within ±1/4 per cent of full scale. It must record rhodamine concentrations from 500 parts per million to 0.01 parts per billion, ±0.01 parts per billion.

Deep-sea plankton sampler.................................12   41–70

To sample plankton and record physical environmental data at all depths (see Exhibit 5).

Shipboard gamma ray detector of nuclear waste in the sea:.......13   52–108

To identify and measure abnormal gamma ray concentrations at any depth, capable of being sent to depths of 6,500 fathoms and recording depth to ±1/4% of full scale.

Oceanographic radioactive water sampler....................14   62–130

To collect 15-gallon samples of water at any depth. Container and associated gear must be constructed of noncontaminating material. It must be capable of being opened and closed by remote operation from shipboard by one or two men.

Underwater camera.......................................15   42–88

To provide single-frame and stereo close-up photographs at depths of zero to 6,500 fathoms. Must have suitable arrangements for providing light and general environmental knowledge. Must record on each frame the date, time, location, camera attitude, and camera direction.

Sea-floor sampling system...............................16   41–59

Including at least the following: small "grab" samplers, short corers (zero to 15 feet), long corers (zero to 100 feet), light and heavy-weight dredge, *in situ* sampling devices (capable of obtaining an undisturbed sample of the water/bottom interface, including retention of ambient pressure), and to operate at any depth to 6,500 fathoms.

Sea-floor geothermal probe..............................17   40–65

To measure heat flow characteristics and values across and within the sea-floor sediments.

Instrument Systems	Priority	Market

Shipboard oceanographic survey system.................... 1   52–110

A system incorporated into a single vehicle to be lowered from a ship to measure and record simultaneously depth, temperature, sound velocity, light absorption, density, subsurface currents, magnetic intensity, and the ion concentration of oxygen, salinity, nitrate-nitrogen, phosphate-phosphorus, and silicates.

Precision navigational control system......................2   60–115

A precise navigational system with world-wide, continuous coverage.

Master oceanographic shipboard data-logging and -processing
system.. 3   34–51

A complete system to provide on-board data-analyzing, logging, processing, and storage capability.

Towed subsurface instrument system........................ 4   42–85

Unit to be towed by a ship at speeds up to 15 knots and depths to 2,000 feet, including sensors for temperature, salinity, sound velocity, and depth.

Exhibit 3 (Concluded)

Instrument Systems	Priority	Market
Air-sea surface interface environmental data-recording system... 5		52–93
To measure major environmental characteristics of both water and air at the interface.		
Marine seismic receiving system.......................... 6		37–74
For shipboard geological investigations.		
Underwater television system for sea-floor investigations....... 7		27–68
For continuous observations in both coastal and deep-water location.		

signed by the ICO on the basis of the urgency of the requirement for the information that item would provide and did not reflect any judgment as to the speed with which each item might be developed. The market estimates for each item were made by the ICO on the basis of projected requirements of the various agencies, institutions, and services which need the data provided by each item. The accuracy and flexibility demanded of these instruments is of a high order. Exhibits 4 and 5 summarize the

Exhibit 4

SUMMARY OF SPECIFICATIONS PREPARED BY ICO FOR CURRENT METER*

1. To be used from a ship which is anchored or "lying to."
2. Depth capability: zero to 6,500 fathoms.
3. To include four modular depth sensor units for zero to 6,500 feet, zero to 6,000 feet, zero to 15,000 feet, and zero to 39,000 feet.
4. Depth accuracy for each module: $\pm 1/4$ per cent of full scale.
5. Current range and accuracy:
    a) Speed: 0.05 knots to 8 knots; ± 0.05 knot accuracy at read-out.
    b) Direction: zero degrees to 360 degrees, ± 10-degree accuracy at read-out.
6. Shipboard monitoring components:
    a) Computer/recorder capable of averaging current over varying time intervals as well as providing instantaneous values.
    b) Visual analogue and digital tape read-out.
    c) Compatible with master shipboard logging and processing system.

* Listed in Exhibit 3 as instrument priority 2.

Exhibit 5

SUMMARY OF SPECIFICATIONS PREPARED BY ICO FOR DEEP-SEA PLANKTON SAMPLER*

1. To be towed from under-way ship at speeds of zero to 15 knots and depths of zero to 6,000 feet.
2. Net capable of being opened and closed on signal from ship.
3. Net screen (mesh) size capable of being adjusted remotely from ship to achieve at least six screen changes per cast.
4. Water volume through net measured to accuracy of ± 1 per cent.

* Listed in Exhibit 3 as instrument priority 12.

Exhibit 5 (Continued)

5. Depth measured from zero to 6,000 feet with accuracy of ±1/4 per cent of full range.
6. Temperature measured from −2 degrees centigrade to 35 degrees centigrade, ± 0.1 degree centigrade.
7. Data read-out compatible with master shipboard data-logging and -processing system.

specifications of two typical instruments to show the order of accuracy desired.

The ICO did not anticipate that "cost-plus" or research and development contracts would be available for the basic design work on these items, or on those of the other two suits described below. It wants a detailed proposal for the manufacture of an instrument, with a firm bid price which can be considered by each potential buyer. ICO will not make any purchases or contract awards. These will be made individually by each user, for the particular needs that user has.

A second suit of instruments described by the ICO was a shipboard oceanographic synoptic system for use by the Navy's Hydrographic Office in connection with the Antisubmarine Warfare Environmental Prediction (ASWEP) system which will, when it becomes practical, operate a world-wide weather network to observe and display information of tactical value for antisubmarine or submarine operations. The synoptic suit of instruments would be placed on ocean station vessels, radar picket ships, and selected fleet units. It would have to provide for the measurement at least of depth, temperature, sound velocity, and conductivity from the surface to 2,500 feet down, and for certain additional interface measurements. It would also have to provide for the preparation of data for rapid, automatic radio transmission. The complete unit would have to be semiportable. The ICO projected the requirements for this synoptic suit at about sixty-six units.

The third instrument suit described by the ICO was for use on "ships of opportunity." These ships would include both military and commercial vessels, and the instrument suit would automatically record oceanographic data along the route sailed by any ship without requiring any significant effort on the part of the ship's force. Sensors would be both ship-mounted and towed. The package would include provision for recording at least the following: echo soundings, temperature at various depths and at the surface, magnetic intensity, waves, air temperature, barometric pressure, relative humidity, wind, and direct and reflected solar radiation. The ICO stated that between 56 and 163 of the "ship-of-opportunity" instrument suits were thought to be needed.

In addition to the instruments and systems on the ICO list of needs, other specific hardware requirements of the oceanographic field have been described by other agencies or by oceanographers themselves. Rarely have any market estimates been made in connection with these items, nor have detailed specifications been prepared for them. However, an immediate need does exist for some number of each one.

The Bureau of Commercial Fisheries made known at the August, 1961, ICO symposium the fact that it hoped that an automatic fish-scale reader could be developed by June of 1962 for use in its studies of salmon. The fish scales in the embedded or protected area from which the measurements are made contain circular ridges or rings on their surfaces. These ridges are formed throughout the life of the fish. Their width and spacing are related to the growth rate of the fish and, typically, to the amount of food available. In the winter, when less food is available, they tend to be narrow and closely spaced, forming annular bands. By counting the number of bands, the age of the fish can be determined. This process is similar to that of determining the age of trees by counting their annular growth rings. The desired automatic scale reader would replace the existing method of having people visually count the annular bands of scales. The Bureau stated that about $50,000 was available for this project.

Several oceanographers expressed the need for an accurate pressure meter for use on the ocean bottom. Ocean-bottom pressure varies, much as atmospheric (barometric) pressure does. Such a device would have to have a high degree of relative accuracy to show small variations in pressure; the absolute accuracy would be of less importance.

Another item desired by oceanographers was a hovering device which, like an unmanned helicopter, could ride a specific temperature or salinity value, or remain at the maximum (or minimum) temperature or salinity point, recording and transmitting its position and other environmental data.

Dr. Richardson of Woods Hole Oceanographic Institution stressed the need for improved ground tackle and mooring systems for research buoys at several meetings in 1961. As of August, he had lost four of the twenty-one buoys which he had placed on the Bermuda buoy line earlier in the year. (Of course, buoy damage rather than mooring system failure might have caused some of the losses.) He had tried various types of ground tackle but felt that, because the problems in deep water were significantly different from those of anchoring ships in relatively shallow bays and harbors, some original deep-water research would have to be done to perfect effective mooring methods.

These items are only a sample of the hardware desired and needed by the marine sciences. Each oceanographer would probably assign different priorities to the various devices described above, depending on his particular field of interest, and would add items especially useful to his work. Despite the documents published by the ICO and other available references, there seemed no way for the prospective manufacturer to learn of or evaluate all the needs for hardware except by spending a great deal of time talking with many oceanographers and actually going to sea with them.

Related Fields

In addition to the area of oceanographic research, many other fields which required hardware for use in the ocean presented potential markets to the manufacturer who developed abilities in dealing with the oceanic environment. Without listing all of these, several examples are given below to indicate the types of opportunities which might exist.

Much of the hardware used by fishermen has not been improved in decades and, in some cases, centuries.

For example, the traditional lobster pot, used almost universally to capture lobsters, is extremely inefficient as a trap. It consists of a box made from wooden slats, with a conical entrance at one end. It is baited with dead fish and dropped in an area frequented by lobsters. The lobsters, attracted by the fish, enter the pot, but they will only remain until they have consumed the fish. They then can, and do, crawl back out. This means that pots must be serviced about every two days, the length of time the bait usually lasts. Could a true lobster trap be designed to reduce the servicing requirement?

Another example from the fisheries is based on the fact that many fish will align themselves with an electrical field, swimming toward the anode. This principle is already being used by the menhaden fishermen. They bring their nets to the surface, drop a cathode to the bottom of the net, and pump the menhaden out through a hose which has the anode attached to its end. Could this principle be applied to the actual catching of fish?

Great opportunities seem to lie in the possibility of gathering minerals from the ocean. Much of the sea floor is peppered with "nodules" of manganese and iron varying from a millimeter to a meter in diameter. It also contains low-grade deposits of cobalt, copper, nickel, and rare earths. Dr. Revelle of Scripps Institution of Oceanography has estimated that the sea floor holds some $500,000 worth of minerals per square mile [8].

The water itself holds in solution a wealth of minerals and chemicals. In addition to the dissolved salts and other common chemicals, each cubic mile of sea water has been estimated to contain 18 million tons of manganese and 25 tons of gold [8].

Could methods and hardware for the economical harvesting of these materials be developed?

Conclusion

Although the manufacture of hardware for oceanographic research and related fields was apparently a highly specialized business, and one which prior to 1961 had not seemed to justify development work on the part of private industry, the increasing publicity given the field in 1960–61 aroused extensive interest among both large and small manufacturing firms. There were still few data on which to base market estimates and profit projections. Both the demand for individual instruments and the timing of the development of that demand were large question marks in the minds of industry representatives, government officials, and oceanographers alike. The demand for hardware would depend on the amount of oceanographic research which would be done over the following years. The research done would depend, in turn, on what hardware was available. The development of the whole program seemed to hinge primarily on the importance placed on oceanographic research by the government.

The various bills introduced in the 1960 and 1961 Congressional sessions had, as mentioned above, been allowed to die in committee before reaching a final vote. However, as shown by the national oceanographic budgets (Exhibit 2), expenditures for oceanographic activity by the various departments and agencies of the government were increasing rapidly. President Kennedy, in his message to Congress on February 23, 1961, and in a subsequent letter to the President of the Senate and the Speaker of the House, emphasized the country's need for more oceanographic research and indicated his personal concern with the marine sciences. It therefore seemed likely that the ocean would continue to get increasing government attention.

Executives of many firms, both large and small, were asking themselves in the fall of 1961 whether they should try to enter the field. If so, when should they do so, how quickly should they proceed, and how should they go about becoming suppliers for this field of oceanography?

BIBLIOGRAPHY

This Bibliography includes the major published sources used in the a preparation of the note, "Oceanographic Instrumentation." It is not intended as a complete list of sources. It does, however, include publications which would be of interest to the prospective manufacture of oceanographic research hardware, including the sources of many of the quantitative data included in the note. Each source is referred to by number where appropriate in the text. Also listed are three articles on oceanography reflecting the expanding interest in the field exhibited by various magazines in 1960 and 1961. These references are included here for the reader who may wish to examine some of these "trade journal" reports on the field. A more complete list of such articles can be found in most business and/or scientific periodical indices.

Government Publications

1. Committee on Oceanography, National Academy of Sciences–National Research Council, *Oceanography: 1960 to 1970* (Washington, D.C., 1959).
2. Interagency Committee on Oceanography of the Federal Council for Science and Technology, *United States National Oceanographic Program, Fiscal Year 1962*, ICO Pamphlet No. 2 (Washington, D.C., March, 1961).
3. Captain C. N. G. Hendrix, United States Navy, and Others, *Required Oceanographic Instrument Suit for Oceanographic Survey Vessels*

(Washington, D.C.: Interagency Committee on Oceanography, August, 1961).

4. United States Navy Hydrographic Office, *Requirements for Shipboard Oceanographic Synoptic System*, and *Requirements for Oceanographic Instrument Suit for Ships-of-Opportunity* (Washington, D.C., August, 1961).

Congressional Hearings

5. Hearings before the Committee on Interstate and Foreign Commerce, United States Senate. 86th Congress, 2d session, on S. 2692, *The Marine Sciences and Research Act of 1959*, April 20, 21, and 22, 1960; 87th Congress, 1st session, on S. 901, *The Marine Sciences and Research Act of 1961*, March 15, 16, and 17, and May 2, 1961.

6. Hearings before the Subcommittee on Oceanography of the Committee on Merchant Marine and Fisheries, House of Representatives, 87th Congress, 1st session, on HR 4340 (an unnamed bill to expand the oceanographic duties of the Coast Guard), April 27, 1961; and HR 4276, *The Oceanographic Act of 1961*, on June 19, 20, 21, 22, and 23, and July 19, 1961.

Periodical Articles

7. "Renaissance in Oceanography," *Electronics*, Vol. XXXII, No. 47 (November 20, 1959).

8. "Down to the Sea: New World for Industry to Conquer," *Steel*, Vol. CXLVII, No 11 (September 12, 1960).

9. "U.S. Seeks Oceanography Instruments," *Missiles and Rockets*, Vol. IX, No. 9 (August 28, 1961).

QUESTIONS

1. Make a literature search with a view to:
   a) Identifying new developments or major shifts in oceanographic interests.
   b) Improving and supplementing the market data.
   c) Identifying leading firms serving the field, if any.

2. Are there new or imminent technological developments that might affect oceanographic techniques or instrument design?

3. Are there recent or potential internal or international political developments that might affect this market?

4. Interpret the market needs and opportunities to a businessman.

ADCOLE CORPORATION

CONSIDERATION OF A NEW AREA OF ENDEAVOR BY A TECHNICALLY ORIENTED COMPANY

ADCOLE CORPORATION was established in 1957 to design and assemble technically advanced electronic equipment and systems. Initially, it employed seven people, five of whom were engineers. By October, 1961, its staff had grown to 27, including 15 engineers, and its gross income for the year ended in June, 1961, had been $360,000. During this period, Adcole's devices had been on about thirty of the country's space shots and the firm had developed an excellent reputation for its ability to design and assemble highly complex electronic circuitry for space-age applications.

However, Adcole's management team realized that the field of missile instrumentation was only one application for its electronic design abilities, and its officers continually watched for new areas which the firm might enter. Dr. Maurice A. Meyer, one of Adcole's vice presidents, had noticed the increasing activity in the marine sciences in 1961. Although he had looked at oceanographic instrumentation two years previously without finding any significant opportunities, he wondered if the field might now have developed to the point that it offered an attractive market for Adcole.

Company Background

Adcole Corporation commenced operations in July, 1957, in Cambridge, Massachusetts. Its founder, President, and majority stockholder was Addison D. Cole, who had left a position as Vice President and Director of Engineering at the Advanced Electronics Company.[1]

His initial staff at Adcole consisted of five highly experienced electronics engineers (three of whom had also been with Advanced), a contract administrator, and the company clerk. Cole chose these men because of the special capabilities and broad experience they had in designing electronic systems and associated circuitry.

One of the major reasons that Cole had founded his own firm was that he wanted to recapture the engineering "freedom" which had been lost at Advanced in recent years. The growth of that firm had led it to become

---

[1] Name disguised. Advanced Electronics was a firm which had been started after World War II to work in the forefront of the developing technology of electronics. It was based in Massachusetts and in 1957 had sales of about $10 million.

more formal in its organization and to require much more specialization from its staff. As Dr. Meyer put it: "The businessmen took over from the engineers." In Adcole Corporation, Cole tried to maintain an atmosphere in which highly competent engineers would enjoy working. He felt that in so far as was possible within the limits imposed by the economic needs of maintaining a going concern, men should be allowed to work on projects which were interesting to them. He also believed that an engineer should be allowed to work on an entire project from start to finish, rather than being asked to do only a small portion of many projects in assembly-line fashion. In 1961, Adcole was still a company run by engineers for engineers, and Cole wished to keep it that way as it continued to grow.

When Cole established his company, he felt that two major routes were open to him. He could attempt to sell services or to sell products. A firm organized to sell services could start with a relatively low capitalization and would incur a relatively small risk. A company seeking early sales of proprietary products would require a much larger capital structure to finance product development, production facilities, and a sales organization. It would run a relatively high risk; but if it was successful, its profits might be significantly larger than those of its more conservative brother.

Cole felt that his firm might follow a path which would yield the best of both of these routes. Therefore, Adcole's long-term plans were divided into three "phases." The following paragraphs, quoted from a description of the company prepared by members of its management in 1961, explain the plan in detail.

Phase 1

In the first phase, engineering work is sought on a contract basis. Almost any type of work may be acceptable, provided it is honest and can be done at a profit. To obtain such work, the main need is for a highly competent technical staff. Every effort is made to build a good reputation and establish the basis for a continuing flow of work from the government and other sources. As early as practicable in this phase, some areas of the electronic field should be selected for concentration. The surest way to continue to get work is to develop the capacity for doing something that is in reasonable demand better than almost anybody else. For a small company, this can be achieved only by some specialization.

Phase 2

After a competent organization of at least modest size has been established and is selling its services on a profitable basis, attention should be given to the development of proprietary products. Generally, at this point the engineering work for others will have developed or partially developed some items that can be sold. These may have a limited market but may nevertheless be attractive because little or no development cost is required. The income from the business will begin to support a modest effort on new-product development. Much of this kind of activity constitutes a reimbursable cost on government contracts. Management should be on the alert for new-product opportunities. The best climate for originating these ideas is within a competent organization busy on engineering work. At some time in this phase, provided the capital is available, it may become desirable to expand the product development activity beyond that supportable for current income. Such an investment may well be desirable, provided the new-product prospects indicate adequate potential; however, at no time should such an investment be so large as to represent a crippling blow to success should the prospect fail to materialize in part or in full. Fundamental to this method of operation is the theory that an active, competent engineering organization will inevitably generate fine new products. Since successful new products will simply move a company from a position that is good to one that is better, there is no justification for taking large risks.

Phase 3

This phase is reached when the company is doing a large volume of profitable business with 50 per cent or more in proprietary products. Income from the operation must provide enough margin to provide for expending 5 to 10 per cent of the gross on research and development. Management must maintain a high order of technical ability in the staff, to keep the company abreast of the advancing technology and remain alert to new opportunities.

Adcole executives realized that in practice, no sharp division would exist between the three phases. In October, 1961, the company had a level of contract income sufficient to support a staff of fifteen engineers, had built up a good reputation for its electronic design capabilities, and had become familiar with many of the environmental problems connected with space exploration. Adcole had also developed several devices for the Air Force which management considered to be of a proprietary nature, although Adcole had no special rights in connection with them other than its technical know-how. It had also developed a medical electronic item. Its major sales efforts were still spent in getting contract development work to allow it to continue the process of broadening its engineering staff.

Adcole's sales had grown steadily during its four-year life and, except for the first year, had always yielded a profit. Income statements for the period are given in Exhibit 1.

Products and Engineering Abilities

Most of Adcole's work had been on two types of items for the missile industry. The largest of these two in terms of total billings was space instrumentation to be used on missiles, rockets, and satellites. The firm also had designed and built special purpose test equipment for use in connection with missile launchings.

Adcole's work on space instrumentation had been done primarily for the Air Force. However, the firm was seeking contracts with the other government agencies in the space business and had recently bid, as a

Exhibit 1

ADCOLE CORPORATION

Summary of Operations for the Four Years from May 20, 1957,* to June 1, 1961
(In Thousands)†

	For the Fiscal Year Ended			
	1958	*1959*	*1960*	*1961*
Gross income	$55.3	$143.0	$187.5	$359.7†
Costs and expenses	76.8	132.5	172.6	352.7
Income (loss) from operations	($21.4)	$ 11.4	$ 14.9	$ 7.0
Other income, net	1.2	3.1	3.9	4.1
Net income (loss) before federal income taxes	($20.3)	$ 14.5	$ 18.8	$ 11.1
Federal income taxes applicable to above income	....	3.7	6.0	3.6
Net income (loss) before special credit	($20.3)	$ 10.8	$ 12.8	$ 7.5
Special credit—federal income tax reduction from carry-forward of 1958 operating loss	....	3.7	1.5	....
Net income (loss), including federal income tax reduction from carry-forward of 1958 operating loss	($20.3)	$ 14.5	$ 14.3	$ 7.5

* Date of incorporation.
† May not be additive due to rounding.
‡ Divided among product lines as follows (in thousands):

	Sales	Profit
Space instrumentation	$280	$ 16
Test equipment	80	10
New-product line	...	(15)§
Total before Taxes	360	11

§ Expenses incurred in developing new products, primarily the heart pacer.

subcontractor, on a special purpose radar unit for the Apollo moon-shot program. This device would indicate the missile's distance to, and velocity relative to, the moon during its approach.

Most of this work had been of the research and development type, done on a cost-plus-fixed-fee basis. However, this work had led to the development of specific hardware items for space use which could be sold on a fixed-price basis. These items were:

1. *Retarding Potential Analyzer.* A sensing device[2] for measuring solar radiation, ion, and electron distributions in space. Knowledge of these factors is important to determine the nature of the space environment for space vehicles and to help define the forces governing weather and communications.

2. *Solar Aspect System.* An optical electronic device to measure the orientation of a rocket or missile relative to the sun.

[2] The term "device" as used here means the total apparatus for doing the job at hand, i.e., the sensor or transducer plus the associated electronics.

3. *Electronic Commutator.* A device used in rockets and satellites to accept the output signals from a number of separate instruments and switch them in continuous sequence to a radio transmitter. This allows fewer radio channels to be used in relaying data from a given number of instruments to the ground.

The electronic test equipment that had been made by Adcole was all of the special purpose type. The company had only become involved in this area in 1960. Most of the units built were devices used for testing gyroscopes used in the inertial guidance systems of ballistic missiles. These units, which measured and recorded gyro drift (error), were only a small part of the total electronic equipment used in testing gyros, and Adcole was doing work on several of the other devices employed. Adcole was the only manufacturer of the drift-recording unit in the country, and realized margins of between 20 and 30 per cent on it.

The firm had also made certain other special test equipment, including a tracking system simulator used to provide artificial stars for testing star-tracking navigation systems. It had done some preliminary research work on several general purpose laboratory instruments; however, the firm's management team felt that it should wait until it had greater financial resources before undertaking active development work on such a group of instruments.

Adcole engineers had spent a significant amount of time on several other new-product lines. The greatest amount of this work was in the field of medical electronics, an area which interested Cole personally. The firm had developed several electronic heart pacers to provide artificial stimulation in cases of heart stoppages. One was a portable device which could be used by any doctor. It consisted of an external unit a bit larger than a pack of cigarettes and two "electrodes" in the form of needles. Several of these units had been used successfully in Boston hospitals. The second type was for internal implanting in a patient with permanent heart trouble. It was powered by a battery which would last approximately five years. The complete unit was only the size of a book of matches and could be sewn under the arm of the patient. The first of these units used in a human being was placed in a small boy in October, 1961. Cole had done most of the engineering work in connection with these medical units. Now that their design was perfected, he planned to sell or license manufacturing rights on the pacers to some firm with manufacturing facilities and the appropriate channels of distribution.

Dr. Maurice A. Meyer, who had joined Adcole in January, 1961, as a Vice President, was also working on several new products. One of the areas in which Dr. Meyer was interested, and in which he had previously done a great deal of work, was in Doppler radar navigation systems. He had developed a proposal which Adcole had submitted to several government services and agencies for an airplane traffic control and landing system utilizing the Doppler principle.[3] He had also done work on a device to aid small-boat and possibly submarine navigation, which worked on an underwater sonic Doppler principle.

Several other members of the company were also working on various radar devices, and Adcole currently had a $70,000 engineering contract with Raytheon Company for work in this area.

Dr. Meyer stated that the firm's major abilities lay in the design and engineering of systems and associated electronic circuitry to perform complex functions. Most of Adcole's work was in designing the "electronics" which would take the original signal from a transducer or sensor[4] and make it perform the job required (e.g., operate a control mechanism or a read-out device). In a very loose sense, this might be compared with the circuitry which transforms the pushing of a key on an electric typewriter into a printed letter on a sheet of paper. Adcole would not make the key, the paper, or any of the components which lie in between; it would, however, design the system, and it employed technicians who would assemble it from purchased parts.

Sales Organization

Because of the high engineering content in Adcole's contracts and the highly specialized nature of this engineering work, the company's engineers constituted its primary selling force. The members of the Adcole staff kept in contact with government scientists, engineers, and project officers connected with the programs which might have need for their particular abilities. These "informal" contacts provided information on new opportunities to submit bids or proposals, allowed Adcole engineers to "sell" their abilities, and helped them to keep up to date on technical advances in their fields.

In 1961, partly in preparation for the greater sales effort which would be required by the firm's move into phase 2 of its long-term plan, and also to provide help with the job of staying abreast of new space developments, the firm added Harry Lowell to its staff. Lowell, a graduate of the business and engineering administration program of the Massachusetts Institute of Technology, had worked as a sales engineer in several fields other than aerospace prior to joining Adcole, and was given the position of Contract Administrator.

---

[3] The Doppler effect refers to the change in the observed frequency of sound, light, or other waves caused by motion of the source or the observer. When the distance between the source and the observer is decreasing, the frequency observed is higher than that actually being emitted, and vice versa. The Doppler frequency shift is proportional to the relative velocity between the source and the observer.

[4] A transducer is a device which transforms one type of energy to another, e.g., a microphone which transforms sound waves into electrical impulses. The term "sensor" is often used to refer to those transducers which are used to "sense" or measure an environmental variable such as light, radioactivity, etc.

Also in 1961, Adcole retained the services of a group of sales representatives to help in obtaining new business, especially government research and development work.

Financial Aspects

In October, 1961, Cole felt that his firm's financial position was satisfactory for its current method of operating. In addition to the original capitalization of $25,000, $24,000 of paid-in capital had been added subsequently, and the company had built up an earned surplus account of $16,000. Substantially all the stock was owned by members of the management team, with Cole being by far the largest stockholder. Adcole's financial condition in June, 1961, is presented in Exhibit 2.

The officers of the firm realized that additional paid-in capital would

Exhibit 2

ADCOLE CORPORATION
Balance Sheet, June 30, 1961
(In Thousands)*

ASSETS

Current assets:		
Cash...		$ 14.8
Accounts receivable.......................................		67.4
Unbilled expenditures and accrued fees on cost reimbursement contracts..		52.1
Costs incurred on fixed-price contract plus estimated profits profits thereon......................................		4.1
Prepaid expenses..		2.7
Total Current Assets.................................		$141.1
Cash surrender value of officers' life insurance.................		3.1
Equipment, at cost:		
Laboratory equipment and tools...........................	$21.3	
Office furniture and equipment...........................	5.5	
Leasehold improvements..................................	0.5	
	$27.3	
Less: Accumulated depreciation...........................	3.1	24.2
Product development costs, capitalized portion.................		11.4
		$179.8

LIABILITIES

Current liabilities:		
Unsecured note payable (bank)............................		$ 10.7
Accounts payable...		65.8
Contract advances..		14.0
Accrued liabilities..		24.2
		$114.7
Stockholders' investment:		
Common stock (no par)	$49.1	
Retained earnings..	16.0	65.1
		$179.8

* May not be additive due to rounding.

probably be required to finance the move into phase 2 of their plan. They were giving some thought to an issue of stock and had spoken to several investment houses, but felt no great urgency to rush into the capital market.

Physical Facilities

Adcole occupied about 4,500 square feet of office and laboratory space in a small building across the street from the Massachusetts Institute of Technology Instrumentation Laboratory in Cambridge. Cole felt that this space might allow the addition of about ten more people to the Adcole organization before new quarters became necessary.

In addition to offices and engineering space, these facilities included an area for the assembly of the devices which Adcole produced. Because much of its work was in miniature electronics, and of one-of-a-kind or low-volume items, Adcole's assembly space was merely a number of work benches. The production force consisted of six technicians, who assembled the devices directly from electronic blueprints and wiring diagrams. Although these technicians had to be highly competent to construct finished products directly from the engineering prints in the Cambridge area, there was apparently no shortage of men who could do this without requiring extensive training by Adcole.

Consideration of Oceanographic Instrumentation

In 1959, when he was Director of Advanced Development and Chief Engineer of Advanced Electronics Company, Dr. Meyer had examined the field of oceanographic instrumentation. He had found that at that time the amount of money being spent by the marine sciences for electronic devices, or for items which might use electronics, was extremely small. He did not feel that this level could justify an effort on the part of the Advanced Electronics Company in the area.

However, his interest in the field continued, and the increased level of activity in the marine sciences in 1961 made him decide that another look at oceanographic instrumentation might be advisable. Therefore, he attended a September symposium on the subject held at Woods Hole and examined some of the material which had been recently written on the needs of oceanography, such as that prepared by the Interagency Committee on Oceanography for its symposium in August, 1961.[5] As mentioned above, he was already working on a device to aid small-boat navigation which might also have an application in the oceanographic field.

From his first brief look at the development of the marine sciences, he felt certain that a significantly greater amount of money would be spent

---

[5] See "Oceanographic Instrumentation", which precedes this case.

on oceanographic and related activities in the future than had been in the past. It seemed reasonable to believe that the increased activity would create a need for more instrumentation, including electronic devices. However, he had not been able to determine the answers to such important questions as: How much money? When would it become available? Who would spend it, and on what?

Dr. Meyer recognized that the small size of the Adcole organization limited the number of areas in which the firm could make a commitment. It had built up an excellent reputation in the missile electronics field, an area which promised to continue its expansion. (*Business Week* estimated that government spending for space activities would increase from less than $2 billion in 1961 to $7 billion in 1965, and that about 50 per cent of these funds would go to electronic ground support, guidance, and control systems.)[6]

However, notwithstanding its present position in space electronics and the expected growth of the field, Dr. Meyer felt that Adcole should not concentrate all its efforts there. He stated that Adcole's abilities lay in being able to design electronic systems to perform complex and technically advanced functions. Although Adcole had an excellent staff, there were many other electronic engineers in the country and many engineering companies which would flood into any growing area of the electronics field. This made it extremely difficult for any firm to keep for long an unchallenged position in any significant segment of the field. Meyer stated in October that competition was increasing rapidly in many phases of the aerospace industry, and that he expected this trend to continue.

Dr. Meyer felt that one way a small electronics engineering firm would continue to be successful was for it to get into new fields early in their development, "skim the cream" off the business, and be prepared to move on as soon as the opportunities became generally recognized and the "crowd" started to arrive. He thought that oceanographic instrumentation might offer this type of opportunity for Adcole. This market did not seem to be large enough yet to justify a concerted effort on the part of large firms; and to the extent that this was true, Adcole could develop a lead in the technology of the field in the immediate future. Furthermore, Dr. Meyer felt that lines of communication could be established more easily between the engineers in companies of Adcole's size and the oceanographers than would be possible in major corporations, and that these lines of communication would be far more effective.

There were, of course, other factors to be considered. Cole stated that a small firm which developed an early lead and/or significantly superior abilities in a small market might gain an unchallenged position. Larger

---

[6] "Space," *Business Week*, August 19, 1961.

firms might be unwilling to spend the time or money required to capture such a market in view of its limited potential.

Cole also felt that a firm of Adcole's size should try to make its investments in areas which would provide a pay-back period of a relatively few months. He felt that the lack of severe financial pressures during Adcole's life had been in part due to the fact that the firm had been careful in this respect. Both these sentiments were reflected in the three-phase plan developed by the firm and quoted above.

At this time the firm was beginning to move into phase 2 of its plan, and more attention would be put on finding proprietary items. Chester G. Kuczun, Vice President and Chief Engineer, was particularly interested in this aspect of any new field of endeavor. One of the questions he asked about oceanographic instrumentation was: "What proprietary products can be developed there?"

Dr. Meyer knew that any decision by Adcole's management team concerning the oceanographic instrumentation area would be made to a very great extent on the basis of his recommendations. He was the one who had become interested in the field, and the others would tend to rely on his familiarity with it to guide their thinking. Although the firm was busy and its staff could easily use its time in other areas, Adcole was in a position to spend time developing an oceanographic instrumentation capability if the potential seemed to justify such a move.

Dr. Meyer felt that Adcole engineers had the ability to develop any electronic systems which might be needed in the field, and that the environmental problems of the ocean would be similar enough to those of space to allow them to solve any special problems relatively easily. However, most of their past work had been in designing the "electronics" of various devices and instrument systems rather than in developing the basic sensors and transducers. He knew that in the oceanographic field, many of the basic sensors needed to build accurate instruments were not available. He wondered if Adcole should get into this less familiar area, or if better sensors would soon be developed by others.

Dr. Meyer could not answer many of the questions which he knew should be considered before any active move was made into the field of the marine sciences. He felt that significant opportunities might exist for Adcole in the field but knew that he should have more information before committing any large amount of the firm's resources, either time or money, to the area.

In October, 1961, Dr. Meyer had collected substantially the same information given in the note on "Oceanographic Instrumentation,"[7] and had in his files most of the sources listed in that note's Bibliography. He thought that a thorough analysis of these data in the context of Adcole's

---

[7] Preceding this case.

abilities would indicate whether or not further interest in oceanography was justified. If a potential market for Adcole did not exist, he did not wish to waste further effort on the field. If it did, he wanted to determine what, if any, additional information he should have and to develop a realistic plan for getting it. He also hoped to gain a general idea of the particular areas within the marine sciences which seemed to offer the greatest potential opportunities for Adcole.

SHALE OIL HALT[1]

UNION OIL is closing down pilot plant because it says crude oil glut bars full-scale operation.

Union Oil Co. of California, the chief enthusiast for extracting oil from shale, will close down its $9-million Grand Valley (Colo.) pilot plant at the end of the month.

Main reason for the shutdown, according to Union Pres. A. C. Rubel, is today's oversupply of crude oil, which has depressed prices. The company feels it now has gained all the operating knowhow it needs from the pilot project. But in light of market conditions, it apparently isn't ready to gamble $300-million on a full-scale 50,000 bbl.-a-day shale oil plant.

Union Oil is confident shale oil some day will become a paying proposition. It says it was making good progress in knocking costs down to a competitive level with crude oil. According to the company, partly refined shale oil is superior in product value to many of this country's crudes. After the pilot plant shuts down, the company plans to keep its technical staff together to prepare more exact data on mining and retorting costs.

Technical Gains. On the technical side, Union Oil reports these achievements from the 14-month pilot plant operation:

Upping production during the retorting stage from 350 tons of shale to 1,000 tons a day. This yields 750 bbl. of shale oil daily.

Cutting mining costs through mechanization to 50¢ a ton ($1 a bbl.).

Simplifying the retort design—and getting the equipment to run automatically—thereby cutting operating costs by two-thirds and lowering the probable capital outlay for a full-scale operation from $8,000 to between $3,000 and $6,000 per bbl. (compared with $9,000 for well-produced crude).

Rival Is Optimistic. Although Union Oil's decision to shut down its pilot project is a definite blow to shale oil's fortunes, a rival company still is optimistic that a shale oil industry is feasible now. Oil Shale Corp. of Carson City, Nev., this week released the results of a two-year pilot plant study conducted for it by the University of Denver's Research Institute. The company says the study indicates that shale oil can be produced in Colorado and delivered to the West Coast for $1.42 to $1.92 a bbl. (Posted price for crude oil in California runs about $3 to $3.25, but because of the oil glut actual prices have been lower.)

---

[1] Reprinted from the July 12, 1958, issue of *Business Week* by special permission. Copyright, 1958, by McGraw-Hill Publishing Co., Inc.

SECTION IV

On the Use of Advanced Technology

Are Our Factories Really Automated?

The average manufacturing system of 1956 (exception—some process industries) can be regarded as no more than a crude assemblage of unintegrated bits of mechanism. These mechanisms themselves may reflect the utmost in the mechanical art of our times. Still, when collected under one roof and directed toward a particular production end, they are anything but a machine-like whole. For each element of machinery introduced is an independent mechanism, usually having little integration with the system outside its immediate environment. The production line has evolved essentially as a random and uncoordinated accretion of constraints brought about through individual machines and brief mechanized sequences.

A hundred years from now the average factory of our day may be regarded as having been no different in philosophical concept from the factory of 1850. In that earlier time men were equipped with hand tools and a comparatively low proportion of power mechanisms to accomplish the production process. Today the proportions have reversed—there are few hand tool operations and many powered machines. This difference between these 1950 and 1850 factories, however, is largely one of the stage of individual mechanical art, not of design philosophy. (Although the 1950 factory does reveal strong consciousness of the need to establish optimum arrangements of machinery in terms of time and distance.) Only in a relatively few plants has the emphasis been on designing the production line as a machine-like entity. Usually, "design" has meant *the collection of equipment* for a production sequence—not *the synthesis of a master machine.*

JAMES R. BRIGHT

FROM: *Automation and Management* (Boston: Division of Research, Graduate School of Business Administration, Harvard University, 1958).

COLONIAL CABINETS FURNITURE COMPANY (A)

IT WAS APRIL, 1958, when Peter Shelby, 36, General Manager and son of the founder and owner of Colonial Cabinets Furniture Company, picked up a large folder entitled "Plan for Conveyorization of Finishing System." He spent the next half hour studying the proposal and then asked his secretary to call in Ed Woods, Chief Engineer, and Steve Mills, Production Manager. When they arrived, he greeted them with:

I'm glad you were able to complete this finishing room modernization plan so quickly. It looks good to me. However, I have a couple of questions about this conveyor installation before I approve the whole project. Automating the finishing line seems like a promising idea. During my past three years of selling in Michigan, I heard so much about automating the automobile industry that I'm convinced we ought to move that way, too. However, the automobile people told me of some pretty expensive mistakes in automation programs. We can't afford to redo our plant like they can. Since I was selling in the Midwest when the project was started, I'd like you to run over the background so I'll understand all the thinking behind your proposal.

Ed Woods, 38, then outlined the history of the project. He pointed out that Colonial Cabinets had been a very conservative southern manufacturer for many years, and that quality, irrespective of time, had been the philosophy:

However, you know that the last few years weren't like the early fifties for us. We used to have a six- to fifteen-month backlog; now the sales orders are much more erratic; the backlog has dropped to a few months, if that much. On the other hand, we have doubled production since 1949, and it seems to be climbing. Next year could be good, according to sales estimates given to us.

Your father called all of us together last December, just before he retired. I guess you heard the gist of it. He made three points: (1) that our success lay in a high-quality line, and we should not forget it; (2) that we were growing out of this collection of old buildings, and we'd have to reorganize and modernize sooner or later; (3) that he was afraid that gradually rising labor costs here, and some smart competition, meant we'd have to do some real cost cutting. He said he was too old [Mr. Shelby, Sr., retired at 82] to handle this kind of thing, so he was calling you back to take over. He wanted us to get started on new plans right away.

Woods went on the review a two-year expansion program involving an expenditure of $400,000, a large amount for this company. It included new woodworking machines, air-actuated presses, powered hand tools, and certain major facilities.

1. *Rearrangement of Rail Storage Tracks.* This was done so that incoming cars of green lumber could be unloaded directly onto the kiln trucks to be rolled into the drying kilns. Three handlings of green lumber were cut to one

542

at a savings of $4.00 per thousand board feet. Consumption was currently 60,000 board feet per week. The cost of the change was $35,000.

2. *Conveyors in Machine Department.* A large amount of rough lumber was used as core wood for veneered pieces. The Machine Department had crosscut saws, planers, jointers, ripsaws, and glue wheels on which successive operations were performed to cut the lumber to width and length, to dress it and glue to size. Hand trucks, lift trucks, and pallets had been used to move the bundles and stacks of material from one machine to the next.

The new system was essentially conveyorized movement of rough lumber through crosscut and planing operations, with some automatic work-feeding and removal, and conveyorized movement to and from the rest of the machines. The old system required 27 men to turn out 42,000 board feet per week. Now, 22 men would turn out 60,000 board feet per week. The conveyor system was largely made by Woods's maintenance shop people, and the cost was less than $4,000.

3. *Frame Plant.* Instead of buying frames for upholstered furniture, Colonial would spend $30,000 for machinery to build its own. This would be installed in an existing unused building at a cost of $20,000. Savings were estimated at $9.00 to $10 per frame plus $1.00 inbound freight per frame. (Upholstery was done in another plant five miles away.)

4. *Conveyorized Finishing System.* This was the largest single item— $150,000—and it applied to the most costly and important part of Colonial's business—the finishing of major cabinet pieces such as dressers, tables, and beds. The system was based on an overhead chain conveyor suspended from trolleys riding on a monorail. Every 88 inches long the conveyor chain a pallet or tray was suspended at a height of about 18 inches above the floor. Pallets were large enough to hold a major piece of furniture such as a chest, dresser, table, or bed headboard. A traction wheel suspended from the ceiling would drive the conveyor. Thus the system would automatically move workpieces through the succession of finishing operations (which involved spraying, staining, sanding, wiping, rubbing, and drying) at a steady rate. Spray booths and force-drying ovens were provided to mechanize and speed some of the processing. Force-drying also would reduce dust spots sometimes picked up during air-drying.

Peter Shelby questioned this plan quite closely, and Steve Mills spoke up:

We need this conveyor and the force-drying ovens to increase output in the finishing room. Right now, we can't produce over 250 case units [meaning major cabinet items] per day because we are air-drying cabinets overnight, and we haven't storage space for more than a 250-piece work-in-process load. The Machine Department and the Cabinet Department can turn out at least 50 per cent more if we just give them more manpower. Finishing is our bottle-neck. A piece is now three days going through finishing. We'll cut that in half.

We're also going to make some very good savings on labor, as you can see from comparison of Exhibits 1 and 2, which show the old and new manning tables. I've always felt that there was a lot of waste motion in our old layout, and it's clear that the conveyor will do this "moving" business for us; and I suspect that the pacing we get from it will improve things.

Woods broke in: "Did you notice that the table [Exhibit 2] shows the work force needed for full-speed operation? Let's see, that would mean how many pallets a day coming out of the Dulux oven? Hmm, yes. If we're running 60 inches per minute for eight hours and there's a pallet

Exhibit 1

MANNING TABLE OF EXISTING FINISHING PROCEDURE

Operation	Men	Description
1. Elevator..............	1	Furniture was brought up from the cabinet room by elevator. It was then unloaded and moved 25 feet to the first operation.
2. Stain edges...........	1	An operator applied stain with a brush to the edges of the drawers and doors, and then shoved the pieces 50 feet along the floor to the first spray booth.
3. Apply stain...........	2	At the first spray booth, stain was applied by an operator and his helper. The helper brought the furniture into the booth with a lift truck. The two men lifted it onto a turntable, and the operator applied the stain with a spray gun. The two men then lifted the piece off the turntable, and the helper moved it 50 feet with the hand truck to a drying area.
4. Dry stain...........	..	Approximately thirty minutes was allowed for drying the stain.
5. Sand stain............	4	Four men secured the pieces from the drying area, moved them 25 feet to their work area, sanded them, and shoved them 20 feet along the floor to the filler area.
6. Apply filler...........	2	Two men, working with brushes, applied filler to the pieces. One of them then shoved the pieces 15 feet along the floor to the wiping area.
7. Pad and wipe........	5	The excess filler was wiped off by five men. One or more of these men then moved the pieces 15 feet to another wiping area.
8. Wipe and pick........	5	Five men continued the wiping, using brushes and picks to clean out the corners and beaded moldings. They then shoved the pieces 25 feet to a drying area.
9. Dry filler...........	..	The furniture was allowed to stand overnight for drying of the filler.
10. Apply sealer..........	2	A helper from the sealer spray booth brought the furniture from the drying area to the booth (50 feet) and helped the operator lift it onto the turntable. The operator applied the sealer with a spray gun. The two men lifted the piece off the turntable, and the helper moved it about 50 feet with his hand truck to a drying area.
11. Dry sealer..........	..	About thirty minutes was allowed for drying the sealer coat.
12. Sand sealer...........	5	Five sanders secured the furniture from the drying area and moved it about 25 feet to their work space. After the sanding was completed, they pushed the pieces 50 feet along the floor to the glazing area.
13. Apply and wipe glaze..............	6	The glaze was applied by a group of six men working in pairs. Two men placed a piece on a low work bench. One man applied the glaze with a brush; the second man followed immediately behind him and wiped off the excess glaze until the exact color blend desired was obtained. The two men then took the piece off the bench and shoved it along the floor 50 feet to a drying area.
14. Dry glaze...........	..	The glaze was allowed to dry overnight.

Exhibit 1 (Concluded)

Operation	Men	Description
15. Apply shade..........	2	A helper from the shading booth picked up the furniture at the drying area and hauled it 50 feet with a hand truck to the booth. Operator and helper placed the piece on a turntable. The operator then used a spray gun to even out any dark and light places resulting from the glazing operation. The two men lifted the piece off the turntable, and the helper moved it about 25 feet with his hand truck to a drying area.
16. Dry shade........... ..		About thirty minutes was allowed for drying the shade coat.
17. Apply Dulux*........	2	A helper from the Dulux booth picked up the furniture at the drying area and hauled it 50 feet with a hand truck to the booth. Operator and helper placed the piece on a turntable. The operator then applied the Dulux finish coat with a spray gun. The two men lifted the piece off the turntable, and the helper moved it about 75 feet with his hand truck to the Dulux drying room.
18. Dry Dulux.............		The Dulux was dried for a minimum of six hours at a temperature of 125 degrees Fahrenheit.
	41	Total labor force required to finish 250 major pieces per day.

* Dulux was a special synthetic finishing material developed by the Du Pont Company working in co-operation with Colonial Cabinets. The Company began using it in 1940. The construction of the drying room to maintain the temperature at 125 degrees Fahrenheit cost $2,500. Use of the Dulux, however, made it possible to reduce the quantity of finishing compound used and resulted in savings of several thousand dollars a year.

every 88 inches, we'll get about 327 cases per day against our present 250. We've sure broken that bottleneck!"

Shelby pointed out that present sales were, except for occasional peaks, averaging 250 case units per day, and the goal was ultimately to lift sales to 375 case units per day. This meant that the conveyor could not meet the intended goal by about 50 units. Woods said:

That's true; and although we could put more men on the line, we can't speed up the conveyor because five feet per minute is the limiting speed, fixed by the time that pieces must be in the drying ovens. Also, we can't put pallets much closer together on the chain because of the size of the pallets needed for our larger cabinets, as well as necessary working room. To meet production peaks of 375 units per day, we'll have to work one to two hours overtime, but that's much cheaper than building a new plant or expanding the length of the ovens and maybe the spray booths.

Steve Mills eagerly mentioned:

There's another kind of output gain that doesn't show up at first glance. For thirty years, I've been yelling, begging, and praying for more careful handling in the Finishing Department. You can see on our old layout [Exhibit 3] that we have over fifteen handlings and moves during finishing. We put bumps and scratches into the furniture during these moves, and then spend time and money taking them out. I estimate we'll cut out 90 to 95 per cent of this handling damage. The conveyor is going to take work through all these jobs with just two handlings—onto the conveyor at the start, and off after the

Exhibit 2

PRODUCTION ENGINEERING DATA FOR CONVEYORIZED FINISHING LINE

Schedule of Operations, Manning Table, and Approximate Allotted Times, Operating at Full Speed

Operation	Men Needed	Equipment Required	Total Time
1. Spray stain............... 1		Spray booth	2.8 minutes
2. Stain air-drying...........			6.4
3. Stain oven...............		Oven at 115 to 125 degrees Fahrenheit	12.0
4. Stain cooling.............			24.0
5. Stain sanding............. 2			22.0
6. Spray filler............... 2		Spray booth	2.8
7. Filler pad, wipe, pick, and inspect................ 6			58.0
8. Filler oven...............		Oven at 140 to 150 degrees Fahrenheit; humidity 25 to 35 per cent	98.4
9. Filler cooling.............			46.0
10. Spray sealer.............. 1		Spray booth	2.8
11. Sealer air-drying..........			6.0
12. Sealer oven..............		Oven at 115 to 125 degrees Fahrenheit	25.0
13. Sealer cooling............			11.2
14. Sealer sanding............ 2			24.0
15. Spray glaze.............. 1		Spray booth	2.8
16. Glaze wiping............. 3			30.0
17. Glaze oven..............		Oven at 140 to 150 degrees Fahrenheit; humidity 25 to 35 per cent	97.4
18. Glaze cooling............			50.0
19. Spray shade.............. 1		Spray booth	2.8
20. Shade air-drying..........			10.0
21. Spray Dulux............. 1		Spray booth	2.8
22. Dulux air-drying..........			15.0
23. Dulux oven..............		Oven at 125 degrees Fahrenheit	6.0 hours
Total labor force........20			

MISCELLANEOUS DATA

1. The space available for the new finishing conveyor was to include the existing Finishing Department plus the adjacent warehouse room (compare Exhibits 3 and 4).

2. Maximum speed at which the conveyor could be run was five feet per minute. Pallets were hung from the conveyor on 88-inch centers.

3. "Total time" shown for cooling and drying operations represents the minimum time required to achieve a satisfactory finish. All other times represent the number of minutes the engineers believed each piece would be available in the work area assigned to that operation when running at maximum conveyor speed. Thus, these times do not necessarily represent the man-minutes of work to be done on each piece.

4. The hanging pallets were to project about 24 inches from the center line of the monorail conveyor on the loaded side and about 12 inches from the center line on the back side.

5. The minimum turning diameter in which the monorail conveyor could reverse its direction was estimated to be about 48 inches.

6. Bedrails were to be finished separately and not run on the conveyor. Mirror frames were to be hung on hooks between the pallets. The edge staining was to be done in the cabinet room before the pieces were placed on the conveyor.

Dulux air dry. We've always had some finish trouble because of poor air circulation when units were set aside to dry. We'll eliminate that by oven drying.

I've talked to the Ford engineers who designed their automated engine plant in Cleveland. Good results have led them to install similar overhead monorail chain conveyor systems for moving engine blocks through the assembly operation. They tell me that they absolutely can count on improved quality because the engines are not banged together or dropped. If they get a 5 per cent scrap reduction with heavy engine castings, think what we can expect in furniture! I look for a saving of 90 per cent on in-process damage. We should get by with one touch-up man instead of three. Oh, yes, I almost forgot to mention that they cut their lost-time accident rate in half. Of course, we don't have the problem of weight that they do, but I look for a little better safety record, a distinct improvement in quality, and a reduction in repair costs.

Mills went on to say that he and Woods had visited over 20 plants, about 15 of which were furniture plants; the others were noted for application of continuous conveying to manufacturing or assembly work. "Ed and I are absolutely convinced that we must get into more automation, or costwise we'll be left behind. Of course, we'll keep the old spray booths for finishing bedrails, which are too long for the conveyor, for specials, for repair, and for emergencies."

Peter Shelby then looked over the new layout (Exhibit 4) and asked questions about the space allotted to various operations, the cost of individual pieces of equipment, and the manning and working procedures. He then wanted to know the pay-back on the finishing room conveyor.

"You'll have to tell us," said Ed Woods, "what sales output you want to use—the present 250 per day or the maximum of 327 per eight-hour day, or your sales goal of 350 per day with overtime."

The three men decided to prepare some economic justification figures on the first two conditions. They considered that manufacturing cost averaged about 75 per cent of the sales income and consisted of 50 per cent materials, 25 per cent labor, and 25 per cent burden cost. Gross sales income at the 250 rate averaged $32,000 per week, and a 7 per cent sales commission was paid out of this.

Man-hours required to increase case goods output in departments other than the finishing room would be, they thought, roughly proportional to the amount of increase. Average pay rate in the plant had climbed from 30 cents per hour in 1940 to 75 cents per hour in 1947, to $1.05 per hour in 1958. However, finishing was the most highly skilled job in the plant, and men in this department averaged $1.40 per hour.

After completing their calculations, the executives discussed questions of operation and performance. Shelby concluded: "I'm all for your plan and am convinced we must automate to keep labor cost down, and to get more out of the same old plant. My only concern is that we haven't gone far enough. I assume you two are satisfied that you can make the system work. How soon can we have this installed?"

Exhibit 3

PATH FOLLOWED IN EXISTING FINISHING PROCEDURE

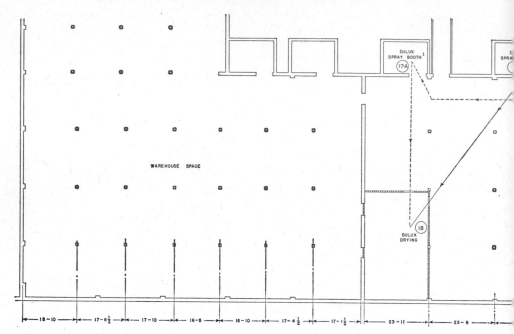

* The two Dulux spray booths were used interchangeably. In some cases, two finish coats were applied.

Woods assured him that if he would approve the project at once, the conveyorized operation would be in full swing by October or November at the latest.

Over half the work force at Colonial had more than 20 years of service with the company, and a dozen had worked over 50 years for the firm. There was no union, and labor relations were excellent, although turnover was definitely higher than it had been before the war.

The working day was eight hours, with an additional half-hour lunch break. The firm shut down for a two-week vacation (paid) and style change in July.

Exhibit 3 (Continued)

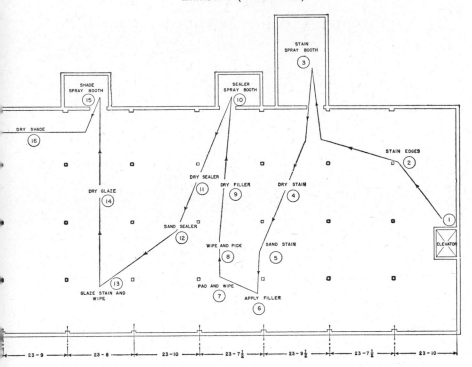

Exhibit 4

LAYOUT FOR FINISHING ROOM CONVEYOR

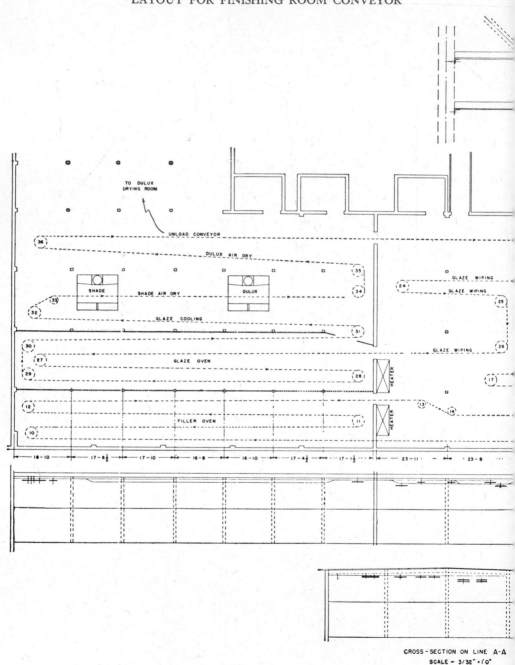

CROSS-SECTION ON LINE A-A
SCALE = 3/32" = 1'0"

Exhibit 4 (Continued)

TI
28

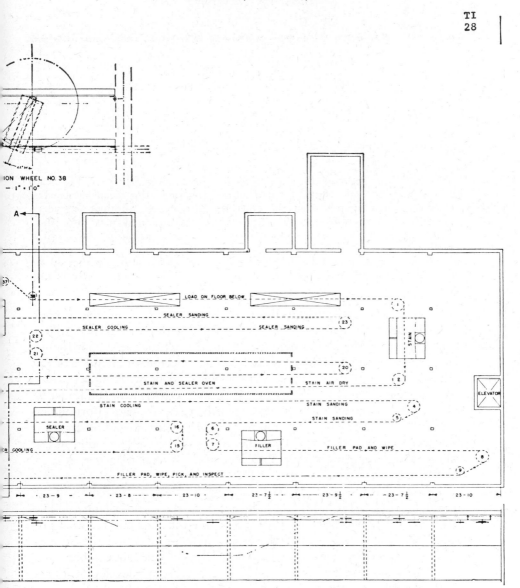

NOTE: The original drawing has been reduced in size. Therefore, the actual scale of this cut must be obtained by using dimensions along the length of the building. From this, the student can determine the distances traveled in various departments.

AMPEX CORPORATION

TIME: 2:15 P.M.
DATE: Thursday, January 23, 1958
PLACE: Office of the Manufacturing Division, Ampex Corporation

Andy, I just received the 2:00 o'clock status report on the VTR head assemblies. Every one of the "control heads" inspected this week has been a reject. It's clear by now that the changes made by the product engineers haven't solved anything—in fact, they may have created new problems. Furthermore, with all these experiments going on, production has slowed to a crawl. I think we should develop a new plan of action for you to present to the meeting at 4:30 today in the front office. Get together with Ray to try to work something out, and then we can talk it over at 3:30 here in my office.

With these words, Larry Burn, Assistant Manager of the Ampex Corporation's Manufacturing Division, asked Charles V. (Andy) Andersen, Manager of Manufacturing Operations, to look for a new approach to solving a problem which had rapidly become the center of attention of the company's operating executives. Andersen would be working with Ray Heidenreich, General Foreman of the Assembly Department and leader of a special task force which had been organized to co-ordinate efforts aimed at correcting the situation. At 4:30 that day, Heidenreich and others from his special committee would be gathering for their daily meeting in the office of the company's Vice President and General Manager, Robert Sackman.

The problem was this: A severe drop in the yield of good units in the manufacture of VTR heads had suddenly occurred early in January. The VTR was the video tape recorder, a machine for magnetic recording of television images and one of the major new products of the Ampex Corporation. The "head" was a small but critical subassembly in a complete system selling for $45,000. After years of development and design work, and enthusiastic acceptance of the product by the broadcast industry, the manufacture of a production model began in November, 1957. Production was planned to fill a backlog of orders for one hundred systems by the end of April, 1958. Seven systems had been completed in November and six more in December. By mid-January the output rate was expected to reach one per working day. The output of heads, however, virtually ceased early in January. Only three systems could be shipped during the first three weeks of that month. On January 23, seven

552

packaged and crated systems sat on the shipping dock awaiting the addition of heads so that they could be shipped. At the same time, eight more systems were undergoing final inspection and would shortly be ready for shipment if heads were available.

COMPANY BACKGROUND

The Ampex Corporation manufactured and sold professional-quality magnetic tape-recording and reproduction equipment for sound- and data-recording purposes in the broadcast and phonograph record industries, laboratory instrumentation, many military applications, and industrial control.

Ampex recording equipment, since its introduction in 1948, had represented the accepted standard of quality in the broadcast industry. Instrumentation products, introduced in 1950, tapped a substantial market and by 1957 accounted for two thirds of sales volume. The company was the outstanding manufacturer in its field, holding 85 per cent or more of the business in most markets in which it competed. The lowest priced product sold to the user for $495, and instrumentation products sold for unit prices averaging $15,000. Most units were sold on a "systems" basis, as a custom-designed combination of standard modular sections.

The Ampex Corporation had been founded in 1944 by Alexander Poniatoff. Since the firm's only product was for military use, the end of World War II forced a search for a new market. At that time, Poniatoff had decided to design and build a high-quality professional type of magnetic recorder that would offer rugged and reliable service in daily use. The success of the first model created a need for additional funds, which were furnished in 1948 by a private investment group. In 1950, George Long, a partner in the group, left his position with a San Francisco bank to become Treasurer of the Ampex Corporation. He subsequently became Executive Vice President, and then, in 1956, President and chief executive officer. Poniatoff at that time was elected Chairman of the Board of Directors.

Growth of sales volume resulting from the development of new products had been important throughout the ten-year history of the firm. Sales volume grew from $400,000 in fiscal 1950 to $30 million for fiscal 1958. Personnel and facilities expanded apace. The original facilities, only 9,000 square feet, were abandoned in 1951 for a 25,000-square-foot plant. In 1958, operations occupied fourteen buildings and a total of 267,000 square feet of space in Redwood City, California. Balance sheets and income statements are given in Exhibits 1 and 2.

The company's engineers worked on the frontiers of knowledge in their field, utilizing new technology to develop new and improved products. Nearly $1.4 million had been spent in 1957 on research and experimental expenses. As a result of these research efforts, Ampex had

Exhibit 1

COMPARATIVE CONSOLIDATED BALANCE SHEETS, YEARS ENDED APRIL
30, 1953–57

(Dollars in Thousands)

	1953	1954	1955	1956	1957	Pro Forma 1957*
ASSETS						
Cash	$ 103	$ 403	$ 402	$ 704	$ 1,011	$ 3,993
Accounts receivable	745	617	1,583	2,034	5,561	5,561
Inventories	1,065	2,355	2,032	2,742	7,603	7,603
Prepaid expenses	36	49	65	107	202	202
Total Current Assets	$1,949	$3,424	$4,082	$5,587	$14,377	$17,359
Investment in ORRadio Industries, Inc.	....	....	....	....	.....	820
Equipment and leasehold improvements	295	498	837	1,033	1,200	1,200
Depreciation	104	168	265	398	560	560
Net equipment and leasehold improvements	$ 191	$ 330	$ 572	$ 635	$ 640	$ 640
Unamortized debenture expense	16	15	95	80	.....	135
Total Assets	$2,156	$3,769	$4,749	$6,302	$15,017	$18,954
LIABILITIES						
Notes payable	$ 460	$ 735	$	$ 850	$ 2,000	$ .....
Accounts payable	312	611	512	712	2,055	2,055
Customers' deposits	....	....	....	125	314	314
Accrued liabilities	156	288	365	510	1,051	1,051
Accrued profit-sharing contribution	....	....	....	....	390	390
Federal and Canadian income taxes	218	57	391	312	1,147	1,147
Total Current Liabilities	$1,146	$1,691	$1,268	$2,509	$ 6,957	$ 4,957
15-year 4½% debentures due November 1, 1969	....	....	1,500	1,400	.....	.....
10-year 6% debentures due October 1, 1962	645	635	....	....	.....	.....
15-year 5% debentures due July 1, 1972	....	....	....	....	.....	5,500
Capital stock—par value	120	207	264	267	361	367
Capital in excess of par value	58	1,023	1,138	1,235	5,721	6,152
Retained earnings	187	213	579	891	1,978	1,978
Total stockholders' equity	$ 365	$1,443	$1,981	$2,393	$ 8,060	$ 8,497
Total	$2,156	$3,769	$4,749	$6,302	$15,017	$18,954

* The above pro forma balance sheet gives effect to significant financial transactions in the three months subsequent to April 30, 1957, namely, private sale of $5.5 million of 5 per cent 15-year debentures, payment in full of a
$2 million bank loan, and acquisition of 28.6 per cent of the outstanding shares of common capital stock of ORRadio
Industries, Inc. This will be reduced to approximately 25 per cent after exercise of outstanding options held by
others.

Exhibit 2

CONSOLIDATED INCOME STATEMENT, FISCAL YEARS ENDED APRIL 30,
1953–57

(Dollars in Thousands)

	1953	1954	1955	1956	1957
Net sales	$3,548	$5,418	$8,163	$10,197	$18,737
Cost of sales	2,630	3,980	5,446	6,508	11,648
Gross profit	$ 918	$1,438	$2,717	$ 3,689	$ 7,089
Expenses:					
Selling and administrative	$ 447	$ 946	$1,355	$ 2,045	$ 3,061
Research and experimental	119	369	502	927	1,381
Interest—debenture and other	50	53	97	109	45
Total Expenses	$ 616	$1,368	$1,954	$ 3,081	$ 4,487
Income before profit-sharing contribu- tion and before income taxes	$ 302	$ 70	$ 763	$ 608	$ 2,602
Profit-sharing contribution	....	....	....	.....	390
Income before taxes	$ 302	$ 70	$ 763	$ 608	$ 2,212
Income taxes	213	44	397	296	1,125
Net Income	$ 89	$ 26	$ 366	312	$ 1,087

developed an advanced line of instrumentation products, a revolutionary machine for recording video images, and an advanced unit for recording digital information to be used in electronic data processing.

ORGANIZATION

Operations were centered at Redwood City, except that in a nearby community a wholly owned subsidiary, Ampex Audio, Inc., manufactured certain models for the consumer market. Robert Sackman, as Vice President and General Manager, held operational responsibility for all activities in Redwood City. The organization, in early 1958, included six autonomous divisions: two product divisions, the Manufacturing and the Quality Control divisions, a Finance Division, and a Research Division.

Each product division was responsible for planning, developing, engineering, and selling its line of products. The Professional Products Division managed the line of audio and video recording equipment used in the broadcast and recording industries. The Instrumentation Division sold a variety of standard and specially engineered systems for varied industrial, laboratory, and military applications. Both divisions performed marketing functions, that is, advertising and selling their lines of products, plus engineering functions in the development of new products and the modification of existing models to meet new or special needs. In the normal procedure for development of a new product, the product division held full responsibility for all work from initial conception through completion of approved design blueprints. At this point the Manufacturing Division assumed responsibility for development of methods and processes, and production of the first units.

In a forecast prepared at the beginning of October, 1957, management projected a sales volume of approximately $30 million for the fiscal year ended April 30, 1958. Approximately 55 per cent of this volume would come from the Instrumentation Division, with the remainder equally split between the Professional Products Division and the Ampex Audio subsidiary. Subsequently, however, a sharp reduction in procurement by the Department of Defense had a substantial effect on the volume of incoming orders at Ampex. The backlog of unfilled orders fell from $11.4 million at April 30, 1957, to approximately $7 million at December 31, with the result that 150 production workers were laid off just before the end of the year. A summary report prepared by Sackman in December offered the following comments:

The initial order upswing in the Instrumentation Division did not continue in November. To meet our year-end shipping goals, we're depending upon a substantial expected government order in January plus some upswing in one-at-a-time orders for standard instrumentation products. A very significant downward change in orders received for the Professional Products Division occurred both in professional audio equipment and in orders from Ampex

Audio subsidiary. This significant change in our expected product mix has brought a number of risks. Principally, they are that we will be dependent upon shipment of one hundred video tape recorders for achievement of goals for the fiscal year and dependent upon certain instrumentation orders for the remainder during this period.

Finance Division

The Finance Division was responsible for purchasing, central personnel management, and certain other service functions, as well as the traditional financial and accounting services. Thomas Taggart, Treasurer, had left the position of Manager of the Finance Division temporarily in early 1958 to accept another assignment in the company.

For the fiscal year ended April 30, 1958, the Division had forecast a profit margin of 5 per cent on the expected $30-million sales volume. To finance the usual seasonal accumulation of inventory in the latter part of the calendar year, the company borrowed $1.5 million in September, 1957. Cash in banks was forecast as follows: a low point reached at the end of November, with balances rising thereafter to $500,000 at the end of January. It was expected that $500,000 could be repaid on the loan in February and the remainder repaid during March without reducing cash in banks below $500,000. The company's trust indenture on the recently issued debentures required that long-term debt be held below 75 per cent of total stockholder equity and that current assets be maintained at a minimum of one and a half times current liabilities.

Manufacturing Division

The Manufacturing Division, employing 1,100 people, was responsible for methods, fabrication, and assembly in the manufacture of the company's products. The Division's organization in 1958 was as follows: There were four department managers reporting to the manager and to Larry Burn, the Assistant Manager. Thomas Taggart, Treasurer, became Acting Manager of the Manufacturing Division on January 1, 1958. Lennert, the Manager, was on an eight-month leave of absence while attending an advanced management training program at Stanford University. The Manufacturing Division used 145,000 square feet of space in the largest of the buildings occupied by the Corporation.

All Ampex tape-recording equipment consisted basically of three things: a mechanical tape transport, electronic circuitry, and a recording head. Company policy was to produce these three types of components as standard modular units and store them in a finished-goods inventory. The recording systems then were assembled to order and checked out just prior to shipment. In assembly, the modular units were withdrawn from storage and mounted in a cabinet with appropriate electrical and mechanical connections. The Manufacturing Operations Department was responsible for fabrication of parts, assembly of modular units, storage, and

Exhibit 3

ILLUSTRATIONS OF STANDARD MODULAR UNITS

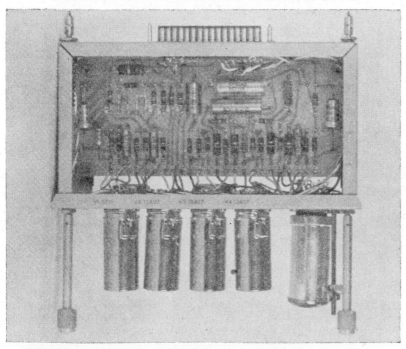

Bottom View, Plug-in Electronic Module

Operator Aligning Standard Audio Recording Heads

Exhibit 4

ASSEMBLED INSTRUMENTATION RECORDING SYSTEM

final assembling of recording systems. Illustrations of modular units and assembled systems appear in Exhibits 3 and 4.

In the manufacture of modular units the Ampex company distinguished between standard products and special products. A standard product was defined as "one that is fully tooled and processed to be produced by relatively unskilled workers on a repetitive basis." This meant that permanent tooling existed in quantities sufficient to produce the unit on a standard production basis and that design prints, operation sheets, and other instructions showed the full details of methods, materials, times, costs, etc., for the product. In contrast, a special product would be produced by relatively skilled workers whose ability offset lack of detailed instruction in manufacture of the item.

The plant was organized in accordance with the basic processing steps: parts fabrication, assembly of electronic components, mechanical assembly, final assembly, check-out, and shipping. In addition, a special department was devoted to head manufacturing, and another to painting and finishing exposed sheet metal parts such as those in the recorder's case.

Production Planning. The Production Planning Department employed 140 persons in the control of manufacturing operations. The product line in 1958 included 230 standard modules—subassemblies—utilizing thousands of component parts. For each module, each month the product division responsible furnished a forecast of expected sales monthly for three months and quarterly for the next six months.

Production runs for standard modules usually included 50 to 100 units, although lots as small as five units for a special filter or as large as 500 units for a common power supply were scheduled. For a standard module the Department commonly allowed three months from the date of the sales authorization for fabrication of the metal parts. Thus, both purchased and fabricated parts would be expected to be on hand in the Mechanical and Electronic Assembly departments at the beginning of the fourth month after release. On this basis the finished modules would go into finished stores prior to the end of the fourth month. In the Parts Fabricating Department, lot sizes were generally larger than those for assembly departments because of multiple use of a given part in one module and the use of the same part in several modules. Although a parts inventory was not planned for any but parts destined to be used in scheduled assembly operations, some accumulation resulted from overruns due either to underestimation of yield or to scheduling of an economic lot size.

For special products, according to the production-planning executives, time rather than cost was the important criterion. The special product usually was an adaptation of one of the company's standard modular items. Rather than planning production as in the case of standard products, the company would, in effect, give a rough sketch to the toolmaker and say: "You make the parts." In the same way, assembly was done by relatively skilled men working from rough instructions.

Engineering Department. The Manufacturing Engineering Department was responsible for processes and methods, tools, plant layout, and product packaging. The Department included some 30 engineers and five tool designers, plus 28 men staffing the tool and die shop on a two-shift basis. The Department's functions in the cycle of new-product development began after the final design of the product had been approved by the product division concerned. However, prior to that point, one of the manufacturing engineers would work as a liaison man with the product division's design development group. Then, when design blueprints had been prepared, formal responsibility would shift from the product division to the Manufacturing Engineering Department. Manufacturing engineers then prepared bills of material, standard operation sheets, and an assembly manual, designed and constructed necessary tools, and prepared appropriate time and cost estimates. Finally, when the product had been fully tooled and processed, responsibility would shift to the Manufacturing Operations Department.

The manufacturing engineering manager felt that his Department had to work within a relatively short time period to put a new product into production. Usually, the company expected to be ready to ship units four to five months after final design prints had been prepared. To expedite this, the Department's liaison man with the product division group would usually become the lead man (or perhaps be the only man) in processing the project when it shifted to Manufacturing Engineering. According to the engineering manager, one of the liaison man's important functions while working with the design group was to estimate costs and to give advice that would orient design toward economical specifications.

The Department tried to develop tools and methods that would offer maximum flexibility in manufacturing operations. For example, assembly of standard products was usually designed to be carried out on a line basis but with a relatively long cycle time—15 to 30 minutes. In recent work, the Department had been tending toward a 30-minute cycle because experiments had indicated that there was not a significant learning improvement in the shorter cycle. For reasons of flexibility in scheduling and manufacture, it was better to have fewer operators on a line and thus a longer cycle time.

Manufacturing Operations Department. Charles Andersen was Director of Manufacturing Operations and thus directly responsible for all production activities in the Redwood City plant. Andersen had joined the company in 1950 as an hourly worker and had been promoted through several supervisory positions. In January, 1958, the plant was operating a partial second shift in most production departments. The area and personnel of each department are listed in Exhibit 5. The company paid an average hourly wage of $2.00 for assembly workers and more than $3.00 in the machine shop. Two thirds of the prime cost of production, however, was in purchased material.

Andersen described the Ampex plant as "just a gigantic job shop." "We produce hundreds of products and thousands of parts," he said, "but they are all in very short runs averaging, perhaps, seventy-five units." To do this, he felt that the entire organization had to remain very flexible. At the same time, he emphasized that quality was of prime importance in producing Ampex equipment. "That's our only excuse for being in business."

Line supervision was carried out by nineteen foremen and assistant

Exhibit 5

MANUFACTURING DIVISION—AREA AND PERSONNEL

Department	Area Occupied (Square Feet)	Number on Payroll, January, 1958 First Shift	Second Shift
Administrative	2,500	17	..
Production control	2,500	64	3
Material control and receiving	5,000	63	5
Traffic and shipping	4,000	32	1
Engineering	6,000	59	..
Tool and die	6,600	28	16
Machine shop	13,000	47	38
Sheet Metal shop	8,400	28	10
Paint and finish	9,000	49	0
Head assembly	8,400	55	5
Mechanical assembly	6,500	56	..
Electronic assembly	14,000	309	74
System assembly	5,400	19	..
Short run:			
Electronic assembly	1,600	50	..
Mechanical assembly	2,200	19	..
Machine shop	2,400	13	12
Stores and warehouse	43,000	..	..

foremen. The three general foremen were responsible for special products manufacture, standard products fabrication, and standard products assembly. Andersen felt that the selection and development of qualified line supervisors was a key element in the company's management. He said, "We can't have a foreman who's just an average guy, because this company must move too fast. The foreman here is the difference between moving ahead and standing still." All of the foremen other than Ray Heidenreich, the assembly General Foreman, had less than two years' experience with the company, and all but one had been promoted from the ranks of hourly employees. Andersen felt that promotion of these men from within was a very important incentive to hourly workers and supervisors in the company.

The changing nature of the production operation placed unusual pressure on both supervisor and worker throughout the plant. In assembly operations, where a typical line would include 20 or 30 girls, the run frequently would be so short that by the time the last girl got the first piece, the first girl on the line was through with the entire lot. In the machine shops the workers had to be flexible enough to be able to operate several machines. Andersen felt that the company could not afford to employ just a "mill hand" or a "drill-press operator," because the man had to be able to change his work as the product mix and machine loading changed.

The company's standard products machine shop included, among other equipment, 22 turret lathes and five other lathes and screw machines, nine mills, 16 drilling machines, and four grinders. The Special Products Machine Department and the tool and die shop contained smaller quantities of similar machinery. The sheet metal shop contained 18 punch presses, five forming presses, seven welding machines, and a degreaser and belt sander. The Plating and Finishing Department had seven paint-spray booths, two baking ovens, a dry-off oven, silk-screening facilities, sanding equipment, automatic washing machines, chemical process dip tanks, and a 600-foot overhead monorail conveyor. This Department had been relocated and expanded from 5,000 to 9,000 square feet in late 1957. Approximately $130,000 was invested in this project, not only to provide additional capacity but also to insure a consistently high quality in output.

DEVELOPMENT OF THE VTR

Although the development of a magnetic recording technique for television images had for several years been a goal of the broadcast industry, the achievement of this goal represented a great technical challenge for manufacturers of conventional tape-recording equipment.[1] The major limitations in the use of tape were in frequency response, since a video signal covered a broad frequency band reaching to several million cycles per second. The most advanced standard model recorders prior to 1956 would not reproduce frequencies greater than 100,000 cycles. Both the Radio Corporation of America and a project supported by Bing Crosby Enterprises had worked to develop a video tape system. Some publicity was given to these projects, both of which were said to be aimed at perfection of a system to permit movement of the tape at speeds sufficient to obtain a frequency of several million cycles with conventional heads.

Ampex Enters the Field

In early 1952 the Ampex Corporation hired Charles Ginsburg, a young engineer who had been working with a local broadcasting station. Poniatoff felt at that time that the technical problem involved in moving a tape at several hundred inches per second would prove an insurmountable barrier to the work being done in other companies. He did believe that video recording was an achievable goal, however, and Ginsburg went to work to develop a system that would move the recording head as well as the tape in order to get the necessary rapid movement of the tape relative to the head. Ampex adapted under license an existing patent for a rotating drum which swept across a wide longitudinally moving tape. Progress

---

[1] See Appendix A to this case.

came slowly, and in the spring of 1953 the project was temporarily shelved. Work was begun again, however, in 1954, and by 1955 a nucleus of six men were working on the project. In March of 1955, they were able to demonstrate the first working model to the Board of Directors.

All those concerned with the video project felt that it was necessary to perfect a system that would give a picture indistinguishable from "live" television itself. A number of major technical problems had to be overcome before this could be achieved, and most of them pertained to the recording head itself. The system under development at Ampex employed four separate heads mounted on a drum about two inches in diameter which rotated perpendicularly to the tape. Thus the heads were swept at high speed across the two-inches width of the tape. Since the tape itself was moving, the result was a series of slanted parallel lines written magnetically across the tape.

Among the problems faced and surmounted by the development group were development of a special system to modulate a signal to represent the broad-band video signal, a control system to maintain a constant speed in head rotation, manufacturing the heads with the required precision, and controlling the stretch in the tape as it curved around the circumference of the drum in passing the head. Although the initial objectives were to obtain a 2.5-million cycle response at a writing speed of 2,500 inches per second, the final model has a 4.5-million cycle response and a writing speed of 1,500 inches per second. The limiting factor had been the head gap, and the achievement was possible only by the use of a gap one tenth of a mil[2] across.

A demonstration for the Board of Directors in March, 1955, showed them that the product could perform to the high standards that were to be demanded of it. The project continued with additional funds and was moved to a separate building for reasons of secrecy. Ampex hoped to have a prototype for demonstration to the trade at the April, 1956, convention of the National Association of Radio and Television Broadcasters. This goal was met, and the first public demonstration was made in conjunction with the Columbia Broadcasting System the day before the 1956 convention at a meeting of CBS affiliate stations. Just three men outside the company had known that Ampex was working on a video recording system, although video development projects in other companies had been given a good deal of publicity. In Ginsburg's words: "When the CBS men saw this machine, they jumped and shouted; nobody at Ampex expected this kind of reception, but Phil Gundy took out his pad and started taking orders." The machine was formally demonstrated the next day to the entire membership of the NARTB.

One prototype unit was used for all of the demonstrations made in the spring of 1956. Sixteen more prototypes were custom-manufactured later

---

[2] A mil is one thousandth of one inch.

in the year by Ampex engineers; of these, eleven were shipped to the television networks, two to the United States government, and three were used within the company. Recordings made on these machines had two important limitations: They could not be edited, and they could be played back only on the machine on which they had been recorded. Meanwhile, work proceeded on design and development of a production model of the VTR planned for introduction at the end of 1957. The production model would be equipped with an editing device, and tapes made on these models would be interchangeable.

Sales

One sales executive estimated that the potential market for VTR systems would probably average two for every United States television station, with foreign sales possible to British and German firms, which would make the necessary adaptations for their local television systems. Thus, he expected a total potential market in television use of 1,000 to 1,500 units. In early 1958 the ten direct-sales people who handled broadcast equipment coast to coast for the Professional Products Division were concentrating their efforts on the VTR. For each unit sold, the company ran a training program for the broadcast station staffs at Redwood City and, in addition, sent two technicians and an engineer to supervise the system's installation. The only competing manufacturer was the Radio

Exhibit 6

THE VIDEO TAPE RECORDER (VTR)

System Front View

Exhibit 6 (Continued)

VTR Head Assembly

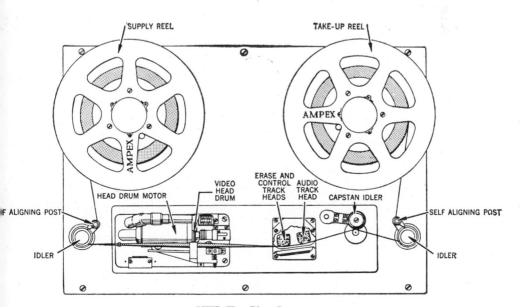

VTR Top Plate Layout

Corporation of America, with which Ampex entered a cross-licensing agreement for certain patents in January, 1958. At that date the production-model Ampex system was being delivered at a price of $45,000, with a color television converter priced at an additional $20,000. Lease-purchase plans were available to stations through an independent finance agency. The Radio Corporation of America video recorder was offered at a $49,500 price, with the color model costing $14,000 extra, according to the Ampex salesmen, who believed that RCA had not completed its first production model.

NATURE OF THE VTR

The video tape recorder was a complex system of electronic and mechanical components weighing more than a ton and occupying a floor console and two equipment racks (see illustrations in Exhibit 6). Eighteen modular electronic units, mounted in the racks, were required for processing the electronic signals in play-back and recording. The console contained the control panel for the system and two key elements: the tape transport mechanism (called the "top plate") and the recording head.

In operation the transport mechanism moves the two-inch-wide magnetic tape past the head at 15 inches per second. The four recording tips are mounted 90 degrees apart on the circumference of a drum two inches in diameter. As the disc rotates at 240 revolutions per second, the tips are swept across the tape perpendicularly to the line of motion of the tape. A vacuum guide chamber helps bow the tape to fit snugly around the circumference of the drum.

The head subassembly, in addition to the rotating drum and four tips, contains a drive motor, a vacuum chamber, a commutator and other switching apparatus, and a photoelectric cell and associated control systems. The entire subassembly is easily demountable as a unit and can be used interchangeably on any system console. The tips themselves had only a limited useful life—about one hundred hours—because of the abrasive effect of contact with the tape. Ampex planned to charge $1,500 for the subassembly, plus $300 for each rebuilding.

VTR Production

The video tape recorder embodied a number of advances in the technology of magnetic recording. With the exception of the head subassembly, however, the component modules presented no unusual problems in manufacture. Three production lots of the modular units had been scheduled to meet the full backlog of orders prior to the April 30, 1958, deadline. The first lot, 25 units of every component but the head, was completed in 1957, and a second lot of 40 units was nearing completion in mid-January, 1958. It was expected that the last of these 40 units would be in finished goods by early February. The last group of 40 was in the parts fabrication stage and due for assembly in March.

The limiting factor to output of systems[3] was the final check-out procedure. Expensive special purpose equipment and skilled operators were required fully to check each system. The procedure took six and one-half days, and only eight production line check stations were equipped as of mid-January. Standard head assemblies were mounted on the systems in check-out, thus making it possible to inspect systems separately from the heads with which they were to be shipped.

The VTR Head

The process for assembly of the video head is illustrated in the assembly drawings in Exhibits 7 and 8. In this process the electric motor was mounted on the subplate along with the other auxiliary components; the rotating drum subassembly was prepared and mounted on the motor; and then the unit was adjusted, the heads polished, and the subassembly inspected. The key element in the head assembly was the drum. Mounted on each drum were four "dimes," specially machined metal discs about the size of a 10-cent coin. On each dime were two grooves which held the tips which made contact with the recording tape in operation.

Assembly of the dime is illustrated in Exhibit 9. The tips were made of alphenol metal, a special magnetic material, and were only 10 mils thick. The two tip halves were aligned on the dime to provide a uniform gap between their facing surfaces. This gap had to be no less than 90 and no more than 120 millionths of an inch across, and its width had to be uniform throughout the 16-mil depth of the gap. The gap itself was one of the critical determinants of the performance of the entire machine. For greatest efficiency, its walls had to be optically smooth and parallel.

The tips were mounted on the dimes with epoxy resin, and then the dime was mounted in the drum on top of a small ferrite coil. This coil served to convert the magnetic flux in the tip material into electrical impulses. The four dimes had to be situated on the drum with an extremely high degree of precision. For proper operation the four tips had to be precisely in the same plane, with all four gaps parallel to each other on a standard orientation. The gaps had to be situated at 90-degree intervals on the circumference, with a tolerance of only 30 seconds of arc.

Two important steps followed the assembly of each head. In the next operation, called polishing, the head was mounted on a top plate with a special abrasive tape which was similar to a recording tape. When the unit was set in operation, the tips were evenly ground as they rotated in contact with the moving abrasive tape.

---

[3] The term "system" denotes the console plus two equipment racks of the VTR, complete except for the head subassembly.

AMPEX CORPORATION

Exhibit 7

ASSEMBLY DRAWING, TAPE RECORDER HEAD

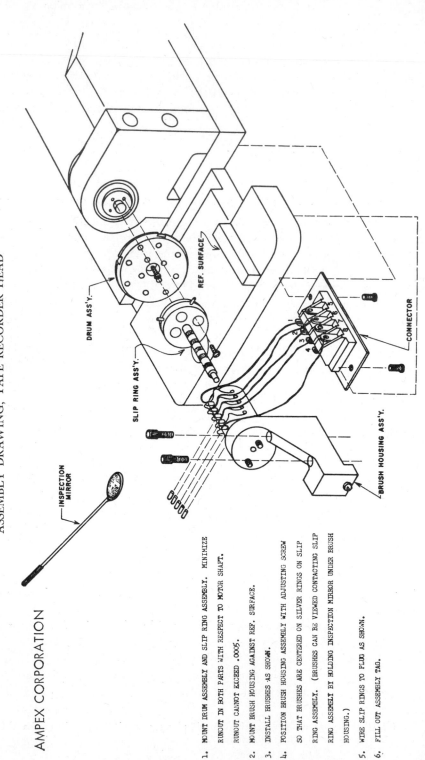

INSPECTION MIRROR

DRUM ASS'Y.

REF. SURFACE

SLIP RING ASS'Y.

CONNECTOR

BRUSH HOUSING ASS'Y.

1. MOUNT DRUM ASSEMBLY AND SLIP RING ASSEMBLY. MINIMIZE
   RUNOUT IN BOTH PARTS WITH RESPECT TO MOTOR SHAFT.
   RUNOUT CANNOT EXCEED .0005.

2. MOUNT BRUSH HOUSING AGAINST REF. SURFACE.

3. INSTALL BRUSHES AS SHOWN.

4. POSITION BRUSH HOUSING ASSEMBLY WITH ADJUSTING SCREW
   SO THAT BRUSHES ARE CENTERED ON SILVER RINGS ON SLIP
   RING ASSEMBLY. (BRUSHES CAN BE VIEWED CONTACTING SLIP
   RING ASSEMBLY BY HOLDING INSPECTION MIRROR UNDER BRUSH
   HOUSING.)

5. WIRE SLIP RINGS TO PLUG AS SHOWN.

6. FILL OUT ASSEMBLY TAG.

Exhibit 8

VIDEO TAPE RECORDER HEAD ASSEMBLY DRAWING

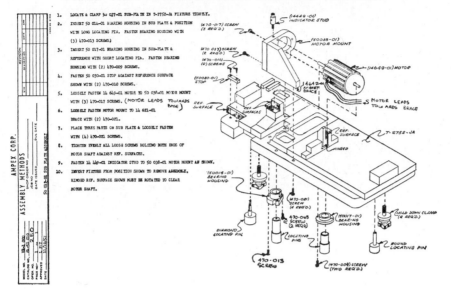

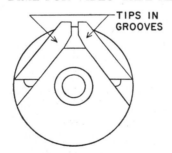

Exhibit 9

DRAWINGS OF DIME FOR VIDEO TAPE RECORDER HEAD

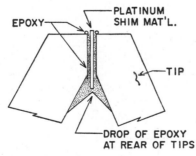

TIPS IN
GROOVES

Simplified sketch of assembled dime,
more than 3 times actual size

PLATINUM
SHIM MAT'L.

EPOXY

TIP

DROP OF EPOXY
AT REAR OF TIPS

Greatly enlarged sketch of tip area of dimes
(Corresponds to extreme top of drawing shown above)

After polishing, the head assembly went to final inspection. Although the subassemblies which made up the head were processed through visual and mechanical inspections prior to final assembly, it was not possible to check the electrical performance of the head prior to final inspection. At this stage the head was mounted on one of three VTR systems available in the Head Department and subjected to exhaustive examination. Among other tests, the head was used to record and play back a standard signal, and to play back from a standard tape. The output of the head appeared on a TV receiver screen and was closely examined for flaws. Inspection took one hour, and each head was inspected three times, with an overnight delay separating two of the tests.

The Head Department

The VTR head was to be manufactured by a group of twenty hourly workers and five inspectors working under the supervision of the Head Department foreman in one area of that Department. Some executives felt that the company's know-how in producing recording heads had been one reason why Ampex had retained the leading position in its field. The foreman of the Head Department, who had been in the Department for two years, said that "in the past, even when other foremen really got into a stew over some new recorder, we never had any trouble making heads. Everything has been smooth and proper all along in the Head Department."

For the VTR head, tooling was designed for an output capacity of 20 units per day, on a two-shift basis. The assembly output was planned to rise to the 20-unit capacity by January as the operators acquired the requisite skills. It was expected that 25 per cent of output would be rejected and require reworking. Performance measured up to expectations during November and December, and 22 heads had been shipped by the beginning of 1958. By that time the early units were being returned for normal rebuilding after the tips had been worn down in use. Until January the Department had produced enough heads to meet the shipping schedule for new systems and to service those systems already in the field.

During the first two weeks of January, only three VTR heads passed final inspection. Output rose to five new heads and two replacement heads during the week ended January 18, but this was still substantially below needs and expectations. As a result, on January 21, 1958, seven complete VTR systems, which were crated and ready for shipment, lacked the requisite head assembly. On the same date, another eight complete systems were ready for check-out.

According to Andersen, the Head Department had been averaging seven assemblies daily in mid-January; but, as he said: "They're lucky to get one through inspection." Of the 40 drums assembled in January, 11 had passed inspection, 15 were abandoned, and 14 were in rework on January 22.

Two principal defects had caused most of the rejects. These were (1) a "waterfall" effect appearing on the picture and (2) low electrical output. While the engineers believed that the waterfall was due to mechanical instabilities in the head, they were uncertain as to the fundamental cause of low output. Charles Andersen commented: "When a head is rejected for low output on one dime, it requires eight hours for rework. It's really frustrating to have that happen when there are three good dimes on the drum. But there's no way to catch it before final inspection."

STEPS TO MEET THE PROBLEM

Early in January a special task force was established to co-ordinate efforts aimed at improving the yield in production of VTR heads. Ray Heidenreich, General Foreman of Assembly, was placed in charge of the special group, which included the foreman of the Head Department and a representative from each of the following departments: Manufacturing Engineering; and the Quality Control, Production Control, and Video Engineering departments of the Professional Products Division. Walter Selsted, Manager of the Research Division, acted as adviser to the group. The task force set out first to confirm that the manufacturing process was under control and in accordance with specifications. Each operation was reviewed in minute detail. Methods and tools were examined and compared with specifications. Raw materials were analyzed. The progress of several head units in process was followed, and the units were examined for mechanical and electrical properties after each operation. The work area itself was thoroughly cleaned to reduce risk of product contamination.

This process of review was completed by January 20, and a few necessary changes were made in the methods being used. At that time, one of the manufacturing executives stated: "Now we're making heads under much tighter control, and we're sure that the process is being executed exactly according to specifications. If these units don't come through, it is a design problem, not a production problem." All units started after this point were marked with red in production records and referred to by the personnel as the "control" heads.

Larry Burn emphasized that the task force was not the only group working on the problem, and that the line personnel had not in any way been relieved of their responsibilities in the matter. Thus the Manufacturing Engineering Department had assigned three men full time and one man part time to the solution of this problem. Furthermore, although the Manufacturing Division held formal responsibility for the product, the engineers from the Professional Products Division had been requested to assist in "trouble shooting." According to Burn: "Manufacturing gave them carte blanche to institute any changes after a thorough evaluation of all techniques."

The View of Top Management

Robert Sackman, Vice President and General Manager, felt that the VTR situation was the prime problem in the company as of mid-January. The problem was an understandable one, he felt, and typical of the difficulties encountered by companies like Ampex working on the frontiers of knowledge in their art. At best, the transfer of a product from the engineering phase to production was a tricky situation. The key element in this situation, as in all problems of this sort, was time—because with enough time, all the "kinks" could be ironed out. "Unfortunately," Sackman said, "in this business, we can't take too much time." He felt that the company's best men had been assigned to the problem, and had confidence that it would soon be overcome. To indicate his personal concern and willingness to co-operate, he began a series of daily meetings in his office with Ray Heidenreich and the department managers concerned. At these meetings the day's developments were reported and discussed.

Sackman felt that the financial aspects of the problem might be annoying; but in the short run, they were inconsequential. The VTR accounted for one half of the planned monthly billings for the remainder of the fiscal year ended April 30. While not concerned with inventory or billings for the next month or two, he did believe that the year-end figures were important goals—measurements against which the company could not afford to fall short.

Market acceptance was an important factor influencing Sackman's views. Ampex had a commanding lead in this product—probably six to eighteen months ahead of the nearest competitor. Once Ampex units went into use in the industry, any competition would have to match the standards of the VTR to achieve interchangeability of tapes.

The Product Engineers' Role

John Leslie, Chief Engineer in the Professional Products Division, shared the viewpoint of most Ampex executives toward this problem. Problems had been expected in production of the VTR, but the magnitude of the problem had been underestimated.

"At best, manufacturing VTR heads is an art," Leslie stated. Engineers had made all of the original and replacement heads for the sixteen prototype systems. They had reasoned that a fully tooled production line would have even less trouble than they had had. "It didn't work that way, though," Leslie said. "We didn't realize the inherent artistry of the engineers who built the prototypes. When the line started up in late fall, the engineers nursed it along; and when all went well for the first week, we all relaxed and went back to our other jobs. Then the yield really nose-dived," he concluded.

Leslie felt that one could not inspect quality into the product; one had

Exhibit 10

VIDEO TAPE RECORDER HEAD—STATUS REPORT*

Shipped in December—18 Units

Total through December—22 Units

	Polishing			Final Inspection			Rework			Passed Inspection				
										Week Ended			Day	
	January 22		January 23	January 22		January 23	January 22		January 23	January 4	January 11	January 18	January 22	January 23
	9:00 a.m.	2:00 p.m.	2:00 p.m.	9:00 a.m.	2:00 p.m.	2:00 p.m.	9:00 a.m.	2:00 p.m.	2:00 p.m.					
Original equipment......None	183† 187†		183† 187† 144	124 134 189 167 201 172†	124 134 173† 172†	134 130† 205†	173† 185† 171 183† 187† 149† 177 130† 194	177 149† 185† 130† 211† 171† 191† 201	177 149† 185† 211† 171† 191† 201 142 133 140 183† 173† 172†	181 122	182	197 196 192 180 188	189 167	124
Replacement heads......	118		...	...	...	116	116 108 110 117 135 197 118 121	116 108 110 117 135 197 121	118 108 117 110 121 197 135			123		

* Numbers refer to serial numbers of units at each stage at specified time.

† "Control heads"—those produced since establishment of manufacturing control on January 20, 1958.

to build it in. Furthermore, there were several places where that quality would come only as a result of operator judgment. For example, in the polishing operation the head was run against abrasive tape. Since there were no objective standards for the time to be spent on the tape, it was up to the operator to decide in terms of the nature of the unit being polished. In addition, the engineers had been able to point out some other aspects of the process requiring extreme care. For instance, handling of the alphenol tips had to be very gentle, as shock would adversely affect the metal's magnetic properties. Furthermore, in mounting the dime on the drum, care had to be taken to insure intimate contact with the ferrite core to insure maximum electrical output.

"We were only called in last week," Leslie said on January 22. "Solving this one will take time, but it is not unsurmountable. We're re-examining our basic principles now to find the first-order problem. Refinements will come later. So far, we've changed several process techniques, but the design is unchanged."

Burn's Appraisal

At 2:15 P.M. on January 23, after talking to Charles Andersen, Larry Burn returned to the latest status report on VTR head production (see Exhibit 10). In thinking through his view of the situation, he offered the following comments to a visitor in his office:

We have the capacity and proven ability to make 20 new heads per day (10 each shift) if there are no delays. Next week, we expect to double capacity by adding a second tool to the bottleneck operation. This month, we've built 40 new drums—passed 11, given up on 15, and have 14 in rework and inspection today. Thus, our yield is 27½ per cent if none of the 14 are good; but allowing for those, we ought at least to get a 50 per cent yield. We're scheduled to turn out 99 good heads this month, 140 in February, and 200 per month starting in April. We've got a meet the schedule. But how?

Producing these heads is more of an art than production. People acquire art with practice. We need to accelerate the abilities and increase the artistry of the production operatiors. Our big mistake was trying to develop the "art" of manufacturing at the same time that we experimented with the tooling on the line. One thing is sure, however; no below-standard head will leave this plant.

APPENDIX A

Principles of Tape Recorder Operation

DURING THE middle of the nineteenth century, James C. Maxwell, a British physicist, discovered that a changing electrical current induces a magnetic field surrounding the conductor carrying the current. This simple principle is the basis for all present-day magnetic recording equipment. Tape recorders function by transporting a magnetically coated plastic ribbon, called the "tape," by a "head" which serves to imprint a magnetic signal on the tape.

Exhibit 11
PRINCIPLE OF RECORDING HEAD

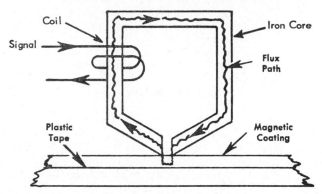

The head may be thought of simply as a piece of magnetic material, such as iron, with wire wrapped around to form a coil as illustrated in Exhibit 11. For this to function as a recording or reproducing head, there must be a "gap" in the magnetic material. Thus a very small cross section of the magnetic material is removed and replaced by a nonmagnetic material such as paper. In addition, the surface of the head near the gap is flattened in the vicinity of the gap to conform to the surface of the tape.

If an electrical current passes through the coil, fluctuations in applied voltage will induce a magnetic field in the head. The intensity of that field will change in direct proportion to the fluctuations in the current passing through the coil. As this happens, the magnetic field will try to bridge the gap caused by the nonmagnetic material and thus complete the circuit. Hence, when a recording tape is placed over the gap in a head, the ferrous coating on the tape serves to complete a path for the magnetic field flowing in the head. As this magnetic field passes through the tape coating, it influences the orientation of the molecules of iron in the coating. Different field intensities will result in different orientations in the tape. If we pull the tape past the gap in the head while passing a fluctuating current through the coil, the imprint on the tape corresponds to the field present in the head at the instant that section of the tape passed the gap. Thus, if a magnetic recording tape moves steadily across a magnetic head while a current is passing through the coil in the head, the resultant imprint along the tape will be directly related to the signal in the coil with respect to intensity and time sequence. Therefore, any fluctuating electrical signal can be represented magnetically on tape.

The signal imprinted on the tape can be "read" from the tape by passing it across the head while there is no current passing through the coil. The changing orientation of the magnetic coating as it bridges the gap in the magnetic head material will set up a slight magnetic field in the head. As this magnetic field fluctuates, it induces a corresponding electrical current in the coil. Thus the signal that had originally formed the imprint on the tape is recreated.

The gap in a recording head is an important determinant of the system's performance. A magnetic field will flow into the tape only when there is a gap in the head (that is, when there is no short circuit to provide any easier path for the field). Furthermore, the head will be effective only for signals the wave lengths of which are greater than the length of the gap. In other words, the process works only when the imprint of one wave on the tape is long enough to bridge the gap in the head. A "wave" may be thought of as representing one complete fluctuation, or cycle, in the signal. As the number of fluctuation per unit time increases, the time duration of each must decrease. Since the tape moves at a constant speed, the length of a cycle, in space on the tape, is proportional to its duration in time. Thus, increases in the maximum frequency which can be recorded can be attained only by increased speed of the tape or by a greatly reduced gap dimension. For example, in the discussion above, it was pointed out that the field in the head is induced by a changing current. If an alternating current changing at a frequency of 100 cycles each second passes through the coil while a tape passes the head at the rate of one inch per second, each inch of tape will bear the imprint of 100 cycles of the signal, and each cycle will then require one hundredth of an inch along the length of the tape. If the gap in the head is one fiftieth of an inch, the length of each wave on the tape will be too small to bridge the gap, and the system will not function. In order to record this frequency, it would be necessary to reduce the size of the gap below one hundredth of an inch or to increase the speed of the tape above two inches per second so that no more than 50 cycles would appear on each inch.

In practice, there are very definite mechanical limits to either the speed at which the tape can be moved or the size of the gap. So far, it has been impractical to reduce the gap below one ten-thousandth of an inch, and that dimension is achieved only with difficulty. With conventional heads and tape speeds of 60 inches per second, a maximum frequency of 100,000 cycles per second can be recorded. At this speed of transport, however, a reel of one-mill tape 14 inches in diameter is exhausted in twenty-four minutes.

There are other performance specifications for a tape-recording or reproducing system in addition to maximum frequency response. One of these is the dynamic range, which is simply the ratio between the maximum signal loudness and the basic noise level in the system. The maximum achievable dynamic range with current equipment is approximately sixty decibels, which is equivalent to a ratio of one thousand to one between the desired signal and undesired noise.

Another common measure of recording performance is the frequency range, that is, the range between minimum and maximum frequency. Present high-quality equipment will reproduce a frequency range of approximately ten octaves, or the equivalent of a ratio of one thousand to one maximum and minimum frequency.

IMPERIAL OIL, LIMITED (A)

J. W. Hamilton, Director of Imperial Oil, Limited, picked up the confidential report just placed on his desk with exceptional interest. Its modest title, "Special Halifax-Montreal Crude Supply Research Project," concealed two especially significant aspects. The project dealt with strategic planning and tactical operation of IOL's tanker fleet—an activity involving many capital investment decisions, some of which were in the order of $10 million. Furthermore, these decisions had to be made in the face of numerous yet critical uncertainties. This final report, which had just been completed and delivered to Hamilton in April, 1958, was intended to provide useful aids to managerial decisions in marine operations.

Second, and in some ways of even more interest to certain IOL executives, this report was the first formal effort of the company's newly created operations research group. What, Hamilton wondered, would be the effectiveness of their mathematically oriented approach to this complex business problem?

Hamilton settled down for a careful study of the report. As he read and examined the exhibits, certain questions came to mind, and he began to make marginal notes as the basis for points of later discussion. Hamilton's copy of the report is reproduced as Supplement A to this case.

Background

The Imperial Oil Company, Limited, was founded in 1880 by several small oil companies in southwestern Ontario. Rapid expansion of the new Company's business led to an acute capital requirement. When funds for expansion could not be found in Canada, they were acquired from Standard Oil Company (New Jersey) in 1898 in exchange for a majority interest in Imperial. The Company continued to expand rapidly, building refineries across the country. In 1919 the corporate name was changed to Imperial Oil, Limited. Standard Oil Company (New Jersey) held, in 1958, nearly 70 per cent of the common stock of the company, with the balance held by over 44,000 shareholders. The company had extensive crude oil production, operated nine refineries with a capacity of 307,000 barrels per day, and sold over 275,000 barrels per day of products and processed crude, making it the largest oil firm in Canada.

A five-year summary of company performance is shown as Exhibit 1. Exhibit 2 reproduces the balance sheet and Exhibit 3 the income statement.

Exhibit 1

IMPERIAL OIL, LIMITED, AND SUBSIDIARY COMPANIES
FIVE-YEAR SUMMARY

	1957	1956	1955	1954	1953
Operating (barrels per day):					
Gross* crude oil production	110,000	119,000	108,000	97,000	90,000
Net* crude oil production	95,000	103,000	93,000	84,000	78,000
Crude oil processed at refineries	267,000	275,000	239,000	214,000	204,000
Canadian crude processed, as a percentage of total	60	60	67	69	57
Crude oil and product importations	126,000	121,000	108,000	88,000	121,000
Sales of products and processed crude	276,000	275,000	250,000	218,000	212,000
Number of regular employees at year end	14,657	14,242	13,696	13,370	13,564
Financial:					
Gross income	$884,569,000	837,373,000	700,275,000	614,550,000	605,504,000
Expenses	$760,122,000	718,494,000	593,810,000	528,067,000	523,713,000
Income taxes on earnings	$ 52,366,000	49,781,000	44,321,000	36,900,000	33,807,000
Earnings after income taxes	$ 72,081,000	69,099,000	62,145,000	49,583,000	47,985,000
Per share	$ 2.29	2.20	2.08	1.66	1.60
Percentage of earnings to gross income	8.15	8.25	8.87	8.07	7.92
Dividends paid	$ 37,728,000	35,890,000	28,366,000	26,863,000	23,878,000
Per share	$ 1.20	1.20	0.95	0.90	0.80
Current funds and inventories	$322,675,000	365,674,000	299,309,000	225,460,000	234,119,000
Current debts	$ 90,790,000	111,183,000	91,697,000	67,682,000	67,951,000
Net current working funds and inventories	$231,885,000	254,491,000	207,612,000	157,778,000	166,168,000
Ratio of current funds and inventories to current debts	3.6	3.3	3.3	3.3	3.4
Property, plant, and equipment less accumulated depreciation and amortization	$488,991,000	429,525,000	372,520,000	331,924,000	291,905,000
Capitalized expenditures for property, plant, and equipment	$103,063,000	97,951,000	80,074,000	74,236,000	67,852,000
Long-term debt	$ 90,776,000	94,170,000	96,628,000	48,986,000	50,919,000
Number of shares issued and outstanding	31,443,000	31,430,000	29,866,000	29,851,000	29,847,000
Number of shareholders	44,544	43,823	43,614	44,734	46,796
Shareholders' investment (book value)	$599,602,000	564,804,000	463,865,000	429,127,000	395,779,000
Per share	$ 19.07	17.97	15.53	14.37	13.26

* Gross production includes, and net production excludes, royalties and oil payments due others on company's share of production.

Exhibit 2

IMPERIAL OIL, LIMITED, AND SUBSIDIARY COMPANIES
CONSOLIDATED BALANCE SHEET

ASSETS

	As at December 31 1957	As at December 31 1956
Current Funds and Inventories:		
Cash...	$ 14,278,549	$ 13,106,026
Government securities, at the lower of cost or market......	14,399,080	64,830,238
Other marketable securities, at cost which is approximately market............	22,634,908	28,285,799
Trade accounts receivable, less provision for doubtful accounts.	96,576,099	95,284,154
Other accounts receivable........	4,268,012	7,616,692
Prepaid taxes, insurance, and rentals...	2,821,040	2,763,734
Inventories, on basis of cost which was less than market:		
Crude oil and refined products.........	138,132,368	130,979,055
Other merchandise.........	7,833,640	6,331,939
Materials and supplies.........	21,731,582	16,476,256
	$322,675,278	$365,673,893
Deferred Funds:		
Mortgages and other deferred accounts receivable, less provision for doubtful accounts.......	15,578,439	10,934,480
Investment in Other Companies:		
Bonds and shares—with quoted market value: 1957—$69,208,160; 1956—$97,190,000. —without quoted market value, less reserve.......	16,012,150	15,933,750
	2,439,935	2,444,489
Funds Deposited with Governments and Others:		
Government securities, at the lower of cost or market........	1,025,831	3,657,811
Cash.........	343,259	223,726
Investment in Plant and Equipment:		
Land, leases, wells, buildings, plant, transportation, and other equipment, at cost........	762,311,619	672,463,670
Less—accumulated depreciation and amortization.........	273,320,724	242,938,267
	$488,990,895	$429,525,403
Deferred Charges:		
Unamortized debt discount and expense........	899,714	948,948
Other deferred charges and credits (net)........	939,894	13,123
	$848,905,395	$829,355,623

LIABILITIES

	As at December 31 1957	As at December 31 1956
Current Debts:		
Accounts payable........	$ 58,390,198	$ 69,272,843
Long-term debts due within one year........	3,420,562	2,397,944
Income and other taxes payable........	22,544,451	32,223,361
Other accrued liabilities........	6,434,552	7,289,156
	$ 90,789,763	$111,183,304
Long-Term Debts (Exclusive of Amounts Due within One Year):		
Imperial Oil, Limited—		
2½% serial debentures, 1949 issue, maturing on December 15, 1959........	1,500,000	3,000,000
3% sinking fund debentures, 1949 issue, maturing December 15, 1969........	40,000,000	40,000,000
Sinking fund requirements: $2,000,000—in each of the years 1960 to 1964, inclusive $2,500,000—in each of the years 1965 to 1968, inclusive		
3⅝% serial debentures, 1955 issue, maturing $1,000,000 February 1 in each of the years 1959 to 1961, inclusive, and $1,500,000 February 1 in each of the years 1962 to 1965, inclusive........	9,000,000	10,000,000
3⅝ sinking fund debentures, 1955 issue, maturing February 1, 1975........	40,000,000	40,000,000
Sinking fund requirements: $2,000,000—in each of the years 1966 to 1970, inclusive $2,500,000—in each of the years 1971 to 1974, inclusive		
Imperial Oil Shipping Company, Limited—3% serial notes maturing May 1, 1959........	275,509	1,170,388
	$ 90,775,509	$ 94,170,388
Other Deferred Debts:		
For employees' annuities........	18,001,251	19,283,737
Potential Debt or Loss Provisions:		
Accumulated income tax reductions applicable to future years........	36,818,685	27,007,123
Fire, marine, and other insurance........	9,962,436	9,962,436
Contingencies........	2,955,653	2,944,809
	$249,303,297	$264,551,797
SHAREHOLDERS' INVESTMENT		
Capital Stock:		
Authorized—40,000,000 shares of no par value:		
Issued 1957—31,442,652 shares; 1956—31,429,887 shares....	$230,039,473	$229,594,469
Capital surplus retained and used in the business........	67,222,821	67,222,821
Earnings retained and used in the business........	302,339,804	267,986,536
	$599,602,098	$564,803,826
	$848,905,395	$829,355,623

Approved on behalf of the Board:
[signed]   J. S. WHITE

Exhibit 3

CONSOLIDATED STATEMENT OF EARNINGS

	For the Years Ended December 31	
	1957	1956
Income:		
From operations	$872,986,952	$830,158,478
From investment and other sources	11,582,524	7,214,712
	$884,569,476	$837,373,190
Expenses:		
Cost of crude oil, petroleum products, and other merchandise purchased, including freight	$488,573,726	$466,367,137
Exploration, operating, and administrative expenses	195,607,467	177,989,961
Taxes, other than income taxes	31,805,958	32,377,257
Depreciation and amortization	39,542,515	37,485,494
Interest and discount on long-term debts	3,214,356	3,283,809
Other interest charges	1,378,089	990,063
	$760,122,111	$718,493,721
Earnings before income taxes	$124,447,365	$118,879,469
Provision for estimated income taxes thereon	52,366,435	49,780,777
Earnings after income taxes	$ 72,080,930	$ 69,098,692
Per share	$ 2.29	$ 2.20

Consolidated Statement of Earnings Retained and Used in the Business for the Year Ended December 31, 1957

Balance at January 1	$267,986,536
Add: Earnings after income taxes—$2.29 per share	72,080,930
	$340,067,466
Deduct: Dividends paid—$1.20 per share	37,727,662
Balance at December 31	$302,339,804

Exhibit 4

ANNUAL REPORT TO THE SHAREHOLDERS

After years of record growth, the Canadian economy entered a period of consolidation during 1957. Business activity levelled off and in the second half of the year industrial production declined. However, the economy continued at near-peak levels, and total employment throughout the year was higher than for any corresponding periods in Canada's history.

To some extent conditions in Canada reflected economic adjustment throughout the free world. Over-supply became general for all basic raw materials. The increasingly keen competition emphasized that Canada's main problem is one of high costs. As a trading nation with a heavy requirement for new capital, this country must be competitive to survive. An output per man second only to that of the United States cannot be sustained unless Canada is able to compete also in terms of output per dollar.

The premium on the Canadian dollar served to aggravate trading difficulties in the past year. However, the free market mechanism will help to bring about a more satisfactory relationship between the Canadian dollar and world currencies, and between domestic and foreign prices. Increasing industrialization

Exhibit 4 (Continued)

in many countries will provide ready markets for many of the materials that Canada produces so well.

During most of 1957 the Canadian oil industry set new records in all phases of its operations. However, as business activity slackened towards the year-end and the weather was unseasonably warm throughout the country, the demands for petroleum products fell below those of the corresponding period of 1956. Product inventories tended to increase and refinery throughput was reduced accordingly.

In addition, crude oil production was affected by the loss of markets that were gained temporarily during the Suez crisis. Thus, production was sharply lower in the fourth quarter, although it averaged 6 per cent higher for the full year.

While crude oil demand declined, potential producing capacity continued to rise. At the year's end crude was being produced at only half of the maximum efficient potential.

The application of United States import quotas to Canadian oil introduced a new difficulty in the marketing of Canada's surplus crude. While the present quotas do not significantly limit Canadian outlets, they create another element of uncertainty about the growth of export markets. It is hoped that in administering the quotas, the United States will recognize the security advantages of Canadian pipe line crude oil supply.

There was surplus refining capacity in Canada and abroad in 1957, and demand fell short of product supply. The consequent high stock position exerted continuous pressure on product prices. In addition costs continued to rise and so the refiners' margins were reduced.

To a considerable degree higher refining costs are due to the improved qualities of motor fuels that are required for present-day cars. However, there have not been corresponding increases in the prices received by the refiners for the improved products. This fact has been obscured by increasing taxes and other charges that enter into the retail prices of gasolines. It is not generally realized that only about half the price that the motorist pays at the pump goes to the refiner who makes the gasoline.

Early in 1958 a Royal Commission on Canada's Energy Requirements met under the chairmanship of Mr. Henry Borden. This Commission is expected to make a comprehensive examination of oil and gas reserves and markets in order to permit a better understanding of the problems by government and public alike.

Imperial's 1957 earnings amounted to $72,080,930. This was a 4 per cent increase over 1956 and reflected the high level of operations during the greater part of the year. Income for the fourth quarter was substantially lower than in 1956. An important factor in the Company's operations was a severe cutback of its crude oil production under Alberta Government regulations which prorate production to market demand. . . . the reduced allowables affected Imperial more severely than most other producers. As a result, the Company's gross production for 1957 was 8.5 per cent less than in 1956.

Because it is greatly affected by changes in crude oil demand, Imperial is particularly concerned with finding additional outlets for Canadian crude. The present problem is exceedingly complex and there is no simple solution for it. Any steps that are taken must be carefully considered in the light of their long-term effect on the national interest.

The Company recorded twenty-four discoveries of crude oil and natural gas in western Canada during the year. Four of these were in association with other interests.

Exhibit 4 (Continued)

The daily throughput of Imperial refineries averaged 267,032 barrels which was 3.2 per cent less than in 1956. The principal influence in this connection was a strike at the Ioco refinery that began in late September and continued for nine weeks.

While total sales increased by only a fraction of a percentage point, there was a more substantial growth in demand for the Company's branded products, indicating recognition of the quality improvements that are continuously in progress.

As part of this quality improvement program, new ultra-modern units called "Powerformers" went into operation at the Sarnia, Montreal and Halifax refineries. Construction of similar facilities will be completed this year at Ioco and Winnipeg, and will begin at Calgary.

There were two major plant developments in the petrochemical field, both at Sarnia. The $5,500,000 detergent alkylate plant went into operation late in the year, and there was scheduled progress in another unit that will be completed this summer at a cost of $28,500,000 to make a variety of other petrochemicals.

The heavy capital demands for new plants and equipment and for carrying on the oil exploration program are indicated by expenditures which totalled $144,000,000 for the year. This compares with $134,000,000 in 1956.

The Company regards prevailing economic conditions as a pause for breath after a long upward climb. Great natural resources and high income levels, together with growing population and public policies that encourage enterprise, assure continued expansion of the Canadian economy. Imperial Oil, by reason of its sound financial position, modern plants and experienced personnel, is well equipped to make the best of present difficulties and to benefit fully when the economy resumes an upward trend.

The continued interest and support of the shareholders is again thankfully acknowledged. The Company now has nearly 45,000 shareholders of whom about 35,000 are resident in Canada and comprise one of the largest groups of the kind in the country.

The loyal and effective work of the Company's employees who number approximately 14,600 is again a subject for grateful comment.

Toronto, Ontario
March 21, 1958

[*signed*] J. R. WHITE
President.

The president's annual letter to stockholders is shown as Exhibit 4. All these exhibits are taken from IOL's 1957 annual report.

Facilities

IOL obtained crude from Canadian fields and by importation, as shown in Exhibit 1. Although all of IOL's needs could have been supplied in Canada, crude was imported from Venezuela as the most economic source because major Canadian producing areas are nearly three thousand miles away in Alberta and Saskatchewan.

For the purpose of this research project, it was assumed that Montreal and Halifax would continue to be supplied by ocean-borne imported

Exhibit 5

TANKER FLEET OPERATIONS, HALIFAX AND
MONTREAL REFINERIES

Total Crude, Tanker-Transported
(Thousands of Barrels per Year)

Year	Imperial-Owned Ships	Chartered Ships	Total
1953	12,250	13,539	25,789
1954	9,013	14,957	23,970
1955	2,252	26,997	29,249
1956	....	36,283	36,283
1957	8,756	30,158	38,914
1958	9,947	29,683	39,630

crude in the foreseeable future. Crude for Halifax was delivered directly by tanker, while that for Montreal moved through the Portland-Montreal pipe-line system. The tanker fleet operation is quantified in Exhibit 5. Refinery data are given in Exhibit 6.

Marine Equipment

At the end of World War II, IOL owned six T–2 tankers.[1] These were gradually eliminated because of their size and relative inefficiency. In 1949 the company built the *Imperial Alberta* of 26,000 dead-weight tons. She proved to be an uneconomical size and was sold in 1955. The long-range plan for the tanker program was then definitely directed toward getting rid of small, old vessels and acquiring larger capacity equipment. In 1957, therefore, the company commissioned the *Imperial St. Lawrence* of 35,000 dead-weight tons. The firm's tanker fleet then comprised the vessels shown in Exhibit 7.

Increasing costs and rising demands began to make IOL executives think of the economies of larger vessels to serve the Halifax refinery directly and the Montreal refinery by way of the Portland pipe line.

Tanker Purchase Opportunity

In early 1957, Imperial Oil had an opportunity to build a 47,000-dwt. tanker under what seemed to be unusually attractive conditions. A base price of $9.4 million and delivery by 1961 were quoted. Escalation provisions of the contract were estimated to cause a maximum cost of $11 million.[2] However, as IOL people examined the economic return of the

---

[1] T–2 tankers were a standard type built in United States shipyards during World War II. They had a speed of 14.6 knots and were of 16,600 dwt. (dead-weight tons). United States and Canadian oil men measured tanker fleets in "T–2 equivalent," as this provided a common denominator. Thus a 17.0-knot, 26,000–dwt. tanker is $26,000 \times 17.0 \div 16,600 \times 14.6$, or 1.8 T–2 equivalent.

[2] "Escalation" was a common clause in shipbuilding contracts to allow for steel and labor price increases during lead times of such length.

Exhibit 6

LOCATION OF REFINERIES AND CRUDE CAPACITIES, EARLY 1958

(Barrels per Calendar Day—Total Capacity, 307,000)

Exhibit 7

IMPERIAL-OWNED OCEAN TANKER FLEET

January 1, 1958

Vessel	Commissioned	Dead-Weight Tons	Speed
Imperial Edmonton	1944	16,490	15 knots
Imperial Toronto	1944	16,475	15 knots
Imperial St. Lawrence	1957	35,555	17 knots

proposal, it did not look quite so attractive against current charter rates.

Hamilton and others were conscious of a distinct cycle in shipbuilding costs. "If we could predict the right time to build, important savings could be made." Charter rates, too, fluctuated widely. "Yet, security-wise, all of us agree it's better for the company to own a large proportion of its own ships."

Operations Research Enters the Picture

During the mid-1950's, Imperial Oil executives decided to get a computer. Delivery in 1959–60 was anticipated. Who would run the computer? If other than routine accounting activities were to be done, who had the requisite mathematical ability? An operations research group clearly was necessary to make the most of computer application to nonroutine problems.

Mathematical analysis of advanced degree had been applied to marketing problems for some years. In view of the impending computer installation, it seemed logical to expand the marketing mathematical group into an operations research group.

"Let's give them a chance," Hamilton and his associates concluded. "We know we need a better method of prediction on tanker acquisitions. Let's have Robinson and his operations research crew explore this particular tanker purchase opportunity and see what they can do."

Accordingly, in May, 1957, the operations research group was told to study the tanker project. The group consisted of Patrick J. Robinson, Dr. George P. Henderson, Dr. Kenneth E. Watt, and Dr. Glen D. Camp (consultant). Biographical sketches are given in Exhibit 8, in brief form.

Under Robinson's leadership, and with the aid of several college undergraduates employed for summer work, data were gathered for a report to advise management on appropriate speed and tonnage for the new tanker. At an early stage the operations research group made a preliminary report, expressing doubt as to whether *any* construction contract should be signed at that time. This conclusion was based on examination of charter rates, world-wide tanker-building programs, and other data. This preliminary report was interpreted by some IOL people

Exhibit 8

BIOGRAPHICAL SKETCHES OF OPERATIONS RESEARCH GROUP

Patrick J. Robinson, the group leader, joined Imperial Oil, Limited, in March, 1948, as a technical analyst and did special project work and supply-demand programming with the newly formed Co-ordination and Economics Department. He took over his present appointment of Co-ordinator of Marketing Research in 1952, and was the founder of operations research activity in Imperial, handling a wide variety of research on marketing and related business problems.

Prior to joining Imperial, Robinson had been senior project and survey engineer with the city engineer's staff of the city of Calgary. He has also had some consulting and direct selling experience not related to the petroleum business. He had initiated a regular lecture series at Ryerson Institute of Technology ten years ago and had been attached to the staff of the University of Toronto for the past seven years.

Robinson studied civil and electrical engineering at the University of Alberta and graduated in mechanical and industrial engineering (B.Eng.) from McGill University. Subsequently, he took postgraduate work in management engineering and computers at Massachusetts Institute of Technology and graduated from the Harvard Business School (M.B.A.), where he majored in finance and statistical control. Robinson was also a trained industrial and cost accountant. He had periodically taken supplementary training in statistics, computers, and operations research. Robinson was the author of a number of papers, articles, and book contributions in addition to his considerable activity in various technical and scientific societies.

Dr. George P. Henderson graduated from the University of Toronto (mathematics and physics) in 1941. After the war, he obtained his M.A. and Ph.D. degrees in mathematics at the University of Toronto. He was a member of the Mathematics Department of the University of Western Ontario for nine years and joined Imperial Oil, Limited, in 1957 in the marketing operations research group. For several years, he had administered correspondence courses for the Society of Actuaries and the Canadian Association of Actuaries.

Dr. Kenneth E. Watt obtained his Ph.D. degree in biology from Chicago. He was a specialist in the growth of populations and marine biology. He joined IOL in the spring of 1957, participated in this special study, and left in December, 1957, to join the Canadian government for biological survey work.

Dr. Glen D. Camp was a professor of operations research, George Washington University, and a consultant in operations research who made visits to IOL in connection with this study. From 1951 to 1956, he had been Director of Operations Research and Consultant to the President of Melpar, Inc. From 1946 to 1951, he was Senior Staff Member, Operations Evaluation Group, Division of Industrial Co-operation, Massachusetts Institute of Technology, assigned to the Office of the Chief of Naval Operations. His Ph.D. degree was taken in physics at the University of California. He was widely known as a leading operations research expert.

as a suggestion that the Marine Department not only should forgo the purchase of the new tanker, but should sell its existing vessels. The Marine Department was not impressed, and pointed out what it considered to be some important omissions and dubious assumptions. Some of the analysis, however, was promising and indicated that the whole crude supply problem was involved. Management instructed the operations research group to broaden the project to take in the entire Montreal-Halifax crude supply activity, including planning and operational procedures.

Reception of the Final Report

After Hamilton completed his study of the final report (Supplement A), he decided to call a meeting of IOL executives who had received copies of the report. The purpose of the meeting was to consider the recommendations of the study, and to form at least tentative ideas on the usefulness of the operations research approach. In opening the meeting, Hamilton remarked: "I don't believe any of us disagree with the need for this type of approach to some of our future decisions. However, we'll certainly have to keep in mind the limited experience of our operations research group outside of the marketing area. To what extent are we willing to rely upon and act on the conclusions in this report?"[1]

---

[1] Definitions of terms used in project report:

Tie-up—When vessels are retained in an inactive state beyond the normal time allowance for dry-docking, repairs, etc., they are considered to be in "tie-up."

Charters—The rental agreements for vessels between owners and users describe participants as "charter parties." The various forms of charter differ principally in the way in which the various costs of operation are divided between the two parties. Exhibit 9 lists the various forms of charter and their major differences.

Exhibit 9

CHARTER PARTIES

Type of Charter	Owner Supplies and Pays for:	Charterer Supplies and Pays for:
Bare-boat charter	Ship only	Crew, stores, repairs, insurance, fuel, port charges, hire
Time charter	Ship, crew, stores, repairs, insurance	Fuel, port charges, hire
Consecutive voyage charter (for a specified time or number of voyages)	Everything	Freight rate per barrel or ton of cargo
Voyage charter	Everything	Freight rate per barrel or ton of cargo

USMC Rate—During World War II the United States Maritime Commission calculated and published tanker freight rates on a uniform basis between most worldwide ports. Although these rates were officially canceled in 1948, western hemisphere tanker operators have continued to use them as a basic yardstick. Market rate fluctuations are therefore expressed, for convenience, in terms of percentage deviations from these basic rates (for example: USMC − 40 per cent; flat; USMC + 50 per cent).

Conversion from Tons to Barrels—Vessel capacities are expressed in deadweight tons. This capacity is measured by the difference in tons (of 2,240 pounds) of

SUPPLEMENT A
SPECIAL HALIFAX-MONTREAL CRUDE SUPPLY
RESEARCH PROJECT

Dr. George P. Henderson   Patrick J. Robinson
Dr. Glen D. Camp (Consultant)

in co-operation with

E. E. Bustard
Capt. J. W. Davidson
A. E. Gendron
G. H. Gilchrist

IMPERIAL OIL, LIMITED   APRIL, 1958

I. INTRODUCTION AND SUMMARY*

A. Introduction

A tentative I.O.L. plan to contract for the construction of a large tanker led to the initiation of this project, approximately one year ago, the major objective being to collect and analyse data which would assist Management in selecting the best speed and tonnage of this proposed new tanker. A secondary objective was to provide a demonstration of the application of Operational Research to produce aids to managerial decision.

It was soon evident, however, that the basic problem was much broader than that of the best speed and tonnage, including at least the question of whether *any* construction contract should be signed at that time. In fact, it was concluded that the various parts of the crude supply problem are deeply interconnected and that any attempt to treat one part in isolation from the others ran a severe risk of yielding misleading results. Accordingly, the project was broadened to that of developing useful aids to managerial decisions on the strategies and tactics of the whole Montreal-Halifax crude supply operation.

---

water which a vessel displaces "light" and when submerged to the "load line." A vessel's capacity for weight cargo (cargo heavier than water) is less than its total dead-weight capacity by the weight of fuel, stores, and water.

Specified volumes of crude oil and its derivatives vary widely in weight, so there is no specific conversion factor from tons to barrels. However, the bulk of the crude oil covered in the case study is of approximately the same specific gravity. For this purpose, then, it would be satisfactory to use 7.3 barrels as equal to one ton of 2,240 pounds. A 47,000-dwt. tanker would have a cargo capacity of approximately 45,700 tons or nearly 335,000 barrels of crude of 30-degree API (American Petroleum Institute rating) gravity.

* NOTE: The following alterations have been made in Supplement A:

1. To save space, these items have been omitted: Table of Contents, list of exhibits, and Bibliography.

2. Because of confidential data, these items have been omitted or altered: Altered —company predictions data in Exhibit 3 and Exhibit 4. Omitted—Exhibit 30, "Estimated Operating Data for New Tankers"; Exhibit 33, " 'Imperial St. Lawrence' 1957 Operating Data"; and Exhibit 35, " 'Imperial Edmonton' and 'Imperial Toronto' 1957 Operating Data."

Despite the interconnections between the parts of this broad problem, it is convenient, for purposes of discussion, to consider the following primary aims:

1. *Strategic Programming of the Tanker Fleet:* Buying, selling and building tankers; and contracting for long-term charter services.
2. *Tactical Operation of the Existing Fleet:* Scheduling heavy repairs, contracting for short-term charter services, day-to-day port and ocean operations.
3. *Assessing New Developments:* Appraising new developments which may significantly change tanker operations.

Apart from the foregoing operational considerations, the secondary objective concerned the method of problem-solving. As a demonstration of Operations Research or Management Sciences this study seems to have run somewhat typically. The initial statement of the problem (Which of two given size tankers should be built considering . . . etcetera?) was essentially a symptomatic statement of the need for scientific evaluation of a wide spectrum of alternative possibilities. The task grew to substantial proportions and only considerable "team" effort and co-operation with the Marine Division and others concerned made its completion feasible.

1. *Strategic Programming of the Tanker Fleet.* There are three major methods of tanker crude supply, namely I.O.L. owned tankers, long-term charters and short-term charters. The relative economic desirability of these methods is not fixed, but fluctuates widely because of large variations in construction costs and charter rates.

Owing to these variations, *there is an obvious large advantage to exploiting the down-swings and, of course, a correspondingly large disadvantage to being penalized by the up-swings.* If these fluctuations were entirely random and unpredictable, then the best that could be done would be to select that one method which, on a long-term average, is most economical. However, the most important result of this study is the clear indication that *these fluctuations are not random and unpredictable, but on the contrary, are causally interrelated and predictable to a very useful degree of accuracy.* Fundamentally, these fluctuations are fully analogous to the oscillations of a feedback-controlled servo-mechanism, the inputs being world tanker demand, tanker construction starts, tanker tie-ups and tanker scrappage, and the outputs being short and long-term charter rates, construction costs, and selling prices. Oscillation is caused by these outputs being fed back as inputs, as in all feedback processes whether physical or economic.

Two major steps are necessary to take full advantage of these oscillations. The first is the development of a degree of understanding of the basic oscillatory process sufficient to permit predictions of useful accuracy. This is accomplished in Section II, "Prediction of Charter Rates and Construction Costs," with details in Appendix A. The second step is the development of a method of comparison, on a uniform basis, of every available strategic alternative (e.g., build a tanker of such-and-such specifications, accept a specific offer of an existing tanker or of a charter service at specified rate, dispose of a tanker by sale or scrapping). This "yardstick" is developed in Section III, "Evaluation of Proposals to Build, Buy, Sell or Charter Tankers," with details in Appendix B, and is there applied to specific proposals such as: build a tanker of specified speed and tonnage, keep "Imperial St. Lawrence," keep "Imperial Edmonton," etcetera. This evaluation is not based solely on current construction costs and charter rates, but instead, takes account of the best available predictions of these costs and rates throughout the remaining lifetime of the tanker being evaluated. This appraisal depends strongly on the value of money in the best alternative use and since this may change from time to time, results are presented over a range of values of this critical interest rate.

The optimum percentage of coverage of its crude oil requirements by I.O.L. controlled tankers is discussed in Section IV, "A Discussion of Controlled Coverage." Sections II, III and IV, together with Appendices A and B, present all results so far obtained on the first and most important objective, Strategic Programming of the Tanker Fleet.

2. *Tactical Operation of the Existing Fleet.* Between the relatively infrequent changes in the controlled fleet (owned plus long-term chartered tankers) the existing fleet is an entity with very slowly changing characteristics. Everything bearing on the optimum operation of this fleet is properly considered under the heading of "tactical operations," and some of these factors are discussed in Section V, "Operation of the Existing Fleet," with details in Appendix C.

The large potential savings characteristic of the strategic programming do not occur in tactical operations; that is, the relevant optima are quite flat and hence the penalties for small departures from these optimum conditions are not severe. Nevertheless, the aggregate of potential small but steady day-to-day savings over the long intervals between changes in the fleet are by no means negligible, and hence this area is worthy of effort, after major strategic considerations have reached a satisfactory degree of development. There is another important reason for close managerial control over tactical operation—the operational data so collected and processed will be most useful in refining the strategic evaluation procedures. For example, it is believed that there is room for significant improvement in the conduct of sea trials on a ship being considered for purchase. This can be done by conducting sea trials on tankers in the existing fleet, the cost of these trials being more than repaid by direct, even though small, improvements in the fleet operations.

Results presented in Section V are not as thorough as would be desired, primarily owing to lack of relevant data. They include consideration of port delays, optimum sea speeds, and possible benefits arising from the use of modern weather prediction capabilities. The basic conclusion in this area is that further detailed study appears to be capable of yielding modest but far from negligible savings and, as previously remarked, a very valuable by-product consisting of an improved basis for strategic decisions.

3. *Assessing New Developments.* In this age of rapid change, technological and otherwise, it is conceivable that new factors might drastically alter the whole picture of tanker operations, possibly even to the point of partially or completely replacing them. Accordingly, it seems essential that Imperial should continue to monitor new developments.

One important part of this area has to do with possible large scale changes in tanker demand caused by new pipelines, changing patterns of production and consumption, etcetera. This is briefly considered in Section II, subsection C, under the heading of world tanker demand; however, the viewpoint there is that of changes in demand caused by economic changes, against a background of present technology.

Another important part is concerned with changes stemming from major technological advances such as widespread use of nuclear-power as a partial or complete replacement for fossil fuels. A third is concerned with possible technological advances in transport itself, such as plastic bags, enormous nuclear-powered tankers, etcetera. A brief discussion of these latter two areas is presented in Section VI, "Assessing New Developments." Considering the time lag likely to be associated with the introduction of any innovation, it is tentatively concluded that strategic programming of the tanker fleet need not at present take account of any such innovations. However, a small continuing effort might well be spent in monitoring new developments to take advantage of profitable opportunities.

B. Summary of Results

1. *The forecasts of tanker charter rates in Subsection II B were obtained by determining a relationship between charter rates and tanker tie-ups.* These predictions indicate that until 1962 there will be an oversupply of tankers in the world fleet and that consecutive voyage charter rates will remain below USMC — 40%. (In the past, charter rates have fluctuated widely, the maximum being four times the minimum.)

2. *European shipbuilding costs are expected to decrease until 1960 at least.* See Subsection II C.

3. *Low charter rates may lead to many construction contract cancellations.* It will likely be possible to take over an existing contract on favourable terms or possibly purchase a suitable vessel at depressed prices. World charter rates, construction costs and the prevailing outlook for owning a new supertanker should be reappraised annually. If a vessel is to be purchased or built, this should be planned in advance of possible upswings in construction costs and charter rates which may be expected some time after 1961. In this connection it might be well to lease at least one shipyard in the Jersey family to provide precious speed and flexibility in building when needed (e.g., the "Universe Leader," 85,000 dwt., was built and launched within eight months).

4. *A review of owned coverage considerations indicates that this factor is not as important as it first appears and should not unduly influence Imperial's planning.* See Section IV for discussion.

5. *A set of guides has been developed to aid Management in deciding whether and when to buy, build, charter or sell tankers.* Section III is in effect a manual of procedures and contains a set of tables and graphs with worked illustrations. These include appraisals of current possibilities such as the dollar incentives to own or sell rather than charter. In the following examples we have assumed money is worth 10% after taxes and have used prevailing tanker values.

 a) The best feasible new tanker (85,000 dwt., 15 knots)—$4,500,000 incentive to buy.

 b) "Imperial St. Lawrence"—$1,400,000 incentive to retain.

 c) "Imperial Toronto"—$900,000 incentive to sell.

 d) "Imperial Edmonton"—$850,000 incentive to sell.

Results for other assumptions can be readily obtained from the tables and graphs in Section III.

6. *Extensive analysis of ships' port-logs shows that turnaround delays at Portland and Halifax are not serious.* However, at La Salina, Aruba, Amuay Bay and Puerto la Cruz, the delays are expensive (see Subsection VI A). Recent contacts with Esso Research and Engineering reveal their interest and activity in studying the first three of these ports. Two of them are apparently already the subject of Operations Research team projects. In view of the delays experienced by "Imperial St. Lawrence" in 1957, Puerto la Cruz probably also deserves study.

7. *When charter rates are low it may be advisable to run the owned and bare-boat chartered tankers at reduced speeds.* In the case of "Imperial St.

Lawrence," savings of the order of $20,000 a year may be possible (see Sub-section V, B). In order to calculate the optimum speeds and obtain firm esti-mates of the savings, it would be necessary to determine the fuel consumption characteristics of the vessel.

8. *The Navigational Weather System operated by Louis Allen Associates, Washington, D.C. was investigated and may prove worth testing* (see Subsec-tion V, C).

9. *Submarine tankers, nuclear-powered tankers, towed plastic containers, very large tankers (up to 500,000 dwt.), tanker flying boats and sea-lines have been considered in Section VI.* Of these, only sea-lines are presently practical. Nuclear-powered surface tankers will likely become economically attractive in the next few years.

C. Previous Reports

1. *A "Preliminary Report" was prepared in May, 1957.* This outlined the scope and basic planning of the overall project, presented a "rough-cut" analytic bounding of the likely feasible solutions and illustrated how available and new information was being compiled and analysed.

2. *In July, 1957 we submitted "An Interim Report on Factors Involved in Decisions to buy Versus Charter Tankers."* This was intended to assist Man-agement in reaching a decision on an urgent question of whether or not to con-tract for the construction of a new tanker at that time.

3. *The present report concludes the study as assigned, and is complete in itself without reference to the two previous progress reports.* It differs in some respects from the details of the former reports and these differences are explained on the basis of better or more recent information.

II. PREDICTION OF CHARTER RATES AND CONSTRUCTION COSTS

A. Introduction

In making decisions regarding the composition of the tanker fleet (owned and long term chartered vessels), it is necessary to have forecasts of future charter rates and construction costs. These predictions are an outgrowth of historical performance and related factors. Exhibit 1 provides some of this information. In the past, when the world tanker tie-ups exceeded about 20 T–2 equivalents, the time and spot charter rates dropped sharply and remained in the vicinity of USMC − 40%. Charter rates go above USMC flat only when tie-ups fall below 10 T–2 equivalents and then rise rapidly when there are no tie-ups.

B. Charter Rates in Terms of Tie-ups

A more useful variable than tie-ups themselves is the percentage ratio of tie-ups to total tanker demand. Exhibit 2 is a scatter diagram of charter rates versus percentage tie-ups. The plotted points represent actual data and the mathematically fitted curve shows the predicted average consecutive voyage charter rate for a given percentage of tie-ups (see Appendix A).

C. Prediction of Tie-ups

Having established an apparent causal relationship between tie-ups and charter rates, the next step is to forecast tie-ups. For several years the changes

Exhibit 1

CONSECUTIVE VOYAGE CHARTER RATES

(Caribbean/U.S. North of Hatteras)

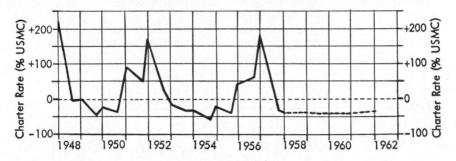

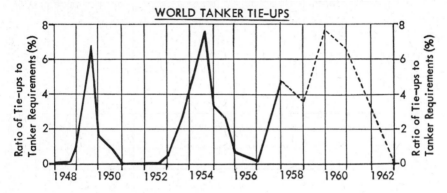

WORLD TANKER TIE-UPS

U.K. AND EUROPEAN TANKER CONSTRUCTION COSTS

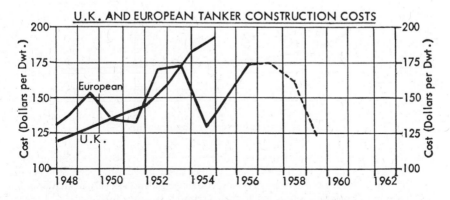

in the world fleet size or availability have been predicted quite accurately. . . .
We have therefore used . . . forecasts of tanker construction and obsolescence
for 1958 to 1965 [see Exhibit 3]. However, there have been rather large departures from the . . . estimates of tanker requirements, as illustrated in Exhibit 4.
Hence we have developed a new method of predicting the demand for tankers
as a pre-requisite for predicting tie-ups.

Our approach to this was to analyse the growth in tanker demand by calculating the ratio of tanker requirements to world crude oil production. We have called this ratio U (measured in T–2's per million barrels of production). This is a measure of the changing pattern of shipments of crude and products. For example, an increase in U means that either a greater proportion of total crude production is being transported in tankers, or the average voyage is longer, or both. Values of U for 1948 to 1956 are shown in Exhibit 5. In 1948 and 1956 there were no tie-ups and tanker demand was taken to be the fleet size. The actual demand was probably only slightly larger than

Exhibit 2

EFFECT OF TIE-UPS ON CHARTER RATES

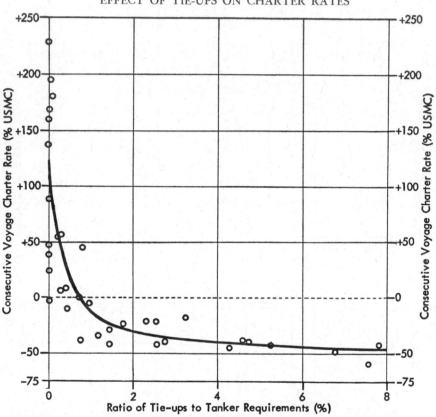

Ratio of Tie-ups to Tanker Requirements (%)

this since there is no evidence of refinery or supply shortages during these periods. We see that, on the average, U has been increasing very slowly and steadily over the nine years plotted and our prediction of future demand for tankers is based on the assumption that this trend will continue.

We would have liked to examine the variations in U before 1948, but no prior information on tanker demand or tie-ups was available. However, we did study a closely related ratio, W. This is simply the ratio of world tanker fleet size to world crude oil production (whereas U is the ratio of world fleet size minus tie-ups to world production). Since the average number of tie-ups is relatively small, U and W behave almost identically as illustrated in Exhibit 6. Seven-year moving averages of W from 1903 to 1953 are plotted

Exhibit 3

ACTUAL AND PREDICTED TANKER AVAILABILITY

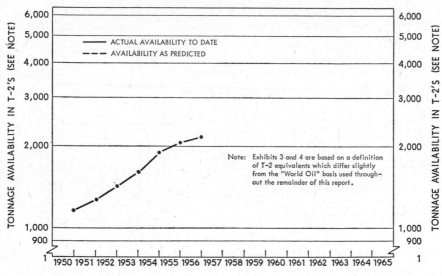

NOTE: Dotted line based on company predictions has been deleted as company confidential material.

and an average trend line has been fitted from 1922 to 1953. In addition the trend line for *U* from Exhibit 5 is shown.

Between 1904 and 1910 the demand for crude, and increases in tanker tonnage, kept pace with each other and the ratio of the two yielded a horizontal

Exhibit 4

ACTUAL AND PREDICTED TANKER REQUIREMENTS

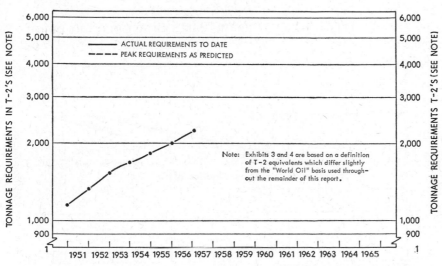

NOTE: Dotted line based on company predictions has been deleted as company confidential material.

Exhibit 5

U, TANKER REQUIREMENTS PER MILLION BARRELS OF WORLD CRUDE
OIL PRODUCTION

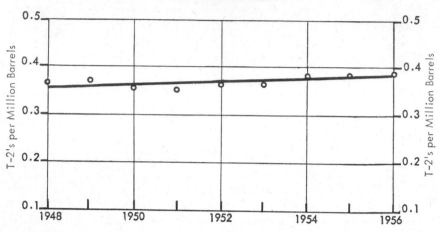

trend. However, between 1912 and 1922 while world production continued
to rise at a uniform rate, much of this was outside the U.S. (where the major
demand existed) and a very rapid rise in ocean borne petroleum transportation
took place. Since 1922, relative stability has existed, with a uniform growth in
crude production and a slightly higher rate of increase in transportation
requirements. The W trend line closely parallels the nine-year trend in U and
the fixed difference reflects the average number of tie-ups. Thus, our assumption that U will continue to rise uniformly appears quite reasonable (despite the
small, regular oscillations about the slowly rising trends).

World crude oil production is shown in Exhibit 7. This graph shows that
production has been growing exponentially since 1942 and the tonnage

Exhibit 6

W, TANKER FLEET PER MILLION BARRELS OF WORLD CRUDE OIL
PRODUCTION

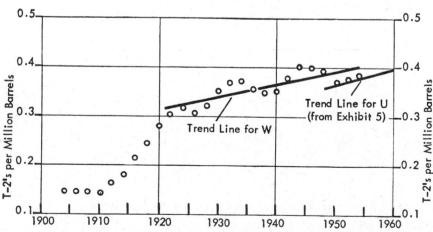

Exhibit 7

WORLD PRODUCTION OF CRUDE OIL

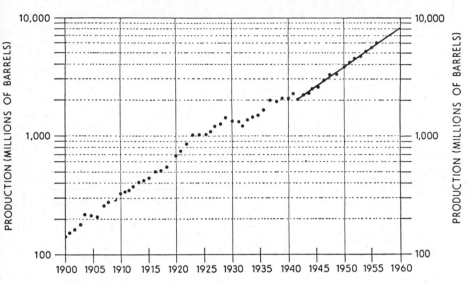

estimates of Exhibit 8 are based on the assumption that this will continue until 1965. However, the rate of growth may decrease in the next few years as it did in 1923 and 1939. Such a reduction might result from the introduction of other sources of energy which could more than offset the demand for petrochemicals.

In addition, the ratio U may reach a maximum and even decrease as the result of one or more of the following factors which are becoming increasingly apparent:

1. In future, U.S. petroleum requirements may be satisfied more by domestic and nearby sources.
2. European requirements may also be met by nearby supplies and even long pipe lines which could substantially shorten the length of the average ocean voyage.
3. Similarly, markets and crude oil developments in other parts of the world may combine to decrease tanker haulage distances.

A falling rate of growth of world crude production and a possible flattening of the U curve, both tend to yield greater tanker tie-ups than our predictions.

Exhibit 8

TONNAGE ESTIMATES

Year	Tonnage Estimates as of First of Each Year (T-2 Equivalents)			Consecutive Voyage Charter Rate Estimates Aruba/US North of Hatteras (% USMC)
	Required	Available	Minimum Tie-ups	
1958	2,760	2,895	135	-42
1959	3,010	3,215	105	-39
1960	3,280	3,535	255	-46
1961	3,570	3,810	240	-45
1962	3,890	4,015	125	-38
1963	4,230	4,220	-10	-
1964	4,610	4,425	-185	-
1965	5,030	4,635	-395	-

The tanker shortages shown for 1964 and 1965 will almost certainly not develop because if requirements are as predicted there will be increased construction in 1962 and 1963.

Where low charter rates are shown there will likely be construction contract cancellations. Insofar as their impact on ship prices and charter rates is concerned, such cancellations have a similar effect to additional tie-ups. If there are construction cancellations it should be possible to take over an existing contract on very favourable terms.

Exhibit 9

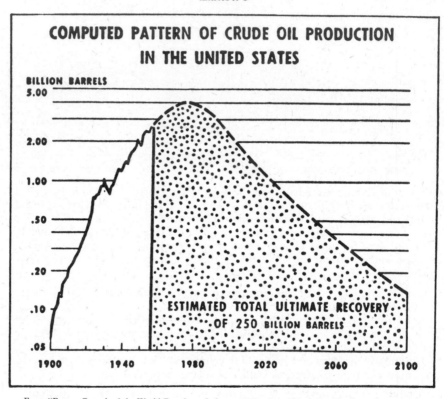

From "Future Growth of the World Petroleum Industry," The Chase Manhattan Bank.

Our predictions only cover the period up to 1965 and what lies beyond becomes increasingly difficult to forecast. However, Exhibit 9 indicates an independent view of U.S. indigenous crude recovery limitations. This exhibit suggests that after 1980 the U.S. will become increasingly dependent on foreign crude as domestic supplies are exhausted. Unless the U.S. demand for petroleum also fell off at this time, the ratios U and W might increase rapidly, leading to a potential shortage of tankers after 1980.

D. *Prediction of Tanker Construction Costs*

The first point of importance is that tanker prices vary differently in different countries. In Exhibit 1 we see that the U.K. tanker price index has increased without oscillations, since 1947. The European tanker price index, on the other hand, has shown two complete oscillations in the same period. Apparently, the reason for this difference is that the U.K. has been the world's preferred shipbuilder. Demand has grown relatively constantly due to long-term building contracts with such large-scale operators as Shell and Cunard White Star Lines, and hence prices have risen very regularly.

This steady rise in U.K. shipbuilding prices has not been projected by a simple extrapolation of the trend since there are numerous economic forces at work in the European and world trading areas which might well alter the future pattern. Any change or break in trend presently foreseeable would tend to flatten or reverse it in the period under study. No satisfactory mechanism for predicting the U.K. prices has been discovered to quantify these observations.

Exhibit 10

PREDICTED AND ACTUAL EUROPEAN SHIPBUILDING COSTS

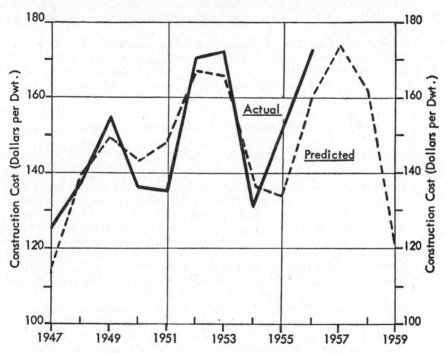

On the other hand, an exhaustive search and analysis has yielded a promising method of predicting European shipbuilding costs. The forecasting procedures and relevant information are discussed in Appendix A and the resulting predictions are shown in Exhibit 10.

In the long range planning of the purchase of tankers, three basic strategies are available. The first, and least attractive, is to buy vessels when the market is at its peaks of fluctuations. The second and most attractive is to buy when the market fluctuates to its lowest ebbs. The third approach is based on a continuous building program which tends to average the peaks and valleys in cost. This method is better than the first, but does not take advantage of the predictability of market conditions. Clearly, the second approach represents an ideal target which can be approximated through careful forward analysis and planning. *On the basis of the foregoing, there appears to be substantial support for delaying any purchase decisions to take advantage of anticipated lower construction costs.*

III. EVALUATION OF PROPOSALS TO BUILD, BUY, SELL OR CHARTER TANKERS

A. General Approach

Before presenting numerical illustrations and working-formulas for routine use, it may prove helpful to discuss the general approach taken and the reasoning that applies.

Suppose that A and B are two proposals to provide ocean borne crude oil transportation. For example, alternative A may be the proposal that a certain tanker be purchased and B, that the same amount of transportation be provided by a specific type of chartering. Both A and B will involve a sequence of future cash outlays.

Let the discounted values of these cash flows be represented by the symbols K_A and K_B respectively. If K_B is greater than K_A then alternative A is better than B and the difference $V = K_B - K_A$ is the dollar incentive to carry out A rather than B. If B were used, the extra expenses of the proposal during its life would be equivalent to an additional payment of V dollars at the beginning of the project. Conversely, if K_B is less than K_A, V is negative, B is more attractive than A and the effective dollar penalty for adopting A versus B is measured by V.

We will present several pertinent examples of the calculation of V, but first there are some general remarks that apply to all the cases considered.

1. For this application, it is necessary to choose the interest rate to be used in calculating the discounted values of the future payments. The proper rate is a matter of opinion and the same individual might choose different rates at different times. However, we believe the correct rate is the one that could be earned if the capital involved in A and B were invested in other operations of the Company. Since this rate is not fixed we will compute V for a range of interest rates.

2. The value of V depends to some extent on the lengths of the voyages that will be made by the ships under consideration. In order to have a uniform basis for comparison we will assume in all cases that crude is being brought from Puerto la Cruz to Portland (2,000 miles). This is also satisfactory for all trips from Venezuela to Portland or Halifax. If Middle East crude were being considered seriously, new values of V and related exhibits could be provided.

3. Instead of comparing plans A and B directly, we will compare each with a standard, basic proposal S. This is particularly convenient when we wish to rank a set of alternatives $A, B, C, \ldots$ The standard, S, is "Obtain the required transportation by consecutive voyage charters on the open market." In accordance with the predictions of Section II we will take the charter rate to be USMC -40% from 1958 to 1963 and we will assume that the average rate over the remaining life of the proposals is USMC flat (which for say a 15 year period will be realistic, especially since any error will be decreased by the discounting factors).

4. In all the examples below, income tax payments have been taken into account at the prevailing rates.

5. Certain costs, which are approximately the same no matter how the crude is delivered, have been omitted from the calculations. These costs, which do not affect V appreciably, are :

   a) Inventory costs for crude in storage and in transit.

   b) The cost of storage tanks in terminals.

   c) The overhead and administrative costs of Imperial's Marine Division and related charges. These costs could vary significantly only if large scale arrangements were made to buy new vessels (which might require more head office staff) or to sell tankers (which might release staff for reassignment outside the Marine Division). However, there have been no indications of such substantial changes and we have assumed that they will not take place. If necessary, the incentives could easily be recalculated to include any contemplated changes in the overhead and administrative costs.

B. Should a New Tanker Be Purchased?

We have developed practical, easy-to-use charts to facilitate comparisons of purchase versus charter alternatives and present here some examples of their use. Both cargo carrying capacity and vessel speed are prime factors influencing the comparative economics of owning alternative tankers. Desirable cargo carrying capacity depends on both moving crude at low cost per barrel and storing it at a reasonable unit cost. In view of this, we considered a set of hypothetical new tankers of four different capacities (35,000 dwt., 45,000 dwt., 65,000 dwt., and 85,000 dwt.) and eight different speeds (11 to 18 knots in one knot steps). Here we mean the speed averaged over weather conditions as encountered on the voyages considered. For each of these ships (A, B, C, etcetera), we consider the proposal, "Let Imperial's wholly owned subsidiary, the Caribbean Oil and Transport Company, buy this tanker and bareboat charter it to I.O.L." As before, S is the standard proposal to obtain consecutive voyage charters at the prevailing rates. For each case V is the incentive to carry out a proposal A rather than S.

Incidentally, there do not appear to be any insurmountable obstacles to serving Halifax by large vessels of 85,000 dwt. or even up to 100,000 dwt. Providing additional fenders and dock strengthening for one of Imperial's berths to accommodate 85,000 dwt. tankers is estimated by the contractor to entail approximately $25,000 construction. Dredging costs would be additional. The latest "Decca" navigational aids are being installed on the East coast and can supplement advanced radar equipment to facilitate safe manoeuvering. Furthermore, the port authorities are apparently anxious to co-operate and accommodate larger vessels. The harbour facilities at Portland are probably going to be revamped to accommodate very large ships, but the timing still appears uncertain owing to the many interests involved.

Estimates of construction costs and operating expenses for the above tankers were supplied by Imperial's Marine Division and are listed in Exhibit 30 [omitted in this book]. The details of the calculation are described in Appendix B and numerical results are tabulated in Exhibits 20 and 32. Graphs of V for this set of tankers are shown in Exhibits 11 to 14. Exhibit 15 shows the optimum speed for each capacity and interest rate and Exhibit 16 gives V for the optimum ships, expressed in dollars and in cents per barrel of crude delivered.

The graphs may be used as follows. Suppose, for example, that an interest rate of 10% has been chosen. From Exhibit 15 we see that the best speed for a 35,000 dwt. tanker is 13.1 knots. But even for this tanker, S is less expensive by 1.4 million dollars. Similarly the best 45,000 dwt. ship has a speed of 14.0

Exhibit 11

V, PRESENT NET INCENTIVE (AFTER TAXES) TO BUY A NEW
35,000 DWT. TANKER

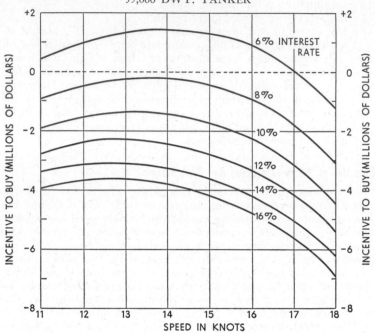

Exhibit 12

V, PRESENT NET INCENTIVE (AFTER TAXES) TO BUY A NEW
45,000 DWT. TANKER

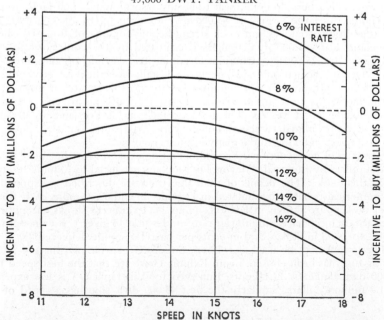

Exhibit 13

V, PRESENT NET INCENTIVE (AFTER TAXES) TO BUY A NEW
65,000 DWT. TANKER

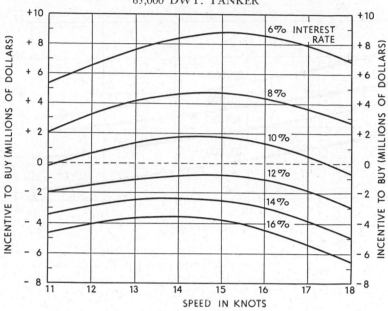

Exhibit 14

V, PRESENT NET INCENTIVE (AFTER TAXES) TO BUY A NEW
85,000 DWT. TANKER

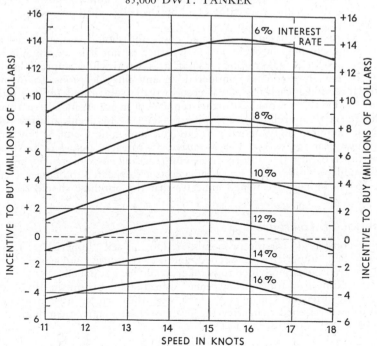

Exhibit 15

OPTIMUM TANKER SPEED

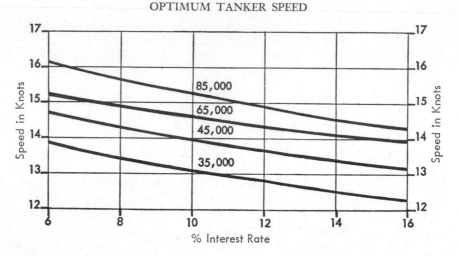

knots and is more expensive than chartering by 0.3 million dollars. We see, however, that buying a 14.7 knot, 65,000 dwt. tanker is better than S by 1.9 million dollars and a 15.2 knot, 85,000 dwt. ship is more attractive than S by 4.5 million dollars.

These graphs can also be used to compare two ships with each other instead of with S. Thus, at 10% the optimum 65,000 dwt. tanker is better than the optimum 45,000 dwt. tanker by 2.2 million dollars. We can also determine the penalty for departing from the optimum speeds. Exhibit 12 shows that at 10%, for 45,000 dwt. ships, a speed of 14.0 knots is better than a speed of 16.0 knots by $650,000.

Exhibits 11 to 16 are based on estimated costs, and should be considered as directional guides to help in deciding (1) whether or not it is worthwhile to build or buy any new tanker [and] (2) if it is worthwhile, approximately what kind of tanker should be considered. In any final decisions, following such initial directional analyses, actual costs may be substituted for the estimated ones used here, to provide a further refinement in appraising alternatives.

The timing of the purchase of a specific tanker may be decided in the following way. Compare the proposals, A: buy this tanker now and B: buy this tanker say one year from now. The incentive, V, to carry out A rather than B is approximately just the difference in construction costs or tanker prices at the times under consideration. Since these costs are expected to decrease during 1958, V will be negative which indicates that the purchase should be delayed.

C. "Imperial St. Lawrence"

We now consider V for the proposals, A: Do not sell "Imperial St. Lawrence" and S: Sell "Imperial St. Lawrence" and use consecutive voyage charters to replace the transportation which this tanker would have supplied.

Actual operating data for "St. Lawrence" were obtained from the 1957 records. These are listed in Appendix B along with the formula used to calculate V. We have assumed that after the present charter agreement with the

Exhibit 16

INCENTIVE TO BUY OPTIMUM TANKERS

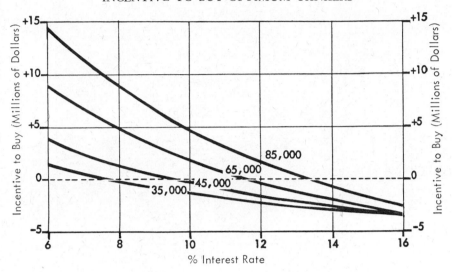

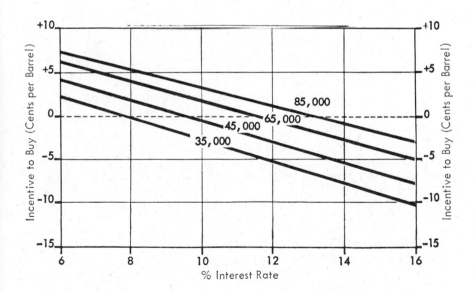

Caribbean Oil and Transport Company runs out in 1962, Imperial's charter rate will be reduced to $1.20 per dwt. per month. Numerical results are in Exhibits 20 and 31, and are shown graphically in Exhibit 17. We see from this latter exhibit that even if I.O.L. were offered as much as 9.0 million dollars for "St. Lawrence," at any interest rate up to 10.5%, it would be better to keep this ship.

Exhibit 17

V, PRESENT NET DOLLAR INCENTIVE (AFTER TAXES) TO
KEEP "ST. LAWRENCE"

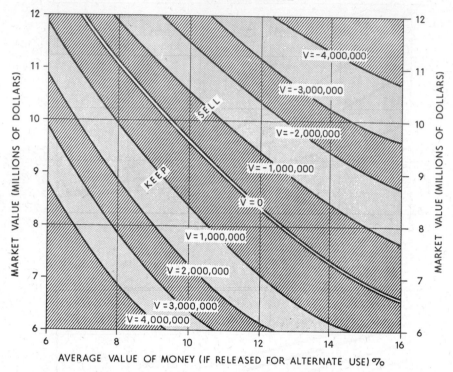

AVERAGE VALUE OF MONEY (IF RELEASED FOR ALTERNATE USE) %

D. "Imperial Toronto"

An analysis, similar to the above, was carried out for "Toronto." Last year's operating data were used (see Exhibit 35). Numerical results are in Exhibits 20 and 36 and are presented graphically in Exhibit 18. This latter exhibit is similar to Exhibit 17 and again provides a family of curves which give the incentive to keep "Toronto" with any combination of interest rate and market value of the ship.

E. "Imperial Edmonton"

Except for 1958 repair costs of $900,000, the operating data are the same as for "Toronto." Numerical results are in Exhibits 20 and 37 and graphs of the incentive to keep are in Exhibit 19.

F. Long Term Charters

Because of the wide variety of long term charter agreements, we have not calculated any numerical examples. However, for any particular proposal, V may be obtained from the estimated cash flows.

Exhibit 18

V, PRESENT NET DOLLAR INCENTIVE (AFTER TAXES) TO
KEEP "IMPERIAL TORONTO"

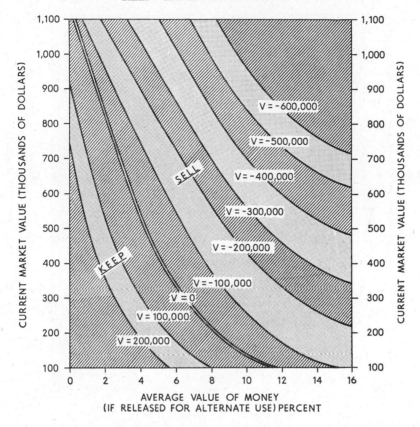

Exhibit 19

V, PRESENT NET DOLLAR INCENTIVE (AFTER TAXES) TO
KEEP "EDMONTON"

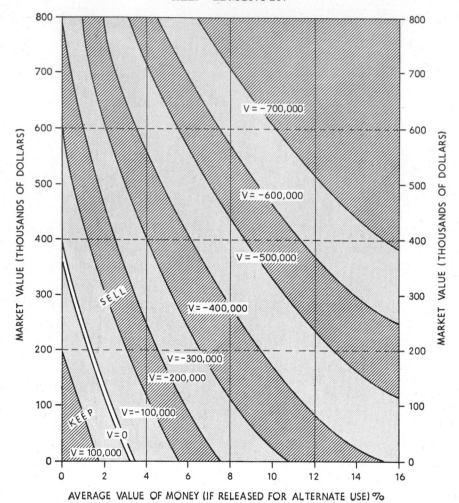

Exhibit 20

NUMERICAL EXAMPLES: DOLLAR INCENTIVES TO KEEP
EXISTING SHIPS IN THE FLEET

V, Incentive to Keep "Imperial St. Lawrence"
(Thousands of Dollars)

Market Value	Interest Rate		
(Millions of Dollars)	8%	10%	12%
7.0.............................3,850		2,400	1,260
8.0.............................2,850		1,400	260
9.0.............................1,850		400	− 740

V, Incentive to Keep "Imperial Toronto"
(Thousands of Dollars)

Market Value	Interest Rate		
(Millions of Dollars)	8%	10%	12%
1.0.............................−530		−610	−690
1.2.............................−660		−760	−830
1.4.............................−800		−900	−980

V, Incentive to Keep "Imperial Edmonton"
(Thousands of Dollars)

Market Value	Interest Rate		
(Millions of Dollars)	8%	10%	12%
0.4.............................−490		−570	−630
0.6.............................−630		−710	−770
0.8.............................−770		−850	−920

Exhibit 21

MAXIMUM ESTIMATES OF REFINERY
CRUDE REQUIREMENTS

(Thousands of Barrels Daily)

1957	Montreal Refinery	Halifax Refinery
1957	70	40
1958	70	44
1959	70	44
1960	70	44
1961	70	48
1962	95	53
1963	120	57
1964	120	57
1965	120	57

IV. A DISCUSSION OF CONTROLLED COVERAGE

A. General Discussion

High controlled coverage is often emphasized as being a desirable attribute of a petroleum company's fleet operations. We have studied the various statements and reports which are available and have not found any factual evidence to justify this position. Our view is that there is no fixed percentage of controlled coverage which is optimum but, instead, that this percentage oscillates slowly as the other strategic variables (charter rates, construction costs, etcetera) oscillate. That is, optimum coverage is a resultant or dependent variable of the fundamental strategic variables. Thus, for example, a reduction of controlled coverage during an interval of low charter rates is not a cause for concern, but on the contrary, corresponds to good strategy just as does a rise in this percentage in anticipation of an interval of high charter rates.

Furthermore, for those who believe a shipper might sometimes go short of bottoms, there has been no evidence of this through the records since the turn of the century. While it is true that spot rates have reached USMC + 250%, such peaks have been short-lived and have provided an enormous incentive to increase the world tanker fleet by construction, conversion, "demothballing," etcetera. *There is virtually no evidence that, apart from brief war time periods, there has ever been a true lack of bottoms to transport all ocean borne crude requirements from 1900 to the present.*

In view of the foregoing, we do not believe that coverage is an overriding consideration in deciding whether to own or charter, but that decisions should be based on the dollar incentives of Section III.

B. *Imperial's Coverage*

When making decisions regarding the controlled fleet, it is necessary to know the present coverage if only to ensure that additional tankers will not increase the coverage to over 100%. This information is given in Exhibits 22 and 23. A possible extension of the Interprovincial Pipeline to Montreal has been arbitrarily shown at the beginning of 1963. It should be noted that the recent proposal to trade Eastern imports of U.S. crude for Western exports of Canadian crude could have the same effect on coverage as the extension of

Exhibit 22

TRANSPORTATION COVERAGE BY IMPERIAL-CONTROLLED TANKERS
(Assuming Venezuelan Crude Supply Only)

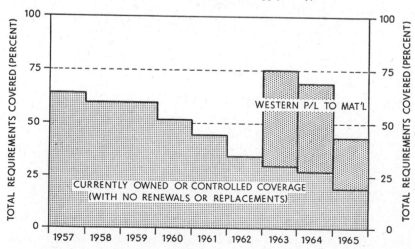

Exhibit 23

TRANSPORTATION COVERAGE BY IMPERIAL-CONTROLLED TANKERS
(Assuming Middle East Crude Supply Only)

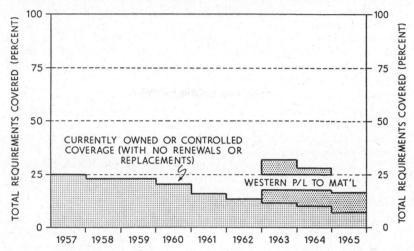

the pipe line. Exhibits 22 and 23 have been based on the following estimates of the future Montreal and Halifax crude requirements.

V. OPERATION OF THE EXISTING FLEET

A. *Turnaround Times and Causes of Delay*

Exhibit 24 gives estimates of the annual cost of the port delays of Imperial ships. The large delays at Amuay Bay, Aruba and La Salina occur when our tankers are on exchange to other affiliates, and hence the cost of these is not incurred by Imperial. However, it does seem worthwhile to note the order of magnitude of these costs. Incidentally, two of the above three ports are now the subject of operations research studies by Esso Research and Engineering.

Exhibit 24

COST OF PORT DELAYS
(Thousands of Dollars per Year)

Port	Berth Congestion	Waiting for Pilot and Tug	Waiting for Shore Orders	Shore Readiness	Doctor	Tide	Totals
Portland................	19	2	0	1	1	0	23
Halifax.................	6	1	1	0	1	0	9
Puerto la Cruz..........	43	8	2	1	0	0	54
Amuay Bay.............	33	12	2	8	2	0	59
Aruba.................	72	24	4	8	0	0	108
La Salina..............	50	12	10	16	4	22	114
Totals............	223	59	21	34	8	22	367

Most of the delay due to berth congestion at Portland and Puerto la Cruz was accounted for by "Imperial St. Lawrence." These costs for this one ship were $12,000 and $37,000 respectively in 1957 (prorated to a full year). The figures were obtained by calculating what the ship's operating costs would have been, and how much crude would have been delivered if there had been no berth congestion.

In addition to the delays, the so-called "normal" turnaround time should be studied. In the case of the "St. Lawrence," an increase of one hour in the average single voyage turnaround time costs $8,000 per year. In this connection it might prove very worthwhile to investigate:

1. The technology of high speed, large volume pumping, particularly with regard to the dissipation of electrostatic charges and the control of vessel trim while loading and unloading.
2. Detailed ship scheduling—which has been assumed efficient for the purposes of this study.
3. The latest types of hoses and connectors (*Petroleum Week*, February 21, 1958).

B. *Optimum Operating Speeds*

The optimum operation of a fleet of tankers involves many factors. However, speed is the most important of these and is the only one considered here. Nominal, but still worthwhile savings are possible by examining individual vessel characteristics and prevailing charter rates and by modifying performance accordingly.

If a given owned or bareboat chartered tanker is run slower than usual, operating costs will be reduced. But the ship will deliver less crude and this will have to be made up by consecutive voyage charters. Thus, when charter rates are low, there may be a net saving if the average speed is decreased. The problem then is to balance marginal operating costs and marginal crude delivered.

The only operating costs which need be obtained are those which change with speed. These are: (1) fuel costs, (2) port charges, (3) repair costs. Unfortunately, we have no data on the fuel consumption of Imperial's tankers when they are operated at different speeds and under different weather conditions. However, we have worked an example based on sea trial data for the "Imperial St. Lawrence." This calculation would be improved if actual operating data were obtained. From the information available, the example yielded the following results (as detailed in Appendix C):

1. The best average operating speed with today's consecutive voyage charter rates is 16.5 knots.
2. The cost curve is quite flat in the region of this optimum speed and a departure of up to 0.5 knots either way results in very little difference in total cost.
3. However, if "St. Lawrence" departs by 1.5 knots either way an annual penalty of at least $20,000 is incurred.
4. While the indicated optimum at today's charter rates coincides with the actual average operating speed for 1957 this may be misleading. If the true fuel consumption and repair data were determined, the optimum speed might turn out to be significantly less than 16.5 knots with a corresponding potential saving.
5. If charter rates return to USMC flat, for example, then with the data employed above, the optimum speed would rise to the maximum possible for the vessel.

C. Weather Routing

A considerable amount of detailed information has been compiled, and a number of conversations held, concerning the pros and cons and feasibility of improvements in operations through "navigating with the weather." The leading professional in this field is Mr. Louis Allen, a highly regarded Meterologist and Oceanographer in Washington, D.C. After many years of Merchant Marine and Naval experience he now operates, as a commercial consultant, "Louis Allen Associates—Navigational Weather System, Meteorologists, Oceanographers."

The procedure used by Mr. Allen is as follows:

1. His staff of specialists prepares detailed forecasts of weather and sea conditions in advance of any particular voyage.
2. He develops data on how the ship behaves under different weather conditions and in loaded and ballast states.
3. The vessel's owners receive a detailed voyage plan which they relay to the ship's master as a recommended routing. Of course the master is free to carry out this recommendation or not as he sees fit.
4. In any case, the Consulting Service tracks the vessel and listens for her routine weather reports. If his route is not followed, Mr. Allen compares the actual results with those which would have been obtained on the recommended route.

The anticipated results of this system may be best indicated by quoting the conclusions of a report being published by the Society of Naval Architects and Marine Engineers entitled "Transoceanic Routing of Ships Based upon Meteorological Forecasts" by Capt. Thomas A. King, Assistant Chief, Division of Operations, Office of Ship Operations, Maritime Administration, U.S. Department of Commerce:

"The concept of navigating with the weather is admittedly not new. The techniques needed in order to achieve the potential promised by advances in meteorology and oceanography, however, are new. These techniques in fact are still in the development stage.

"In ship operations, as contrasted with aircraft operations, where pressure pattern flying has long been established, the problem becomes more complex. The complexity is inherent as the ship operates in two media and one plane, rather than in one medium and a choice of a number of planes. Additionally, since the fastest of ships are relatively slow and lack maneuverability—compared to aircraft—the period of exposure is longer, the forecast more demanding, and the choice of action more confined.

"With this preface, however, it is concluded that recently developed techniques and practices in the application of meteorology to ocean navigation can result in significantly improved vessel performance. This improvement can be achieved in terms of reduced time on passage, fuel economies, less heavy weather damage, safety, and potentially reduced insurance premiums. It is not concluded that all vessels on all trade routes would benefit in equal degree. There are still many refinements and advances to be made in the practical application of this science to ocean shipping. As an example, such advances could be expected through further co-ordination of the benefits to be derived from meteorology with the gains that could be made by more advanced applied oceanography.

"While the seaman, of necessity, is a practical meteorologist, it is doubtful that the true benefits to be derived from all the advances that have been made could be realized without the training of the professional meteorologist. It is further doubtful that full benefit can be realized unless the application of the science is specially tailored to the needs of a particular vessel upon a particular voyage. It therefore is concluded that the maximum benefits can be achieved when a professional meteorologist, with all of the information available, studies the problem of a specific ship about to depart on a known passage and thus arrives at a recommended route calculated to represent the desired balance between steaming distance and weather to be encountered.

"While the frequency and magnitude of savings which can be achieved are not considered to have been determined in the demonstrations under study, it is concluded that the total cost of conducting the demonstrations has been more than balanced by the savings achieved. In the first demonstration alone, where the testing conditions were considered to have been at an optimum, the direct savings alone would more than have paid for the cost of all 27 demonstrations.

"It therefore is concluded that the application of professional meteorological techniques to ocean navigation holds much promise in terms of both economy and efficient operation. Accordingly all interests, both in government and private industry, should consider further exploring and studying the benefits to be thus derived."

Mr. Allen estimates that his service would save Imperial up to $250,000 a year at a cost of $25,000 a year. However, some very real reservations exist in Imperial, regarding the potentialities of this approach for north-south passages. Mr. Allen has offered to carry out (without obligation) a detailed comparison of existing and proposed operational procedures applied to actual voyages of Imperial's ships. This could provide an excellent basis for more informed comments, questions and criticism and might lead to a limited operational experiment.

VI. ASSESSMENT OF NEW DEVELOPMENTS

Crude oil is a very abundant, low value commodity per unit of weight or volume and as such favours the cheapest possible transportation with virtually no premium on speed of delivery except possibly in wartime. These considerations are bound to have a profound influence on the following developments and technical innovations.

A. Submarine Tankers

Submarine tankers have been seriously proposed by naval architects and marine engineers. However, very large submarine tankers would require great quantities of lead ballast, and current naval architectural opinion is that "eventually the stability problem would make the ship impractical." However, one naval architect has prepared plans for a 12,300 ton displacement (5,000 dwt.) submarine tanker, and while the ship would be uneconomic in peacetime, it would have definite tactical advantages in wartime—particularly if nuclear-powered. Nevertheless, Press reports of similar plans for 100,000 tons displacement with 50-knot capabilities are clearly absurd since the machinery involved would fill nearly half the hull and be prohibitively expensive!

B. Nuclear-Powered Tankers

Closed cycle gas turbine nuclear propulsion plants in tankers will require slightly less crew than oil-fired steam plants of equal shaft horsepower due to the elimination of fireman water tenders. Also, nuclear power plants of this type are about 20% more efficient than conventional power plants. While nuclear power plants weigh more, they require much less space than conventional ones (about 40% less, not including fuel which makes the disparity even greater). When the basic development work on this propulsion machinery has been done, it may prove quite superior to conventional types. Hawker Siddely, John Brown Nuclear Construction Ltd. has been formed to build a 60,-000 dwt. nuclear-powered oil tanker and there is considerable interest in such vessels in North America. However, Professor H. B. Benford presented a paper at the November, 1957 A.P.I. annual meeting in which he stated: "The results of the studies make it appear unlikely that nuclear-propelled merchant ships will become commercially competitive within ten years unless costs can be brought down more rapidly than now thought possible."

C. Supertankers

Enormous 500,000 dwt. nuclear-powered tankers have been proposed, but docking problems, inventory costs and the penalty in case of accident are factors to be balanced against very low unit operating cost. Technical problems of unloading at Portland or Halifax might be economically insurmountable, and marine architectural problems exist for these gigantic vessels. However, several tankers of over 100,000 dwt. are reported on order.

D. Nylon Containers

Esso Research, Limited, has been studying the possible use of proofed nylon containers for the transportation and storage of oil. It has been found that economic use of these huge nylon sausages will only be possible if they can be used over and over, preferably for two or more years. Certain technical problems associated with towing the containers through heavy seas need further examination. This system will reduce costs only if the containers are towed by tankers of well over 27,000 dwt. and only if 20,000 tons of crude can be towed. This introduces problems of tow-rope strength and certain navigational and maneuvering limitations. Clearly, this type of transportation is not ripe for commercial exploitation yet but needs, and is worthy of, extensive sea trials and further research and development (e.g., we have suggested investigations of fibreglas reinforced containers and gear as one possible means of improving design and performance). Apart from these developments by Esso Research, Limited, we have a report covering German research and sea trials involving similar plastic containers. This work appears to be more advanced in some respect but not all. Again, Press reports of 600 foot, 20,000 dwt. containers appear decidedly premature and misleading.

E. Sea-Lines

Indications are that sea-lines may be a profitable alternative to normal dock facilities if very large vessels are employed and unexpected harbour or berthing difficulties arise. One such major installation has recently been put into use in a sheltered region of the Eastern U.S. seaboard with very successful results and at a cost estimated between one-half million and one million dollars. A sheltered mooring is necessary near the terminal point to keep costs down. It is doubtful if the need exists in Halifax with other alternatives available.

F. Flying Boats

Flying boats have been used for transporting crude in emergencies but are clearly uneconomic, despite certain speculation on eventual nuclear-power developments.

APPENDIX A

PREDICTION OF CHARTER RATES AND CONSTRUCTION COSTS

1. Relationship between Charter Rates and Tie-ups

Let R be the rate, expressed in percent USMC, for consecutive voyage charters, Caribbean/U.S. North of Cape Hatteras, averaged over a three month interval and let T be the number of tie-ups, in T–2 equivalents at the beginning of interval. Values of R and T are in Exhibits 25 and 26.

Exhibit 25

R, CONSECUTIVE VOYAGE CHARTER RATE, CARIBBEAN/U.S. NORTH OF CAPE HATTERAS, THREE-MONTH AVERAGE (% USMC)

	1st Quarter	2nd Quarter	3rd Quarter	4th Quarter
1948	+230	+137	− 2	− 8
1949	− 2	− 21	−48	−41
1950	− 24	− 40	−37	+ 7
1951	+ 89	+161	+49	+39
1952	+170	+195	+25	+ 2
1953	− 10	− 33	−38	−43
1954	− 38	− 37	−58	−42
1955	− 17	− 22	−42	−29
1956	+ 45	+ 8	+58	+57
1957	+181	+ 32	−34	−58

Exhibit 26

T, TANKERS IN TIE-UP AS OF FIRST OF EACH QUARTER
(T–2 Equivalents)

	1st Quarter	2nd Quarter	3rd Quarter	4th Quarter
1948	0.0	0.0	1.0	13.0
1949	10.6	30.6	89.6	71.5
1950	23.9	20.8	10.8	4.8
1951	0.0	0.0	0.0	0.0
1952	0.6	1.0	1.0	2.3
1953	7.6	12.3	50.5	81.9
1954	89.2	91.1	155.8	164.5
1955	71.2	56.9	58.9	36.2
1956	18.1	8.9	6.9	6.2
1957	2.9	0.0		

The curve of Exhibit 2 was obtained by fitting a function of the form

$$R = a + b/(T/D + c)$$

by least squares. Here, D is the demand for tankers (see Exhibit 27). This procedure gave $a = -51.9$, $b = 0.493$, $c = 0.0028$.

Exhibit 27

	F World Tanker Fleet (Jan. 1) (T–2's)	T Tie-ups (Jan. 1) (T–2's)	D = F – T Tanker Demand (T–2's)	P World Crude Oil Produc- tion (Millions of Bbls.)	U (T-2's per Million Bbls.)
1948............1,268	0	1,268	3,433	0.369
1949............1,274	11	1,263	3,404	0.371
1950............1,391	24	1,367	3,802	0.360
1951............1,507	0	1,507	4,283	0.352
1952............1,636	1	1,635	4,505	0.363
1953............1,775	8	1,767	4,787	0.369
1954............2,004	89	1,915	5,006	0.383
1955............2,244	71	2,173	5,641	0.385
1956............2,398	18	2,380	6,093	0.391

F is from reference 19 of the Bibliography [omitted in this book]; T is from [reference] 21, and P is from [reference] 25.

2. Prediction of Tanker Demand

Let D be the tanker demand, expressed in T–2 equivalents and let P be the world crude oil production in millions of barrels per year. We define U by

$$U = D/P$$

Forecasts of D were obtained by predicting future values of U and P. Values of U for 1948 to 1956 are in Exhibit 27. The least squares straight line is

$$U = 0.3588 + 0.00322\,(t-1948)$$

Exhibit 28 gives world crude oil production, P, from 1900 to 1956 (see also Exhibit 7). The trend line, based on data from 1942 to 1956, is

$$\log_{10}P = 3.313 + 0.03353\,(t-1942)$$

Exhibit 28

Year	P World Crude Production (Millions of Barrels)	F World Tanker Fleet (Jan. 1) (T–2 Equiva- lents)	W Seven Year Average of F/P
1900......................	149	20	
1901......................	167	22	
1902......................	182	25	
1903......................	195	27	0.145
1904......................	218	33	0.145
1905......................	215	34	0.145
1906......................	213	35	0.146
1907......................	264	36	0.148

Exhibit 28 (Continued)

Year	P World Crude Production (Millions of Barrels)	F World Tanker Fleet (Jan. 1) (T-2 Equiva-lents)	W Seven Year Average of F/P
1908	285	37	0.147
1909	299	44	0.144
1910	328	48	0.143
1911	344	50	0.150
1912	352	50	0.163
1913	385	58	0.172
1914	408	77	0.182
1915	432	95	0.197
1916	458	96	0.216
1917	503	108	0.232
1918	504	128	0.247
1919	556	151	0.265
1920	689	182	0.280
1921	766	225	0.297
1922	859	294	0.306
1923	1,016	323	0.314
1924	1,014	337	0.318
1925	1,069	341	0.319
1926	1,097	355	0.312
1927	1,263	371	0.314
1928	1,325	397	0.321
1929	1,486	443	0.338
1930	1,410	468	0.349
1931	1,373	518	0.361
1932	1,310	571	0.369
1933	1,442	579	0.375
1934	1,522	582	0.372
1935	1,654	584	0.368
1936	1,791	605	0.357
1937	2,039	640	0.353
1938	1,988	692	0.350
1939	2,086	752	0.354
1940	2,152	809	0.353
1941	2,221	798	0.365
1942	2,093	796	0.377
1943	2,257	749	0.392
1944	2,292	909	0.399
1945	2,595	1,129	0.400
1946	2,745	1,265	0.399
1947	3,022	1,285	0.404
1948	3,433	1,268	0.398
1949	3,404	1,274	0.388
1950	3,802	1,391	0.373
1951	4,283	1,507	0.370
1952	4,505	1,636	0.374
1953	4,787	1,775	0.377
1954	5,006	2,004	
1955	5,641	2,244	
1956	6,093	2,398	
1957		2,614	

P is from reference 25 of the Bibliography [omitted in this book] and *F* is from [reference] 19.

3. Prediction of European Tanker Construction Cost

Let F_t be the fleet size in T–2 equivalents, in year t. European tanker cost Y_t, is an index to tanker cost throughout a year, t. In contrast, the demand index, $X_t = F_{t+2} - F_t$, is measured as of January 1, so it seemed advisable to combine demand indices for t and $t+1$ in developing a prediction formula for cost in year t. We are more interested in the deviations of X_t and Y_t from their linear trends and it is these deviations which we actually used. The calculations were based on the data in Exhibit 29.

Exhibit 29

Year	Y European Tanker Cost (Dollars per Dwt.)	F World Tanker Fleet Size on Jan. 10 (T–2 Equivalents)
1947	125	1,285
1948	138	1,268
1949	154	1,274
1950	136	1,391
1951	135	1,507
1952	170	1,636
1953	172	1,775
1954	131	2,004
1955	152	2,244
1956	173	2,398

We put

$$X_t = F_{t+2} - F_t \tag{1}$$

The regression line of X_t on t is

$$\bar{X}_t = 78 + 49(t\text{–}1947)$$

and the residual x_t is

$$x_t = X_t - 78 - 49(t\text{–}1947) \tag{2}$$

A slightly different method was used to remove the effect of time from Y_t. Here the regression equation is

$$\bar{Y} = 1334 + 3.382(t\text{–}1947) \tag{3}$$

and the adjusted cost, y_t, is defined to be

$$y_t = Y_t \bar{Y}_{1947}/\bar{Y}_t \tag{4}$$

The regression equation of y_t on x_t and x_{t+1} is

$$\bar{y}_t = 130.1 + 0.1695x_t + 0.1065x_{t+1} \tag{5}$$

Equations (1) to (5) and estimates of F_t from Exhibit 8 were used to predict construction costs for 1957–1959. The results are shown in Exhibit 10.

APPENDIX B

EVALUATION OF PROPOSALS TO BUY AND SELL TANKERS

1. Introduction

Consider two proposals, A and B which involve the transport of the same constant quantity of crude per year for n years between the same ports.

Let the estimated net cash outlays at the end of the t-th year to carry out these plans be $K_1(t)$ and $K_2(t)$ respectively. Then the discounted difference in cost is

$$V = \sum_0^n [K_2(t) - K_1(t)]v^t$$

where

$$v = 1/(1 + i)$$

and i is the interest rate. V is the cash incentive to carry out A rather than B and will be calculated for a range of interest rates. Actually K may include some items which are paid almost continuously (wages, for example). These are multiplied by

$$\overline{s_1}| = i / \log_e(1 + i)$$

to give the correct discounted value.

We will consider in detail, two types of comparison. In the first, A is the proposal that Imperial's wholly owned subsidiary, the Caribbean Oil and Transport Company (hereafter COTC), buy a ship (or keep a ship which it already owns) and bareboat charter it to I.O.L; and B is the proposal that the transport that would be supplied by the ship of A, be obtained by consecutive voyage charters on the open market. In the second type of comparison, A is the proposal to keep a tanker which I.O.L. now owns, and B is the proposal to sell the tanker and transport the crude in chartered ships.

2. Purchase of a Tanker by the Caribbean Oil and Transport Company

Let P be the price of the proposed ship and let M be the annual operating expenses. Included in M are the costs of fuel, repairs, crew wages and benefits, insurance, port charges, stores, provisions and rented equipment. Let the annual income tax saving obtained by I.O.L. chartering from COTC be T and let S be the scrap value of the ship at the end of n years.

Normally, when a ship is 12 years old there are certain extra repair costs. Let these be R and suppose that they will occur m years from the present. (If the proposed ship is now new, m will be less than 12).

If the ship is bought, the cash payments will be:

$+P$ at time zero

$+M$ per year payable continuously for n years

$-T$ per year payable continuously for n years

$+R$ at the end of m years

$-S$ at the end of n years

The expenses M and R reduce I.O.L.'s income tax and since the tax is at the rate of 47.7%, we will multiply these amounts by 0.523. We have then,

$$\sum_{0}^{n} K_1(t)v^t = P + 0.523 M\bar{a}_{\overline{m}|} - T\bar{a}_{\overline{m}|} + 0.523 R v^m - S v^n$$

where $\bar{a}_{\overline{m}|}$ is the present value of an annuity of \$1 per year payable continuously for n years and is given by

$$\bar{a}_{\overline{n}|} = (1 - v^n)\bar{s}_{\overline{1}|}/i$$

Let $r(t)$ be the consecutive voyage charter rate in dollars per ton for the t-th year, for the voyages under consideration; let N be the number of round voyages per year which the proposed ship would make; and let the cargo carrying capacity of the ship be C tons.

If the ship is not purchased, I.O.L. will pay $NCr(t)$ dollars to charter equivalent transport in the t-th year. Thus

$$\sum_{0}^{n} K_2(t)v^t = 0.523\bar{s}_{\overline{1}|}NC \sum_{1}^{n} r(t)v^t$$

and V, the cash incentive to buy this ship is

$$V = 0.523\bar{s}_{\overline{1}|}NC \sum_{1}^{n} r(t)v^t - P - 0.523 M\bar{a}_{\overline{m}|} + T\bar{a}_{\overline{m}|} - 0.523 R v^m + S v^n \qquad (1)$$

We will calculate V for a set of hypothetical new tankers of various speeds and capacities. Estimates of N, C, P, M, T, R and S were obtained from data supplied by Imperial's Marine Division (see Exhibit 30) [omitted in this book]. It is assumed that if a ship were purchased, it would be permanently assigned to the route Puerto la Cruz–Portland. We take $n = 24$ and $m = 12$.

In accordance with the forecasts of charter rates obtained in Section II, we take the rate to be USMC $- 40\%$ or \$1.80 per ton from 1958 to 1962 and USMC flat or \$3.00 per ton thereafter.

Then

$$\sum_{1}^{n} r(t)v^t = 1.80 a_{\overline{5}|} + 3.00(a_{\overline{24}|} - a_{\overline{5}|}) \qquad (2)$$

Values of V obtained from (1) and (2) are shown in Exhibits 11 to 16.

3. "Imperial St. Lawrence"

We will now compare the proposals, A: Keep "Imperial St. Lawrence" and B: Sell "Imperial St. Lawrence" and use consecutive voyage charters. [See Exhibits 31 and 32.]

We use equation (1) of Section 2 where P now represents the present market value of the ship. Instead of attempting to estimate P we have calculated V for various values of P and i.

Actual 1957 operating data were used to determine M, N and C, except that fuel costs were adjusted to conform with the January 1, 1958 price of \$2.65 per barrel (see Exhibit 33 [omitted in this book]).

Exhibit 31

M, ANNUAL OPERATING EXPENSES FOR NEW TANKERS
(Thousands of Dollars)

Speed in Knots	Capacity in Thousands of Tons			
	35	45	65	85
11.........................	844	928	1,082	1,207
12.........................	901	987	1,151	1,287
13.........................	955	1,047	1,227	1,371
14.........................	1,025	1,120	1,307	1,470
15.........................	1,103	1,207	1,407	1,584
16.........................	1,193	1,308	1,533	1,713
17.........................	1,313	1,444	1,698	1,884
18.........................	1,461	1,596	1,879	2,101

Exhibit 32

V, INCENTIVE TO BUY A NEW TANKER
(Millions of Dollars)

Interest Rate (%)	Speed in Knots							
	11	12	13	14	15	16	17	18
35,000 dwt.								
6.........	0.59	1.15	1.46	1.53	1.42	1.06	0.13	− 1.23
8.........	−0.81	− 0.36	− 0.16	− 0.18	− 0.36	− 0.77	− 1.71	− 3.05
10.........	−1.86	− 1.50	− 1.38	− 1.46	− 1.70	− 2.15	− 3.09	− 4.41
12.........	−2.66	− 2.37	− 2.32	− 2.45	− 2.72	− 3.20	− 4.15	− 5.44
14.........	−3.28	− 3.05	− 3.04	− 3.21	− 3.52	− 4.02	− 4.97	− 6.25
16.........	−3.78	− 3.58	− 3.62	− 3.82	− 4.15	− 4.47	− 5.62	− 6.88
45,000 dwt.								
6.........	2.02	− 2.86	3.50	3.83	3.91	3.51	2.73	1.60
8.........	0.07	0.75	1.24	1.44	1.41	0.94	0.11	− 1.03
10.........	−1.40	− 0.85	− 0.46	− 0.37	− 0.48	− 1.00	− 1.85	− 3.00
12.........	−2.53	− 2.07	− 1.77	− 1.75	− 1.92	− 2.49	− 3.36	− 4.51
14.........	−3.41	− 3.02	− 2.79	− 2.83	− 3.05	− 3.65	− 4.53	− 5.69
16.........	−4.10	− 3.78	− 3.60	− 3.68	− 3.94	− 4.57	− 5.46	− 6.62
65,000 dwt.								
6.........	5.24	6.48	7.59	8.38	8.79	8.62	7.90	6.80
8.........	2.15	3.14	4.03	4.61	4.84	4.53	3.73	2.58
10.........	−0.18	0.62	1.33	1.76	1.85	1.44	0.58	− 0.60
12.........	−1.97	− 1.31	− 0.73	− 0.43	− 0.44	− 0.92	− 1.83	− 3.05
14.........	−3.37	− 2.82	− 2.35	− 2.14	− 2.23	− 2.77	− 3.72	− 4.95
16.........	−4.48	− 4.02	− 3.63	− 3.49	− 3.65	− 4.24	− 5.21	− 6.46
85,000 dwt.								
6.........	8.76	10.42	11.91	13.31	13.97	14.31	14.04	12.89
8.........	4.52	5.84	7.03	8.15	8.57	8.69	8.26	7.01
10.........	1.32	2.38	3.34	4.25	4.49	4.44	3.89	2.57
12.........	−1.14	− 0.27	0.50	1.25	1.35	1.17	0.54	− 0.84
14.........	−3.06	− 2.35	− 1.72	− 1.09	− 1.10	− 1.38	− 2.08	− 3.50
16.........	−4.59	− 4.00	− 3.48	− 2.96	− 3.05	− 3.41	− 4.16	− 5.61

R and S were estimated by the Marine Division and T is determined by the charter party between I.O.L. and COTC. Assuming the same consecutive voyage charter rates as above and taking the future life of the ship to be 23 years, we have

$$\sum_{0}^{n} r(t)v^t = 1.80a_{\overline{5}|} + 3.00(a_{\overline{23}|} - a_{\overline{5}|})$$

and equation (1) becomes

$$V = -P + (1705a_{\overline{23}|} - 547.9a_{\overline{5}|})s_{\overline{1}|} - 314v^{11} + 800v^{23}$$

where V and P are in thousands of dollars. The results are shown in Exhibits 17, 20, and 34.

Exhibit 34

"IMPERIAL ST. LAWRENCE"

V = Incentive to Keep the Ship, P = Market Value

i (%)	$V + P$ ($1,000,000)
6	12.75
8	10.85
10	9.40
12	8.26
14	7.36
16	6.63

4. Ships Owned by I.O.L.

Let A be the proposal to keep a ship which is now owned by I.O.L. and let B be the proposal to sell the ship. The only difference between this case and those considered above is in the income tax payments. As before, P is the present market value of the ship, M is the annual operating cost, R is the extra repair cost at time m and S is the scrap value at time n. Let $U(t)$ be the undepreciated capital cost at time t. Assuming that the present 15% rate of depreciation will continue to hold, we have

$$U(t) = (0.85)^t U(0)$$

where $U(0)$ is the present undepreciated capital cost.

For proposal B the payments are:

$-P$ at time zero

$+NCr(t)$ per year payable continuously for n years

$+(0.477)[P - U(0)](0.15)(0.85)^{t-1}$ payable at time t for $t = 1, 2, \ldots$

The last item is the income tax on the difference between the selling price and the undepreciated capital cost.

For proposal A the payments are:

$+M$ per year payable continuously for n years

$+R$ at time m

$-S$ at time n

$+(0.477)[S - U(n)](0.15)(0.85)^{t-1}$ payable at time $n + t$ for $t = 1, 2, \ldots$

$-0.477U(0)(0.15)(0.85)^{t-1}$ payable at time t for $t = 1, 2, \ldots n$, the income tax saving on depreciation

Exhibit 36

"IMPERIAL TORONTO"—VALUES OF P FOR GIVEN V AND i

P = Market value in Thousands of Dollars
V = Incentive to Keep in Thousands of Dollars
i = Interest Rate in Percent

i	V								
	200	100	0	−100	−200	−300	−400	−500	−600
0....................	742	933	1,124	1,315	1,506				
2....................	429	602	775	948	1,120	1,293	1,466	1,638	
4....................		375	535	696	856	1,017	1,177	1,337	1,498
6....................		210	363	515	667	818	970	1,122	1,273
8....................		90	235	381	526	671	816	961	1,107
10....................			139	279	419	559	699	839	979
12....................			65	201	337	473	609	745	881
14....................			7	140	272	405	538	671	804
16....................				92	222	352	482	612	742

Therefore V, the incentive to carry out A rather than B is:

$$V = -0.523 M\bar{a}_{\overline{m}} - 0.523 R v^m + S v^n - 0.477[S - U(n)](0.15)\sum_{1}^{\infty}(0.85)^{t-1}{}_1 v^{n+t}$$
$$+ 0.477 U(0)(0.15)\sum_{1}^{n}(0.85)^{t-1}v^t - P + 0.523_{\overline{s}\overline{n}}NC\sum_{1}^{n}r(t)v^t$$
$$+ 0.477[P - U(0)](0.15)\sum_{1}^{\infty}(0.85)^{t-1}v^t$$

The terms involving $U(0)$ and $U(n)$ cancel and V may be written

$$V = -(P - Sv^n)(0.07845 + i)/(0.15 + i) - 0.523(M\bar{a}_{\overline{m}}$$
$$+ Rv^m - NC\bar{s}_{\overline{n}}\Sigma r(t)v^t) \quad (3)$$

Exhibit 37

"IMPERIAL EDMONTON"—VALUES OF P FOR GIVEN V AND i

P = Market Value in Thousands of Dollars
V = Incentive to Keep in Thousands of Dollars
i = Interest Rate in Percent

i	V							
	0	−100	−200	−300	−400	−500	−600	−700
0....................	399	590	781	973	1,164			
2....................	120	293	465	638	811	983		
4....................		88	248	408	569	729	890	
6....................			91	243	395	546	698	850
8....................				120	266	411	556	701
10....................				28	168	308	448	588
12....................					93	229	365	501
14....................					34	167	300	433
16....................						119	249	379

5. "Imperial Edmonton" and "Imperial Toronto"

Incentives to keep these ships were calculated from the data in Exhibit 35 [omitted in this book], using equation (3). The operating data are based on actual 1957 costs and the repair estimates were supplied by the Marine Division.

For "Edmonton" equation (3) solved for P, is:

$$P = 200v^{12} - [V + 379.2 - (138.1a_{\overline{12}} - 234.7a_{\overline{5}})s_{\overline{1}}](0.15 + i)/(0.07845 + i)$$

The same equation holds for "Toronto" execpt that the term 379.2 is omitted. The results are shown in Exhibits 18, 19, 20, 36 and 37.

APPENDIX C

OPTIMUM OPERATING SPEEDS

1. General Method

Consider a given fleet of n tankers some of which are owned and the remainder of which are under the bare-boat charter. We wish to determine the optimal operating speeds for these ships. If the ships are run slower than usual operating costs will be reduced, but the tankers will deliver less crude and this will have to be made up by consecutive voyage charters. Thus, when charter rates are low there may be a net saving if speeds are decreased.

Actually, the optimum operation of the fleet involves many factors other than speed (assignment to routes, for example). However, we will ignore these other variables and will assume, in particular that all the ships are assigned to one run—Puerto la Cruz to Portland and that the total Halifax and Portland ocean borne crude requirement is expressed as an equivalent requirement at Portland. We will also assume that at any feasible speed, the above fleet, along with the time-chartered ships, cannot deliver enough crude to satisfy this requirement so that there will always be some consecutive voyage chartering.

Let the i-th ship be operated at average speed s_i and at this speed, let the operating costs be a function $M_i(s_i)$ dollars per year and let the crude delivered be another function $C_i(s_i)$ tons per year.

The controlled fleet will deliver crude at the rate of $\sum_1^n C_i$ tons per year

and the consecutive voyage charters will have to provide $R - \sum_1^n C_i$ tons per

year, where R is a constant—the total requirement minus the crude delivered by the time-chartered tankers. If the consecutive voyage charter rate is r dollars per ton, the total cost, K, will be:

$$K = \sum_1^n M_i(s_i) + r[R - \sum_1^n C_i(s_i)]$$

$$= \sum_1^n (M_i - rC_i) + rR$$

Since each term, $M_i - rC_i$, depends on the single variable, s_i, we can minimize K by minimizing each term. Thus each owned ship may be considered separately. Dropping the subscripts, the problem is to choose s to minimize the function

$$F(s) = M(s) - rC(s)$$

where M and C are known functions and r is given.

In calculating M we may leave out those costs which are independent of s (wages, for example). In fact, the only costs which need be considered are fuel, repairs and port charges.

2. "Imperial St. Lawrence"

As an illustration we present some data for "Imperial St. Lawrence" in Exhibit 38. The fuel consumption figures were obtained from the sea trials of "St. Lawrence" and it is not really correct to use them in this calculation because fuel consumption as measured in the sea trials is not the same as consumption under various weather conditions. Therefore, this calculation is presented merely as an example. To obtain the correct optimum speed for a given charter rate it would be necessary to measure the fuel consumption of "St. Lawrence" at different speeds under different weather and sea conditions. The prevailing charter rate, r, is taken to be $1.80 per ton.

Exhibit 38

"IMPERIAL ST. LAWRENCE" OPERATED AT DIFFERENT SPEEDS

Speed (Knots)	Fuel per Day Steaming ($1,000)	Fuel per R.V.* Steaming ($1,000)	Fuel in Port per R.V. ($1,000)	Port Charges per R.V. ($1,000)	Round Voyages per Year
13	0.88	11.4	1.3	3.8	21.62
14	1.03	12.4	1.3	3.8	22.94
15	1.18	13.3	1.3	3.8	24.24
16	1.37	14.4	1.3	3.8	25.50
17	1.62	16.1	1.3	3.8	26.72

Speed (Knots)	Fuel and Port Charges per year ($1,000)	Repairs per Year ($1,000)	M ($1,000)	C Cargo per Year (1,000 Tons)	$M-rC+1606$ ($1,000)
13	357	188	545	722	851
14	401	192	593	766	820
15	446	196	642	810	790
16	497	200	697	852	769
17	566	204	770	892	770

*Round voyage

We see that for this charter rate, the best average speed is 16.5 knots. When the charter rate increases, the optimum speed will increase until the maximum feasible operating speed is reached.

If more accurate data on fuel and repair costs are obtained, it would be worthwhile to calculate optimum speeds for other charter rates, but this example serves to illustrate the possible impact of the method on operating strategy.

SAREPTA PAPER COMPANY (A)

In March of 1962, Joseph Small, Staff Assistant to the Executive Vice President of Sarepta Paper Company, was reviewing the work he had accomplished during the past two years. Small's time was usually divided between co-ordination of staff operations and the institution of cost-cutting devices and procedures.

An industry-wide profit squeeze was just beginning seriously to affect Sarepta, although the squeeze had been in existence for several years. John Upton, Sarepta's President, often reminded his management team of the increasing severity of the situation. Within the past three months the price of one of Sarepta's product lines (making up 30 per cent of its total volume) had been cut on two separate occasions and was presently at a level which Upton considered to be the absolute minimum for Sarepta.

To date, Small's accomplishments consisted of a number of procedural changes around the mill which were clearly improvements but to which, for the most part, it was difficult to allocate specific dollar savings. However, Small believed that his two major improvements, which were materials-handling devices, were showing specific dollar savings through increased manpower efficiency. Small realized that Upton wanted a larger, more tangible savings than anything accomplished to date. He also knew that Upton did not consider any device or procedure which would cause labor relations difficulties or hard feelings among the workers as a prudent way to cut costs unless the resulting savings were necessary to remain competitive.

Small had come to Sarepta in 1960 from Allegiance Chemical Company, where he had worked since graduating in industrial engineering from the University of Maine in 1950. While at Allegiance, Small had specialized in process control and production flow. Although his college training was not in chemistry, his experience at Allegiance had helped him to acquire a good working knowledge of chemistry. As a result, he felt perfectly at home in a discussion of any phase of the papermaking process.

Company Background

The Sarepta Paper Company, located in Wascom, Maine, is a non-integrated,[1] fine-paper company which produces primarily specialty pa-

---

[1] Nonintegrated means that it does not have the facilities to make its own pulp (explained in section on Production [General]).

627

pers[2] for converting customers.[3] The Company was formed in 1880 and was incorporated in 1920. Since its beginning the top management had come from one family, the Uptons, who were also the principal owners. John Upton was the third generation of Upton management. The Sarepta organization was quite often referred to by other paper companies as proud and progressive. Sarepta had developed considerable pride in its line of specialty papers, and it was proud of the reputation for quality that it had in the paper industry. Sarepta's "progressive" label stemmed from the fact that it had been a leader in changing product lines to suit the various needs of customers. Also, Sarepta had been a leader in selling techniques by using its present direct selling method.

The American Paper and Pulp Association (APPA) classified Sarepta

Exhibit 1

ORGANIZATION CHART

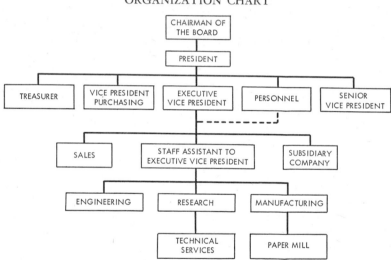

as a medium-sized paper company with a daily production of 175 tons and an employment of approximately 600 persons. According to APPA, there were approximately 85 nonintegrated paper mills in the New England area, and roughly 20 of them had a product mix comparable to Sarepta's. The Sarepta organization chart is shown in Exhibit 1.

Finance

The balance sheets and income statements for 1960 and 1961 are presented in Exhibits 2 and 3. Sales had grown from approximately $12–14 million just after World War II to the present level of $20 million. (Small

---

[2] Specialty paper refers to high-quality grades of fine paper which usually have a specialized application (e.g., Thermofax paper).

[3] Converting customers buy paper and convert it to final form (e.g., wallpaper).

Exhibit 2

BALANCE SHEET

(All Figures in Thousands)

	1961	1960
ASSETS		
Current Assets:		
Cash	$ 506	$ 702
Accounts receivable	2,031	2,104
Inventory:		
Raw material and supplies	1,405	1,510
Work in process and finished goods	2,032	1,831
	$ 5,974	$ 6,147
Prepaid expenses	201	162
Total Current Assets	$ 6,175	$ 6,309
Fixed Assets:		
Land	$ 101	$ 85
Buildings	4,133	3,343
Machinery and equipment	7,205	6,305
	$11,439	$ 9,733
Less: Allowances for depreciation	4,481	3,934
	$ 6,958	$ 5,799
Total Assets	$13,133	$12,108
LIABILITIES		
Current Liabilities:		
Accounts payable	$ 1,743	$ 1,101
Payroll and other compensation	331	306
Profit-sharing retirement plan	44	95
Taxes other than income taxes	110	108
Estimated federal income tax	330	331
Long-term debt due within one year	75	......
Total Current Liabilities	$ 2,633	$ 1,941
Long-term debt	$ 2,025	$ 2,100
Deferred federal income taxes	205	241
Stockholders' equity:		
Common stock, par value $1.00 per share:		
Class A	$ 441	$ 381
Class B	2,407	2,407
Retained earnings	5,422	5,038
	$ 8,270	$ 7,826
Total Liabilities	$13,133	$12,108

had learned from the sales manager that the 1962 sales level had been forecast to reach the $22–24-million level. Because of the unstable profit situation, the expected profit as a percentage of sales was uncertain.) Until 1958, Sarepta was entirely owned by the Upton family. In 1958, 350,000 shares of common stock were sold publicly for $9.75 per share. Sarepta now had over two thousand shareholders, and its Class A common stock was traded over the counter. Prior to this public issue, all expansion and improvements had been financed from either retained earnings or debt.

Exhibit 3

STATEMENT OF EARNINGS

(All Figures in Thousands)

	1961*	1960*
Net sales	$20,985	$19,413
Other income	38	70
	$21,023	$19,483
Costs and expenses:		
Cost of goods sold	$16,815	$15,833
Selling, general, and administrative expenses†	2,823	2,521
Interest	126	97
	$19,764	$18,451
Earnings before federal tax	$ 1,259	$ 1,032
Allowance for federal income taxes (estimated)	654	538
Net income	$ 605	$ 494
Dividend:		
Class A common stock	$ 221	$ 191
Class B common stock	0	0

* Year ended December 31.
† Depreciation: 1961, $567,000; 1960, $472,000.

Marketing

Until 1929, Sarepta's principal product was a magazine grade of paper made for a single national magazine. In addition, there were a few specialty grades which were produced and sold to a small number of customers. At that time, there was no formal sales force. In 1929, Sarepta lost its long-standing contract with the magazine due to a major policy change on the part of the magazine. Consequently, the first sales force was formed, and Sarepta began to push direct selling. Direct selling may be generally defined as selling direct to converting customers who prepare the paper for final consumption (e.g., greeting cards and wallpaper). The alternative to selling direct is the use of brokers, who carry no inventory, or merchants, who stock large quantities of paper and sell to customers of all sizes.

Direct selling had permitted Sarepta to establish a personal relationship with its customers and had kept Sarepta's management aware of the product needs of its customers. The fact that Sarepta had a total of only 125 to 150 customers meant that it was possible for a fifteen-man sales force to serve them adequately. Also, direct selling eliminated the need for an expensive advertising program to support brokers and merchants in their selling efforts.

The thrust of Sarepta's sales effort was based on quality, service, and price. Since the quality was usually specified according to the customers' particular needs, the only places for product differentiation were service and price. Direct selling lent itself to emphasis on service; therefore,

Sarepta was in a good position to take advantage of the attributes of good customer service. Price was dependent on the published industry price level, and the reasonable limits of variance around this level were determined by the cost picture of the company concerned.

Sarepta's product line[4] had undergone a general trend toward more specialty papers since its major change in 1929. In the last six years, there had been a 40 per cent change in the product line, which was an indication of the growing importance of market sensitivity. Exhibit 4 gives the

Exhibit 4

PRODUCT LINES AND RELATIVE SALES VOLUME

Product Line	Volume
1. Offset	14%
2. Greeting Card	12
3. Board lining	3
4. Gumming	2
5. Envelope and stationery	2
6. Lightweight business forms	7
7. Hanging paper	1
8. Direct process	35
9. Photocopy	7
10. Alpha and overlay	11
11. Surgical and X ray	6
	100

relative volumes of the eleven major types of paper produced in 1962 by Sarepta.

Research and Development

Sarepta maintained a small research and development laboratory for the development of new pulps and the investigation of new chemical processes. The objectives were to develop the grade of paper desired by the customer and to assist manufacturing in making the pulp as cheaply as possible. The R & D laboratory employed twenty men on a full-time basis; eight of these were trained chemists and paper specialists.

Production (General)

Sarepta was a nonintegrated paper company, which meant that it lacked the necessary facilities for the production of wood pulp. The over-all difference between a nonintegrated and an integrated process is shown in Exhibit 5.

The obvious difference was what took place before the pulp reached the refiners. As a general rule, only the larger paper companies had completely integrated processes. One of the main advantages of such an operation was that there was more control over the cost of the pulp,

---

[4] "Product line" refers to the different grades of paper.

Exhibit 5

PROCESS COMPARISON

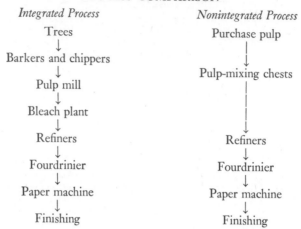

Integrated Process   *Nonintegrated Process*

Integrated Process	Nonintegrated Process
Trees	Purchase pulp
↓	↓
Barkers and chippers	Pulp-mixing chests
↓	↓
Pulp mill	
↓	
Bleach plant	
↓	↓
Refiners	Refiners
↓	↓
Fourdrinier	Fourdrinier
↓	↓
Paper machine	Paper machine
↓	↓
Finishing	Finishing

which meant there was more control over the basic cost structure of the final product. On the other hand, a considerably larger capital investment was required. Nonintegrated paper companies had to operate under the major disadvantage of being dependent on a pulp supplier and having a product cost structure based on the price at which they could purchase pulp.

Sarepta's production facilities consisted of five paper machines, each having different widths, lengths, and operating characteristics. The variations in the designs of the different machines had resulted in some grades being more suitable to certain machines. It may be said, for purposes of production scheduling, that complete interchangeability of product lines with machines did not exist.

Sarepta's production operation was a three-shift, twenty-four-hour-per-day, six-day-per-week process. Because of Maine "blue" laws, Sunday could be used as a normal production day only six times a year. However, maintenance and other "nonproductive" activities could be performed every Sunday. Employees received one and a half times the normal pay for Saturday work and twice the normal pay for Sunday work. Due to a special Sunday cleanup session performed by each shift every third week, and because of the normally scheduled Sunday operation, the average pay for a production employee was considered to be for fifty-six hours at the normal hourly rate.

Each paper machine was manned by a five-man crew which was made up of the following positions and wage rates:

Machine tender	$2.47–$2.63
Back tender	2.26– 2.33
Third hand	2.11– 2.17
Fourth hand	2.07
Fifth hand	2.33

In addition to base pay, these five machine operators plus two additional beater operators (jobs explained in section on Production [Detail]) received a bonus based on a direct incentive system employing standards. The average bonus was equal to approximately 11 per cent of the base wage rate. This is not to imply that there were only thirty-five men per shift associated with production; rather, these were the men directly responsible for the operation of the paper machines. Employees involved in pulp preparation and finishing were also considered production personnel but did not receive a direct bonus. These employees, along with all other hourly employees in the Company, received a plantwide bonus which was determined by a formula based on the direct bonus given to the machine and beater operators.

The production employees were represented by the United Papermakers and Paperworkers Union, and labor relations could be classified as good. Severe unemployment in and around Wascom had affected the attitude of workers toward job security. Sarepta employees were commonly known to be the highest paid employees in the surrounding area.

The crew-type operation of the paper machines tended to create a feeling of pride among the machine operators. They outwardly demonstrated pride in their competence in the "art" of papermaking and their ability to cope effectively with production problems. The production and over-all performance of each crew were thoroughly documented. This record was a necessary part of cost and production control, but it also served as a status incentive among the crews and consequently reinforced the regular bonus incentive.

Production (Detail)

A diagram of the process used by Sarepta is shown in Exhibit 6. Each of the paper machines and its associated equipment were similar to the layout in Exhibit 6, with only minor variations which were necessary to meet the individual machine requirements.

The purchased pulp, which was in sheets of approximately 30 by 50 inches having a thickness of one eighth of an inch, was placed into the pulp mixer in bales to dissolve the solid pulp into the fibrous solution. From the pulp mixer the solution was pumped into the beater chest, where beater-room additives were mixed. A beater engineer controlled the beater as well as the amount and type of additives. Beater-room additives differed according to the grade of paper being produced. Typical additives were rosin, alum, caustic soda, calcium chloride, slime-control additives, and brightness increasers such as titanium dioxide.

The stock, or washed pulp with additives, proceeded from the beater chest to a series of Jordans for refining. (Beaters and refiners were used to condition the fibers in the pulp.) A Jordan, which was a type of refiner, was designed for cutting or brushing and was controlled by the machine

Exhibit 6

PULP AND PAPER PROCESS

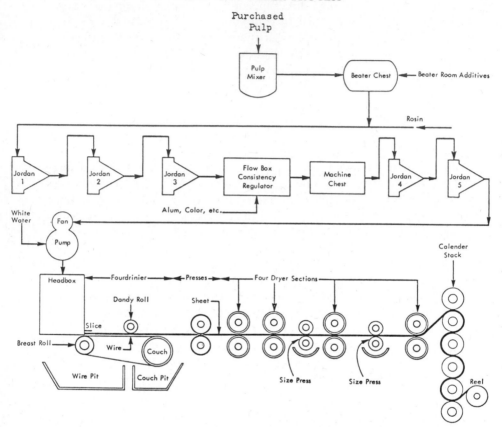

Courtesy IBM Corporation

tender. After the Jordans, the stock passed to a consistency regulator, where the percentage of dry pulp to total solution was controlled. A typical consistency would be 4 per cent by weight. Also, at that point, other additives were added to the stock. The mixing chest, the next step in the process, was simply a holding point for the stock as it was fed into the final Jordans, which allowed the machine tender to make fine adjustments on the pulp fiber. After the last Jordan, the stock passed through cleaners for removal of undesirable nonfiber material; then, it was diluted by recirculating water (known as white water) and was carried to the paper machine.

A paper machine of the Fourdrinier type, as used by Sarepta (see Exhibit 6), was made up of a headbox and wire for forming a sheet from the stock and presses, and felts for smoothing, drying, sizing, and finishing the sheet. The headbox was a reservoir from which all of the stock, both water and pulp, was delivered to the wire as a smooth sheet. The headbox slice opening was adjusted according to the speed of the wire, the consistency of the stock, the desired thickness, and other variables. The wire, which was an endless, moving bronze-wire cloth, allowed the fibers to form a mat or web as the water drained away. At this point, freeness—the ease with which water drained from the web—appeared as a discernible line. The web appeared shiny or wet on the headbox side of the line, while the sheet appeared dull on the other side. The freer the stock, the faster the water drained from the web, and the closer the line was to the headbox.

Control of the sheet formation was of particular interest to Sarepta because of the stringent requirements of specialty papers. Formation—the way the fibers lay together and interlocked—took place on the wire as the sheet was formed by the slice. Only very slight changes could be made in formation after the stock had been deposited by the slice and a sheet formed. This fact points out the importance of the headbox to the success of the operation.

As a sheet moved with the wire, the dandy roll served as a press, while the couch roll, which was perforated and had a vacuum applied to it, sucked water from the sheet. From the couch to the first press the sheet was assisted by a felt which, like the wire, formed a continuous belt to assist the newly formed sheet into the dryers. The press, acting like the wringer on an old-model washing machine, and the dryers, which were steam-heated rollers, served to remove the moisture from the sheet as it progressed toward the dry end of the machine. A typical moisture content of a sheet entering the dryers was 65 per cent, and a typical moisture content of the finished product was 3 per cent. Each section of the dryers was usually kept at a different temperature, with the temperature progression being from low to high as the sheet moved toward the dry end.

Sizing, a material which increased the resistance of paper to penetration by liquids, was added to the sheet at the size presses. The final important point, as the sheet neared completion, was the calender stacks. The calender rolls were critical in determining the final thickness and finish of the paper. The calender stack adjustments were normally made by the back tender.

The reel after the calender stacks was the last point of the continuous process, as shown in Exhibit 6. By means of a special reel arrangement, a full reel could be removed and a fresh reel begun without requiring that the paper machine be stopped. Once a full reel was removed, it was usually rewound and cut into smaller reels. The rewinder was operated by the third hand and was considered a responsibility of the machine crew.

Completed paper was tested to insure that it met the customer's specifications. "Off-spec" paper, paper which did not meet the required specifications, and wastepaper resulting from trial runs and trimming were called "broke" and were returned to the pulp mixer to be re-entered into the process. Approximately 80 per cent of all broke was placed back into the process.

There were numerous tests to which paper could be subjected in order to determine if the proper quality had been achieved. Some of the more common tests, which were universal to the industry, were basis weight, caliper, bursting strength, tensile strength, breaking strength, resistance to penetration by a liquid, finish, and formation. Typical of specialized tests which were made on particular grades of paper according to their expected application were oil penetration, printability, and stiffness. Basis weight, caliper, and bursting strength were defined as follows: basis weight—the weight in pounds of a ream of paper of standard size (a ream is usually five hundred sheets, each 24 by 36 inches); caliper—thickness measured in thousandths of an inch or points of caliper; bursting strength—strength in pounds per square inch, sometimes given in points— Mullen.

Historically, at Sarepta, as in the entire paper industry, operator know-how had been relied upon exclusively for meeting the required specifications. Years of experience had taught the operators how different paper-machine adjustments affected the quality of the paper. An experienced operator would know that basis weight was directly affected by stock flow rate, headbox level, and stock consistency. Also, he knew that caliper was affected by ironing at the calenders, by the presses, and by the draw or differential, which was a result of the slightly higher speed of succeeding sections in stretching or drawing the sheet. Likewise, finish was affected by ironing, by adding certain chemicals to the stock, by spraying starch or other sizing onto the sheet at the sizing press, by varying the drying rate, and to a small extent by a change in the amount of refining.

An experienced operator also relied on such things as the feeling of slipperiness of the stock in the headbox, the location of the water line on the wire, the sound of the machine, the crushing-out at the calender or press rolls (undesirable accumulation of water resulting from excess moisture in the sheet), and a finger test of the relative velocities of the wire and the flow of stock at the slice. According to his best judgment, an operator would relate these intuitive evaluations to the "on-spec" paper which had been produced in the past. These judgments had to be made, since there was no way to check characteristics such as bursting strength, porosity, or printability of paper continuously and simultaneously as the paper was being made. Consequently, the amount of "off-spec" paper produced was practically inversely proportioned to the accuracy of these judgments.

Operator judgment was particularly evident, and necessary, when a grade change occurred. The operator had to preadjust the Jordans, headbox, consistency, wire and machine speed, and slice opening, as well as numerous other minor adjustments. Once the required operating changes had been made, variations in the stock would necessitate changes while the run was in progress.

Production and Cost Data

The elaborate records of production and cost, kept for every paper machine and every shift, were used to compile two cost figures used commonly by Sarepta to determine the effect of down time and off-specification paper on profits. Since time was such an important bench mark in a continuous-process operation, both production and cost figures were commonly expressed in tons per hour and dollars per hour, respectively.

The two cost figures of particular interest were the direct cost per hour and the marginal income per hour. The direct cost included general overhead, direct labor, and other costs which were not believed to change vis-à-vis normal variances in production. Marginal income was the average incremental income received per hour for a full hour of on-specification

Exhibit 7

SELECTED PRODUCTION AND COST DATA

	Paper Machine No.					
	1	*2*	*3*	*4*	*5*	*Total*
Average daily production (tons).........	35	35	30	50	25	175
Start-up time (hours per year)...........	720	330	250	438	95	1,838
"Off-spec" time (hours per year).........	110	210	140	275	150	885
Direct cost* (dollars per hour)...........$	63	$40	$ 82	$ 80	$105	$370
Marginal income* (dollars per hour)......$	131	$83	$163	$185	$211	$773

* These terms are defined in the section on Production and Cost Data.

production. Marginal income was essentially the selling price minus the variable costs, which were essentially raw material and power.

Production statistics which were continually reviewed for possible improvement were start-up time (time required in a grade change to obtain the required specifications) and off-specification time. As stated previously, both of these times depended largely on operator know-how and intuition. Exhibit 7 presents average annual production and cost figures for all five paper machines.

Raw material costs for Sarepta's nonintegrated process usually averaged between $150 to $165 per ton, depending on the particular grade being processed. This cost included an approximate broke reuse rate of 80 per cent.

A New Concept in Papermaking

As Small pondered his cost-cutting chore, he remembered having seen an advertisement for a computerized control system which was manufactured by International Business Machines. Although the advertisement was in a paper-industry trade journal, it was unclear just what benefits could be derived from such a system by a paper company. Since there were no actual systems in operation, there were no specific claims or statements which indicated the degree of success that could be achieved. Two other well-known computer manufacturers had also run similar advertisements. While Small was somewhat skeptical of the possible outcome, he decided to talk to a salesman from each company.

After discussing the proposed systems with the three companies, it appeared to Small that each of the systems followed the same principle— measurement of numerous variables at predetermined time intervals, comparison of measurements against standard data, and notification of intolerable variances between the actual and the standard. The only significant differences between the different systems were price, experience in the field, and service. Before any further detailed investigation was made, Small decided that since IBM's system was the cheapest, and since he thought IBM had a superior reputation for research, production, operating experience, and service in all aspects of computer operation, it should be the system that he would investigate thoroughly for cost-cutting potential. Also, because of the complexity of such an application and the unfamiliarity of Sarepta with computerized process control, Small and the IBM representatives felt that the system should be analyzed with respect to one paper machine. If proved successful, the system had the necessary computer capacity to be extended to the other four paper machines; and then, even greater savings would be realized.

From what Small could see, a computer offered several potential cost advantages to Sarepta. If operated effectively, it would serve as an aid in reducing "off-spec" and start-up costs. Savings realized in these areas would be readily apparent and easily measured. However, Small hoped that the system might also be an aid toward making higher quality paper. Hopefully, new lines could be introduced into the product mix which, before, could not be made to meet required specifications. For purposes of analysis, Small knew that savings in this area could only be expressed as a hope or possible fringe benefit for having the system.

Small analyzed the cost and production data for the five machines (see Exhibit 7) and was convinced from those data that machine No. 4 would be the best to analyze with respect to the control system. However, there were two other cogent arguments for using No. 4. Historically, the crews which operated it were thought to be the most competent and the most likely to co-operate in seeing that the system was used effectively. Also, No. 4 already had more instrumentation than the other machines, making the application cheaper and easier from the outset.

Exhibit 8 presents a diagram of the IBM 1710 system as it would be used by Sarepta. The paper machine would provide the system with actual readings, the card reader would give the standard values, and the 1620

Exhibit 8

IBM 1710 CONTROL SYSTEM AS APPLIED TO A PAPER MACHINE

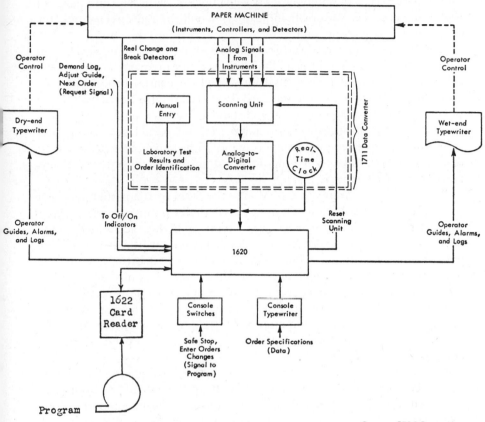

Courtesy IBM Corporation

central processing unit would perform the comparison of data. All readings, both standard and actual, would be printed out by typewriter, with the variances being printed in red. A complete reading of all of the data would occur every fifteen minutes; while every three minutes, variances from the standard would be printed. The operator could also receive a "demand log" (reading on all points whenever he wanted them) and a "break log" (a reading on all points at the time of a paper break).

Typical variables which could be easily measured and recorded were as follows:

1. Temperature
2. Pressure
3. Flow rate
4. Position indicator
5. pH
6. Power
7. Atmospheres of pressure—plus and minus
8. Humidity as a function of dew point

The paper machine sensors (see Exhibit 8), having analog outputs, would pass through transducers first to put their output in the form of milliampere (Ma) or millivolt (Mv) analogue signals. Measurements of the pulse type (i.e., on or off indicators) would be fed directly into the 1620 central processing unit.

The IBM 1711 data converter would receive the analogue signals and convert them into digital form. The digitized measurements (representing actual values) would then be fed into the 1620 central processing unit, which would also receive the standard data from the 1622 card reader and punch. The comparison of actual and standard values would take place in the 1620 central processing unit, and the output would be a typewriter print-out. Typewriters could be located at both the wet and the dry ends of the machine, thereby giving identical information to the machine tender and back tender.

The typewriter print-out would take the form of the partial log sheet shown in Exhibit 9. Although it appeared complex on first glance, a closer analysis showed that the sheet was simply a highly accurate logging device. It could be expanded or reduced to meet the needs of the particular paper machine which was being monitored. Also, it should be noted that the values which were recorded were in units which were familiar to the machine operators. All print-out data were in paper-machine language and not in computer language. For this reason, it was believed that only a minimum amount of training would be required for the machine operator to become familiar with the operation of the computer.

In determining the cost of the 1710 system to Sarepta, Small decided that all costs could be considered as related to the actual IBM equipment or related to the associated equipment such as sensors and computer room. The total purchase cost of the IBM equipment would be $175,000, with service contracts negotiated separately. However, the IBM salesman had not encouraged Small to purchase the equipment; rather, he thought a monthly rental arrangement would be more suitable to Sarepta. The monthly rent for the entire system, including normal service calls, was $4,000. With the rental arrangement, Sarepta would not be obligated for a period longer than 30 days. If Sarepta so desired, it could have the entire system removed with only 30 days' notice to IBM.

After carefully reviewing the condition of all of the instruments currently in use on the paper machine, Small decided that at least $25,000 would be required to purchase new sensors where necessary and to purchase the required transducers to give the system an "80 variable" capability. Small assumed that these expenditures would be capitalized and that a ten-year life was reasonable to expect. Another $25,000 was required to install the sensors and transducers, and to make a room near the paper machines which could house the 1710. Since Sarepta maintenance personnel and carpenters were to perform this work, this second $25,000 was to be a one-time expense as far as Small was concerned.

Exhibit 9

LOG SHEET PRINTOUT

DAILY LOG SHEET

1710 SYSTEM

	DATE	GRADE	TIME	1 / 2	3 / 4	5 / 6	7 / 8	9 / 10	11 / 12	13 / 14	15 / 16	17 / 18	19 / 20	21 / 22	23 / 24	25 / 26	27 / 28	29 / 30	31 / 32	33 / 34
1&2	4-25-62	60110000076220 F BRITE GRT DT	1203	865 / 140	300 / 300	80 / 43	230 / 100	75 / 749		250 / 400	85 / 42	240 / 400	350		85 / 44	130 / 250	200 / 65	1700 / 75	200 / 300	563 / 492
3&4	4-25-62	60110000076220 F BRITE GRT DT	1204	865 / 140	312 / 330	79 / 44	221 / 99	70 / 747		250 / 421	82 / 32	248 / 402	370		90 / 43	132 / 255	205 / 60	1700 / 75	201 / 302	560 / 490
5		1207 V9-69,75 V19-369, 350 V23-91, 85					1210 V27-212, 200												
6&7	4-25-62	60110000076220 F BRITE GRT DT	1211	865 / 140	312 / 350	79 / 44	222 / 99	71 / 740		251 / 420	84 / 32	290 / 402	300		85 / 43	120 / 255	200 / 60	1700 / 75	200 / 302	563 / 490

Line 1 & 2 Represents standard print out

Line 3 & 4 Represents the timed routine print out of the log

Line 5   Represents exception routine

Line 6 & 7 Represents a sheet break print out caused by the sheet break interrupt.

NOTE: Small type will appear in red on computer typewriter.

The operating expenses were more difficult for Small to estimate. Power and general overhead were tentatively set at $50 per month. In addition, two men, schooled in the operation of the 1710, would be required on a full-time basis to operate the computer. Small knew of two men at Sarepta who were suitable for these two jobs, yet both would have to be sent to a three-week computer course. Also, because of recent changes in work assignments, Small believed that it would be necessary to hire only one additional man to fill the two vacancies that would be created.

Small realized that although he had a large amount of information regarding the 1710 system and Sarepta's production operation, he would be unable to make a cost analysis for Upton until he had made one critical assumption. The assumption which faced Small was just how much start-up and "off-spec" time could be eliminated by the computer application. Since there were no other 1710 applications in the paper industry, there was no past experience to draw from. After much deliberation, Small decided that for the purposes of his analysis, he would use a reduction in start-up time of 40 per cent and a reduction in "off-spec" time of 60 per cent. Small felt that such savings would not come initially but would result only from practice and diligent efforts on the part of the machine operators.

In thinking through these assumptions, Small pondered the point of operator co-operation. He knew that job security would not be a source of discontent, for it was obvious that the control system would not eliminate the need for crew members. A system with a closed loop designed to eliminate some of the routine tasks of the crew members (not eliminate jobs) was not even in the foreseeable future. However, Small was afraid there would be resistance to anything that might threaten to remove the "art" of the machine operators' work. It would be like making the skill required to be an artist no longer necessary so that anyone might be a successful painter. Clearly, such a change would have a psychological impact on the employees. Small knew that his proposal to Upton would have to include a method of dealing effectively with any personnel objections that might arise. It was clear that regardless of the accuracy and thoroughness of the control system, it would all be wasted unless the operators were willing to correlate their past paper-machine experience with the printed warnings of the typewriter and take the required action.

Automation and Management

This comparative analysis (of electric lamp and shoe manufacturing) seems to confirm that (a) automation is an evolutionary trend and not an absolute quality; (b) some industries are exceedingly difficult to automate or impractical to automate; (c) widespread "fully automatic manufacturing" is in the far future. There is little doubt, however, that we shall continue to see gains in productivity as the production line is further refined and integrated into a harmonious machine-like whole, even though it is not completely automatic.

For these reasons, the managerial task for achieving automation is not simply that of keeping in touch with equipment developments. It is to pursue productivity improvements on a company-wide front, including design, materials, processes, and marketing practices that will facilitate automaticity, rather than in the machinery area alone.

The major problem for management is to perceive the direction and possibilities for constructing an environment that will support automaticity and to press forward at a rate and in a manner that are economically and technically desirable in their own particular firm, with due regard to easing the impact on the work force.

JAMES R. BRIGHT

FROM: *Automation and Management* (Boston: Division of Research, Graduate School of Business Administration, Harvard University, 1958).

THE FINISHING room conveyor was installed as shown in Exhibit 4 in "Colonial Cabinets Furniture Company (A) (page 550). Operation started on November 12, 1959. Over the next few months the following events occurred:

1. On Tuesday morning of the second week of operation, the operator for the first spray booth had not appeared for work, although it was ten minutes past starting time.

2. At 10:25 A.M. on a Thursday in early December, the chain of the conveyor from which the pallets were suspended snapped, and six pallets spilled their cabinets on the floor. The conveyor was stopped. A quick check showed that a pin joining two chain links had sheared and something inside the gearbox driving the traction wheel had broken.

3. Inspection reported peculiar finish bubbling to occur on a few pieces out of each day's run. These were found each morning on units that were in the ovens at 5:00 P.M. the previous evening. The defect was traced to the sealer coat. A check with finish specialists strongly suggested that the sealer-sprayed cabinets could not be left in the hot oven much beyond the prescribed drying time.

4. The conveyor loaders who placed the cabinets on pallets in the first-floor cabinet room took a lunch break to go downtown. When returning, they had a flat tire which caused them to be about fifteen minutes late.

5. After two months, inspection advised that a number of dealer complaints, coupled with their own investigation, made it clear that sanding was not being done properly after the staining operation.

6. After three weeks a delegation of men requested an interview with the plant manager. They complained that they had tried patiently to "live with" the conveyor system, but that the working conditions were too much for them. Personal time was severely restricted. The suspended pallets swayed and turned, and did not provide the steady work base they needed. They were unable to give the extra time needed for touching up troublesome spots. They disliked the "pressure" of the continually moving work. They had no freedom on the job, etc. Several "old-timers" said that the conveyors "made them nervous."

7. A paint salesman offered a new finish developed by his firm. It was a stain that provided a distinctly superior finish at half the present cost of

stain. It was to be applied after the filler operation, and needed to air-dry for about fifteen minutes. Oven drying was distinctly deleterious.

8. On January 15, Peter Shelby was quite upset when the monthly accounting figures still failed to show the expected labor savings by at least six men.

9. The sales manager called Steve Mills, the Production Superintendent, from Chicago, and advised him to prepare for a 1,000–3,000-unit order on TV sets. A high-quality TV set manufacturer was going to try a short experimental run of de luxe 24-inch-tube sets and a few color-tube sets. The large tubes were quite big and deep, and offered "a great opportunity for fine-quality, large wooden cabinets." The television set manufacturer thought that cabinets would be about 38 inches deep and have lengths of 36 inches and 72 inches (for phonograph-TV combination units). Steve Mills was asked to advise his fastest delivery time if management would authorize interruption of the regular production schedule.

IMPERIAL OIL, LIMITED (B)

J. W. Hamilton's Notations on Crude Supply Research Report

As J. W. Hamilton, Director of I.O.L., studied the report given as Supplement A in "Imperial Oil, Limited (A)," page 588, he made notations in the margins or on exhibits. These notations are reproduced in Exhibit 1.

Exhibit 1

Page Number in This Text	Location in Original Report (Supplement A)	Hamilton's Notations (As written by him in the margins)
590....	Subsection A–2 opposite sentence "For example. . . ."	See page 613.
591....	Opposite subsection B–1.	Subject to great error Exhibit 2 (p. 594).
591....	Opposite subsection B–5 (a).	Load? Discharge? Repairs? Dry dock? No facilities available to Imperial except in U.K.
591....	Opposite subsection B–7.	Only true if fuel saving is greater than existing charter rate.
592....	Subsection A. "20 T–2" was circled.	120! Spot, yes; time, no.
594....	Subsection C, opposite word "assumption," last line.	Sensitive to political and project (e.g., pipeline) decisions.
593....	Exhibit 1 (p. 593), bottom chart.	Construction costs exceeded 200 in 1957 for European yards, 263 in U.K. Were dips due to subsidies in European yards?
594....	Exhibit 2.	If curve were lowered slightly, it would hit −50 rate. Do tie-ups cause rates? Or is it something else, or both?
595....	Exhibits 3 and 4.	Should we attempt a specific forecast or extrapolated trend?
599....	Exhibit 10 (p. 599).	Will wages and steel costs drop sufficiently to allow costs to drop as predicted (despite formula in Appendix A [p. 619])?
600....	Paragraph III,A.3., "USMC flat" was circled.	High.
604....	Subsection B, last paragraph.	Additional tankage, unloading facilities, tugs, etc.?
604....	Second last paragraph, III,B.	"May" should be "must."
602....	On and beside Exhibit 11.	(Hamilton made arrow marks on the horizontal scale at 14 knots and at 16½ knots.) Construction costs? Interest rate equals value.
604....	Exhibit 15 (p. 604). Hamilton drew in large size on this exhibit:	?

Exhibit 1 (Concluded)

Page Number in This Text	Location in Original Report (Supplement A)	Hamilton's Notations (As written by him in the margins)
610....IV, Subsection A.		Factors such as labour, contractual, and other problems? Rationing has occurred—may be true over-all—individual companies have been hurt.
612....Subsection B. Hamilton underlined "*modifying performance accordingly.*"		Once you've bought the ship, the characteristics are fixed.
612....Second paragraph.		Tie-up costs?
612....Subsection B.1.		Exhibit 11? Exhibit 15? [See pp. 602 and 604.]
614....Middle of page.		Marine Department claims weather runs west to east, not north to south. No advantage! Possibilities of getting prevailing north-south wind are nil!
616....Subsection F.		Flying saucers?
619....Top of page.		Does F take supply or demand into account? Utilization of fleet?
620....$+P$ at time zero.		Surely distributed over construction period.
623....Subsection 4. Hamilton circled "15 per cent" and added question mark.		?

After making his specific comments to the I.O.L. executives reviewing the report, Hamilton also raised the general question: "Have long-range wage and inflationary trends been ignored or adequately considered throughout this report?"

SAREPTA PAPER COMPANY (B)[1]

THE SAREPTA Paper Company was a nonintegrated paper company that produced specialty papers for sale to converting customers. In the first three months of 1962 the effects of an industry-wide profit squeeze had worsened to the point that John Upton, Sarepta's President, feared a decline in earnings for the year.

In 1960, Joseph Small, Staff Assistant to the Executive Vice President, had been assigned to institute cost-cutting devices and procedures where possible within the limits of the practices which were acceptable to Upton. During March and April of 1962, Small collected cost and technical information relevant to the application of an IBM 1710 control system as a potential cost-cutting aid. There were no similar installations in the paper industry, so he was forced to make several assumptions concerning possible savings which such a system might reasonably be expected to yield. In early May, Upton assigned Small the specific task of formalizing the proposal and making recommendations as to what Sarepta should do.

As a starting point in preparation for the final study, Small decided to review what he called the "triangular life" of a new proposal. In his opinion, new proposals were either being worked on in the capital expenditure procedure, discussed in the daily production meetings, or discussed in the weekly meetings with Upton. Therefore, these three phases made up Small's triangle. By outlining exactly what occurred in each of these three activities, Small hoped to establish a framework to follow in laying out his proposal. Hopefully, this framework would insure that he had considered all pertinent factors. Also, Small was particularly interested in reviewing the minutes of the last meeting with Upton, for he was sure that they contained more constructive ideas about the 1710 proposal than the data about any other meeting.

Procedure for Making Capital Expenditures

The capital expenditure procedure might be classified as relatively simple and without rigid guidelines. Anyone at any time at the level of supervisor or above could initiate a request for a capital expenditure. Presumably, anyone at a level lower than supervisor was free to make

---

[1] See "Sarepta Paper Company (A)," for a description of the Sarepta Paper Company, the technology of paper production as related to Sarepta, and the IBM 1710 control stystem.

informal requests to his supervisor. If the supervisor was of the opinion that a proposed expenditure had merit, he could place the request into the formal procedure. Obviously, in a company the size of Sarepta, there was a considerable amount of informal exchange among personnel. Consequently, a supervisor could air his or his subordinates' ideas among other members of management before any formal action was taken.

Capital expenditure requests proceeded through the Sarepta organization as shown in Exhibit 1.

Exhibit 1

Supervisor
↓
Department Head
↓
(Engineering Department)—Perform economic study
and prepare proposal
↓
Staff Assistant to Executive Vice President
↓
Executive Vice President
↓
President

As shown in Exhibit 1, the Engineering Department performed the critical function of determining the relevant costs and savings of proposed expenditures. Also, it was responsible for selecting the way in which expected earnings were to be presented in the capital expenditure proposal. However, the Engineering Department did not pass judgment on the proposals and consequently was not a decision step in the capital expenditure process.

There was no specified limit which was budgeted annually for capital expenditures only. Proposals requiring investments of up to $1,000 could be approved by Small. Those proposals which required investments greater than $1,000 but less than $5,000 could be approved by the Executive Vice President. All other proposals could be approved only by the President.

Sarepta's policy as to the limit which could be spent annually was purposely kept flexible. Upton believed that if a particular expenditure was needed, if the return on investment was reasonable, and if sufficient funds were available, then it should be approved. Nothing which met these criteria was ever rejected simply because a specific budgeted amount had already been spent.

Sarepta did not use a prescribed method for determining the return on a proposed expenditure. Savings were often difficult to determine precisely, so a single required rate of return on investment was discouraged by management. Sizable expenditures were sometimes made with little or no figures to back them up; however, a straight return on investment was

Exhibit 2

MINUTES OF PRODUCTION MEETING, APRIL 27, 1962

Total value produced, $56,320—tonnage, 166.8.

Number 1 Machine

This machine had three major changes.

Number 2 Machine

Approximately one-half hour was lost patching the wire. Mr. Smith informed us that the wire would be taken off this week end, even though it has not run its full life. Approximately 1¼ hours were lost on electrical trouble due to defective coil in the DC generating equipment.

The density on copy paper was slightly higher than standard; however, the good formation offsets this feature.

Number 3 Machine

Approximately 8,000 pounds of paper is being held pending the calendering of the sheet. Some Scotch tape was introduced into the system, and it is felt that most of the 8,000 pounds can be released after the finishing of the paper.

Number 4 Machine

The direct process paper has had the Titanox cut down from 70 pounds to a total now of 35 pounds. The opacity and brightness are still in range. This drop in Titanox represents an approximate saving of $8.00 per ton.

Number 5 Machine

A trial using a slurry of Zeolex, Titanox, and NuClay was tried on three pulpers. Fifty pounds of Zeolex at 7 cents a pound was substituted for 50 pounds of Titanox at 25 cents a pound. The opacity and ash were held at satisfactory limits during this trial. However, the paper showed a bubbly appearance and is being kept separate. It has not been determined that this slurry has caused this bubbly appearance, and further trials will be made to determine whether this type of procedure can be used. If successful, this would represent an approximate $9.00-per-ton saving.

On the Swartz order, the paper appears to have streaky, bad edges. This will be further investigated prior to shipment.

General

X100 Clay. It was discussed that a trial of X100 clay, a publisher's offset, be made as soon as a carload of this material can be received. The approach will be to employ 50 pounds at the start and see what effect this has on our opacity and retention. An additional 50 pounds will then be used in subsequent runs; and to start with, no more than 100 pounds per pulper would be employed until we determine how severe the abrasiveness and dusting action of this material will be on our offset papers.

Slush Broke and Starch. Mr. Brown pointed out in reviewing the

Exhibit 2 (Continued)

---

pads being taken from slush broke that we are still getting indications comparable to those that were obtained before washing was done on the broke.

Trial Pulps. Mr. Smith requested that on all new pulps we receive in the mill for trials, we order a quantity of 25,000 pounds in place of the existing 4,000-pound lots. This would give Manufacturing a better chance to evaluate the merits of this pulp.

Claflin. It appears in all aspects that this piece of equipment can be satisfactorily used in our operation. The potential savings of our power on this unit is in the range of $25,000–$35,000 per year.

Shipments for today were 410,133 pounds. Average shipments to date, 340,433 pounds. Average production, 345,193 pounds.

Total broke usage for today was 51,933 pounds.

JOSEPH SMALL

---

calculated when possible. Often, these figures were a matter of much discussion before a capital expenditure decision was made.

Daily Production Meetings

Monday through Saturday, Small conducted a production meeting at 11:00 A.M. Manufacturing, Engineering, Research and Development, and Technical Services each had one representative at this meeting. Discussion usually centered around the past day's production and any difficulties that had been experienced. Also, the progress and relative success of various cost-cutting equipment and procedures under trial were usually discussed briefly. Exhibit 2 presents the minutes from a typical daily production meeting. Each day the minutes were prepared as shown in Exhibit 2, and copies were distributed for retention to the executive vice president and each of the persons in attendance.

Weekly Meetings with the President

Every Monday at 12:30 P.M., Upton met informally with the executive vice president, the manufacturing manager, the engineering manager, the treasurer, the manager of research and development, and Small. These meetings began with lunch but often extended well past the lunch hour.

Since Small had been working with the information related to the IBM 1710 control system for two months, the basic idea, the technology, and the over-all philosophy of the 1710 had been discussed haphazardly from Monday to Monday. On May 7, 1962, Upton surprised the group by asking each member for his candid opinion of the 1710 system. He assured the men that since this undertaking was so different from anything yet done by any paper company, each of them was entitled to have any strong feelings, pro or con, expressed before any more time was devoted to the matter by Small. (At the time of the meeting, Small still did not have exact savings figures prepared, yet he was confident that they would be significant.)

MR. SMITH (MANAGER OF MANUFACTURING): Sir, as you know, I have worked in a paper mill since I was 18 years old; and during these past thirty-three years, I have worked at practically every job in the mill. Of course, the majority of my work experience has been on the paper machines. I guess you might call me an old-fashioned papermaker who considers that this is the only way to make a living. Since I have been with Sarepta, I have seen many new ideas come and go, and I've even had a few myself. Sometimes, they were nothing more than slight modifications of wire and machine speed; other times, they were complicated procedures which were supposed to permit my men to handle the finished rolls and sheets more efficiently. Please don't get me wrong. I'm not against change. As a matter of fact, I have supported most of the new ideas which have come up. Yet, I cannot say that I'm entirely in favor of this computer thing.

My men, just as I did, have spent the best years of their lives learning how to make paper of higher and higher quality. Some of you call the skill we have acquired "the art of papermaking." It doesn't matter to me what you call it; the important thing, as far as I'm concerned, is that it does exist. When a machine tender ends his shift for the day and fills out the production records, he can't help but feel a little bit proud when he has outdone the previous shift. Likewise, he can't help but become irritated when the day has been bad. You're probably saying to yourself that any damn fool on a bonus system would and should feel that way. Sure, the bonus means something, but I'm talking about something more than that. Unless you have done it, it's hard to realize, but there is a feeling of accomplishment attached to making good paper that is greater than the pleasure of a few extra dollars of bonus money. As I said, I'm not against the change, but I can't help but object to this proposal. My men are competent and understanding, but I'm sure that Sarepta is paving the way for trouble if it tries to impose on the machine operators some sort of mathematical hocus pocus that will remove the so-called "art of papermaking." Having devoted their lives to papermaking, their skill is all they have. I know times are hard for Sarepta; and I, like many of my men, own stock in this company and want to see it prosper as much as anyone. Can't we concentrate our cost-cutting efforts somewhere else? Let's not cut our own throats. I hope I haven't cut my own throat, but you asked for my opinion. I have tried to state what I honestly believe is best for Sarepta.

MR. BROWN (MANAGER OF RESEARCH AND DEVELOPMENT): As an opening comment, let me say that I know each of us appreciates the sincerity of Mr. Smith's statement. He has sharply pointed out a fact which must be reckoned with before the 1710 system can be used by Sarepta or any other paper company. As a matter of fact, Mr. Smith's statement is a perfect introduction to my opinion as to what should be done with the 1710.

I believe that Sarepta should definitely obtain the system and apply it to one of our paper machines. However, I think it should be done as a research project and not as an aid to production from the outset. It seems clear to me that since we are dealing with something entirely new, with an infinite number of unknowns, the logical thing is for the Research Department to be in charge. This may sound heretical, since we're all concerned over our profit position. It really isn't, nor is it just a bold word for a luxurious R & D effort. In my opinion, we need to be as thorough and systematic as possible. Consequently, this should be done by establishing a carefully controlled series of tests to include determination of the proper number and position of sensors, and the degree of success which can be expected from telling a machine operator what and how much to adjust in order to get a desired result. Sure, this would take several months, at least six to eight months; but when it is finished, we would know exactly where we stand and what to expect in the future. We might even find out the whole thing is a flop, but that is the purpose of research. By proceeding under the auspices of research, the public will view failure as a scientific find; but if we go "hog wild" into a production application, a failure could mean a serious setback vis-à-vis public relations. The public, our market, could construe such a result to mean that we lack certain basic production competences or something like that, which all of us know is not true.

How does all of this fit into Smith's comments? Smith has expressed deep concern over the psychological implications of the 1710. By having it initially attached to the paper machine but not an integral part of the production process, the operators will have a chance to learn from the beginning what the system is all about. We could even conduct special classes to insure that every one of the men is fully informed as to the intentions behind such a system.

The men will not be losing their skills; rather, they will be applying them under a slightly different situation. The paper they make will hopefully be of higher quality and greater quantity than in the past, so there will be something to which the men can look for a sense of pride. However, if they do not understand and appreciate the philosophy behind the entire operation, they may resist it from the start, and failure is certain. Again, I say let's make it a research project and put it through its paces under rigid scientific investigation.

MR. BUTLER (MANAGER OF ENGINEERING DEPARTMENT): Both of these gentlemen have pretty well covered many of the points I had on my list; however, I still think there is another viewpoint. Mr. Brown's plea for a research project approach has certain excellent points about it. However, to me, it seems that the thrust of his argument is built around insurance against damage from failure. We in the Engineering Department like to think a little more positively about our undertakings. In my opinion, the computer should be under the Engineering Department for several reasons. The basic layout and wiring of the sensors will be done by Engineering, so we will be familiar with the project from the ground up. Another more important reason is that the greatest amount of formal mathematical training is found in the Engineering Department, as opposed to the training in chemistry found in the Research Department. Since the system is based on mathematics, it would seem logical that Engineering personnel would be the easiest to train for the testing and operation of the system. However, I do agree that whoever takes over the computer must carry out the orientation program mentioned by Brown.

MR. WALTERS (TREASURER): My comments will be short and to the point. The last two speakers have assumed that there will be a computer acquired. I can tell you now that we can make all of the sweeping statements about a profit squeeze that we like; but until we start looking at some figures and try to get some additional profit, we are going to stay in that squeeze. Admittedly, gentlemen, I don't understand all of the technical problems associated with the manufacture of paper, although I can clearly see the importance of Mr. Smith's comments. For that matter, I'm not even a step in the capital-budgeting procedure. As it is, I'm the man who has to try to cover up the mistakes and show a profit where possible.

I don't intend to imply that because the 1710 may not show a profit immediately, it should not be considered for its long-range potential. I just want you fellows to try to put this thing into some kind of a dollar perspective before you get too "carried away." Don't forget we do have stockholders; this is a business, not a government-subsidized proving ground.

MR. SMALL (STAFF ASSISTANT TO THE EXECUTIVE VICE PRESIDENT): I think Mr. Walters' statement is well put, and I must take the blame for the fact that you gentlemen have not received specific figures of expected costs and savings. I expect to have these soon. Hopefully, that will be by the end of the week.

Since all of you have heard me expound so often on what I think the virtues of the system are, I believe it would be best for me to not make any further comment at this time. I'm sure Mr. Monroe and Mr. Upton have some remarks that would be more appropriate.

MR. MONROE (EXECUTIVE VICE PRESIDENT): I think we can all appreciate the problem that Small is having in trying to get a reasonable savings figure. The fact is that there are a lot of unknowns, and no one has the answer to them. While I can't shed any light on better ways to determine savings. I would like to mention one point. Smith has brought out a very realistic objection. He has raised this objection from the standpoint of the psychological effect it will have on the men. Let's carry that point out a little further. Assume that the men resort to the "old standard"—the labor contract—for protection. We could be opening the gate to labor troubles. They might first scream, "Higher wages"; then would come a special factor to compensate the men for lost time should the computer be temporarily out of order. Job security will probably not be a big issue at first, but it could come to the point that some pretty ridiculous clauses would have to be added if for no other reason than to appease the workers and give them reassurance.

Labor relations have been excellent for the past few years. Oh, occasionally, we have had to give in and accept some demands that seemed unnecessary; but all in all, I think we should consider ourselves fortunate. Just look around at our dying textile neighbors. They are a good example of what can happen when labor is allowed to call all the shots with respect to technological change. The question is whether we can keep ourselves from being put in the same position.

MR. UPTON (PRESIDENT): Well, now I know what to expect the next time I ask each of you for a frank opinion. All of you have one, and a lot of good arguments to back it up. That's the way I like it. I must confess that I did not expect such an outward discussion. I think perhaps this is indicative of the nature of this thing we are dealing with. It seems to leave no one in the gray area; you are either white or black.

Gentlemen, as President, I probably feel the profit squeeze more acutely than any of you. I must weigh the risk of an added expense against the advantages of success to Sarepta.

I am a little surprised that none of you stressed the public relations possibilities. We are in an industry that is starved for ways to differentiate its products. From the marketing standpoint, it would seem that this is an excellent "gimmick" by which Sarepta might identify itself, if not its products. As Brown mentioned, there is always a certain amount of risk which must be accepted whenever something radical is tried. Even if we try it as a pure research project, we will probably be hounded by paper trade journals for a story. It's a little presumptuous to think that we can conduct this operation as some sort of secret endeavor. We don't have to encourage publicity, but it will be impossible to keep the final results from our market. We will just have to appraise how serious we think the threat to our reputation really is. Also, we have to recognize that an early entry and success in this field could give us a feather that we could wear in our cap for a long time. But is the feather going to bring us more profits?

From what I've heard today, I'm convinced that we need to get down to brass tacks and take some kind of action. Therefore, Small, I want you to formalize your proposal and have it ready for me by four weeks from today. Feel free to make assumptions, but make sure you state them and show why you think they are reasonable. I suggest that after you have made your initial analysis, you form a committee made up of the men present today and carefully go over it. There will be some disagreement, but I hope that you can work out some sort of proposal that will be suitable to you. My first interest is to do the right thing for Sarepta, and then my interest is in trying to do it in a way that is suitable to you.

SECTION V

Technological Planning and Forecasting

TECHNOLOGICAL PLANNING AND MISPLANNING*

By M. P. O'Brien

Some Definitions

The words "research" and "development" have been used together so generally as to imply that R & D is a single activity. In reality, there is a fundamental difference between them—in objectives, in their relationship to the needs of society, and in the viewpoint and intellectual characteristics of their practitioners.

A problem of semantics has resulted from the tendency toward "inflation" of terms—drafting is called design; design is called development; development is called research; and true research must be modified for clarity and called "basic research." For the purposes of this paper—and not as an attempt at semantic precision—the key words will be used in the following sense:

> "Science" embraces both the accumulated knowledge of the physical world and the work of extending this knowledge.
>
> "Research" describes the process through which new facts and relationships in nature are discovered.
>
> "Engineering," like science, has a broad connotation which makes simple and precise definition difficult. In this context, it may be described as the process of designing, developing, and building specific equipment and systems—a bridge, an engine, a radar, an electric power system.
>
> "Development" describes a phase of design in which the objective sought is beyond the current state of the design art and in which novel design concepts are evaluated and improved by experimentation, usually guided and evaluated by analysis.

The distinction made is that scientific research seeks facts and generalizations, while engineering development is directed toward specific tan-

---

* AN EXPLANATION TO THE READER: in September, 1961, a two-day conference on "Technological Planning at the Corporate Level" was held at Harvard Business School. One of the twelve speakers was M. P. O'Brien, Dean Emeritus, Engineering, University of California at Berkeley, who spoke informally under the title shown above. During his talk a power failure cut off the lights and air conditioning; but despite these handicaps, Dean O'Brien held the audience of 125 corporate officers and R & D managers spellbound by the uniqueness of his concepts. A vigorous question and answer session followed, in which O'Brien defended and amplified several points. Later, a formal copy of his talk was provided for the proceedings. Here, we include portions of the talk and discussion of special significance to students of management. His observations deserve consideration in the case issues and exercises in this textbook.

J. R. B.

gible results—ultimately to be embodied in hardware. These notes deal with development work and not with scientific research.

. . . .

Conflict between Profits Now and Profits in the Future

An accounting department casts up statements of sales and manufacturing cost, of taxes, amortization, capital charges, and other factors measurable in dollars, and reports a profit or loss. What such profit and loss statements omit is an appraisal of the concurrent loss or gain in other assets not measurable in dollars; among these is the store of potential and actual new technological products which *may* produce profits in the future. The more novel and the more potentially profitable a new product is, the more visionary and impractical it appears when first proposed. The present value of future profits from a novel idea, not yet demonstrated, is difficult to express in terms which a qualified accountant would include in the profit and loss statement. Unfortunately, the negative side of new-product development—the cost—is measurable by the accountants in terms everyone can understand.

Development work reduces profits now in the *hope* of sustaining profits in the future, but there can be no certainty that these hoped-for profits will materialize. Merely spending money on staff and facilities, and on design and testing, may produce only interesting but unprofitable results. Effectiveness in assessing the state of technology, in selecting potentially profitable products, in estimating the market available and the timing, in planning and executing a development program, in forecasting the manufacturing cost in production, and in introducing the new product all require knowledge, experience, intuition, and much luck. The managers of a technical business are understandably hesitant about cutting deeply into present profits to support development work because they face many uncertainties, including not only the potential profitability of the product but also the capacity of their organization to achieve the desired results at acceptable cost in time to exploit the potential market.

The conflicting demands imposed by the need for present profits and for the assurance of future profits through new developments is reflected in attitudes within the organization. The operating units are responsible primarily for producing a profit *now*—and there is frequently a personal *financial* incentive toward maintaining current profits at as high a level as possible. The success of the development and design organization, however, requires that its effort be supported at the expense of profits now; this group must argue for its needs, usually as a minority among the managers, offering only hopes in return for dollars. When business is good, its efforts are not regarded as crucial; when it is poor, they are too expensive.

The two extremes are, on the one hand, to spend nothing on product improvement and new-product development and to exploit the existing product line to the limit; on the other, to apply the entire net income to development work. As products and product lines go through their life cycle from exciting novelty to maturity and ultimate extinction, the balance between profits and expenditures for development work should change; with luck, the management adjusts this balance to optimize present and future profits.

. . . .

The decision regarding how much to spend from current income to *develop profitable products for the future* must be made in terms of *this* business at *this* time; there is no generally valid formula to be applied. Companies competing in the same field of technology may have sound reasons for different decisions in this respect—and these several courses of action may all be successful.

The Growth of a Technology

We have all witnessed the introduction, growth, and maturity of new technologies: the internal-combustion engine and the automobile, electric power, photography, synthetic fibers, and many others. This characteristic cycle has been shortened in recent years. Progress as a function of time, measured by dollars spent, by number of workers, by number of technical publications, or in any other representative manner, can be represented by an S curve in which four phases of growth can be distinguished:

1. *Invention or Concept.* The greater the ultimate value of the idea, the more fantastic the idea seems when first proposed; once disclosed, other means of achieving the same end are conceived and tried. Feasibility studies and experiments show promise but unacceptable performance. The state of related science and technology is frequently controlling, especially in materials.
2. *Rapid Growth.* If the idea is sound, one or more designs appear which are made to work. Capital becomes available for growth. Many competitors take the field; the concept is refined, simplified, reduced in cost; and production increases rapidly in volume. Competition in ideas sifts out the best combination of technique, materials, and performance. Income from sales permits increased development efforts and refinement of product.
3. *Consolidation and Approach to Maturity.* The number of competing concepts is reduced as some prove superior to others; the number of competitors is decreased as the weaker ones, usually pursuing inferior concepts, drop out or are absorbed. The winning design or designs have been established; manufacturing costs and sales promotion receive the main attention.
4. *Maturity.* Improvements in the product are minor, occur at increasing intervals, and are relatively expensive for the gain achieved. The market is saturated. A few competitors remain.

This cycle of events is well known. It is described here because this changing environment should influence decisions regarding the strategy to be followed in developing new products and the decision regarding resources to be committed for this purpose. In the early phase the profits may be large, but so are the risks, and the casualties are numerous. The risks may be limited by holding off until later phases and then "buying in" through purchase of designs, patents, or going companies. It is difficult to assess the current status of a maturing technology—and what seems to be an approach to maturity may be altered by an innovation—but there are symptoms and trends which are indicative. In the mature phase the momentum of usage and of heavy investment deters abrupt and drastic change; the innovator in these areas must be prepared for a costly and time-consuming effort to supplant the old concept with a new one.

The Evolution of a Development Project

Development projects—large or small, major innovations or minor improvements—follow the same sequence of steps, which are described below as a straightforward sequence but are in reality a series of approximations, with feedback from subsequent steps to refine the concepts and assumptions made earlier. Furthermore, the relative effort which must be devoted to each step will vary with the novelty of the design concept. These steps are as follows:

1. *A technical-economic objective* (or a technical-military objective) is identified, a task which involves the interplay of what is possible and what is needed; of costs and benefits; of requirements and capabilities. Will the benefits justify the costs? What benefits? What costs?

   If the objective is extremely novel, as were radar and the atomic bomb, the first question to be answered is whether or not the desired result is physically possible. Scientific knowledge and mathematical skill are required to identify the key problems, to design critical experiments in order to obtain the necessary data, and to analyze the test results. After the question of physical possibility is answered, the feasibility and practicability can be analyzed and the objectives of a development program formulated in terms of one or more concepts which would —in principle, at least—attain the objective; a design concept is created. The cost of the subsequent development program and the value of the product developed are influenced enormously by the quality of the work in this first phase. Hasty decisions to rush into hardware before a firm, scientific base is provided are costly in money *and time*.

2. *Analysis of the design concept* to express the environmental conditions quantitatively and to specify the characteristics of the subsystems, the components, and the materials is the first step in a *preliminary design*. The basic concept is necessarily qualitative and schematic in form, and— although theoretically possible—may require conditions which are not practically achievable. For example, power from controlled nuclear fusion has been shown to be a possibility by idealized experiments, but the pressures and temperatures required for the reaction are beyond those which can be contained by solid boundaries; various concepts for magnetic containment have been proposed and studied analytically and experimentally, without conclusive results as yet.

   This example is extreme in its degree of novelty, but all development projects are in essence similar, in that the objective cannot be achieved through the existing state of the design art—and one must proceed by concept, analysis, and test through *all* the areas of uncertainty until at least one solution is found for *every* problem. Analysis and test are not possible until a design concept has been created for each part and for the whole system or device.

Practical considerations which usually become important at this stage in a development project are the cost, the time required, and the probable performance. The cost of analysis and experiment in the preliminary design phase of an advanced project is not inconsequential, but it is small as compared with the amount necessary to proceed from this point to a working prototype. The sponsors of the project, whether in government or in industry, wish to limit their commitment by "definitizing" the program; but the questions asked cannot be answered, even approximately, until the major uncertainties are resolved, and not conclusively until the prototype is tested. Judgement based on experience, intuition, and mutual confidence is essential to avoid an impasse at this point.

The preliminary design and the related developmental analysis and experimentation add enough to the existing state of the art that a working prototype can be designed in detail.

3. *Detailed design* is the process by which instructions are prepared for the purchase of materials and parts, for the fabrication of components, and for assembly of the prototype. Frequently, detailed design is started in parallel with preliminary design, particularly when long lead-time items are involved, but the work is subject to constant correction and modification as the preliminary design evolves, until the time arrives when the preliminary design in hand is judged to have a reasonable chance of doing the job; then comes the agony of freezing the design. From this point on, proposed improvements must be rejected if they cause delay—but they must be considered. The groups in preliminary design and development must inject their knowledge into the detailed design; and in the course of doing so, they conceive new and different approaches, until they come to regard the design in progress, but not yet brought to test in a prototype, as an obsolete "klunker"—and it may be so if the project management is not discriminating. The most economical course of action usually is to carry the first design to test as quickly as possible and to accumulate improvements for an advanced version because the prototype test is likely to reveal many troubles which were not anticipated.

4. The *prototype* is put to test, redesigned to eliminate defects, retested, and, with luck, brought to an acceptable level of performance.

As a project proceeds through this sequence from concept to prototype test, the cost and the number of workers required in each step, and the number qualified for the work, increase greatly. Skill and thoroughness in developing the preliminary design will effect substantial reductions in the cost of the detailed design and the prototype test. One step is not more important than the others; they are all essential.

The preliminary and detailed design of a prototype requires choices of materials and components which will be difficult to change in the production version without excessive cost. Choices made by designers which had little effect on performance may affect production costs to a substantial degree.

The Project versus the Functional Organization

When only one project is undertaken at a time, the problems of organization are relatively simple, but as the number of projects increases, the same scientific and engineering talents and the same technical services are required on several projects concurrently. A functional grouping of the organization—development, design, testing, computing, fabrication—may conserve manpower and make available to each project greater competence than would be available if each project were self-contained.

This reasoning about a functional organization has merit, and the principle can be applied successfully when the succession of projects involves only variations and improvements of a single concept. It is the engineering organization appropriate to a mature area of technology.

A novel concept cannot be developed through the medium of a functional organization. The statement is made categorically because the writer knows of no exceptions—a separate and autonomous group is essential—and it is important that this group control the budget as well as the technical work. The project group may be small and may call on a functional organization for many services, but it must at least be competent to carry through the preliminary design and establish quantitative subordinate objectives for the detailed design, to plan the component and prototype tests, and to evaluate the results of work done by others.

The Project Engineer

The individual who manages a development project must have the viewpoint of an engineer—a compelling interest in achieving the tangible end result with the least effort—whatever may be his education, his professional society membership, or his job description. Physicists, chemists, and mathematicians, as well as graduate engineers, have served successfully as project managers; in general, an engineer should be best qualified for this assignment, provided that he qualifies in other respects. The starting point of a development project is a solution in principle; the end point is a solution in hardware. The requirement is to traverse the intervening distance at minimum cost and in minimum time.

Development work ranges in character from improvements of an established product to highly creative applications of recent scientific discoveries. Generalizations about the knowledge and experience of a project manager are difficult to formulate beyond the obvious requirement that he be familiar with the scientific principles and the analytical and experimental methods pertinent to his problem. He cannot be an expert in all the related fields, but he must know enough to recognize, and depend on, others who are really experts and to be decisive in avoiding interesting but unproductive scientific side issues. Advanced projects, especially those which require a team effort involving scientists, mathematicians, and engineers in the early phases, represent a particularly difficult problem of management because the engineers who have the production viewpoint and the managerial skill are frequently found to be lacking in the requisite knowledge of science and of the viewpoint of scientists. The scientist, on the other hand, is inclined to be satisfied with solution in principle and to view with distaste the plodding effort required to realize a design in hardware, especially when many attractive improvements have appeared after the design was frozen.

·   ·   ·   ·   ·   ·

Pioneering work in a new area of technology must overcome so many obstacles—physical feasibility, hostile expert criticism, inadequate finances, market development, and so forth—that the successful director of such work must exhibit personal qualities which are rare and often annoying to others. Self-confidence to the point of arrogance, single-minded dedication to the job, impatience with adverse criticism, and disregard of side effects and minor obstacles are characteristic of such individuals; the exacting task of executing a pioneering effort successfully seems not only to require these qualities but to accentuate and harden them. There have been exceptions to this generalization, but not many. Large technical-scientific organizations can, in principle, compensate for the scarcity of such individuals through group direction of the work and through changes in the director at appropriate times, but such organizations usually come into being after the pioneering work in a new field is over.

·   ·   ·   ·   ·   ·

Control of a Project

The over-all objectives of a development project have been discussed in general terms, but a few more comments on the subject are appropriate as a background for a discussion of project control.

A development project is usually expensive—at least relative to the resources of the sponsor—and the results sought should be of such character as to justify the cost and the risk. Timidity can lead to products which are quickly obsolete and not worth developing. On the other hand, if the goal of the first prototype is so advanced as to require many innovations simultaneously, the time and cost may become so great before encouraging results are obtained that the project loses support. A recent example of this situation was the nuclear-powered airplane, for which the objective was an operational airplane capable of supersonic flight—and the longer this first objective was in force, the more difficult it was to back off to a more reasonable initial target. The first objectives should be difficult but achievable in reasonable time—and the prototype should be designed and put to test as quickly as possible after preliminary design indicates a reasonable chance of success.

The process of delineating objectives must be carried through to the subsystems, components, and all related tests in quantitative terms, with target dates and budgets for each. Without this type of co-ordination, the groups within a project can drift apart, each achieving a sound design but one not compatible with the over-all requirements. The tendency to explore interesting side issues, to delay the matching of components at an interface, or simply to forget the quantitative objectives requires constant attention from the project management.

The lead time between concept and prototype test, the money involved, and the desire for early availability of the product require that important projects be *audited* at intervals, thoroughly and by an individual or group with the knowledge, experience, and time to probe all phases of the work. The stakes are too high and the chances for failure too great to assign the objectives and the resources and to await the final result. The project manager should welcome an audit as an independent check on his situation, and the higher management had better be wary when a project manager resists audit.

There are many observable check points in the course of a development at which predicted and actual progress can be compared, such as successful completion of tests of key components, of preliminary design, of release of drawings, and so forth. At some of these points the rate of expenditure will increase rather abruptly; and they are, in general, the effective points for thorough audit.

Control of the funds—and comparison of the expenditures with the degree of completion—is a complicated task. The accountants can supply the figures for expenditures and commitments, with some delay and some uncertainty over the indirect costs to be adjusted at the end of the year; but the sum required to complete the work can only be estimated. It is not uncommon for the project organization to estimate the percentage completion as roughly equal to the percentage of the budget spent—a happy situation until the money is gone and the work is incomplete. Reappraisal, at intervals, of the work yet to be done and of the related costs is a more reliable approach, and this reappraisal is best accomplished in conjunction with a technical audit.

Development engineers dislike schedules because they imply that a problem will be solved—a breakthrough achieved—by a certain date. True, one cannot predict the date of an invention or of the desired results of analysis or experiment, but one can schedule the construction of facilities and components for test and the program of testing. It is an interesting fact that tight schedules are frequently met when taken seriously, sometimes with the aid of invention on schedule.

Development projects tend to cost an amount proportional to the elapsed time from concept to completion of prototype test. . . . Economy seems to demand that development projects move ahead steadily at the maximum pace feasible, once a thorough preliminary design has been completed.

The Chance for Success

. . . .

There must be a reasonable balance between income and the amount risked on new-product development. The chance for success with whatever resources can be available, large or small, can be enhanced considerably by two means: (1) an effective organization devoted to technical-economic analyses and (2) a systematic search for development ideas—a technical "scouting force." These items should be the first charges against the development budget, however small.

Technical-Economic Analyses

Appraisal of a proposed development project requires an objective technical-economic analysis, starting from the physical problems of development and manufacture and carrying through to sales and profit, to provide management with a basis for decision. The expense of this work can be prohibitive if every proposal is subjected to complete analysis. Frequently, a single unfavorable factor may be decisive in eliminating a proposal; skill and intuition are essential to identify key elements of the problem early and thus avoid fruitless work. The process of decision making regarding the expenditure of funds on a novel development is a circular one. The questions raised usually cannot be answered without cost, possibly including the cost of experimentation, but the availability of funds hinges on favorable answers to these questions. A usual situation resulting from this impasse is that the technical proponents of an idea, who know little about markets and less about manufacturing costs, cast up a set of figures, usually optimistic, which cover only half the problem. Management suspects the figures—both because of their source and because of their rosy hue. It is amazing how many proposals, good and bad, in large and small development laboratories, have remained suspended in this fashion for long periods, costing some money but making no progress, for lack of a mechanism of appraisal in which the management has confidence.

A series of approximations should characterize the technical-economic analysis. If preliminary screening uncovers no absolute barriers and the first guess at profitability is encouraging, the proposal should be scrutinized in more detail to identify the problems requiring analysis or experiment. Work on these problems should provide the basis for subsequent appraisal, and so on, until the project is completed or abandoned.

Fifteen years of association with development work have strengthened my conviction that the minimum requirement for success in new-product *acquisition* or *development* is competence in the technical-economic analysis of new product proposals. There are, to my knowledge, few organizations which do this type of work routinely and effectively.

The Search for Ideas

The preceding notes dealt with the appraisal of ideas for new products. Scouting for new ideas also needs attention to assure an adequate number for appraisal and selection and as insurance against being "scooped" by a competitor. Suggestions from internal and external sources, published literature, patent disclosures, and other sources do provide ideas in quantity, but possibly not of the quality needed. A scouting force—appropriate in size and caliber to the objectives sought—is a desirable adjunct to a development organization, possibly as a secondary assignment for some of the technical staff, but on an ordered plan and with continuity of effort and contact.

These two suggestions may appear to be feeble approaches to the problem of assuring a succession of new products; but done effectively, they will yield a higher return per dollar spent than any other part of the development budget. Without this type of guidance the development dollars may yield only interesting novelties, not profitable products.

By constantly searching for new product ideas, and by appraising them objectively in the light of the company's circumstances—cash position, competition, know-how, and so forth—the risk assumed and the chance of success can be matched to the resources available so as to yield a profit now and assure a profit in the future.

. . . .

The Age of the Decision Makers

A delicate but important subject for discussion here is the relationship of the age of the decision makers to the character and scope of the development program.

Age brings experience and sound judgment. "Experience is the best teacher"; "Old men are wise and young men impetuous"; and so on through all the clichés, aphorisms, and old wives' tales which the elders have used for generations to restrain their juniors. True, judgment is important, and years of experience should bring sound judgment. It is also true, unfortunately, that experience tends to be specific and to limit a man's vision to a narrow area. It is difficult to keep the mind open to innovations and to sift out of past experience those considerations which are pertinent to a new problem. The problem is particularly acute in men who have themselves carried through important development projects earlier in their careers. Development work is a tough way for an engineer or scientist to make a living. It is a type of work for young men, requiring discontent with the past and unbounded optimism for improvement.

Uncertainty is their constant companion. Age brings a desire for stability, an impatience with constant change, and a weakening of the imagination and the creative urge. Obviously, top management must control this process and cannot let the development organization proceed without restraint; but in the process of decision making, it must assess not only the experience of its advisers but their recent record of open-mindedness about innovation.

Another problem of age—and one involving top management itself—is a lessened interest in new developments as the responsible managers approach retirement. This attitude is a human one, but it should be recognized and, if possible, circumvented. Age alone tends to produce this result, and it is reinforced by the realization, mostly subconscious, that money taken from profits now will not appear as profits from new products before retirement.

. . . .

Q. You mentioned the desirability of making technological audits. Where do you find the technological auditors?
A. By borrowing for a limited period people who are knowledgeable in the field—from engineering, manufacturing, sales, finance, other projects—depending on the nature of the problem. Large organizations have enough qualified individuals who are between long-term assignments to staff a few audit teams. This assignment is good experience for prospective project engineers. A small, continuing secretariat is helpful, but the team members should be changed frequently—with just enough carry-over in membership to provide continuity in procedure and basic approach. There are matters of protocol affecting the groups audited which must be established and observed.

The results achieved by such audits depend primarily upon the extent to which the next higher level of command gives serious consideration to the conclusions.
Q. How can you control or plan development?
A. It is clear that one cannot schedule discovery or invention. However, once the development objective has been established and the key technical problems identified, one can plan experiments; from these experiments, one can plan the design and manufacture of test equipment, and so on. Planning development work to this extent cannot be as precise in time and cost as the planning of a production program—and the plans must be subject to change—but proceeding on a development program without a plan, schedule, and estimate of cost usually turns out to be a costly and time-consuming process.

There is also the consideration that men frequently are creative under pressure—and continual pressure to meet a schedule is good.

Let me remind you that these comments pertain to development work and not to research—basic or applied.
Q. Do not most businesses have a research department?
A. Companies in the technical field generally maintain a *development* organization, but not many support what can properly be called *research*. Inflation of terms has caused drafting to be called design, and design to be called development, and development to be called research—to the confu-

sion of everyone. What most companies urgently need is a good engineering design organization. A limited number can afford advanced development work on their own. Very few can justify research in these days when the *research* programs of the largest industrial organizations are a tiny fraction of the national total research expenditure.

Q. Technological results have to be sold. Additional capital is needed to develop ideas. What about examining the value of investment or expected return on research? One product may show a substantial pay-off; another none. This leads to the need for experimental research, doesn't it?

A. Again, there is a semantic problem. When a product can be identified as the outcome of experimentation, I would refer to the process as development and not research. Development work intended to yield new products should be guided by forecasts of sales and profits which assume that the reasonably optimistic forecasts of performance will be realized. Experimentation on the key technical problems refines the knowledge of physical performance and permits improvement in the forecast of the market, and so forth. No matter how murky the view ahead may be, it is worth the effort to project costs out to the production stage still early in the development cycle; and to correct it as new data become available.

One thing to remember is that busy operating organizations, including their integral engineering and laboratory groups, almost never develop radically new products. Current problems cause such pressure that long-range development is usually disregarded by them—until they run out of products, as sometimes occurs. New products can be expected only from organizations dedicated to this end.

Q. Who, then, will do basic research and finance it?

A. There is little basic research now being conducted in industry. There are a few large companies which have supported truly basic research in fields related to their business; other basic research is found in industry, but is limited in scope and direction. However, in the aggregate, this work is small as compared to the basic research of the universities, the research institutes, and the government laboratories. Whether this situation is desirable or not, it is the practical result of the combined effect of uncertainty over research results, competitive pressures within industry, and the availability of government funds for these research institutions. Under existing financial and political conditions, I am convinced that industry is unwise to spend its own funds for basic research. Industrial efforts should concentrate on applying the results of research to new developments and to the related applied research.

Who, then, should do the research; and how should it be financed? Government support of basic research is not deeply imbedded in our system, and I think industry should base its plans on this fact. Furthermore, the funds for basic work are available only to nonprofit organizations —or substantially so. It will become increasingly important for industry to influence the distribution of these funds so as to support a steady advance in all branches of industry.

In making these remarks, I was concerned not with what the situation ought to be, but rather with what it really is.

Q. Did you say that we should push men through the development activity and into production work?

A. Yes, and for several reasons. In the first place, development work is probably the most demanding and unrewarding phase of technical industry; few men are competent, and even fewer remain so over a long period. There are exceptions; but in general, it is suited to young men, and "graduation" to other technical work such as engineering, manufacturing, or marketing should be normal.

Another consideration is that the development and production of truly novel products usually bring in some problems in technical sales, in manufacture, in product service. At the outset, at least, only developmental groups are qualified to handle these problems. It is effective to move the men—or some of them, at least—along with the product to avoid discontinuities between functions.

A third consideration is that decisions made in the development work tend to make commitments which affect manufacturing and marketing. Some individuals in the development group should have had experience in these areas, and this end can be accomplished by allowing some to follow the product through—and then return to development.

Q. What is your distinction between research and development? The need for probing into new principles?

A. Development work is aimed at specific objectives, beyond the state of the art, at results that you can use commercially or militarily.

Q. Aspects of research, then, must be more focused toward the commercial end point?

A. The confusion between research and development is more than a semantic question; it is producing a real effect in the inefficient management of the national research and development programs, and is resulting in costs which are greater than necessary for the same end results.

Q. We need better selection of development objectives?

A. The chance of a hit is very low if you just explore in general. Conversion of research results into useful hardware is an important activity—as important to the nation as research. We need to place more emphasis on the work of the engineer.

Q. Is it possible and better to change your project leaders before a project gets into trouble?

A. That's what I hope we can be smart enough to do.

Q. Real research is something for other companies? I think there's some inconsistency in your position. You're saying that we should go around searching in various laboratories and the various universities. And as I recall from college, you won't even get in the front door unless you were doing research on your own because research people just won't bother to spend the time of day with you.

A. I didn't give the whole paper in my talk. I said you had to have a "ticket of admission." You must have some people on advanced work *all* the time.

Q. Right, but what I'm saying is that if you summed up all the tickets of admission, if everybody simultaneously made the decision they weren't going to do research—I think this country would be in sorry shape. I think this country's going to be in sorry shape unless it gives real attention to the research end of things.

A. This possibility does not frighten me because I do not regard much of what is now done in industry as research. Most of what is called research is really development work aimed at rather specific objectives. When I say this, I do not mean to depreciate what industry is doing, but only to point out that it is not properly called research.

It is my impression that there would be available to industry an adequate number of scientists to maintain contact with basic research—if industry recruited, either as consultants or on a full-time basis, scientists who have passed the stage of active research. Many companies have done so. However, you may be right in believing that in the long run, some basic research in-house may be necessary to maintain this "ticket of admission."

. . . . . .

Q. I'm concerned about a couple of things. First, the remarks made this morning to the point that results that come out of research have to be sold because additional capital is needed to develop them. Second, the fact that research isn't desirable in most companies. To my mind, the fact that we can abrogate our responsibility to co-operate or estimate the value of the results by hiding behind a budget must be forestalled. I'd like to offer a suggestion to help this come into being, namely, that we put more burden of responsibility on the engineering people and the marketing people in the upper division. We should think well ahead in the context of studies such as the first speaker this morning, Dr. Raymond, mentioned. To be more specific than that, what energy do we save? Not what assembly of black boxes do we play with? And if we have research results with these certain characteristics, the idea comes to a business review. Then turn these over to the marketing people and the production people to assess the value of the problem if solved. By looking at our research in its more fundamental aspects and quantitatively relating it to product possibilities, one project might show substantial pay-off. Only two or three great technological developments are needed, if successful. I think we can place a dollar value of prospective return on the problem, and thus get a differential consideration of the value of research without your people saying where research will pay off. Thus, we may see some research as possibly paying off in several areas. Almost certainly, it will hit in some one of these areas.

A. We certainly have a semantic problem here, because one cannot think about what I call research in this fashion. Research seeks an end which is not known; that's why it's research. If we used your ideas and said "development," then perhaps it might work. But I'm convinced that no operating organization, through its main chain of command, will ever come up with *radically* new products.

Q. You mean that existing organizations are normally too set on their problems to know what they're talking about?

A. If you talk to them about future new products when business is good, they are busy getting their product out the door, and they don't want to bother with you. And when business is slow, you can't sell them a development project. My thesis is that any company in the technical field ought to have at least a minimum staff thinking ahead, defining long-range goals, and evaluating these goals in the light of scientific discoveries. But if you put a dollar value on the problem which the operating divisions define as the one they'd like to get solved, you won't get any questions about scientific progress, because it isn't their problem *yet*.

Operating divisions are busy with the product. If you ask them what they want, they'll polish their antiques to the nth degree. That's all they can see. "I'm having trouble with this part now, and I want something that'll last twice as long!" That's their argument, in essence. Well, they ought to do that work themselves. *Anything they can define for themselves, they ought to do for themselves in their own engineering group.*

I've spent fifteen years on this kind of work. If you want to develop new products, dedicate some people to this end. If they don't develop new products, they don't eat. When this work is in an operating division, they will say: "We were so busy putting out fires that we didn't have time to go think about new products." I could name some men in pretty big research laboratories whose directors have told me: "We spend three quarters of our time putting out fires." And these are supposed to be research groups! Now, if they are mixed in with the operating people, the pressure of the day-to-day product line is severe: "We're having trouble, and the first team has got to get out there. Drop your long-range stuff, and get this fixed now!" That's what happens, and logically so. Novel products are not likely under such circumstances.

. . . .

Q. I'm asking who is going to pay for it [basic research]. You say we must sponsor this research more and more through government channels.

A. I don't say that's the only way to do it. I don't say a company which can afford it shouldn't; some should and do. However, if I were responsible for spending the money of a company with, say, $200 million in sales and corresponding profits, I don't think I would let myself be talked into basic research. The chance is too small that the results would be beneficial *to that* business.

Q. Several times, you've alluded to the possibility of pushing research men through the development activity in order to get effective management of new projects.

A. Oh, yes, Mr. Smith talked about that. I think practically all engineers ought to come in through the development organization.

Q. You've come to this several times. I was wondering if you'd like to discuss it just a little bit more, because it's a pretty serious change of concept for some of us.

A. Transfer of the technical information *with the people* when the project moves from laboratory to production is the key argument. If you feel you've got a package ready for development, you'd better transfer the key people. Otherwise, you will run into a barrier, and the next group will say: "Well, we didn't invent this. We've got to review the whole situation. Our reputation is at stake." So you lose time and waste money.

Q. Among creative scientists, there is the possibility, of course, of starting many arguments that way. Who gets to move? Who gets to stay? These things aren't just accepted!

A. In basic research laboratories, there are some men who should stay there permanently. But most of the industrial labs are engaged in development work. The men I am thinking of are in that part of the business and ought to go on with the product. Some day, they should be managers of an operating unit.

Q. . . . In engineering organizations I think that research contracting under government sponsorship has caused us to make these activities very inefficient and unproductive. And today, there's increased ability to maintain our organization by putting in better communications and providing more service to the greater number of engineers. You can get more out of it for less dollars. I'm with you 100 per cent on this need for financial measurement in technical things.

A. (Dr. Raymond.) I call it "stupid arithmetic." But it happens to be very worth while to go through this stupid arithmetic in any situation. Too many R & D and management people don't even go through the elementary economics of their projects. They never ask: "What'll happen if this is good?" They get so intrigued with the fact that this is a new technical possibility that they never realize that it may not be worth an economic damn.

Q. My question basically is whether or not you can make these very refined distinctions between research and development. I think that probably successful development calls for some probing-around for new principles. This probing into development cost will deteriorate into excess paper work very rapidly. I wonder if you wouldn't agree?

A. Oh, I agree with you. I've gone through things pretty fast. What I'm saying is that development work is aimed at specific objectives. The development man gets his data and goes on. The research man gets intrigued with the subject and wants to round it out and write a paper on this general phenomenon. That, of course, is a good thing if you're a scientist; but for the development project, it's financial murder.

Q. What you're essentially saying is that the objectives of the research simply must become more focused as they move toward the commercial end point.

A. I said the development must become more focused. I really think semantics creates a problem. . . .

Q. If you look at the men coming out of graduate school with physics, and particularly in the electrical engineering segment, etc., the very best men wouldn't take the job in the kind of area you just described. Now, I want to know how you're going to get them.

A. Well, I don't know how you're going to get them, but I think we're hurting bad for the shortage of them. It is my feeling that the whole development program (and I mean development) in this country is costing at least twice what it should because of this shortage.

Q. I think it's the other way around. I think if we'd spend the money on examining the development end, we'd do a better job of selection before we started off on half of these projects. That's where we'd save money, not in the basic research end. We should open basic research wide, then do a very careful job of selection at the development end—which is the expensive end, as you pointed out.

A. True; but you represent a pretty big company and can exploit most of what you find. But many companies—and I'm thinking about the whole range of companies needing new products—many companies are participating in the whole area of research. The chance of hitting with basic research in their own area is like setting a pencil on end and expecting it to fall at the 360-degree mark. If they explore in general, the chance of hitting something in their own field is terribly poor.

Q. I don't know about exploring in general, but I bet their chances of success are a lot better if they'd spend a little more of their investment on the research end that you're talking about, including digging 'way back to the roots and picking the one that makes the best sense, instead of just picking one at random.

A. You're going to make me read my whole paper.

Q. Have you been saying that we've had too much talk about science and scientists, and too much glamour about research, and not enough emphasis on making things happen in the production end?

A. I really don't think we're giving too much emphasis to research. But we are not giving enough emphasis to the technique of converting research results and resulting design concepts into hardware which is usable. And that's a very difficult problem. Development is the most difficult occupation I know of. You get little credit because many of the results "leak" out into the operating departments. If things go well, some other manager replaces you because you got fouled up on production or something, and he comes along and gets the firm out of difficulties. In research, you can go in many directions at once, and this floundering isn't noticed. That's the way it should be. Development is aimed, and must produce results. So I don't want to give the impression I'm against development. I just want more attention to translating ideas into producible products.

QUESTIONS

1. Compare O'Brien's definitions of research and development with those in the Gibson, McCrory, and Novick readings. Is there a conflict?
2. Why is it important for management to understand the distinction between research and development?
3. What are the effects of conventional reward systems for managers on development progress? On the exploration and adoption of radical, new concepts?
4. Study the events in "Photon, Inc. (A) and (B)," in the light of O'Brien's comments on technological planning. What are your conclusions?
5. What are the merits of project versus functional organization?
6. Do you concur with O'Brien's concept for staffing new product developments? What problems might occur? How would you handle these problems?
7. Design a "technological scouting" program for a specific firm.
8. Identify at least three major hypotheses of innovation suggested by O'Brien. Are they confirmed by other items in this book or your experience?

Shall Scientific Research Be Planned?

Even those who are most anxious to introduce the maximum of planning into the control of scientific research agree on its failure in regard to discoveries of the greatest importance. J. D. Bernal says:

"In any survey of the business of scientific research, general lines of advance can be seen and fairly probable conclusions drawn from them. What cannot be seen are the possibilities of fundamental, new discoveries and their effect in revolutionizing the whole progress of science. The practical problem is to see that science advances on the widest and most comprehensive front, being prepared to accept and use as welcome gifts the radical discoveries that come its way."

This is in fact, of course, the abandonment of planning. It is these very revolutionary discoveries that make it impossible to plan the future of science.

When looking back, it is very easy to see how science could have been planned. Looking forward, all we can do is to continue to spread the frontiers of our knowledge and, as Bernal says, "to accept and use as welcome gifts the radical discoveries that come in our way."

Phillips points out that since progress is made by trial and error, and its extent is therefore proportional to the number of trials, the conditions most favorable to progress will be those that favor the greatest number of trials. These conditions will be those where the number of independent thought centers is greatest, that is, the conditions of maximum individual liberty. This is the true reason for the importance of personal liberty; progress depends on liberty. It is also the reason for the failure of any system for planning scientific research. The increase in efficiency of operation achieved by planning is balanced by the loss of independent thought, with a consequent diminution in the trial of ideas.

C. E. K. Mees, Vice President
in charge of Research
Eastman Kodak Company

FROM: *The Path of Science* (New York: John Wiley & Sons, 1946).

TOP MANAGEMENT GUIDES FOR
RESEARCH PLANNING*
By James Brian Quinn

WHAT KIND of guidance can and should top-level management provide in the planning of its research operations? Its most essential activities[1] in this sphere are:

1. Establishing meaningful objectives for research.
2. Seeing that the organization is attuned to the company's major long-term technological threats and opportunities.
3. Developing an over-all business strategy into which research is integrated.
4. Developing a procedure which evaluates research projects in light of company goals and capacities.
5. Organizing research and operations for a maximum transfer of technology from research to operations.

This paper will analyze why each of these activities is critical, what problems each involves, and how these problems can best be overcome.

OBJECTIVE SETTING

As with any other aspect of industrial planning, research planning should begin with the establishment of the targets the activity is to shoot toward—over-all organizational objectives. But in most organizations, there is great confusion over the nature and use of objectives in planning. What are objectives? Why are they needed? How do they come into being? Where and why do failures occur in establishing objectives for research? These are common questions. If we can dispel some of the major misunderstandings about these issues, perhaps management can avoid one of the most common pitfalls in research planning—inadequate objective formulation.

* Author's note: This paper is based on a two-year study which included interviews with over 120 top research, operating, and planning executives in thirty-five major companies in the chemical, electrical, electronics, basic metals, and pharmaceutical industries. The author gratefully acknowledges a research grant from the Alfred P. Sloan Foundation.

[1] These activities have been developed into an integrated research planning system in James Brian Quinn, "Long-Range Planning of Industrial Research," *Harvard Business Review*, July–August, 1961, substantial parts of which are reproduced herein by special permission of the publisher.

What Are Objectives?

Objectives are targets or goals. They state the results that the organization or any of its components should accomplish. Objectives do not take just one form. They should exist at all levels in the organization in a definite hierarchy.

At the top of the pile are the relatively permanent "value objectives" of the total organization. These link together the value premises which should guide the organization's actions. They state the firm's desire for employee happiness, value of products, honesty to all, profits to stockholders, etc. These are selected by the owners or general management for the whole organization and generally express some distillation of the moral values of the times (although you can always have value objectives like those of the Al Capone organization which are rather individualistic). While value objectives may well serve as guides for potentially errant managers, they are of relatively little use in planning.

But in business enterprises—immediately subordinate to the value objectives—there is a group of "over-all business objectives" which are critical to the planning process. These establish the intended nature of the specific business enterprise and the directions in which it should move. These over-all business objectives are somewhat less permanent than value objectives, but nevertheless usually stand for years. General management should, of course, establish these objectives because they are targets for all elements of the organization.

Below this level are a series of less permanent goals which define targets for each organizational unit, its subunits, and finally each activity within the subunit. The critical objectives here are those at the "over-all business objective" and the "organizational objective" levels. Formulation of both is a top management responsibility. Below this level, top management's concern is just to see that those who establish goals keep them consistent with higher level objectives.

Why Define Objectives for Research?

There are three overwhelming reasons for setting clear objectives for research:

1. Objectives provide the only usable criteria for judging the adequacy of research plans. If present (or proposed) programs will not propel the company to its goals, they must be replanned. For example:

One large company set as its goal a 10 per cent annual sales growth rate. Because of the company's size and the nature of its markets, antitrust laws foreclosed the possibility of acquisitions. Growth therefore had to be internally generated. Market planners thought that if present products were given adequate technological defense and were skillfully marketed, the company would achieve a 2 to 3 per cent growth rate because of population factors. But research planners evaluated 85 per cent of current R & D programs as essentially defensive. By a simple ratio analysis, it became obvious that the company was in effect expecting each dollar of offensive R & D—i.e., the other 15 per cent of its program—to yield approximately $25 per year of new-product sales. To expect such a high impact ratio was entirely unrealistic. Consequently, the company had to reassess thoroughly its offensive programs and its total program balance.

2. Objectives allow self-planning in creative organizations. They do not *constrain* action like other plans, i.e., policies, procedures, or methods. Properly established, objectives tell the organization *what* it is to accomplish, not *how* to do it. Creative persons are thus left free to select their own approaches to needed solutions.

3. Objectives provide the only criteria by which actual research performance can be judged. On a national level, we have an outstanding example of the confusion that is caused when this maxim is not followed.

The U.S. missile program was conceived primarily to support goals of national defense and scientific investigation. Whether or not the decision was a good one, the program initially was not intended particularly to enhance the national image in the eyes of the world. The R & D program as drawn up and executed appears to be meeting successfully the goals originally set for it. Hence, it should be considered a success. But suddenly, the goal of national publicity has been retroactively applied. The result is disillusionment and confusion.[2]

How Do Objectives Come into Being?

Granted the need for objectives, how do they come into being in an organization? They can originate in three different ways: (1) by "enunciation," i.e., by management's carefully assessing the organization's future purposes and communicating these in an organized system; (2) by "appeal," i.e., by subordinate groups' submitting proposals to management until its pattern of decisions indicates that an organizational objective exists (even though not formally enunciated); (3) by "external imposition," i.e., by outside pressures such as the government, labor unions, or the international situation forcing the company in certain directions. In most complex organizations, objectives originate by all three methods.

But consistent management decisions are the only way to keep an established objective in existence. Once decisions begin to contradict understood objectives, the organization cannot direct itself toward the goal with confidence. At this point the utility of the objective—no matter how clearly and how often enunciated—has ceased. Enough decisions consistently contradicting a given goal will eventually create a new goal. Until then, confusion reigns. Consequently, all key decision makers must have a clear idea of the firm's objectives and back these with consistent decisions throughout the organization.

---

[2] This argument is developed in depth in Ralph E. Lapp, *Man and Space—The Next Decade* (New York: Harper & Bros., 1961).

Key Problems in Establishing Objectives

Let us look at some of the major causes of failure in establishing objectives for research and some of the approaches specific companies have found useful in dealing with these problems. The most common failures can perhaps be classified as follows:

1. *Objectives change too often.* Managements allow "urgent competitive pressures" to dominate decisions. Hence the whole organization becomes oriented to the "profit now" objective and overdiscounts—or ignores—future needs until they become crying present realities. Thus, longer term fundamental and applied research either lack guidance altogether or are essentially converted into short-term service activities supporting current marketing or production goals.

2. *Objectives are distorted by the organization.* This problem can never be completely overcome. For each time an objective is transmitted from one person to another, the person receiving the transmission reinterprets the objective within his own framework. Thus, small distortions introduced by somewhat inconsistent top-level viewpoints are likely to be amplified by each link in the chain of authorities transmitting the objective down into the organization. Researchers can only self-direct themselves meaningfully if these distortions are minimized by careful management action.

3. *Objectives are too general.* A most common problem where objectives are enunciated formally is to express them too vaguely for use as planning guides or criteria for judging action. Such overgeneralized goals usually take the form of "value objectives." But too frequently, even "over-all business objectives" are thought out in such vague terms as "growing as rapidly as possible," "diversification in any profitable direction," etc. While not imposing constraints on research, such objectives do not help stimulate research in desired directions.

4. *Objectives can be too specific.* Some organizationally immature operations overplan research by setting goals in too great detail. Such goals take either of two forms: (*a*) specific materials, pieces of hardware, test measurements, components, etc., demanded by operating groups; or (*b*) step-by-step experimental goals. Such goals occur when operating or staff groups dominate the research function. The obvious result is that research is constrained in its approaches to problems, since it is told *how* to do the job, not *what* is to be done.

The experience of several companies may demonstrate some interesting ways of attacking these problems.

On the issue of the short-term orientation of decisions, the chairman of the board of one large concern said: "Any damn fool can make a profit for a month—or even a year—by gutting the organization's future. Top management's job is to keep the company 'future-oriented.' We try to do this by using a complex of *long-term* management controls. We play down the use of current profit and return standards in any rigid sense. And we purposely use intuitive judgments concerning how well each operating unit is building its organization and technology to meet future demands. So far, we have resisted taking on board members from banks and financial houses because we think such people overemphasize current profits at the expense of future strength."

A pharmaceutical company reports that its president and chief technical executives visit the central laboratory once a month and talk with individual researchers about their work and evolving company goals and needs. The executives get to talk to each researcher about once a quarter. The company reports that the activity is a real stimulus to researchers because they feel management has a positive interest in their work and they genuinely understand company objectives.

A large company has both a centralized planning group and divisional planning groups. The central group reports to an executive committee consisting of general corporate managers. Each year, to initiate the company's planning process, the executive committee—with the help of central planning—draws up and circulates a statement of general corporate goals for the next five years. Targets for each division are included as a part of the statement. Before formal division planning begins, appropriate representatives of the executive committee personally discuss these targets with each division manager and his planning manager. Each division then draws up a set of plans—supported by budgets—to meet agreed-upon goals. All plans are screened by the central planning group and then sent to a long-range planning committee (of the executive committee) for final co-ordination into the corporate plan. The corporate plan then becomes the basis for appraisal of budgets, and the division goals expressed within it become standards against which division performance is evaluated.

Types of Objectives Needed

Fortunately, the kinds of objectives which are most vital to research planning can be established—with proper care—to avoid the pitfalls noted above. A later section on "The Research Mission" will describe the kinds of "organizational objectives" which should be considered for research. Formulation of these logically follows the forecasting of technological threats and opportunities and the establishment of a research strategy. The following examples will illustrate what "over-all business objectives"[3] are most critical to research planning and what issues these should resolve for maximum effectiveness:

The Kinds of Businesses the Company Wants to Be In. These can be best expressed in terms of the kinds of markets the company will sell in and the functions its products must perform for customers. Thus an "electronics" company should consider whether it will be in the "communications" business, the "industrial controls" business, the "consumer appliance" business, the "quality laboratory measurements" business, etc. Each of these businesses requires a different kind of research backup in terms of program scope and balance. Obviously, a broad-based company will seek a position in several such busi-

---

[3] The author has amplified some of these in "Long-Range Planning of Industrial Research," *op. cit.*

nesses simultaneously. This simply means that it should be careful to back each with the research needed to accomplish its goals.

Method of Growth Intended. Is growth to be achieved by acquisition, merger, internal development, or a combination of approaches? Each approach carries different financial and organizational commitments and affects research program size and balance.

Direction of Growth. Is the company to grow vertically toward markets or raw materials, or horizontally into new areas at the same level of distribution? Should it find new fields or further penetrate present markets? Should the company be a broad-line producer or specialize in limited fields? Should it hedge cyclical products with countercyclical products, etc.? Such considerations obviously affect the internal balance of the research program tremendously.

Rate of Growth. Recognizing the limits of its personnel, resources, and markets, how fast should the company reasonably hope to grow? What should the timing and pattern of such growth be in each market area and over all? This requires careful thought because too rapid growth can be as dangerous as too little growth. Unless all resources, including technology, are carefully built up to support a new market position, the company will be easy prey to a slower moving competitor with better developed backing for his product or service.

Allowable Dependence on Supplies. Are the company's raw-material markets stable, or should alternative materials be sought? Is competition among vendors sufficient to insure technical progressiveness and low cost? Are individual vendors strong enough to support technical programs of their own, or should these be supplemented? Management must decide how much of a risk it is willing to take on supplier relationships. A company can often gain some degree of control over its supply markets and individual suppliers by obtaining superior knowledge of the properties of purchased materials, processes for manufacturing purchased items, or possible substitute items. Again, the company's goal of "independence of supply" affects research program scope and emphasis.

The Kind of Capital Structure Desired. Particularly in smaller companies the desired capital structure affects the length of time the company can wait for research pay-offs, the amount of technology the company can exploit without damaging ownership goals, the degree of risk the company can assume on projects, etc. These, in turn, influence total program size and balance on long-term versus short-term projects.

The Degree of Stability Desired. Because of stock price considerations, ownership needs, banking relationships, etc., a given company may desire earnings and sales stability as opposed to more rapid but risky growth. The degree of stability needed will affect the emphasis placed on more "sure-fire" applied projects and smaller impact technology which may sacrifice potentially greater gains for lower risk.

Other Business Objectives. Other objectives commonly stimulate or restrict certain research programs. These include the desired company image, its intended size, the allowable degree of government control, the percentage of market to be held in total and by geographical areas, the degree of technical flexibility desired, the price-volume and profit-volume markets the company wants to be in, the degree of decentralization intended, the company's desired size, and rate of return on investment.

Obviously, initial decisions concerning objectives will be modified as information from later planning stages becomes available. But orderly research planning must begin with a clear understanding of the directions the company wants to go and the confidence that these directions will not be constantly changing. Without such guidance the program will inevitably drift toward studies that fascinate individual scientists, toward pet projects of key executives, or toward sales service—or similar short-run activities—which bear little relationship to long-term company needs.

DETERMINING TECHNOLOGICAL THREATS AND OPPORTUNITIES

Research must be responsive to technological flows from three sources: the *scientific community* generally, the company's present and potential *customers,* and the company's *competitors.*

Let us see what is involved in assessing the threats and opportunities offered by each of these three flows. . . . What kinds of organizations have been found useful for forecasting technology? What kinds of information should management expect forecasters to consider and to provide for the planning process? And what kinds of problems are encountered in forecasting technological threats and opportunities?

Concepts of Technological Forecasting

The first thing to emphasize is that forecasting is *not* planning. Forecasts assess future environments and the mutual impact of these environments on the company and the company on the environments. Planning occurs later when management takes forecast information and converts it into goals, policies, programs, and procedures which guide action. Forecasting can be delegated to staff groups. Planning from the forecasts should always be a line of activity. Planning requires that action decisions be made and followed up with authority delegations, assignments of responsibilities, and controls to see that these assignments are carried out. This is where many "planning programs" fail. Staff planning groups anticipate problems or foresee opportunities. They evaluate alternatives and even recommend action in reports which are carefully "accepted" by management. But then nothing happens. Line managers continue to make decisions as if the staff group's analysis—and the problems and opportunities themselves—never existed. Top management thus should see that technological forecasts are used for decision making, or else it should not waste money on them.

Another important point: Management is interested in forecast accuracy, not precision. No one can forecast the precise technologies which will be needed and available three to seven years ahead. Yet management decisions on staffing new knowledge areas, planning exploitation of present research results, making major organizational changes, and so on, demand such lead times. Fortunately, what such decisions require is information about the *direction* future technology is likely to take and the *probable ranges* of technologies which might be faced. As the future unfolds, early long-range decisions can be modified, nullified, or reinforced—provided sufficient flexibility has been built into initial plans. Forecasters can be expected to provide accurate enough range forecast information for these early plans to propel the company in proper directions.

Finally, unlike other areas of forecasting, mathematical formulations are almost worthless in technological forecasting. The requisites are human judgment, a knowledge of the scientific field under study, a real sense of the economic implications of science, and imagination without stargazing. To be effective, each phase of such forecasting must be the specific responsibility of some competent individual or organization. Let us see what kinds of approaches have been used in evaluating each of the three technological flows affecting research.

General Scientific Environment and Competitive Technology

Forecasts of the general scientific environment—and the impact of competitive science in particular—may take several possible forms. The following examples offer an excellent overview of major approaches:

Some companies have developed grids[4] of all the basic sciences which might potentially impinge on their operations. On a preset schedule, they review each scientific field on two bases. First, they investigate whether the science (1) is beginning to show promise of breakthroughs; (2) is highly active, with major contributions being made rapidly; (3) is slowly approaching saturation; or (4) is scientifically dormant. Second, they evaluate whether the science is developing in directions which appear to be more (or less) closely associated with the company's long-term goals. These two parameters help determine whether a given field needs increased or decreased emphasis in the company's fundamental program. Such reviews are made by the company's most competent available scientist(s) in each field, with such outside support as the company may feel is warranted.

Other companies select for study specific knowledge areas which researchers or executives think might eventually impinge on their company's operations. Staff groups then assess the scientific potential of these individual fields and their potential economic implications if certain solutions are found. An individual study could take several man-months and usually involves an investigation of the "state of the art," important knowledge gaps, the current work being done, the magnitude of the field's potential economic impact, and the availability of qualified personnel to man the field.

Many studies—both within and outside of industry—have projected the future state of the art in various technological fields. These have attempted to estimate what technology will be needed and available in such end-use fields as computers, automatic production devices, transportation, space, communica-

---

[4] One such check list is provided by the Specialties List of the National Register of Scientific and Technical Personnel.

tions, energy, etc.[5] The technique most commonly used in such studies is to forecast critical sociological factors whose change will create a certain set of demands for technology. Present technology is compared with these needs, and gaps are noted. The forecaster then identifies the missing key facts which compose these gaps. Present fundamental and applied programs indicate which of these problems are being worked on and with what seeming progress. Past experience with similar problems provides a basis for determining the probability of success and the potential timing of solutions. Then, by cataloguing significant breakthroughs and trends, the forecaster can extrapolate developing knowledge into the future and estimate the future technical configuration of the field under study.

Many companies evaluate competitive technology both formally and informally. In fundamental research, liberal publication policies and free informal exchanges make it relatively easy to evaluate the scope of competitors' programs. Many research directors say they know to a man who is working on what in competitors' fundamental research. Several companies keep accurate tabulations of publications and patents by competitors and break them down into knowledge areas to assess competitive progress in critical spheres. Many companies make annual product comparisons to identify where their products are superior or need defensive support.[6]

Forecasts of the scientific environment are typically provided by one of three organizational devices: (1) a staff analysis group, (2) a research committee, or (3) an *ad hoc* special study group. Each approach presents its special advantages and problems. Two interesting combination approaches illustrate solutions some companies have found useful.

Several research directors indicated success in having research scientists assist a respected staff group in preparing forecasts. They say this approach both utilizes the special skills and information sources the staff group has and forces the researchers involved to think rigorously about the potential of their scientific fields and their contributions to it.

The vice president of research in one electronics company annually assigns a team of newly hired Ph.D.'s to study the potential impact of its own scientific specialties. As new personnel, they are not influenced by past company biases. Their report goes directly to the research committee.

Customer Needs

Of all possible technology flows, the company is most interested in those which impinge on the needs of its present and potential customers. Projecting technology to support present lines is not uncommon. As a matter of routine, some market research groups look ahead to customer needs three to five years in the future. But too often, market research groups get bogged down in problems of the present. Some of the more

---

[5] Published examples include Lapp, *Man and Space—The Next Decade;* Harrison Brown, *Challenge of Man's Future* (New York: Viking Press, 1954); Hans Thirring, *Energy for Man* (Bloomington: Indiana University Press, 1958).

[6] Several systems for doing this are found in James Brian Quinn, *Yardsticks for Industrial Research* (New York: Ronald Press Co., 1959).

sophisticated *organizational devices* to insure a longer term orientation to the needs of present and potential customers include the following:

A chemical company invites its customers' technical and management personnel to seminars at which they discuss their developing scientific problems and learn about the sponsor's own current research programs. The company then tries to meet defined needs through its own R & D program and through co-operative research with customers.

A.T. & T. has long supported a sizable systems-engineering group which (on the basis of demographic data, call information, system problems, anticipated new means of communication, and so on) expresses needed future technology in terms of "black boxes" (of known performance characteristics) to be developed by R & D. The group must constantly look far enough into the future to keep adopted technology from creating system-wide bottlenecks 10 to 20 years ahead.

One company has a long-range marketing research group of technical people whose sole responsibility is to contact those charged with long-range thinking in customer and potential customer companies. On the basis of this information, it tries to meet future technical needs—three to ten years ahead. The group claims to be able to spot needs and opportunities that customers themselves cannot see because of operating biases and the fact that they are constantly putting out technological "brush fires."

Some specific *techniques* used in identifying areas where longer term research could propel the company into new or expanded markets are also interesting:

A glass company considers those properties of its product (glass) which are unique unto it, i.e., exceptional tensile strength, chemical resistance, translucency, ductility, etc. It then seeks to identify present and potential markets in which consideration of one or more such properties is a dominant factor. Its applied research program then seeks glasses with intensified properties needed to meet recognized market needs. Its fundamental program seeks primarily to isolate further and to understand the properties of various glasses.

A basic metals company, by extensive field research, seeks to identify those applications where its products can most nearly be substituted for the dominant competing product. It then identifies the performance limits which preclude its present product's entry into the desired market. Where economically feasible, applied research works on the improvement of these performance limits. Fundamental research investigates the phenomena limiting the performance of the metal's compounds and alloys.

A chemical company seeks what it calls "the critical operating characteristic" of each of its major products. This is the characteristic which—if improved slightly—will most dramatically influence product sales. This becomes the focal point for applied research. For most products the nature of this critical characteristic is said to remain stable over a moderate—two- to five-year—period.

Such market research guidance helps stimulate long-range research in useful directions but does not constrain scientific approaches by over-detailing the specifications of needed products.

Top Management Considerations

Obviously, top management does not need to be involved in the details of technological forecasting. But it should expect research planning to be based upon adequate forecast data and to see that proper organizational devices exist to provide it. These organizations must look far enough ahead to allow research planning adequate lead time and not be overly biased by short-term considerations or by traditional ways of attacking problems. The effects of the latter kind of bias can be tragic. For example:

In a large chemical company a product area had been disregarded as "too small relative to our operation" to be worth the company's while. A brief discussion established the fact that if certain solutions could be found, the product had an annual potential of $10 billion. This sounds fantastic, but the company had only considered the traditional way of doing things in the market under consideration. It had not thought about what chemistry could do to change the field totally.

Significantly, the *most profitable opportunities* and the *most serious threats* offered by technology frequently come from looking at old problems in entirely new ways—not from traditional approaches gently mutating accepted technology. As examples:

The indigo industry was subverted not by traditional dye sources, but by the development of synthetic dyes through chemistry. Polymer research—not agricultural research—recently transformed the textile field and the rubber business. Solid-state physics is revolutionizing electronics. Plastics are on their way toward transforming the housing, packaging, and metals fields. The accidental discovery of penicillin brought a whole new approach to the attack on certain medical problems. Psychology has recently made dramatic advances —not because of traditional therapeutic techniques, but because of chemistry.

Finally, technological forecasting must take a broad enough viewpoint to insure that research planners recognize the opportunities and threats posed by change in the general economic and sociological environment. This means that they must consider trends in economic conditions, the demographic structure, shifting expenditure priorities, the role of government in the economy, public and legal attitudes toward business, international affairs, future labor conditions, and so on. Analyses of such factors have led particular companies to research policies which more limited commercial considerations would not have dictated. For example:

Some companies are beginning to orient some of their technological thinking toward arms control. This move is based on a changing U.S. and international attitude toward such activities, as well as the growing potential of a multibillion-dollar business in arms control devices.

Demographic analyses have shown the need for research into many fields: geriatrics, nonfossil energy sources, synthetic foods, recovery of water and chemicals from the sea and air, water purification, sewage disposal, traffic control, exotic sources of food and raw materials, and chemical means for contraception—to name only a few.

Recognizing potential public and legal pressures, some companies have established broad fundamental research programs and even entire laboratories for the primary purpose of producing technology for the public good. Others take on certain defense or health contracts—outside their normal spheres of interest—on a nominal (or non-) profit basis and contribute resulting knowledge to the public domain. Some companies restrict research and growth which would apply to areas that might create cries of "giantism" or "stifling competition." Many freely exchange basic technology with competitors, although this induces a higher degree of competition in markets they could otherwise dominate.

STRATEGY FOR RESEARCH

The next major top management consideration in research planning is to develop the over-all business strategy which research is to help support. An initial problem here is that the concept of strategy itself is so often misunderstood.

A strategy is a plan so complete that it takes into account possible countermoves of opposition groups. A strategy is an *implementing* plan. It supports an objective—or set of objectives—by determining *how* the organization can best achieve its desired ends in the light of competitive (or other) opposing pressures and its own limited resources. Every competitive organization which survives in the long run must be stronger in some respects than its competitors. Conversely, its competitors must exceed its strength in certain areas, or else they would not survive.[7] The essence of strategic planning, then, is to marshal the organization's resources so that its comparative strengths are emphasized and the opposition's comparative strengths have the least negative effect on the organization.

This means, in research, that no company can be pre-eminent in all technological fields. Because of limited resources, each company must expose itself to some risks and pass up some opportunities. The research strategy problem is to establish—in the light of expected competitive action—whether the company should (1) concentrate its research efforts, (2) remain "on the grapevine" (in touch) with the scientific community, or (3) virtually ignore developing technology. Each company's peculiar strengths, weaknesses, and objectives will determine its optimum strategy. Let us look at the typical considerations in research strategy.

Major Research Programs

First, the company must minimize serious technological threats to its existence. As a starting point, it looks at positions which must be defended

---

[7] Of course, if either party is nurtured by a benevolent third party—such as the government or fate—it can have no comparative strengths and survive.

at all costs. Then it saturates these areas with research. Almost every company has a few lines or processes which are its "bread and butter." These must be defended with strong research commitments until design maturity eliminates returns from research or the company decides to phase out the products or processes themselves. Carefully forecasting customers' technological needs and watching competitive programs will indicate areas which need heavy developmental and applied research support. Cataloguing the limits of knowledge supporting these areas helps to delineate fields for strong *longer range* research efforts.

For example, one large, limited-line electronics equipment manufacturer said:

"Our company got into fundamental research because things were becoming too complicated to continue without it. We needed to know the physical limits of certain kinds of matter in order to develop machinery which could operate at increasingly high speeds and with increasing complexity. Purchase of our kind of equipment is a straight technical decision. The fastest, most reliable equipment for a job will sell. No other will. Consequently, whoever first obtains the basic knowledge in our field will dominate it. And we cannot afford to lose our present number one position. As a result, 80 per cent of our fundamental program is now on composition-of-matter problems which we think pertain to our one primary equipment line. We try to exceed competitors' talent commitments in all these problem areas."

Next the strategic plan outlines areas where optimum technological opportunities exist. Top management must determine these by a critical analysis of the company's particular strengths and weaknesses. Examples from the chemical industry illustrate three completely different strategies in actual companies:

Company A tries to make itself indispensable to its customers by high performance of its chemicals and special services. The company refuses to make chemicals which may face fierce price competition. The company makes only high-margin specialties whose volume is too small to interest the industry's giants. It sells mostly to small companies, which tend to regard company A as their own research department. To do this, company A must keep intimately in touch with its customers' needs and be a research leader in a few scientific fields tailored specifically to these needs. The company backs up its carefully restricted research program with a team of engineers highly specialized in flexible small-plant operations.

Company B only enters fields requiring the complex technical skills it already has and/or raw materials to which it has special access. Its real strength lies in exploiting highly competitive situations by applying offbeat process technology. Consequently, the company plans to grow only in fields with large, long-run volume potentials, not in those having short-term, high-margin potential and high technological obsolescence. The company backs up its strategy with a strong raw-materials and process-oriented research commitment. It attempts to expand its range of technical skills slowly, but develops great depth in each skill it takes on.

Company C combines research with an acquisition strategy. After World War II the parent company found itself with large amounts of cash, but with heavy investments in overseas resources and low-margin cyclical products and services. The company decided to diversify into the chemical field by acquisition. After several successful acquisitions made on a somewhat random basis, the company found itself with successful operations at both ends of the chemical spectrum—chemical specialties and heavy chemicals. But to fill out its line and provide profit stability, it needed intermediate-range—medium volume and margin—chemicals. With this as a target company C started a long-range research program to provide (1) the know-how to back up acquisitions of desirable small companies in these fields and (2) new intermediate-range chemicals on which to build a new division of its own.

Such considerations determine where a company's program should be strongest. Here the company must exceed competitors' talent commitments—not necessarily their dollar commitments—area by area.

Grapevine Programs

The strategic plan must also insure (1) that sudden advances in certain areas of science will not catch the company unawares and completely demolish a major segment of its business, and (2) that the company does not overlook exceptional exploitation opportunities offered by rapid developments in new scientific areas. Such is the function of "on the grapevine" or "connecting" programs. These programs keep the company aware of impinging technology so that, as major advances occur, it can move rapidly to (1) force competitors to cross-license otherwise damaging technology, or (2) develop market positions for itself and, at the same time, avoid pre-emption by competitors.

Research groups in each "connecting" area tend to be small. But they must be staffed with first-rate men who can be on the informal grapevine that exchanges scientific information freely. These men must make contributions themselves, and the company must allow them maximum freedom to publish and to participate in scientific meetings. Two examples will show how this element of strategy is implemented in practice:

One large company considers its laboratory a "window on the world." The laboratory's primary function is "to be in the main stream of pertinent science in order to be able to appreciate the implications of new science as it becomes available." This means that the company can initiate crash programs in time to avert developing technological threats and can move rapidly to use new technology which is relevant to its operation. To be in the main stream of science, the company feels its laboratory must contribute "a fair share" to fundamental knowledge in all areas which might impinge on its operations. It therefore makes sure its program scope includes all active related sciences. And the company liberally encourages its researchers to publish their own scientific contributions.

A large chemical company uses a planning technique it calls the "limit forecast." In effect, it annually surveys all pertinent scientific fields and plans its program so that it can never take more than five years to catch up with major new technology hitting its field from any unconventional source. Such planning is possible because of (1) the company's own substantial financial capacities, (2) inertia in its markets, and (3) long lead times in the industry caused by sizable investment requirements. The company feels that a five-year crash development program could put it into a good position to deal with any major threat either through cross-licensing or direct competition.

Problems in Strategic Planning

While the above concepts are straightforward, strategic planning is fraught with hazards. Let us look at the more common and significant problems in strategic planning for research.

The first big problem is determining objectively the critical strengths or weaknesses of the company. Two approaches are provocative:

A medium-sized electronics company made a study of the relative *market penetration* of its various products. The products with high penetration and profit return were considered successful. Those with low penetration *or* low profit return were considered unsuccessful. Top management tried to assess what factors had contributed most to the success of "successful" lines. It also analyzed what factors had caused the failure of "unsuccessful" lines. It then tried to assess why the leading competitor was most successful in each area where the company had failed. The study indicated that the company's strengths lay in designing special components for precision jobs and selling such items direct. Its weaknesses were in competing in mass markets where low cost and advertising "pull" techniques were important. It then started a program to "spin off" the latter activities and to retrench into specialized markets backed by a fast-moving engineering group and pilot-scale plants.

A coal company used an *investment analysis* approach. It found that its investments were almost exclusively underground. Because of the technological maturity of the field, management felt further investments in the highly competitive underground operations would offer limited returns. It decided to do research which would yield aboveground investment opportunities leading to special market positions. With this broad goal, its research was most successful.

Unless a company adequately assesses its particular strengths and weaknesses and develops its resources properly around these, it will eventually be a "me too" operation, unsatisfactorily trying simply to meet competition on all fronts.

A second major problem: Many managements do not recognize that—in organizing the company's resources—a "growth through research" strategy must be backed by entirely different kinds of financial and organizational commitments from more conventional market development or acquisition strategies. The research approach requires (1) that management think in terms of a five- to seven-year pay-back period instead of the two- to four-year period common to other investments, (2) that management be willing to make research investments with less certain information and a potentially higher risk than normal operating investments, (3) that a flexible long-term capital plan be developed to meet the unpredictable investment spurts and long investment cycles characteristic of research, (4) that operating departments be more technically oriented and highly co-ordinated to achieve maximum benefit from research technology, and (5) that the over-all organization be planned to grow flexibly from within rather than through acquisition of entire experienced operating units from outside. Lack of such long-term thinking has often caused research failure in companies dominated by "merchant" or "financial" management whose approach is geared to near-term profit considerations.

Finally, strategic thinking is frequently biased by "the way things have always been done." This leads to problems like the following:

1. Many companies tend to balance their R & D programs to match present product-line sales or investment patterns rather than building programs to meet maximum technological threats and to take advantage of greatest technological opportunities.

2. Few companies tend to balance their investment risks by purposely taking on extremely high risk projects a certain percentage of the time. Instead, they tend to research traditional products on traditional sets of components and fail to look for really offbeat approaches which could upset the whole field. Although scientists themselves frequently would like to take a broader range of risks, they are often constrained by management's attempting to hold research to too detailed a profit contribution standard over too short a time base. Conversely, by limiting the scope of their research, these companies are simultaneously (and often unwittingly) exposing themselves to the threat that an entirely new technological approach taken by an outsider could completely upset their traditional market positions.

3. Few companies have defined their research strategies broadly enough to defend themselves adequately against the eventual costs of "gadget changing and molecule manipulation" short-term technical orientations. Business is the institution our society has established to take its risks. In fact, the only logical justification for "big business" besides economics of scale—and these are surpassed as soon as a company decentralizes—is to take risks other economic units cannot. Perhaps the paramount element of risk taking today is in the scientific and technological spheres. Yet—despite a significant change in attitude in recent years—too few companies have really faced up to supporting the truly long-term research which is needed to keep U.S. industry in the technological forefront. Instead, much of such research is still forced onto institutes, the federal government, and educational institutions. In the long run, this exposes business to several extremely unpleasant possibilities:

a) Specific industries can be more easily attacked by public groups with the eventual goal of greater public control over the businesses' operations. For example, the pharmaceutical industry today would undoubtedly be less prone to attack and eventual regulation if it could point to significant fundamental research contributions as justifying high margins and returns. Despite truly impressive developmental accomplishments, the industry does not enjoy as favorable a scientific image as it easily could in the eyes of the public or the medical profession.

b) The groups supporting longer term research will eventually control large areas of basic knowledge and can make business subject to royalty payments and/or specific controls if they use such knowledge. Atomic energy is a case in point.

c) The government itself has another wedge to use in entering open productive competition with private enterprise. It has already entered the power-producing field (not by this route, however) and now has powerful technological entrees into the air transportation and satellite communications fields should it choose to use them.

d) The total long-term research done in the U.S. may not be adequate. The result can only be that eventually certain foreign countries will usurp desirable markets which would otherwise belong to U.S. businesses.

e) Even in considering U.S. markets, many companies tend to overlook or discount rapidly developing *institutional* markets and the potential of new *public* consumption areas.

Such threats may in the long run be among the most serious of all strategic considerations for business.

Top management must overcome these serious difficulties and develop a broad research strategy which minimizes technological threats from present and potential competitors yet maximizes the company's own potential gains from the use of technology.

The Research Mission

The research organization can support any given strategy in a variety of ways. And it is up to top management to specify which types of support it expects from research. Is research to be the dominant source of new product and process ideas, or is this the function of sales or operating managers? To what extent should research simply service present products and processes? Is research to be the technological arm of management, consulting on all aspects of the company's technological situation? Or should research be just a highly skilled pool of technical specialists available to answer problems beyond the talents of divisional personnel? To what extent is research to support itself through patent income? Is research to provide a scientific "intelligence service" to keep the company aware of impinging technological threats or opportunities outside the sphere of traditional operations? To what extent is research technology to be the basis of new product growth, new processes, or a general technological reputation for the company? Answers to such questions are crucial in designing a research program which best fits the company's needs.

By not defining the research mission carefully, many managements, in effect, set research adrift without specific responsibilities in the overall organization. Like any other organization, research can and must be held accountable (over a suitable period of time) for accomplishment of a particular portion of the company's goals.[8] *Proper definition of corporate goals, strategies, and the research mission provide a firm basis by which management can hold the research organization responsible for specific accomplishments. Yet, if properly developed, these plans do not constrain the scientific approaches research uses in carrying out its mission.*

PROJECT SELECTION

Next, top management must be sure that it has a project selection procedure which fits research into company goals. The process, of course, is exceedingly complex and requires much intuitive judgment, but project selection for an integrated research program essentially follows a three-step sequence: planning technology (1) for present products, (2) for foreseeable new products, and (3) for entirely new applications.

Present Products

The process begins by assessing the technology needed to support present lines two to ten years in the future. The first step is prediction of the company's potential market for each product class. Partly, this involves assessing what technology will keep the products attractive to customers despite inroads of substitute items, competitive technology, and changing customer needs. Customers' technical needs and potential competitive technology are defined by the technological forecasting techniques already noted.

Planners then compare present technology with needed technology and identify gaps. If enough key facts are available to fill these gaps, defensive development or applied programs can be introduced (or continued) to fulfill established needs in the shortest possible time (usually within two to five years) and with a high probability of success. But if key facts are missing, the company will have to undertake "support" studies in the specific disciplines underlying needed technology.

Because scientific areas within which these studies are needed can often be rather clearly defined, their probability of technical success is usually reasonably high. Average lead times often lengthen to three to seven years if support studies are introduced. But past experience in the specific scientific areas supporting the product should be used as the guide to expected lead times and the number of people needed to staff each area. Regardless of whether the developmental or the combined developmental-support-fundamental approach is used, planned technology for existing lines proceeds from recognized needs to specific programs.

New Products

In a dynamic technological environment, however, present products—plus planned acquisitions—are unlikely to fulfill all company goals (see

---

[8] See Quinn, *Yardsticks for Industrial Research.*

Figure 1). The next step is to find new market applications for present or new technology and then (through the forecasts noted) identify the specific technology needed to fulfill these applications. The needed technology is again matched against present technology, and gaps are noted. As before, the gaps can be attacked by either of two methods— "support" research or development. Before making substantial commitments to either approach, the company should make exploratory

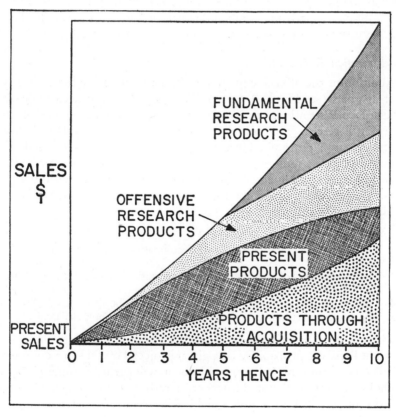

Figure 1

investigations to determine the technical feasibilities of the various possible courses that are open to it.

As in the case of present products, if exploratory work indicates that enough key facts are known, development and applied programs can be undertaken with a high probability of success and a probable impact within two to five years. If key facts are missing, support programs in defined areas can be initiated. Again, experience indicates the general probability of success and lead-time pattern in any given area, and specific project sizes are based on this estimate. These factors are typically determined by intuitive judgments. Only when research has reached quite applied stages are mathematical projections at all useful. But even in applied work, experience indicates that while time schedules can be met by massing personnel on projects, budget estimates are only accurate within broad ranges.

Again, note that planning new lines first identifies market needs and then works back to sequential programs to meet these needs. Thus, optimum levels for both present and new product support are best developed by aggressively (1) seeking specific market needs, and (2) analyzing past experience in technological support areas to obtain the best possible estimates of success probabilities and project cost.

Fundamental Research

Addition of the offensive program still may not enable the company to meet its goals (see Figure 1 again). The company may need technology which develops entirely new applications, beyond the scope of those presently foreseen. The company then needs a "fountainhead" fundamental research program. Here the planning process is reversed. First, technical planners must identify scientific areas which may provide the foundations for commercial end products compatible with company goals. Within these fields, management should support specific project inquiries based on:

1. The rapidity with which technical advances are occurring.
2. The competence and enthusiasm of company personnel in the particular field.
3. The availability of qualified persons to staff scientific areas new to the company.
4. The anticipated amount of information yet to be discovered in an area.
5. The relative pertinence of the area's knowledge to company goals.

There is no alternative to an element of faith in planning fundamental research. Here the probability of a given project's leading to a commercial end product is low or unknown. Either it will yield "commercializable" technology, or it will not. However, a rather stable percentage of the projects undertaken in a given field will frequently have commercial implications. Several companies with mature fundamental programs made statements like the following: "We can predict with some accuracy that we will have one major new capital-absorbing development as a result of fundamental research in that area next year. We don't know what the development will be; we do know we can expect it."

Despite the fact that many companies have analyzed their experiences over a long period of time and have come up with ratios showing so many dollars of sales (fixed investment or profits) per dollar of research, I know of no company which has found enough reliability in such ratios to use them rigorously for planning specific fundamental programs. Nevertheless, intuitive, order-of-magnitude judgments of these relationships, *scientific field by scientific field*, must—and do—underlie all determinations of whether the company has enough fundamental research to meet its goals. Management should, of course, bring to bear any data which may help reveal possible trouble spots in the fundamental program. But it should avoid using any figures rigidly. Ultimate decisions on this element of program balance must be left to trained scientists in whom management has confidence.

Detailed fundamental research planning, indeed, occurs from the "bottom up." Each researcher should be encouraged to select his own specific inquiries within his scientific specialty. Since these researchers should know more about their specialties than anyone else in the company, management's primary control is to make sure that their judgments are tempered by those of competent scientific executives who understand company goals and needs.

A large chemical company stated how its management gives the researcher maximum scope in selecting inquiries, yet does not lose control of this critical planning process:

"We expect the individual researcher to come up with project proposals within the area of his specialty. He discusses any new idea with his director. If the director is enthusiastic, he suggests that the researcher make a literature search, perform exploratory investigations, and report back in one month. If at the end of the month the area looks promising to the researcher and a small committee of research directors, the researcher is allowed to go ahead for another three months. His progress—and the promise of the field—is then checked again. If things are encouraging, he is given a commitment for six more months' work. The six-month review is the last informal review. If the project continues, it is thereafter reviewed annually by the research committee in the appropriate budget review cycle."

Other Technology

Although fitting projects into goals has been described in terms of sales and/or profit goals and present or new product lines, similar approaches are used to fit other technology into company goals. If specific needed technology can be defined, the program develops from the desired result back to the specific research project. If specific technology cannot be defined, the company plays the probabilities that fundamental research in broad scientific areas will produce applicable technology. These concepts apply whether the technology is for new processes, new raw-material sources, greater human safety, improved product quality, information for the public good, or any other of research's many possible outgrowths. The important factor is to work *from* company goals *to* a balanced research program that will meet these goals.

Program Balance

The final stage of project selection is balancing the final package of projects to meet company goals and strategies. So many detailed decisions are involved in the planning process that intended final program balance may be lost if management does not step back and take a careful overview of its final program. It must see that emphasis is balanced among:

Phases of effort—by seeing that long- and short-term goals are supported by adequate fundamental versus applied versus developmental research. More fundamental stages must feed new scientific possibilities to later stages and must find principles which are bottlenecking more applied programs. Applied and developmental programs should provide concrete evidence of research pay-off in the near future.

Offensive versus defensive research—by making sure that the company is giving adequate attention to growth goals versus maintaining present businesses. This breakdown applies only to applied and developmental phases because earlier phases cannot be identified as to results sought.

Product lines supported—by subdividing applied and developmental programs to see whether each present and potential product line is getting sufficient offensive and defensive support to fulfill its particular subgoals.

Operating divisions supported—by seeing that each division's needs receive adequate attention when divisions and product lines do not coincide (as in the refining, distributing, transporting, and producing of oil).

Scientific areas—by insuring, particularly in fundamental phases, that program scope includes all scientific fields presenting major long-range scientific threats or opportunities within the company's sphere of activity.

Types of results sought—by supporting goals with the proper levels of product technology, process technology, raw materials technology, public-good technology, pursuit of general scientific understanding, and so forth.

No mathematical techniques can tell managers what the "right" balance is for their program. What is right for one company is wrong for another. The proper balance for any particular company depends solely on its goals, capacities, and strategies. These must be determined by seasoned management judgments. But this balance must not be regarded as a rigid cast. As certain project areas begin to produce results, they should receive added emphasis. Others become less attractive and must be de-emphasized. The result is a constant dynamic rebalancing as the program progresses. In fact, one sure sign of program weakness is a static balance of emphasis over a long period.

RESEARCH TO OPERATIONS

One more crucial area for top management advanced planning is in facilitating the transfer of technology from research to operations. Two sets of biases tend to restrict this transfer. On one hand is the researcher, who often either does not recognize the commercial implications of his work or will not release his work until he has covered all of its possible scientific ramifications. On the other hand, operating groups often term research technology "impractical" because it was "invented by people who don't understand operating problems."

Perhaps the most insidious restriction appears when operating managers—many of whom are held to profit or "return on investment" standards—resist taking on research ideas which will add marketing or engineering development costs to their operations in the short run, despite the long-run desirability of such ideas. Involving operating personnel in program planning and reviews tends to enhance their understanding of research progress and prepares the way for transfer of research technology to operations. Beyond this approach and the usual exchange of reports, individual companies have found the following organizational devices useful:

A large chemical company has formed a development division which it refers to as a "large flexible plumbing and cooking establishment." The development director is held to a profit responsibility. He makes his profit by pilot plant production and sale of new products conceived in research. As soon as a product or process is successful in development, the appropriate operating division can request that the product be transferred to it. The development director has to try to pull other research ideas up to commercialization as soon as possible to continue making a profit. Consequently, there is a positive impetus to get ideas out of research, and operating managers do not resist taking on proven profitable ideas.

A pharmaceutical company pays the researcher a percentage of profits on any idea commercialized and encourages him to follow the product or process through to commercialization, if he has the talent and interest. In effect, the company sets up a small new profit center and operating division for each new product. The researcher thus has an interest in pushing his ideas, and there are no operating managers to resist taking on new products or processes.

By simple accounting entries a steel company segregates the "debugging" or "market introduction" costs of a new operation and puts them into a separate pool which is not charged directly to any operating division. These costs are only amortized to the specific operation after it has had sufficient time to get established.

A large electronics company emphasizes that the managers of its decentralized operating divisions are not held to a short-term profit standard, but are held to a complex of standards, an important one of which is "technical progressiveness." Management judges technical progressiveness by comparing each division's actual use of research technology against an estimate of how much research-produced technology *could have been* used by the division —the standards being, of course, subjective.

Such devices assist the transfer of technology from research to operations. But they are not total solutions in themselves. Optimum transfer of research technology to operations will occur only when research is properly integrated into the company's over-all plans by the kind of top management co-ordination outlined above.

SUMMARY

Top management's function in research planning thus is:

1. To provide research with a clear understanding of company goals and stategies, and to define a specific mission for research within the context of these plans.

2. To see that appropriate organizational arrangements are made:
   a) To assess carefully the major technological threats and opportunities the company faces.
   b) To facilitate transfer of research technology into operations.
3. To develop a project evaluation procedure which results in a balanced package of projects to meet company objectives.

From this point on, management must continuously evaluate its program to see that both research and operating units carry out their intended functions in developing and utilizing technology to support company goals.

QUESTIONS

1. Set research objectives for Photon, Inc., at the conclusion of the (E) case. (Prior study of the full Photon series is necessary.)
2. Prepare a statement of research policy and research objectives for Union Oil Company as of 1960. Assume that the shale oil project has been successfully completed, but that the Board of Directors and management have concluded that a full-scale production program on oil shale is not desirable now.
3. If your work in a business policy course has steeped you in an industry or a company, establish research objectives for a company on which you have background.
4. As a term project or major report effort, form a team of engineers, scientists, sociologists, and economists among your fellow students to examine *scientific* and *engineering* progress of significance to a given firm.

   Suggestions: Note the varieties of approach suggested in Quinn's paper. Choose a limited product area such as a material, a component in an energy system (e.g., conductors), or food preservation.
5. Study a common consumer product, and identify desirable functional improvements or additional features needed.

   Suggestions: Typewriter, dishwasher, 35-millimeter slide projector, etc.
6. As far as possible, identify the kinds of development programs and research programs needed to realize the improvements identified in (5) above.
7. How can management evaluate the scope, quality, and appropriateness of its research work? Its development work?

Who Should Make Research Decisions

The best person to decide what research work shall be done is the man who is doing the research. The next best is the head of the department. After that you leave the field of best persons and meet increasingly worse groups. The first of these is the research director, who is probably wrong more than half the time. Then comes a committee, which is wrong most of the time. Finally there is a committee of company vice-presidents which is wrong all the time.

C. E. K. MEES, Vice President
in charge of Research
Eastman Kodak Company

FROM: R. M. Lodge, "Economic Factors in the Planning of Research," November, 1954. Cited by permission from *Sources of Invention,* by Jewkes, Sawers, and Stillerman (New York: St. Martin's Press, 1959).

NATURAL RESOURCES PROJECTIONS AND THEIR CONTRIBUTION TO TECHNOLOGICAL PLANNING

By Joseph L. Fisher and Hans H. Landsberg

TECHNOLOGICAL PLANNING—that is, planning for the creation, development, and adoption in industry of new and improved technology—lies near the heart of economic growth for the individual firm and for the whole country. This kind of planning, both within firms and in certain public agencies, has spread rapidly in recent years. A number of private firms and government agencies have notable long-range planning programs. Among these may be mentioned public (investor-owned, government-regulated) utilities, major steel companies, air lines, federal government construction agencies, and larger municipalities. Public electric power utilities and gas pipe-line companies examine market possibilities twenty or more years ahead and schedule the construction of new capacity and the introduction of new technology. Federal construction agencies such as the Corps of Engineers maintain six-year advance programs of construction projects; more general planning for rivers and harbors work and for other purposes extends much farther into the future.

For the most part, advance planning, private or public, pertains to the opportunities and problems of particular organizations and the products or services they deal in. Frequently, the specific plans are not put in the larger context of the industry, geographic region, or national and world market *in a systematic and disciplined way*. We are aware that the trend is definitely toward the preparation of more comprehensive technical and economic information relating to the future, but much more could usefully be done.[1]

A distinction needs to be drawn here between what we call natural resource projections and technological planning. By natural resource projections, we mean disciplined, systematic forward estimates of demand for and supply of land in its various uses—crop and grazing land, urban

---

[1] National Planning Association, *Uses of Long-Range Economic Projections: Some Survey Findings,* Technical Supplement No. 5, National Projection Series (Washington, D.C., August, 1960). Almost 90 per cent of the respondents in this survey, chiefly larger enterprises, reported that they used long-range projections of the general economy in their planning. But the major portion of the business community probably does not make use of such projections, according to the survey.

land, recreation sites, forest land; water, energy commodities, and metallic and nonmetallic minerals—both individual items and general categories. Demand and supply estimates for the various items are interrelated to take account of substitutions among them, and are consistent with projections of the broad capability of the economy in terms of its labor force, investment rates, productivity, foreign trade, and the like.

By technological planning, we mean, as noted previously, the rational taking-account of all factors relevant to the creation, development, and adoption in industry of new and improved techniques, products, or services. The process of technological planning may be subdivided as follows:

1. Identification of problems and opportunities (preliminary technological and economic appraisal).
2. Research.
3. Development (pilot operations with materials and cost records kept).
4. Definitive economic appraisal (costs, markets, pricing, economies of scale and joint production, competition).
5. Scheduling and budgeting of the innovation.
6. Actual adoption in industry (organizing the capital, labor, raw materials, etc., to do the job).
7. Periodic evaluation.
8. Ideas for further technological planning.

Throughout, there will be a concern for education and training of personnel for all phases of the process of technological planning.

The focus of our paper will be on natural resources projections, as these are derived from and adjusted to more aggregative demographic, technologic, and economic projections. The general methodology for making natural resources projections will be explained briefly, and a few specific projections for 1980 and 2000 will be presented. A number of possible resource shortages which come clearly into view in this systematic looking-ahead will then be considered in more detail. These problems represent challenges and opportunities for technological planning. The last part of the paper will suggest in several major resource fields a number of newer technological prospects which are already, or soon may be, important subjects for technological planning.

The most significant point the paper will try to make is that technological planning for specific purposes in particular firms and agencies can be done more effectively against a backdrop of systematic, long-term projections of the demand for and supply of natural resources. These projections can furnish a useful framing or perspective for the technological planning of the particular firms and agencies. This will be especially true for firms which develop basic resources or process raw materials, plus those firms closely connected with such activities, and firms that are in the business of creating substitutes, such as various branches of the chemical industry.

Natural Resource Projections for the Years 1980 and 2000

The basic inputs for the economy, as well as for individual firms, are labor and enterprise, capital, and resources, including raw materials. All are necessary, although, within limits, one may be substituted for another. Estimated demand for any one of these, or for any subitem, must be accommodated within projections of the over-all capacity and performance of the economy. Further, there must be internal consistency among the amounts, spatial and industrial distribution, and scheduling of use of the various components. On the supply side, requirements will have to be met out of the existing and potential number of people, their skills, the supply of savings and investment funds for capital formation and replacement, and the amounts, distribution, and potentialities for resource and raw materials. Technology and economics form the bridge between estimated demands and the levels and manner in which they are satisfied. With advanced, promptly adopted technology, requirements can be filled more quickly and efficiently. With the skillful balancing of the variety of supply possibilities with estimated demands, with careful attention to the estimating of net returns of alternative courses of action and to the economies of scale, the development of the economy can proceed along economic lines.

Projections of demand for and supply of resource and raw materials can form one important basis for technological planning and economic adoption in industry. The accompanying table presents estimates for 1980 and 2000 of the demand for a number of important resource and raw materials. Projections are also presented of population, labor force, gross national product, and investment. These may be thought of as a portrayal of the likely capability of the economy for 20 and 40 years ahead. Within these aggregative projections, and consistent with them, the demands for the more specific materials have been worked out. The economy has been divided into three parts along its vertical dimension; major end-use categories, such as food, shelter, transportation, heat and power, and the like; intermediate materials which have been carried some distance in processing from the basic resources but are still not highly specific in use, such as lumber, steel, and aluminum; and the more basic resources and raw materials, such as land in its several major uses, water, and relatively unprocessed minerals and fuels. Figure 1 illustrates our estimating system in such a way that some of the interrelations may be visualized.

In the larger study from which these estimates have been drawn, demands for specific materials, as well as the more aggregative items, are presented in ranges: high, low, and medium. The medium projections are presented here, although for many analytical purposes the high or the low is more significant. For example, the low demand projection for agricultural products indicates the surplus acreage that we might expect to have on our hands should the assumptions on which the low projection

SELECTED ECONOMIC AND RESOURCE ESTIMATES

	1960	1980	2000
Economic Aggregates:			
Population (millions)	180	245	330
Labor force (millions)	73	102	140
Households (millions)	53	73	100
GNP ($ 1960 billions)	503	1,060	2,200
GNP per worker ($ 1960)	6,900	11,500	15,500
Government expenditures ($ 1960 billion)	100	240	550
Private investment ($ 1960 billion)	73	150	320
Personal consumption expenditures ($ 1960 billion)	330	660	1,320
Intermediate Products:			
Meat consumed (billion pounds)	29	46	65
Cotton produced (billion pounds)	7.5	10.4	16
Automobiles produced (millions)	6.6	11.6	24
New dwelling units (millions)	1.5	2.7	4.2
Steel produced (million tons)	100	175	280
Construction lumber produced (billion board feet)	31	48	79
Fertilizer consumed (million tons of nutrients)	8	21	42
Basic Resource Requirements:			
Cropland, including cropland pasture (million acres)	442	437	455
Forest land, commercial (million acres)	484	484	484
Grazing land (million acres)	700	700	700
Outdoor recreation land (million acres)	44	75	136
Urban land (million acres)	21	32	45
Timber (billion cubic feet)	11	21	36
Fresh-water withdrawals (billion gallons per day)	250	340	480
Fuel (quadrillion BTU's)	45	83	138
Oil (billion barrels)	3.2	5.3	9.7
Coal (million short tons)	398	607	698
Natural gas (trillion cubic feet)	13.1	25.8	35.0
Iron ore (million short tons)	125	200	320
Aluminum, primary (million short tons)	1.8	7.8	19.5
Copper, primary (million short tons)	1.7	2.4	3.9

Source: Taken from work in progress at Resources for the Future. Medium-level estimates only are shown.

rest turn out to be the path of the future. It marks the outer limit of the range of problems that public policy may have to deal with.

Conversely, in the case of energy and some other materials, the high projection suggests the earliest date at which one or the other of the commodities involved might begin to show the effects, in terms of cost, of approaching depletion. Also, a projection that delivers a verdict of adequacy at all three ranges suggests quite a different degree of confidence or urgency for policy-making purposes from one in which adequacy is indicated at only one or two levels.

The methodology employed in making these estimates may be illustrated by examining briefly one particular chain of estimates stretching from the over-all economic projections through end-use projections to intermediate products and basic resources. The demand for housing (2.7

How the U.S. will grow — 1960 to 2000

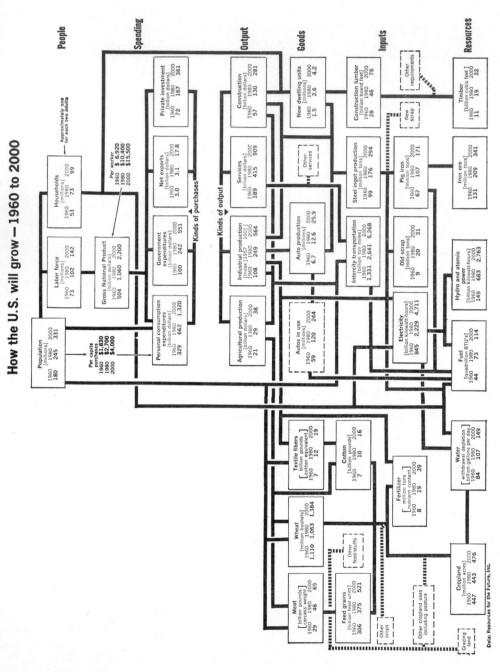

Figure 1

Data: Resources for the Future, Inc.

million new units in 1980, 4.2 million new units in 2000) is derived from the projections of population, its age distribution, family formations in particular years, income, and other characteristics. It is also related to supply factors, such as the age specific distribution of the housing stock, the likely replacement rate, upgrading and improvement of units, the possibility of new types of supply altogether, such as second houses, and so on. Throughout, historical trends and relationships are employed for developing the future estimates.

The demand for the intermediate product, lumber, is derived from the demand in specific years for housing and other types of construction which require lumber. These, in turn, have been drawn from estimates of the demand for the end products into which these other uses of lumber flow. Generally speaking, the range in the demand estimates from high to low reaches its maximum at this intermediate product level, since the possibilities for materials substitution are greatest at this cross-sectional level. Thus, we have had to come to terms statistically with the possibility of the substitution of steel, aluminum, tiles, plastic boards, and the like for lumber, as well as of the substitution of composition boards and paper products, both of which may be made of wood.

The final stage is to consolidate all the demands for the intermediate product, lumber, in such a way that these can be traced back to the demand on the forests. The othe main strands of demand, in addition to lumber, are from pulp and paper products, plywood and composition board, railroad ties, pit props and poles, fuel wood, and several others. The over-all demand, expressed in cubic feet of wood, provides in rough form an estimate of how much wood will have to be cut in a given year and—with due allowance for amounts uncut, and uncuttable, and wasted— how much will have to be grown. More meaningful is the presentation of demand, not for the total amount of wood, but for the amount of timber required and growing stock suitable for the several major intermediate products.

Turning to the supply side, such factors have to be examined as the existing stock of saw timber and other types of timber, differential growth rates among species and sections of the country, rates of cut, efficiency in processing and use, and other technical factors. Beyond this, attention has been given to the possibilities for imports and exports and, most difficult of all, the likely path of adjustment to cost and price changes. Over past years the cost and price of lumber, generally speaking, have been rising in this country relative to the cost and price of other construction materials, such as steel, aluminum, and cement.

Our perspectives on demand and supply of lumber for the future would indicate that in all likelihood the requirements we have calculated cannot be met on the basis of the contemporary supply pattern and practices, but only with sharp improvement in the utilization of existing forest lands. Failure to act undoubtedly would tend to raise the cost of the forest products, certainly of lumber. Even such actions as now seem possible would probably prove insufficient to check this tendency. Thus the past price trend is likely to continue.

It is obvious that this development would have its repercussions on the demand as we have projected it; but in our projection technique, there is no provision for "feedback" to the demand projections from the judgment of adequacy—or lack thereof—through their effect on price. Rather, we consider the likely consequences of demand trends and supply outlook for the cost and price situation. The rate at which the use of substitute materials may increase is one of the unknowns; this depends largely on technological planning within the relevant sectors of industry and the rate at which the cost differential between lumber and its competing materials tends to increase.

Cost must here be understood in the widest sense, not simply in terms of dollars and cents per pound or square foot of material. Substitute materials typically permit the adoption of novel techniques in design and use. This affects the designer, the builder, the producer of construction materials, and, last but not least, the consumer who must be prepared to accept the consequences of change. Thus, cost per physical unit is only the starting point, but by no means the most pertinent standard of comparison.

The substitution rate depends also, of course, on improvements in forest management practices, conservation in the processing and use of lumber and other forest products, the possibilities for larger imports, and ultimately on developments in forest genetics and physiology which may result in hybrids that will grow trees much larger and faster.

In this construction-lumber-forest complex, as in others, the American economy is notable for its willingness to seek substitutions and new sources, and to accommodate readily to them. This is fine for improving the economy but very hard on the making of accurate projections. This characteristic of substitution furnishes scope for technological planning and is the hallmark of an enterprising economy. A major objective of government policy is to stablize this aspect of the economic environment at a high level through appropriate laws and regulations, and to enhance thereby opportunities for creative forces of development and growth.

RESOURCE PROBLEMS AND PROSPECTS AHEAD

Our general conclusion drawn from this kind of a systematic demand and supply look-ahead is that for several decades, there will be general adequacy of resource and raw materials in this country, *provided* there is no catastrophic war, *provided* there is a continued flow of education and research and a continued flow of technological innovation (including discovery, substitutions, conservation, and so forth), and *provided* access to sources in other countries remains open. The provisos are extremely important and will be examined later. Furthermore, the finding of general over-all adequacy does not mean that there will not be severe problems for particular materials at particular times and in particular places. Nor does it mean that sufficient supplies will be forthcoming without considerable effort in research, technological planning and development of many kinds, strenuous conservation efforts, and further improvements in management across the board. Indeed, these problems will challenge the most imaginative thinking and effort of both business and government.

A few of the more important resource problems and opportunities ahead will be considered here; each presents challenges for technological planning.

Energy

Over the length of our national history, energy resources, while never altogether easy to win, have been ample to support rapid economic growth. Projection ahead in this field, as in others, is hazardous, but the picture which emerges from recent studies shows general adequacy—i.e., the meeting of projected demand without significant increases in real cost —at least until around 1980 for the various energy-using sectors of the economy (such as households, industry, and transportation), with supplies being drawn from substantially the present conventional sources.[2] This is in sharp contrast to the record of the past century, during which the major source of energy for the economy has shifted sharply from a predominant reliance upon wood more than a century ago to coal at the end of the nineteenth century and lasting until after World War I, and since then to oil and gas, which now supply 70 to 75 per cent of the total.

Beyond 1980 to the end of the century the outlook has to be uncertain, primarily because depletion, in the sense of rising cost, of the leading contemporary sources of energy—domestic crude oil and natural gas—is strongly indicated. Looking back at the history of crude oil supply and demand, one naturally hesitates to make such a judgment. Discovery of new deposits of oil has confounded every prophet who went on record predicting the early depletion of this resource since oil first flowed at Titusville. Yet it is beyond dispute that the amount of oil and gas in the ground is finite; and it is likely, therefore, that at prospective rates of consumption, even in the face of optimistic assumptions regarding improvements in the technology of both discovery and recovery, cost of energy will begin to feel the effects of depletion of domestic oil-bearing formations before the century is out.

---

[2] The statistical background for this and the following paragraphs on energy is to be found in Schurr, Netschert, *et al.*, *Energy in the American Economy, 1850–1975* (Baltimore: Johns Hopkins Press, 1960), and in the forthcoming *Resources in America's Future.*

The response of the economy is less certain, for there are various evasive maneuvers on the horizon, some in direct substitution of oil and gas, some through indirect displacement. First of all, technology will undoubtedly postpone the effects of depletion through improvement in finding and recovery of oil and gas. Recent years have seen substantial improvements in secondary recovery techniques for underground oil. Given the attention now lavished on this technique and the fact that in the past, pools have given up at most one third of their content, there is good reason for anticipating that secondary recovery will continue to increase in importance and, 10 to 15 years from now, will supply perhaps as much as one third of the total consumption. But this will merely postpone, not prevent, depletion. Its effect on costs, in the longer run, may be mitigated or even offset entirely through the exploitation of shale and tar sands, the liquefaction or gasification of coal, and the use of nuclear and other unconventional forms of energy. Finally, world reserves of oil and gas—less explored and depleted than those in the United States—offer the possibility of supplementing domestic supplies, even though rising demand in the developing countries will undoubtedly claim a rising share of oil and gas throughout the world. Which particular combination of these elements will be the path of progress will largely depend upon relative advances in technology, as these are reflected in cost, and upon institutional factors.

The possibilities for large-scale use of shale as a source of liquid fuels are very good. The research and pilot operations have already been carried out in the Colorado plateau. While there are problems of scale, location, water supply, and transportation, it appears evident that usable liquid fuels can be produced from shale at a cost of no more than 10 or 20 per cent higher than liquid fuels from conventional underground sources. The development of tar sands, found in large amounts in the western prairies of Canada, while not as far advanced in terms of pilot plant operations, is widely believed to be at least an equally feasible source for large amounts of liquid fuels, held back principally by a serious locational handicap.

Economic conversion to liquid or gaseous form of one of our most abundant fuel resources, bituminous coal, which has been losing its markets for direct use as a solid fuel, is another goal toward which technology might well be oriented on a large scale. Success would make available, not in the Rockies or in the Canadian prairies, but in the heart of the country, a long-term source of liquid fuel for which vast markets are likely to persist for decades. The know-how exists, but the cost is presently prohibitive. A breakthrough here would both revive an ailing industry and secure the energy base of the economy for a long time to come.

Nuclear energy does not hold its greatest promise in substitution for liquid and gaseous fuels, and this seems to point to the need for technological planning which will, by some sidewise displacement process, permit nuclear energy to contribute toward meeting an incipient liquid-fuel problem. For example, further development of use of nuclear-produced electricity in space heating could result in a saving on fuel oil and gas. Nuclear energy may be substituted on a wide scale in the propulsion of ships. Conceivably, process heat from nuclear sources could be used in the extraction of liquid petroleum from oil shale. Direct use of nuclear energy for the propulsion of automobiles, buses, and trucks seems to present almost insuperable difficulties because of the need for heavy shielding, but it is possible that the indirect substitution process may take over. With further improvement of the fuel cell—powered by, say, hydrogen—and with the hydrogen produced with the aid of nuclear heat, it may become both technically and economically feasible to engineer a series of fuel cells for the purpose of moving automobiles and other land vehicles.

Further off in the distance are the possibilities for application of solar energy in certain uses. Conversely to nuclear energy, which is a very highly concentrated form of energy, solar energy is widely dispersed and has to be collected or concentrated if it is to become useful for new purposes. A far-ranging development program is now getting under way, and it is a distinct possibility that by the end of the century, solar energy may have entered some parts of the economy in a significant way.

Figure 2 presents estimates of the demand picture for 1980 and 2000 (and actual figures for 1960) for the several energy commodities and indicates also the major uses to which they may be put. Technological planning may find some guidelines in this set of projections. In a sense the economy will have a breathing time for the next two decades, during which conventional energy sources will suffice; thereafter, rather massive substitutions of new sources or techniques may have to take place if substantial cost increases are to be avoided. Discovery, research, and development programs, it would seem, may be laid out in a thoughtful and resonably unhurried manner with the hope that they will produce results in about twenty years.

Water

Projections of the uses and sources of water supply can also furnish a framework within which technological planning in certain industries may operate more effectively. Unfortunately, past statistics of water use, supply, and cost are very scant and do not support future projections as well as one might wish. Furthermore, national projections of water demand and supply have far less meaning than regional or river basin projections, primarily because water cannot be transported from one basin to another in large amounts. For this reason a finding of over-all water adequacy for the whole country is not particularly meaningful or helpful. Further difficulties arise from such matters as the definitional

PROJECTED ENERGY DEMAND, BY SOURCES AND ECONOMIC SECTORS

C — COAL (INCLUDING AMOUNTS CONSUMED IN ELECTRICITY GENERATION)
O — OIL
G — NATURAL GAS
E-HN — ELECTRICITY BASED ON HYDRO AND NUCLEAR SOURCES
AS — ALL SOURCES (INCL. NGL, NOT SHOWN SEPARATELY)
E-AS — ELECTRICITY FROM ALL SOURCES

(IN BTU X 10^{15})

SECTOR	1960						1980						2000					
	C	O	G	E-HN	AS	E-AS	C	O	G	E-HN	AS	E-AS	C	O	G	E-HN	AS	E-AS
RESIDENTIAL	1.6	2.7	3.7	0.4	8.6	2.0	2.8	2.5	7.2	1.8	14.6	5.4	2.7	1.8	7.2	5.3	17.2	9.1
COMMERCIAL	1.2	0.9	1.2	0.2	3.6	1.2	1.6	1.3	2.2	1.0	6.3	2.9	1.5	2.4	2.2	2.6	8.8	4.4
TRANSPORT	0.1	8.3	0.4	—	9.6	—	—	16.9	0.8	—	19.3	—	—	35.0	1.1	—	38.3	—
INDUSTRY	5.4	1.6	4.8	0.7	12.9	3.7	8.8	2.7	10.2	3.1	26.4	9.4	11.1	3.9	18.8	10.7	49.8	18.3
TOTAL (INCLUDING SECTORS NOT SHOWN)	10.4	18.0	13.6	1.6	45.5	8.8	15.9	29.8	26.7	6.9	83.5	20.9	18.3	53.4	36.2	21.3	138.0	36.4

Figure 2

difference between water that is withdrawn, used, and returned to streams and water that actually disappears in use through evaporation and transpiration. Figure 3 illustrates the outlook in a tentative way for two selected regions: the Ohio River region in the East and the Colorado in the West.

From this sample look-ahead, several problems emerge clearly. The Colorado region, like most western regions, with the notable exception of the Pacific Northwest, which is supplied adequately by the Columbia River, either faces water shortages already, or will face them in the near future. In the Colorado River basin, for example, water disappearance is already about 15 times the dependable flow (flow that is available 95 per cent of the time), and water withdrawals exceed dependable flow by close to 30 times. It will be noted in Figure 3 that projected disappearance is about the same as average flow throughout the period shown, and even exceeds it slightly at times. Water supply, on the average, therefore, is now fully used up or almost so, and the prospect is that this will continue. Additional dams and reservoirs and further regulation of flow can affect water use by raising the dependable flow, which in turn can yield such benefits as increased hydroelectric capacity, but cannot affect average flow, which sets the upper limit over the long run to water disappearance. These observations about water disappearance in the Colorado make no allowance for maintaining some minimum amount of flow for diluting pollution which, though not now large compared to eastern rivers, will undoubtedly increase in the future. The upshot of all this, despite confusion caused by terminological and measurement difficulties, is that the Colorado region now faces a severe water shortage problem that may well handicap economic growth.

In the Colorado River basin, as well as in most of the other basins in the West, the largest water use is irrigation farming, averaging nearly 90 per cent of total withdrawals over all the western regions. Recent economic research indicates that irrigation is a relatively low-value use of water in the West as compared to industrial, municipal, and even recreational use of water. One study, recently completed and now nearing publication, focuses on the economics and alternative use of new water supply developed in the San Juan River of northwestern New Mexico. Under a variety of relevant and apparently realistic assumptions as to place and pattern of use, including the possibility for economic transmountain diversion of this supply to the Rio Grande Valley for use in Albuquerque and the other more populated parts of the state, it turns out that water used in industry might have the effect of increasing state income as much as forty times that of using the water for irrigation. Furthermore, use of the water for recreation might return six times as much in state income.[3]

This and other recent analyses point clearly to the main western water

---

[3] Nathaniel Wollman et al., The Value of Water in Alternative Uses (to be published by the University of New Mexico Press).

PROJECTED WATER REQUIREMENTS
AND FLOW: TWO REGIONS
1980 AND 2000

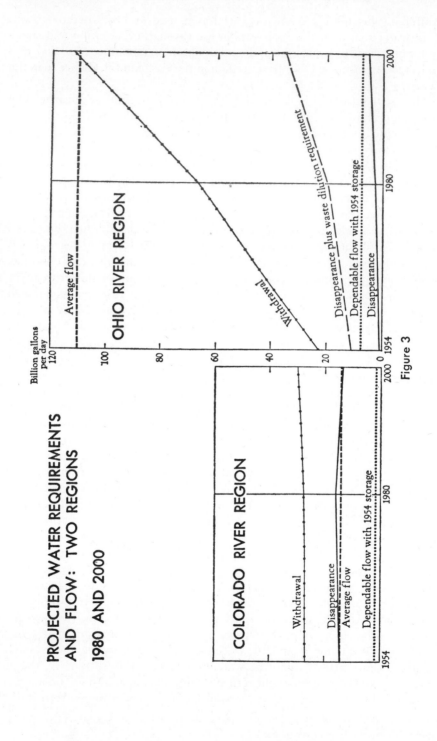

Figure 3

problem: that of shifting the emphasis in water use from irrigation to other uses, principally municipal, industrial, and recreational. These uses can support higher costs and prices for water supply; more jobs can be made available per unit of water used, and more population can be supported; and as an added bonus, most of the water used for such purposes is returned to streams, whereas in agriculture some 60 per cent actually disappears into the atmosphere.

Other measures may be taken to improve the western water picture. Research on water conservation across the board can yield major returns. One interesting possibility is the use of hexadecanol and other monomolecular film-forming substances, which spread rapidly and easily over the surface of reservoirs to reduce evaporation losses. The gains here can be very great; Lake Meade, formed by Hoover Dam on the Nevada-Arizona border, now suffers a loss of over one million acre-feet each year from evaporation. A protective film could probably reduce this loss considerably, although experiments to date do not permit an accurate estimate of the feasible reduction. Other possibilities include the reduction of the number of phreatophytes, which are useless water-using plants and trees, further improvements in irrigation canal linings, vegetation control of the upland portions of river basins, and integrated management of surface and ground water. More physical and statistical research on artificially induced rainfall apparently is needed before anything definite can be said about this possibility.

In much of the eastern and middle part of the country the problem appears to be not so much one of sheer supply as one of supplying reasonably clean water. This characterizes the Ohio River region, as shown in the chart. Despite fairly sizable efforts on the part of many municiplities to prevent and abate pollution, the problem seems to be gaining rather than receding in most places. Pollution takes a variety of forms, including biological, chemical, and sedimentation. A recent preliminary study indicates that the requirement of water supplies to maintain minimum flows in eastern rivers, thereby flushing and moving sewage and other forms of pollution downstream into the salt water, may overwhelm all other uses within a few decades.[4] This possibility, or rather probability, shows up clearly in the chart on the continuously rising line of disappearance plus waste dilution requirement, most of which is the latter. These estimates are based on the maintenance of a standard of water purity of at least four parts of dissolved oxygen per million. Admittedly, this is a rather high standard for highly populated industrial areas, but it seems consistent with good standards of public health, improved recreation, and the aesthetic desires of many people for clean water. Also, it is quite feasible technically. Technological planning for the introduction and

---

[4] Nathaniel Wollman, *Water Supply and Demand*, Committee Print No. 32, U.S. Senate Select Committee on National Water Resources (Washington, D.C.: U.S. Government Printing Office, 1960).

improvement of pollution treatment processes and for pollution prevention measures will undoubtedly have a high pay-off in years to come; indeed, these will be necessary if estimated future water requirements are to be met in a dependable way.

Other Resources

The same kind of story that has been presented in energy and in water can also be told in the other resource fields. One interesting and rather new possibility is to be found in the outdoor recreation field. As a result of a rapidly growing population, high levels and increases in income per family, greater mobility of people, and shorter work weeks and longer vacations, the amount of time and money spent in outdoor recreation has been increasing very rapidly during recent years. Statistics are scant, but they seem to point to a growth of somewhere between 6 and 10 per cent annually in the use of outdoor recreation areas and facilities, ranging all the way from city parks and playgrounds to the magnificent national parks and forests. Indeed, outdoor recreation has become a large-scale growth industry. Continuation of this rate of growth over the next few decades seems altogether likely.[5] It involves not only the direct use of land and water areas but numerous ancilliary industries, such as the small-boat and outboard motor industries, outdoor sports equipment of many kinds, construction of summer homes at beaches, lakes, and in the mountains, and so on. Estimates of demand for outdoor recreation as affected by location, age and income distribution of the population, distances traveled, amounts spent, and the like can provide the basis for technological planning in industries related to this activity. The employment of certain standards of use, expressed in man-days of use per acre or per dollar of investment in facilities, or in some other way, makes it possible to translate anticipated demands into requirements for additional outdoor recreational acreage and facilities of many kinds, all of which call for technological planning and investment.

Similarly, a future demand-supply picture can be built up for the various metallic and nonmetallic minerals, agricultural crops, forest products, and chemical materials of various kinds. With few exceptions, our demand projections in the metal field point toward the continuing need for new discovery or, alternatively, for commercially feasible methods of using low-grade ores, if dependence upon foreign supplies is to be avoided. It is interesting in this connection that a few months ago, we were visited by a representative of a major U.S. oil company who was seeking advice as to the likely future demand for various metals. His interest, it turned out, was motivated by the fact that his company's staff of geologists greatly

---

[5] See Clawson, Held, and Stoddard, *Land for the Future* (Baltimore: Johns Hopkins Press, 1960), chap. iii. Also Marion Clawson, "Methods of Measuring the Demand for and Value of Outdoor Recreation," Resources for the Future Reprint No. 10, 1959.

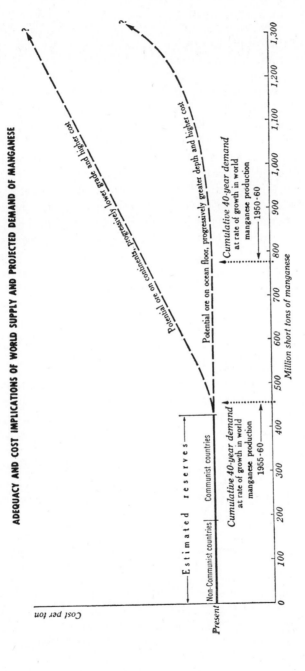

ADEQUACY AND COST IMPLICATIONS OF WORLD SUPPLY AND PROJECTED DEMAND OF MANGANESE

Figure 4

exceeded the foreseeable need for their services in the oil business, and that the transfer of the technology they had developed in oil and gas exploration to metals exploration seemed a worth-while investment. Ideas as to future demand and supply can thus give the impetus to transfer of existing technology as well as to creation of new technology.

In the case of manganese, to illustrate more fully one of the metals for which this country is almost wholly supplied from foreign and generally remote sources, even the resource situation of the world as a whole is not such as to assure continued production for the balance of the century. Depicted in Figure 4 are world reserves, that is, the metal content that can be recovered at present levels of cost and technology, conjectural cumulative demand through the year 2000 at two different levels, and potential ore, that is, occurrences not now commercially minable. If the data reflect and project the situation at all correctly, then it is clear that technology must aim at three things: (1) to facilitate discovery of additional reserves; (2) to reduce the cost level at which potential ore, including that now accumulating in steel mill slag heaps, can be mined; or (3) to tackle production of the nodules on the ocean floor, which experts claim are even now within economic reach, provided venture capital of substantial magnitude can be attracted to this proposition. Failing progress along these paths, one must be prepared for a gradual increase in the cost and price of manganese around the world, and in the free world above all.

As a final word along this line, it is interesting to note that the outlook for basic agricultural crops for the next decade or longer is for continued oversupply. In a sense, therefore, the future picture in agriculture is quite different from that for many of the raw materials. Even here, however, some clues for technological planning can be found. For example, what are the possibilities for new or increased use of basic agricultural crops in industry for the production of alcohol and fuel, fabrics and paper, and so on. In this paper, we do not attempt to fill in the full picture for agricultural crops, metals, energy sources, water, or any other resources, but merely indicate a few of the possibilities for the future.

SOME CONCLUSIONS FOR TECHNOLOGICAL PLANNING

A number of promising lines for technological planning and resource development have been opened up in the preceding sections dealing with the resource trends and visible problems ahead. A more careful sighting-in on these opportunities could result from a periodic review of the demand and supply projections, taking into account the effects of changing technology on the demand and supply outlook.

One thing that emerges clearly from this kind of look at resource and raw materials in the American economy is the need to maintain and increase basic research in the physical, biological, and engineering sciences.

and in economics and the other relevant social sciences.[6] For example, geological survey work must be continued and accelerated so that there is maximum chance that new ore bodies will be discovered. The same is true of hydrologic surveys which form the basis for water development. Research in entomology leading to the control and elimination of insects which are harmful to trees and crops has enormous potential for increasing the supplies. Genetic research in both agricultural plants and trees holds promise of large augmentations to supply in the more distant future. For example, physiological and genetic research done during recent years with the pines (some of which has been supported by Resources for the Future) indicates that as we come to understand more about the flowering and germination of the trees and the possibilities for hybrid strains, we may expect considerably more rapid timber growth over many of our forest areas. Research in solid-state physics is opening the way to "molecular engineering" of essentially new construction and other materials by means of which strength, durability, and other characteristics may be greatly improved in relation to volume and weight. Other work in molecular physics holds the promise of developing monomolecular films which can be spread on the surface of reservoirs to reduce evaporation losses. Research and development for desalinization of sea water and brackish water are now proceeding on a fairly wide scale under government auspices. As more information is derived from pilot plant operations of several types, significant cost breakthroughs may be achieved.

Research is needed also in the social sciences and can be expected to pay off handsomely. In economics, basic research is needed in methodology for estimating impact of specific technological innovations in specific industries and regions, and on related activities. There would be important gains if the demand-supply projections framework outlined earlier in this paper could be improved and redone periodically—say, every three years—by an agency of the government. This makes up the economic and resource framework within which technological development takes place; it should be elaborated and maintained. Benefits and costs of research itself need much more profound examination than they have been given thus far, as do the estimating of benefits and costs of particular development projects and sequences of projects.

Research has to be fed not only with funds but also, and most important, by a stream of highly educated and motivated young men and women. Educators and scientists, almost unanimously, have been calling for more such persons and for a higher quality of training. Without increased attention to this factor the whole process of technological planning will not be adequately sustained.

---

[6] Total research and development expenditures have increased some threefold since 1953 and now are running about $14 billion a year. For trends in research (basic and applied) and development expenditures during recent years, see various publications and releases of the National Science Foundation.

A few additional selected lines for technological planning and resource development may be indicated, each of which offers promise for the more distant future. It is always risky to place too high a bet on any one such line; on the other hand, it is even more risky for a business firm that wants to maintain and improve its position over the future to neglect these less certain possibilities. On the horizon in the energy field, for example, exciting work is being done on various types of fuel cells, magnetohydrodynamics, thermionics, secondary and tertiary oil recovery, and nuclear energy, as well as along more conventional lines. In the minerals field, one may mention improvements in steel making through the replacement of air blasts by oxygen and even direct reduction, the possibilities of getting nodules of manganese and phosphates from the ocean floor, and the development and use of semiconductor ceramic materials. In the water field a scanning of the horizon shows many possibilities in water conservation, as noted earlier, in the recycling of water in industrial processes and the substitution of air fin for water cooling, long-distance and transmountain transportation of water, the integrated management of surface and underground water, and better sequence and timing of projects in river basin development. In forestry, quick-burning and other new techniques for control of less desirable species is but one example of technological planning leading to improved management of a basic resource. In wood products, new particle boards, precut lumber for modular construction, and the like offer economies.

For these and other "farther out" possibilities an emphasis on basic research becomes of highest importance. A portion of each research and development budget could well be devoted to the more remote and offbeat projects, as well as to the basic understandings from which new insights arise.

Obviously, the fuel that keeps the engine of technological development running is an expanding, high-quality program of education and training in the engineering schools and the industrial training centers. Without this, the rate of advance cannot be maintained, let alone increased. This is true in resource fields as in others. Enough has been spoken and written on this subject that it needs no further attention here.

A final point needs to be made explicitly. Technological planning for natural resource and raw-material development may be done in terms of the United States, North America, the western hemisphere, or the world. It would probably be possible to operate an advanced economy within the United States or North America alone, but the costs would be high. Low-grade taconite, concentrated at high cost, might have to be substituted for richer imported ores if the United States alone, as a source of iron supply, is considered. Similarly, alumina would have to be extracted from domestic clays. Manganese, nearly all of which is now brought in from overseas, would have to be mined at perhaps five times the cost from domestic sources, refined from tailings, or got up off the floor of the sea in nodules. Synthetic products would have to be substituted for industrial diamonds, and although the man-made product is in some respects an improvement over nature's, this is by no means universally true. Tin in tin cans would have to be replaced entirely by glass bottles and paper cartons as scrap recycling diminished. Tea and chocolate would disappear from the table, and so would coffee unless Latin American sources were retained. Tourist travel abroad would die out.

Furthermore, the United States depends on export markets overseas for one third to two fifths of its cotton, wheat, rice, and tobacco production; for only a slightly smaller but growing share in food fats and oils; and for substantial amounts of its exports of machine tools, electrical equipment, and other highly processed items. Elimination or drastic reduction of the United States export trade would severely dislocate large segments of the domestic economy; it would interrupt industrial advance and gains in living levels in other countries, with most serious repercussions politically as well as economically.

In practical terms, therefore, it is out of the question to undertake either natural resource projections or technological planning in this field except on a scale which includes international trade and investment in raw materials. Anything less would greatly aggravate the resource problems of the United States for the foreseeable future.

. . . .

Q. You spoke of the possibility of a lumber demand going from, I believe, 31 to 79 billion board feet, and you commented that you didn't think this was going to be possible with our current way of doing things. We're also acquainted with another study made by the Stanford people in which they give some figures that give the opposite picture: that in the long run, we will not be using as much lumber; that lumber as we know it will possibly be off, I think, by about 6 per cent. So I wonder if you'd comment on how we get these diametrically opposed viewpoints from people who are supposedly looking at the same basic data.

F. (FISHER). This doesn't surprise us, of course, that different "experts" looking at the same data come up with a different view. This is the spice of our existence in business and in economics. Partly, I think, it's methodological, and partly not. I have not examined the Stanford study very recently, and perhaps you have.

We, very purposefully, have followed a methodology which does not close up the gaps that are incipient when demand, say, exceeds supply. Obviously, as you move forward through time, these gaps do close. Looking back, supply always equals demand. We have chosen a methodology which will open the gap to the fullest possible view because this is an indication of an emerging problem. The more difficult the problem looks in these terms, the more necessary it is for somebody to do something about it in the direction of substituting aluminum or steel or tiles; or in substituting lower grade lumber, composition boards, and so forth, for high-grade lumber; or in directing attention away from those products that embody a lot of lumber. It's in the methodology, probably, that the main difficulty comes. And our methodology is not the same as theirs.

L. (LANDSBERG). Yes, this is largely so. I could outline various provisions under which you could come closer. There's one particular point that I might use to illustrate this point: If you assume a geographic shift in timber production from the East to the West, that is, when a higher percentage is lumber from the West than is now the case, you come much closer to closing the gap. How fast you can do this realistically is a problem. At the same time, unless you assume substantial changes in management, in fire prevention, and in disease prevention—in other words, in forestry technique—you can see that your cumulative drain will almost exceed your forest supply by the year 2000, if your demand continues unchecked in that direction. We know that one of two things will happen. Either price will go up and discourage demand, and we will have substitution; or we will be forced into a large-scale program of improvement in forest management. This is the kind of thing I tried to point out. To pick one figure, at which we think in a given year demand and supply will come together, is not as important to us as identifying the problems involved.

F.   I might add this: In this case and in many others the national picture is not too revealing. You have to get down to regional terms. This is obviously true in the case of water demand and supply. It happens also to be true in the lumber-timber complex. The big reserves presently are in the West, mature timber that no longer is growing very much. The rapid growth is in the East in second and third growth, where the young trees just grow faster. A kind of rational approach looking at it in these broad terms would be to continue lumbering in the West, clear out the trees that aren't growing very fast to make way for young growth, and then move to the East. But these adjustments are difficult; and all we've done is, we hope, to enrich understanding of the general situation within which business can maneuver and change can take place.

Q.   Dr. Fisher, as an economist, would you consider it the government's duty to do something about this?

F.   Well, I don't accept the "government" as implied in the way you put the question. The government is us. It is business; it is labor; it is everybody in the political sense. It may well be that additional government policy and investment will be called for. This is not to say that strenuous effort may not also be called for from business. My own bias is in favor of the business system handling it to the extent possible, but I don't see a dichotomy, really. The business system, I hope, will close the gaps within an improved framework of government policy. Now, this could lead us into quite a discussion, and so I'll stop with that.

Q.   I'd like to question the things you said ought to be questioned, that is, the assumptions of leaving the feedback out. And it goes a little bit like this: If you leave the international feedback out, as you said you did for the energy study in which we needed only relatively crude data, won't we run into just a simple assumption? That the population growth in the rest of the world is equal to that of the United States right now? That the standard of living will become what the United States standard of living is today? . . . which are fairly reasonable assumptions. Then we come out with some very drastic differences on these energy reserves from those that you show. And I don't think we can estimate the reserves because the spread we found in our company studies, from the optimistic to the pessimistic, gives a range of answers from ten to one.

F.   Let me say one thing. In the generalization we made about general adequacy of energy supply, we meant it to apply to this country *with the proviso* that we import about what we do now. But now—

Q.   We're on my thesis of why we ought to put the feedback in. Isn't this kind of sticking your head in the sand and saying that you automatically have to be—

F. Let us take the energy case and, if you like, put in some of the feedbacks in terms of discoveries, reserves, and possibilities in other parts of the world.

L. In this energy instance, we have considered the international scene in terms of what might happen through 40 years of consumption. Will there be anything for us even if we want it, and at what price? This is the problem, I presume, that you are referring to. We have a very nasty problem trying to figure out what the rest of the world can consume in the next 40 years.

As for the ranges of estimates, they don't particularly upset us; we present the low, medium, and high figures not in order to indicate margins of error or to be optimistic or pessimistic. The figures are not that at all. They are simply results of different assumptions—different possible paths. We think the medium figure is most likely, but neither the low nor the high is unlikely. A range of this kind is not indicative of how much our estimates may be off. Rather, we say that under a different set of assumptions which we outline, it may even go that high or that low. So in this respect, this "high" is not so frightening.

Q. No, it's not frightening, but you kicked a number around on energy. Wouldn't the people in this room have to take your figure into account before they retire or not take it into account? This becomes important, because you've got to project such findings in terms of whether this is something that's going to happen in your lifetime or not happen in your lifetime.

Q. What complicates the picture much more is the current international military situation. This has placed a fairly high technical price on energy plans, and this is going to spur the development of power reactors.

Q. I question your 1975 figure on nuclear energy. Isn't it low?

L. Not really, when you look at it in terms of presently installed capacity and the time it takes to make a real dent in it through additions of plant. I might say our estimate for the year 2000 might be of interest. It is that roughly 50 per cent of all electrical energy would then be nuclear energy. This, in turn, is barely 15 per cent of all energy consumed. In terms of this projection for the year 2000 of total energy, you don't get far by 1975 in nuclear energy and even by 2000, not as far as one might offhand be tempted to anticipate.

Q. I notice you gave transportation no credit at all. . . .

F. Yes; but again, shipping is a very small part of energy consumption. It's the advantage of this sort of across-the-board analysis that you can really afford to concentrate on the important things. You don't have to worry too much about the small fields.

QUESTIONS

1. Study Figure 1. What major needs and problems for the United States are indicated for 1980? Will these needs be significantly sharper by A.D. 2000?

2. What significant relationships do you detect on Figure 1?

3. What actions at this time, if any, do your conclusions suggest for (a) a public gas and electric utility company, (b) a large holder and producer of pulpwood timber in northern New England, (c) a manufacturer of home-building materials, (d) a manufacturer of large materials-handling

systems for the mining, stockpiling, and loading of bulk materials, (e) a producer of electrical generating and distribution equipment, (f) the National Park Service, (g) a firm that produces air-pollution-removal devices, (h) the commissioner in charge of the collection and removal of rubbish for a major city, and (i) a large dairy products processor and distributor in eastern Pennsylvania?

4. Study Figure 2. What conclusions do you draw for firms associated with the production and distribution of energy?

5. Study Figure 3. What business opportunities are suggested? What government actions and decisions would you monitor if you were guiding a firm according to your suggestions?

6. Make a library study of a natural resource position of major importance to a specific firm. Prepare a report for top management of that firm, and include action recommendations.

   Suggestions: Choose a large producer of a material, of energy, or of equipment vital to a particular natural resource user.

The Ethics of Fame[1]
By William J. Coughlin

Fame and honor, in this nation at this time, all too frequently are considered inseparable. They are not. It is possible to have fame without honor and honor without fame.

We are reminded of this by a news item concerning Army Maj. Lawrence R. Bailey, who has received the Bronze Star and Purple Heart following his release by the Pathet Lao after months of brutal treatment.

You may recall the news photographs of Maj. Bailey being carried on a stretcher from the aircraft that brought him home.

The citizens of the major's hometown of Laurel, Md., recently tried to present him with an automobile as a token of their appreciation. Declining, Maj. Bailey suggested the money be used to establish a scholarship fund.

We could not help but contrast the major's action with those of our seven astronauts.

We are well aware that the astronauts are brave, courageous and dedicated men who wear their fame with proper public humility. But they have shown a singular lack of character when it comes to the question of profiteering on their fame.

We are weary of speculation in motels, apartment buildings and other real estate. We find little to admire when the directors of a large aerospace firm almost come to blows over the possibility of investment by the astronauts. We find nothing noble in the renting by NASA of luxury apartments with wrought-iron stairways and a 50-ft. swimming pool under the guise of Houston "working quarters" for the astronauts. We find nothing to applaud in the rejection of the offer of free homes in Houston—after acceptance of the real-estate promoter's scheme became public.

[1] From an editorial reproduced by permission, from *Missiles and Rockets*, November 5, 1962.

We find nothing but revulsion in the deal which set the whole thing in motion, the half-million-dollar sale of exclusive rights to their personal stories to *Life* magazine. They have sold their stories and the stories of their wives to the highest bidder in a crass commercialization of man's first step to the stars.

The astronauts can aver they were badly advised by their business manager—and they were. They can say they were poorly led on this matter by their superiors at NASA—and they were. But these men of space are supposed to be the finest of our land, men of Homeric stature who are leaders and advisers in matters of honor in the best classical tradition.

They should need no business manager, they should require no advice on this. Where is the strength of character to lead the nation, not to follow the unethical advice of others?

The seven gentlemen are the first into space, but they have left the path littered with unpleasant debris. Let them take a day away from the centrifuge and study what the philosophers have to say about the ethics of fame.

. . . . . .

They alone are not at fault. It is to the discredit of our industry and our society that we let these men be tempted by the cheap profit motives of a mass magazine, that we did not advise or lead them better. But if these are men of true greatness, they must be the leaders and set proper standards for others. To date, they have failed, not in bravery and accomplishment but in honor and reputation.

. . . . . .

THE PLANE MAKERS UNDER STRESS[1]

By Charles J. V. Murphy

"Cease all study, design, development, fabrication, and test work toward the B–70 weapon system in wing strength in accordance with the Master Phasing Schedule. Proceed with design, development, fabrication, and test work to produce one XB–70 for the earliest possible flight date consistent with tentative funding ceiling. Terminate immediately all subcontracts. . . . "

That order from the Air Materiel Command at Dayton, Ohio, was teletyped to an Air Force project officer at the North American Aviation plant at Inglewood, California, at the start of business on the morning of December 2, 1959. It struck down a project on which upwards of six thousand men were working at full tilt, and on which half a billion dollars had already been irretrievably committed. But the order did more than just wipe out an enterprise already reaching into hundreds of plants across the nation. It also decreed an end to an era that has uniquely expressed U.S. power and technical competence.

The B–70 Valkyrie was the last heavy bomber the U.S. had in development. It was also the last important tactical airplane under urgent development by an American airframe manufacturer. When that message reached J. L. Atwood, North American Aviation's President, as it instantly did, he could not altogether contain the shock, although the substance of the order was not a surprise to him. There had been a telephone call from the Secretary of the Air Force the afternoon before, putting Atwood on notice that the decision to give up the B–70 as a full-blown weapon system had been regretfully taken, and formal notice to that effect would presently be sent to him. But Lee Atwood wept all the same.

He had reason. North American's future as a prime airframe contractor rested on the B–70. For nearly five years the company had been mobilizing its engineers and partially tooling up in the expectation of producing a manned bomber system for the Strategic Air Command that would begin to replace the B–52's after 1965. Powered by six engines, each generating 30,000 pounds of thrust, equivalent in their whole output to about one third the power put out by the great generators at the Hoover Dam, the

[1] Reprinted by special permission from *Fortune* magazine, June, 1960; copyright by Time, Inc.

new bomber could fly at three times the speed of sound (about 2,000 miles per hour) at 80,000 feet or so, and could flash into the Soviet hinterland and back in six hours, with a single refueling over the polar latitudes. A total investment of between $6 billion and $7 billion for the system in being was taken for granted, and a network of some ten thousand subcontractors and vendors was in the process of being constructed.

From these prolonged exertions and ardent expectations, there will emerge in due course only a single prototype plane, or what the military call a test vehicle. Of what the B–70 system might have been, the only physical evidence is a full-scale mock-up that fills a huge hangar at Inglewood—a symbol of a famous industry under stress.

Into the Wild Blue Yondermost

The airframe industry is perhaps the most remarkable industry ever to evolve under the auspices of American enterprise. In a single breathless generation, it became, along with the aeronautical-engine makers, the largest single employer in U.S. manufacturing. Its planes dominate the air routes of the world. More than any other industry, it was responsible for Allied victory in World War II and has since borne the racking responsibility for the defense of the West. Its natural leaders, "the primes," include six great companies: Douglas with headquarters at Santa Monica in the Los Angeles area, North American at Inglewood, Lockheed at Burbank, Boeing at Seattle, Martin at Baltimore, and Convair, now a division of General Dynamics, at San Diego. Ranged about them are, or rather *were*, seven smaller primes. They are McDonnell at St. Louis; Republic and Grumman situated close together on Long Island; Northrup at Hawthorne, in the Los Angeles area; Fairchild at Hagerstown, Maryland; Chance Vought at Dallas; and until its recent demise, Bell at Buffalo.

Most of these companies are now in grave trouble, the big with the small. The trouble and stress, paradoxically, have come in the midst of plenty. Just about as much money as ever is flowing from the Pentagon into the defense industries. But unfortunately for the airframe companies, which year in and year out depend upon the military for 80 to 85 per cent of their sales, a diminishing share of the stream is going to them. It is the specialists in military rockets and space technologies that are emerging as the principal beneficiaries of the strategic patterns being developed for the 1960's. These are the companies that are expert in the chemistry of high-energy fuels; in the technology of metals and plastics, which provides the means of devising a shielding for a nuclear warhead or a man-carrying capsule that will allow it, after being flung thousands of miles through upper space, to be brought back through the earth's envelope at velocities up to twenty times that of sound without being burned up; in the techniques of miniaturizing computers and radio transmitters that can be trusted to aim a hundred-ton projectile within a mile of the desired target or to relay a signal 50 million miles from the vicinity of Mars; and in all the other scientific disciplines as well that have made possible the vault into space.

All of the major companies, and indeed even the smaller ones, have made a heroic effort to master these new technologies. By and large, they have succeeded. Most of the great plane builders are no longer emotionally or even financially anchored to the airframe assembly line alone; they, too, are grappling with the challenge of outer space. Lockheed, to take a single newsworthy example, is not only the maker of the now famous U-2 reconnaissance plane; it is also prime contractor for the Samos and Midas satellites, which may make traditional reconnaissance wholly obsolete. All the same, the swift military transition to rocket strategy, and the fact that it came in the midst of the industry's own leap from piston-engine planes to jets, have presented the aircraft makers with problems of unparalleled severity: problems that everywhere are certain to call for redeployments of capital and manpower and effort on a scale perhaps never before known to a basic U.S. industry.

The need for such redeployment is no longer a matter of pride but of stark necessity. While few industries have grown faster than the airframe makers, none is now involved in deeper financial perplexities. The charts that follow dramatize the changing fortunes of six representative companies. Taking the industry as a whole—defined here as all of the primes except Convair—the figures are no less revealing and startling. Between 1950 and 1959, sales of these twelve top plane makers rose from about $1.2 billion to $7 billion—up nearly 500 per cent as against a 90 per cent increase for all U.S. manufacturers. While sales still remain at high level, backlogs are now crumbling, and profits have tumbled sharply. In 1956, profits for the industry ran to $166 million. In 1959, they were down to under $67 million, not much more than they were at the start of the Korean war build-up.

An even more revealing sign of the industry's ebbing financial strength is the drop in the ratio of earnings to net worth, the test of its capital-formation power. In 1954 the companies we are considering earned a whopping 28.3 per cent on a net worth of $646 million. Last year, they earned only a meager 6.1 per cent on $1.1 billion. Traditionally, these companies have been better off than most manufacturers by reason of the fact that much of their work is done on tooling and in plants provided by the U.S. government. Their aggregate investment in fixed assets is currently carried at only $500 million, compared to $1.2 billion put up by the Air Force and Navy. Yet this substantial advantage has not stemmed their decline. Indeed, according to a tabulation of the First National City Bank, aircraft companies as a group now rank tenth from the bottom in forty manufacturing classifications, between brewing and building, heating, and plumbing equipment, in terms of earning power on the stockholders' equity.

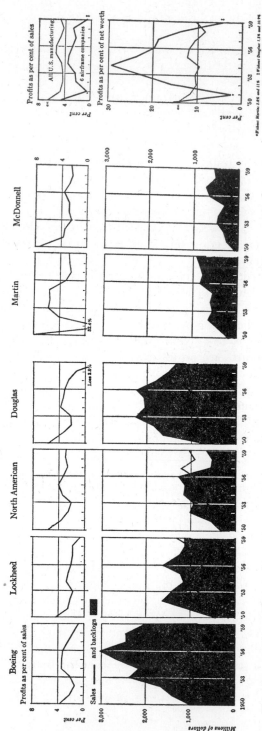

These charts are a financial analysis of five of the great "prime" airframe contractors and one smaller one. McDonnell of St. Louis. McDonnell has been included in the analysis because its business in the last three years has been running at a high level and is, in fact, close to that of Martin. Convair has been left out because its parent company, General Dynamics, Inc., does not break out Convair's operating record from its consolidated statement.

Sales of the six companies analyzed rose rapidly in the past decade from $833 million in 1950 to $5.8 billion in 1959. But the backlogs of Boeing, Lockheed, North American, and Douglas, which went up and up until 1956, have fallen off sharply since; only Martin shows a generally upward trend. Meanwhile, profits fell from $138.8 million in 1957 to $41.4 million by the end of 1959; and since 1954, profits as a per cent of sales (upper charts) have flagged. Of recent years, for special reasons, Martin and McDonnell have made a better profit showing on sales than their larger competitors. But as indicated in the upper chart at far right, returns on sales for the six are discouraging. Returns on net worth for the group are still more revealing. In 1954 the profits of the six ran to 29.2 per cent of invested capital, or far above the average for all U.S. manufacturing. In 1959 profits on invested capital plunged below 5 per cent, as against 10 per cent for all manufacturing.

For this turn in fortunes, there are two causes. The proximate cause is the huge write-offs that Douglas, Boeing, and Lockheed have each had to take on their commercial jets. Even allowing for the technical misfortunes that have overtaken Lockheed's Electra turboprop, the jets have been a huge success for everybody but their designers. The combined write-offs for development costs and inventory write-downs so far total almost $500 million, with more, but fortunately not much more, still to come this year. It was chiefly this exigency, combined with the fact that all of last year's commercial deliveries were at prices below actual factory costs, that accounted for Douglas' loss of $34 million last year and $6.9 million more in the first quarter of this year, and for the drop in Boeing's and Lockheed's profits. Nor has Convair escaped. While it no longer publishes separate profit statements, it is known to have written off some $75 million in development charges on its 880 jet transport in the past two years.

The Pentagon Disposes

Initial losses on commercial aircraft, however, are nothing new in the airframe industry. The deeper trouble lies in the declining emphasis on traditional airpower in the national strategy, and in the shift in procurement from aircraft to great strategic-range ballistic-missile systems. Premonitions of this change came in the early fifties, but the shift itself gained real momentum in 1957, the year of the Sputniks. After that, nothing was quite the same. True, the military are still spending a good deal of money on airplanes. The budget of the Department of Defense for fiscal 1961 calls for spending about $6 billion on planes and related equipment during the next twelve months, or only 10 per cent less than the industry got in the fiscal year that ends this month. But the Pentagon's request for "new money" (i.e., new obligational authority) for airframes has already dropped sharply to only $4.7 billion, or about 25 per cent less than a year ago. Five years ago the Air Force and Navy were absorbing about 8,000 new planes per year. In the coming fiscal year, however, they plan to buy a total of only about 1,300. Moreover, in the same period the number of models ordered has dropped from 44 to 21.

By contrast, the weight of the money being sluiced into the missile systems is increasing. In the coming fiscal year the Pentagon will spend nearly $3.5 billion on missiles (just about what it did in fiscal 1960); but there will be nearly $600 million more in new money (making about $3.8 billion) for expansion of this category than was provided last year. Even more indicative of the shift from planes toward the so-called "exotic" systems is the money budgeted by the Pentagon specifically for research and development. Here, military spending is already moving at a rate approaching $4 billion annually, with the major share going to missile and space systems of one kind or another. When to these sums is added the $600 million the National Aeronautics and Space Administration expects to spend on its independent projects, the annual outlay on military missiles and space rockets already exceeds that for planes. If the B–70 is not reinstated as a system, or if the next administration is not persuaded that a truly effective "little war" capability demands a jet airlift and more versatile tactical planes, the ratio in 1963–64 could well be: missiles and space rockets, 75 per cent of the federal defense procurement dollar; planes, 25 per cent.

The great aircraft manufacturers, as already indicated, have made a determined effort to meet this shift and to switch their business around. Douglas, for instance, is now doing perhaps 50 per cent of its business in other than airframe work; North American and Lockheed are about 40 per cent over into new fields; and Martin is 80 per cent converted into missile and electronics work. Nevertheless, there has been a tremendous fall in total backlogs and profitability for the industry as a whole. In 1956 the backlog of orders for twelve of the industry's prime producers was about $11 billion, tripled from $3.5 billion in 1950. Now it is less than $8 billion. The airframe makers have moved over into space, but they have clearly lost business to other and newer companies in this field.

Junior Partners

They have also lost something else, which has been even harder for them to swallow, namely, their accustomed position of primacy in the management of the great military programs. In World War II, they not only produced planes in enormous quantities, subcontracting parts to other companies, but they had virtual control of the design and the development of what they were making. The advent of rockets abruptly upset this historic pattern of the industry. In the case of the Atlas, the first of the great ICBM systems, the Air Force originally asked Convair to manage the job in the customary way. However, when Atlas was raised to top national priority in 1955, it became necessary to achieve simultaneous breakthroughs in propulsion, electronic control and guidance, and re-entry techniques. To guarantee a sure and rapid outcome, the government turned to other companies that had the necessary *expertise*.

Specifically, the job of "system management" was given to the Ramo Wooldridge Corporation, a brand-new outfit that had been formed by two physicists, Drs. Dean Wooldridge and Simon Ramo, who had done a brilliant job at Hughes Aircraft in the development of the Falcon missile. This company, in effect, became a new kind of prime, leaving Convair with a junior role of fabricating the rocket structure and fitting in revolutionary components—the nose cone carrying the nuclear warhead, the guidance gear, and the rocket engines—which were made by still other outsiders. This new arrangement was soon extended still further. Through an autonomous subsidiary, Space Technology Laboratories, Ramo Wooldridge (now Thompson Ramo Wooldridge) became the master manager not only of the Atlas program, but of the Thor, the Titan, and the Minuteman as well. All this galled the primes; and to placate them, a modified arrangement is now being considered. A nonprofit corporation, patterned after the RAND Corporation, is being set up by the Air Force to take over the management of future inventions. This may reduce jealousy about Thompson Ramo Wooldridge's special position, but it will scarcely restore the aircraft makers to their erstwhile independence.

More serious still, it is much more difficult for the primes to make big money out of the new programs and to justify their huge establishments than it was when they made only planes. In the past, their principal source of earnings was the classical one—*value added by manufacture*. Here they could expect, once they had passed over to "incentive" fixed-price production contracts, pretax earnings of about 10 per cent on volume. But the big money in rockets and space, at least for the time being, is R & D money; as a fabrication job, even the tallest rocket offers relatively little work for the eye-filling orchestration of men and machines on the factory floor that has been the industry's forte. Martin, for example, is the master assembler of the Titan ICBM, which weighs 222,000 pounds on the launching pad. But 90 per cent of this is fuel. The actual hardware, consisting of engines, guidance, skin (or airframe), and nose cone, weighs only 15,000 pounds; and the wafer-thin aluminum skin, which is the only part Martin will actually fabricate, except for parts of the control and ground operating gear, weighs only 8,000 pounds. Moreover, the present maximum military requirements for the Titan call for only some three hundred vehicles, a tiny figure compared to the thousands of planes that were turned out on a single production run.

Floor Space for Sale

Indeed, the Titan and Atlas programs together are scheduled, while they last, to produce in airframe equivalent only about three million pounds of metal processed annually. By 1963, when perhaps only a half-dozen types of tactical aircraft will remain in production, all of the nation's military requirements for both rockets and planes could, according to certain tentative calculations, be supplied by an annual output of 30 million pounds of airframe equivalent. This will be less than 60 per cent of the industry's current rate, and it could all be supplied from 25 million square feet of floor space, or but 24 per cent of the 105 million square feet now in use. This is a somber prospect for an industry that produced a billion pounds of airframe in a single year in 1944, and about 150 million pounds a year at the height of the Korean build-up.

To be sure, the weight of fabricated metal is not in itself the full measure of the role played by the primes. Many of them, as already indicated, are charged with integrating and marrying on the factory floor the systems and subsystems that make up the completed product as well as bringing the system to operational status, straight through the R & D firings at Cape Canaveral. In this case, they make pretax profits rarely exceeding 6 per cent of the aggregate cost of the work assembled, or only about half as much as they earned from long runs on the airframe assembly lines. And when the R & D side of the fee vanishes and the missile is ready to go into production, the actual returns may be disappointing on the assembly job. With the emphasis overwhelmingly on engineering, the great labor agglomerations collected about the primes are on the verge of being stranded. The future look of the factory floor can be conjectured from the fact that in the missile plants the ratio now is about one engineer to every production worker.

And these are not the only discouraging circumstances. The old saw in the airframe industry that a plane was already obsolescent as it left the drawing boards is, if anything, even more apposite to the new inventions. Atlas, scarcely operational, is being overtaken by Titan, which is being overtaken by Polaris and Minuteman, which in turn may be overtaken, while the Minuteman is still in the R & D stages, by a more advanced concept just beginning to emerge. The risk, moreover, of promising projects never quite attaining the hardware stage, except in test quantities, is high. Competition everywhere is sharp. Whenever a prime makes a bid for a job, it not only encounters practically all the other members of its club, but also the new system and subsystem specialists—GE, Westinghouse, Thompson Ramo Wooldridge, Litton, Avco, Remington Rand, and Burroughs.

So the crisis is deep, and if the airframe makers are to meet it, there will be need for all of their proved ingenuity, resolution, and ability to adapt to new circumstances. How they are responding to the challenge, of course, varies tremendously from company to company. One of the smaller primes, Bell Aircraft, has already struck its flag; another, Fairchild Engine & Airplane, is tottering, with sales down to less than $115 million last year. Other companies—notably Republic Aviation and McDonnell— have done much better, by reason of special circumstances, but they too are braced for trouble in the fairly near future when their present production runs out. The central struggle for survival, however, is going on among the great primes.

. . . .

No well-rooted U.S. business has ever known change on the scale and in the complexity and suddenness that is now being experienced by the airframe industry. In a very real sense the prime movers in this business are going through not one but two revolutions at once. Propelled by their own genius for innovation, these great companies are now in the process of completing for commercial aviation, as they had earlier completed for the military, the difficult transition from piston to turbine power. Meanwhile, they have been overtaken by a still greater change in U.S. military strategy—the epochal shift from manned aircraft to military and space rockets.

Most of the leading plane companies have to a greater or less degree moved over into the new space technologies, and some have contributed brilliantly to them. Nevertheless, the double revolution now in progress has impaired sales, backlogs, and, more important, profitability. In 1954, . . . profits after taxes of twelve of the leading prime aircraft manufacturers ran to $182.6 million, or 28.3 per cent of net worth. In 1959, profits were down to $66.9 million, or only 6.1 per cent of net worth, a good deal lower than the average for all U.S. manufacturing companies.

Moreover, while profits may eventually be recouped, it seems highly doubtful whether the airframe companies can continue to put to use the huge facilities and enormous pools of manpower that they have traditionally employed. The characteristics of the industry in the recent past were not just its engineering skills but also its long production runs of both military and commercial aircraft. In the new era that is emerging—conditioned, on the one hand, by the immense power of the nuclear warhead and, on the other, by the swiftness of obsolescence in still fluid technologies—there will be much less need for quantity output. The total production of ICBM rockets for the Atlas and Titan programs, for instance, is not likely to exceed six hundred units, not counting, of course, the additional small numbers that will be diverted into space projects. These numbers are indeed insignificant when compared to the thousands of planes to which the industry has been accustomed.

Space projects, to be sure, cause great sums of money to be spread through the defense industry. The Titan and Atlas programs are together going to cost about $10 billion. But only a small fraction of this sum, perhaps no more than 10 per cent, represents the actual factory cost of fabricating the rockets themselves. The balance is being spent elsewhere—on research and development; on the enormously expensive ground control gear needed to maintain the rockets in constant readiness on their pads and to prepare them for action; and in the costly construction of the sites where the rockets are being deployed. In these flourishing areas, and in the design and production of the vital components of the new weapons, the primes, by and large, have been at best fractionally represented, although some of them are beginning to push hard for a bigger share. Wherever they turn, however, they bump hard against the broader competition of specialists in electronics and other technologies.

The ability of the traditional aircraft makers to meet this kind of competition, and to reshape their corporate strategy accordingly, of course, varies enormously from company to company.

QUESTIONS

1. Granted all the wisdom of hindsight, what indicators (technological, political, economic) could have been suggestive warnings to the plane makers of possible serious future developments? Consider the 1944–1960 period.

2. Assume that as a member of a major airplane manufacturer's top management, you had identified each of your "indicators" at the time they occurred. (a) Explain *exactly how* you would continue to monitor this development. (b) At what point, amount, time, or other measure will this indicator call for action?

3. At what point was the total situation clear enough for any plane-maker management to take action steps?

4. Who in a corporation is supposed to do this kind of thinking? How should it be fed back to the firm for review and action?

5. Design an appraisal program, procedure, and organization for a specific firm to monitor its technological environment so as to identify significant opportunities and threats.

Clarke's Law

When a distinguished but elderly scientist states that something is possible he is almost certainly right. When he states that something is impossible, he is very probably wrong.

Perhaps the adjective "elderly" requires definition. In physics, mathematics, and astronautics it means over thirty; in the other disciplines, senile decay is sometimes postponed to the forties. There are, of course glorious exceptions; but as every researcher just out of college knows, scientists of over fifty are good for nothing but board meetings, and should at all costs be kept out of the laboratory!

ARTHUR C. CLARKE

FROM: *Profiles of the Future*, New York: Harper & Row, 1963.

THE PREDICTION OF TECHNICAL CHANGE[1]
By S. Colum Gilfillan

PREDICTION USUALLY requires counting, dating, and measuring, and so plunges us at once into semantics, the perpetual bugbear of statistics, the endemic disease that more or less infects all our figures. For statistics begins with counting, and counting begins with definition of the thing to be counted—and inventions can hardly be defined. Patents are not quite so bad, and we shall taken them up later. Inventions, like many things and notably people, don't stay the same, but are perpetually evolving, growing, squirming out of their definitions. . . . Suppose we consider television. That sounds simple, since we all know what television is. Or do we? Was it already television in 1847 when Souvestre satirically predicted it? Or did it begin in 1877 when the first apparatus was built, or in 1882 when the scanning disk was added, or in 1901 when Fessenden designed a wireless system? Or was it Zworykin's modern cathode ray receiver of 1929 that constituted the invention of television, with the kinescope, and some experimental broadcasts the next year? Or is our date 1928 or 1937 when regular broadcasting began? Or should it be some future date when with color, three-dimensional vision, binaural hearing, and worthy programs, the art will at last enter the prodigious destiny of the home theater? And is this television, at whatever stage, to be counted always as one invention? . . .

Definition of Invention

What is a television system, anyway? Does it include the wireless inventions and radiotelephony? Then it reincorporates and carries on those older arts. And if we think of television as including the photoelectric cell, and electricity, and copper wire, and drama, we shall have to place the beginning of the invention thousands of years back.

But, you may say, those earlier inventions, like radio and copper wire, were not television, but only parts of it. You may frame your own definition of television, according to which it would have begun, say, in

---

[1] This article is part of a paper delivered at the Conference on Quantitative Description of Technological Change at Princeton, April 6–8, 1951. The Conference was sponsored by the Committees on Economic Growth and on Social Implications of Atomic Energy and Technological Change of the Social Science Research Council. Condensed from S. Colum Gilfillan, "The Prediction of Technical Change," *Review of Economics and Statistics*, November, 1952, pp. 368–85.

1927, and you may find other people agreeing with you. And similarly, you may pick a definition and date for the radio, meaning more accurately radiotelephonic broadcasting, and including with the receiving sets the transmitter and whole art that goes with them, and perhaps the factories and companies that make radio equipment, and retailing and repair services, and the broadcasting arts, studios, and companies. Such a broad definition of radio seems right for economic studies, for it names an economic unit that advances together. You would define the phonograph similarly. But then you would become confused when you realized that modern phonographs are often part of a radio receiver, and always supply the main source of broadcasts, and the modern orthophonic phonograph was invented as by-products of the telephone, electron tube, and movie, and is largely built of similar or identical parts with radio and in the same factories. So how are we going to date, count, and measure the phonograph and those other inventions separately, if we cannot define or see them separately?

And similarly when we try to foresee the future of inventions, say of radio and television. Remembering how the radio largely displaced the phonograph, but then combined with it, and how television is displacing but also combining with the movies, we should predict that television— which combines the radio, phonograph, movie, stage, concert hall, arena, and soon, I think, the home-printed newspaper, too—will largely replace the radio, the same television set which will then be called the audiovisor, gushing music and oral soap opera during the day, grand opera during the evening while the family has time and darkness to look, and at other times printing microfilm newspapers, sounding air raid alarms, and serving as phonograph, program recorder, and dictaphone letter writer. In such a machine for all the kinds of mass communication and some other purposes, are we counting and dealing with seven inventions, seven machines, or one machine and invention? In predicting the future, should we say that the radio is going to decline under the competition of television? Or should we say that the radio will go right on, costlier and more influential than ever, but in new, expanded forms, including more elements than ever, and the same old invention will have a new name, such as the audiovisor, or home theater?

•   •   •   •   •   •   •

An invention may be continued in forms even more diverse. Let us take, from a precious page of American history, Shreve's invention of 1816, the Mississippi packet boat, including a feature later added to her. She seems today to have vanished beneath the waters of Old Man River. But no—a part of her is flying overhead, in every commercial airplane! For a vital feature of these is the governmentally imposed standards and inspection for safety; and this was introduced into American culture by the Steamboat Inspection Service called forth in 1838–52 by the river perils and high-pressure engines used in those steamboats. Surviving, too, are the snag boat Shreve invented to clear the Mississippi channel, and probably some other inventions from the Mississippi steam complex. You may deny that some of these are parts of the Mississippi packet boat, and you may be right, for who can *prove* the proper use of a word?

. . . .

Lag between Invention and Use

After this long and dire warning, let me now attempt some statistics on invention, confessing in advance that they are "rotten," but hoping they are better than *no* idea of magnitude. I concluded in my book that while inventions are impossible to define, save arbitrarily, from the viewpoint of their physical science nature, since each embodies many principles, each subject to infinite gradation, yet inventions and invention can be hazily defined as linguistic and other sociological phenomena, evincing the central grouping tendency characteristic of biological phenomena. For men tend to talk and think alike, and to standardize their manufactures instead of building all the intermediate forms, such as those that might unite a ship and an airplane by a continuous series of intermediate forms.

The statistics of invention, then, that I shall present, are unreliable, based on highly subjective and imperfectly informed judgments on what are the names, definitions, dates, and importance of inventions. One group of 19 were the most useful inventions introduced in the quarter century before 1913, as selected by vote of *Scientific American* readers.[2] I found geometric mean intervals: between the date when the invention was first thought of and the first working machine or patent, 176 years; thence to the first practical use, 24 years; to commercial success, 14 years; to important use, 12 years; or say 50 years from the first serious work on the invention, to important use from it. As a check on these averages, I have reckoned two other lists of inventions I had prepared for other purposes. The first, of the 75 or so most important inventions of 1900–1930, prepared for Professor Ogburn and *Recent Social Trends,* gave a median lapse of 33 years between the dates of the first working model or patent and the date of commercial success, in place of the 24-year geometric mean above. The other list covers 209 of the 500 most important nonmilitary inventions from 1787 to 1935. Its median interval, between the first serious work and commercial success, for the inventions started before 1900, is 37 years. The arithmetic mean was much longer, 117 years, even after adding 900 years to each ancient date, to close up the relatively stagnant period of the Dark Ages. Three modal points were noticed, one for the anciently started inventions and others at 55 and 35 years. With

---

[2] *Scientific American,* 109 (1913), pp. 163, 243, 352. Cf. Gilfillan, *Sociology of Invention* (Chicago, 1935), p. 96.

the inventions begun *after* 1900, the gestation period was much shorter, only a mean of 9½ years, doubtless largely because of the time limitations imposed, since the invention had to be recognized as important by 1935, and yet have been begun not later than 1900. There may also be reflected a speeding-up of the inventive process.

So much for the gestation period, from the first patent or other embodiment to commercial success in modern form. An earlier period, from the first conception or prediction of the invention to its first embodiment, if this period is worth attempting to measure, figured out 176 years for the inventions of 1888–1913. A more important period to measure comes after the gestation period, from the first commercial success to "important use," assuming that those terms can be sufficiently defined. It figures out at a mean of about 10 years for the 46 ascertained inventions of 1782–1935, compared with 12 years for the 1888–1913 list.

Causes of the Lag

Why have good inventions been so slow to develop, from the point of first essay to that of practical success? It has not usually been because they were not wanted. For these inventions we have been counting were all considered important and were usually much wanted; they were by no means average inventions, but the best. Almost all could be called fundamental rather than improvement inventions; and there is our clue. Because they were fundamental, striking out in new lines, they were hard to carry through to the point of practicality, and took a long time. Then, because they took long, they overran the 14–18-year period of a patent grant, so that only the latest added improvements received patents that ran into the period of commercial success, which alone could give a considerable financial reward or even much psychic reward of widely recognized achievement. Thus, almost all the inventors in question had to work for nothing in cash, and little in fame. And they could foresee that their labors would probably go unrewarded, and their outlays probably never be repaid. Fundamental inventions, like the steamboat, airplane, helicopter, and television, are particularly expensive ones. So men with brains enough to succeed in quests as hard as the Holy Grail's will perceive the odds they face, and do something more promising instead. Or if they try nonetheless, continued failure, dissuasion, and bankruptcy will in most cases bring them to a halt, as with almost all the inventors who built thirty-four steamboats before Fulton's success.[3] We told television's history, with work beginning in 1877 and yielding no money reward or reimbursement of expenses until a few years ago. There is the helicopter, which goes back to a Chinese toy, the flying top, and to Leonardo da Vinci's unworkable idea, followed much later by many rational experiments in the nineteenth

---

[3] Gilfillan, *Inventing the Ship* (Chicago, 1935), pp. 91 ff.

and twentieth centuries, parallel with the airplane, to practical use on a leash in World War I, successful flight by Focke in Germany in 1938, and commercial success by Sikorsky in America in 1940, with a magnificent destiny still to begin, and I think ultimate merger with the airplane.

Almost any great invention has had the same story. Suppose we speak of one that most people have never heard of, because it is still "in the doldrums" of work for love—the voice-operated writing machine. I don't know when that idea began, but a book of 1892[4] told what it would do (as well as all about television). Fessenden got it writing after a fashion in 1907, and Flowers[5] in 1916 got it to write a line that could be read. A typewriter manufacturer was reported backing the invention, but why should he, or anyone who is speculating for profits? Lastly, the Bell Telephone Company, with a tighter monopoly and longer purse and views than any other source of commercial invention, and with new motives—of understanding the nature of speech, enabling the voice to operate switchboard mechanisms, and coding speech for transmission on a narrower band width—has taken up this half-century-old problem and produced the vocoder, useful for them, but not answering our problem. A voice-operated typewriter is being worked on by another inventor; but besides its great mechanical difficulties, it will require a completely phonetic spelling, and that people learn how they really pronounce their own language—two major social difficulties. So, after half a century the invention's realization is probably still well in the future, though its utility would be enormous, and its achievement probably possible speedily if we set our resources to it.

I could name other babies begging for a chance to grow to greatness— the print-reading machine, the telharmonium and other musical instruments of unprecedented powers, electricity direct from heat or sunshine or burning coal in the mine, under-ice navigation, the unsinkable ship or cabin, three-dimensional color photography immediately developed, more of synthetic foods and feeds, hydroponics (soilless agriculture). The trouble is simply that neither the patent system nor any other commercial institution we have pays anyone to work on such a fundamental invention in any but its ripest stages, nor even reimburses their heavy expenses to the few fools and heroes who do tackle it. . . .

What *can* be done to develop rapidly a fundamental invention, by using governmental resources and direction, has been shown recently by the American, British, and German armies, creating not only the atomic bomb but an atomic power plant, radioisotopes, jet and turbine-propelled and supersonic planes, rockets and superrockets, guided and homing missiles and torpedoes, radar, the proximity fuse, magnetic and acoustical

---

[4] Max Plessner, *Ein Blick auf die grossen Erfindungen des 20. Jahrhunderts,* I: *Die Zukunft des elektrischen Fernsehens* (Berlin, 1892).

[5] *Scientific American,* February 12, 1916, p. 174.

mines, magnetic submarine detection from the air, the "walkie-talkie," the "snorkel," the transported breakwater, and pipe lines laid across the English Channel.

While nonmilitary fundamental invention remains a colossal neglected opportunity, it brings us one small benefit: It makes almost easy the prediction of what inventions civilization will be adopting a generation or two hence. For instance, the automobile age, with its universal mobility, its suburban living, the decline of the railways, and the need for great boulevards for automobiles and trucking, was pretty well foreseen by H. G. Wells in 1901, when automobiles were but scarcely known. He made it the chief theme of his book *Anticipations*. We have spoken of some anticipations of television which go back for centuries in the stage of mere expressed desire, and for 73 years of practical work. I published an article on its future myself 40 years ago, and later found the book (cited above) on the future of such arts written by the German engineer Plessner in 1892, which leaves little more to be said on what television will do. He overlooked only the animated cartoon and scientific drawing and advertisements. We could cite endless examples of successful prediction of the future achievement merely by describing the inchoate, not yet practical inventions of the present.

.   .   .   .

Duplicate and Equivalent Invention

Having seen by now how invention is no longer the sporadic and inscrutable act of heroic single inventors, but a regular business and branch of business or government, like a drafting department or promotion department, in which teams of varied specialists are ordered by noninventive superior officers to attack certain problems, with good expectations that they will successfully invent in the desired lines, we are ready to observe two more characteristics of invention, most significant for social science and prediction, namely, *duplicate* invention and *equivalent* invention. Duplicate inventions are those where a more or less identical solution is invented independently, with a tendency to rival findings about the same time, when the social need and the basis in prior arts have built up to it. Duplicate inventing is a perfect proof of the social (versus the individual) theory of invention, as was perceived by 1855 and perhaps in the 1600's.[6] It has been commonly proved by Ogburn and Thomas[7] or other lists of historically duplicated inventions. But better evidence is first the frequency of "interference actions" in our Patent Office, where two or more applications covering partly the same invention are filed within the couple of years an application is usually pending there. In active fields the percentage of such interferences rises to ten or even

---

[6] John Coryton, *A Treatise on the Law of Letters Patent* (London, 1855); and perhaps Thomas Reade, *Inventa Adespota*, an unfound work quoted in 1661.

[7] In William F. Ogburn, *Social Change* (1922), Pt. 2, chap. v.

more.[8] But when the coincidence of time is not so close, so that an earlier one of the duplicating inventors had already got his patent, or in some way his invention had become known, than all later applicants should simply be refused patents. This is enormously frequent, being the main reason why half the American patents applied for are never issued. We are including here under duplicate invention the more frequent situation which patent lawyers call "want of invention," meaning that the proffered device, though somewhat different from anything before, finds each of its ideas sufficiently nearly anticipated, so that no flash of genius or rare luck would have been necessary for the somewhat new but not very difficult combination. Still more multitudinous must be the cases where the inventor found out he had been anticipated *before* he reached the advanced stage of patent application; and the incalculably numerous cases where he could and would have made the invention, as you and I could start inventing the gas turbine, but he is stopped by knowledge that it is already invented.

The other principle, that of equivalent invention, we may perhaps call mine because others have not developed it much (Principle 36 in the *Sociology of Invention*). Even better than duplicate invention, it proves the importance of the social forces back of invention, and provides a means for predicting the social effects of inventions and guessing at their time of arrival. By equivalent invention, I mean inventions different in physical principles, yet accomplishing much the same end, as, for instance, truth may be carried across a totalitarian boundary by inventions as different as radio and unmanned leaflet-distributing balloons, and by many other means. Equivalent inventions commonly arrive in groups to meet some newly realized social need. I count 21 radically different means of flying into the air, 18 means of contraception without counting chemical differences, eight different basic starts on geophysical prospecting, six ways to make uranium explosive, of which two were used, six different principles for mechanical stokers, all started before 1850, beside still other means for ending the terrible trade of hand stoking, such as pulverized, liquid, and gaseous fuels, the internal-combustion engine, burning coal underground without mining it, and so forth.

The principle of equivalent invention, which is as easily proved as it is universally overlooked, shows first of all that inventions are not the prime causes of social change, as Marxians and engineers tend to claim. For if so, how account for the inventions coming in functional groups? One solution would rather tend to inhibit all others, as less needed after one way has been found. Only if there are behind history some larger forces—geographic, biologic, sociologic, economic, and *generalized* technologic—could we explain how these whole functional groups of equivalent inventions come to be found about the same time, lifting us into the

---

[8] A. D. McFadyen, "Why Nobody Can Steal Your Invention," *Popular Science Monthly* (April, 1939), pp. 86, 234.

air on such varied wings, sending inquiring feelers deep underground without boring a hole, and solving the ancient Malthusian problem by so many means simultaneously, once the social situation was prepared for birth control by the lowered death rate and rationalized religion. Inventions are only partly prime forces. For the most part, other and more general forces come first, set the stage, and sound the call for inventions to meet certain newly perceived needs; whereupon inventors step forward with their solutions, some duplicate, others unlike but functionally equivalent.

Now, see how this principle of equivalence helps in our present problem of prediction. If I may use a personal example, in 1937, writing on the prediction of inventions and their effects for Ogburn's government book, *Technological Trends and National Policy*,[9] I listed 25 unlike means, invented or begun, by which airplanes could cope with fog, and added:

With all these 25 different means apparently available for conquering fog, we may quite confidently predict that by some means or other fog will be effectively overcome for aviators soon. We may be confident even though several of the 25 means should turn out to be worthless, and no others be added by future invention in this now very active field. And hence we have a firm basis for predicting the social effects of aviation without danger from fog.

So today, fourteen years later, airplanes are flying through and landing in fog with considerable facility, using at least nine of the means listed, and expecting soon to rely chiefly on a new means, radar. This was not in my list because while then existent, it was secret and unknown. But the closing statement provided for other equivalent means to be invented, as was obviously to be expected when 25 had sprung up in the few years since aviation began. The principle of equivalent invention allowed correct prediction of the result to be attained, the airplane's victory over its nemesis fog, even though the means—the inventions which would accomplish it—were most obscure. There was a competitive race between a score of inventions; it would have taken a much better judge of technical horseflesh than I to foretell the winner; it seems now the first prize will go to still another, a dark horse named Radar, by Man o' War out of Britannia for dam; but the equivalence principle enabled predicting the victory, and the time, which might have been named more accurately than just by the word "soon," and all the social effects to flow from fog-freed aviation could have been predicted.

Since ill acquaintance with technology and inability to predict winners in a race of improvement are common failings, with present company not excepted, let me give another example of how my own ignorance was saved by that blessed principle of equivalence. I published an article in

---

[9] U.S. National Resources Committee, *Technological Trends and National Policy* (1937), with the chapters on "The Prediction of Inventions" and "Social Effects of Inventions," by Gilfillan, pp. 15–38, esp. p. 22.

1912 on the future home theater,[10] predicting it would arrive by 1930 in two rival forms: television with the sight and sound both sent over the telephone wire, and the "disk and film" form of home "talkie"; but the two would sometimes be combined to broadcast a "talkie." It turns out that the telephone wire is incapable of carrying so much—radio is the right medium; the disk and film are too hard to handle and keep synchronized; sound on the film is a much better solution, but still too expensive and tricky for wide home use. All these facts, including radiobroadcasting, were known to a few people in 1912 (except that sound film was not useful till 1922); but I was young and without technical training and so didn't know. Nevertheless, by grace of equivalent inventions, I and others long before me were right as to what technical achievements would be accomplished (for example, movies with talking, color, and stereoscopy, and their broadcasting into homes), and so I could be right (and did not predict badly) as to the social consequences that would flow from those technical achievements. I was much too optimistic as to time of perfecting and wide use of these very difficult, fundamental inventions. Timing is always difficult to predict, and will be discussed later.

Prediction of Invention

We claim, then, that the principle that inventions come in functionally equivalent groups usually makes it easier to predict the effects of invention than to foresee the invention which will have the effects. Behind the inventions are the greater social and basic technical forces which not only bring forth the group of inventions, but also induce the same effects through means other than inventions. For example, we spoke at the start of an audiovisor machine, which could bring into most homes not only a speaking, moving, colored, three-dimensional theater, concert hall, church, school, museum, arena, and reporter's and traveler's vantage points, but also print microfilm newspapers, and serve other purposes such as phonograph, spoken letter taker, projector for microfilm books, and so forth. Social consequences flowing from the wide use of such an audiovisor would include a great enlightenment of all classes not too poor to own the machine, a tendency toward national standardization of attitudes and interests, and a vast political power in the hands of whoever controls the broadcasting services and radio chain facilities, allots the few available band widths, runs the censorship, and perhaps goes so far as to control the programs. If any group of men controls all the most-used facilities for quick, newsy, attractive, inexpensive mass communication, propaganda, and entertainment, they will control the main door to people's minds, and thereby control their minds and everything. If we may compress the political effect of the home theater into one word, it will be totalitarian.

But now, observe that this tendency is not coming through the audiovisor alone. All other inventions for mass communication, such as

---

[10] "The Future Home Theater," *Independent*, 73 (October 17, 1912), pp. 886–891, il.

color, microfilm and other improvements in printing, the long-playing and high-fidelity phonograph and talking book, the radio chain broadcast, color "talkie," educational film, and complete canned lecture—all have the same effects in some degree. And so do inventions not for mass communication at all, but for bettering point-to-point communication and transportation across wider areas, such as the long-distance telephone, airplane, and trailer vacation. And finally, the same effects of national standardization and totalitarian power are brought by changes that are not invention at all, but such changes as growth of wealth, monopoly, education, and philosophies congenial to organization, rationalizations, socialism. Due to these wider and basic philosophic factors, it is clear that the audiovisor will present very different programs and have different influence according to the sort of country it is in—very different in largely capitalist, commercial, competitive, freedom-loving, and rich America from what the same machine would stage in poor and communist Russia, or poor and Catholic, theocratic Spain. Therefore, to predict the future political effect on a country of the audiovisor, we shall need to foresee the country's *whole* political future, taking account of all pertinent inventions as well as of the one in question and its functional substitutes, and considering all other influential factors, both fixed ones like climate, slowly changing ones like wealth and racial capacity, and quickly change-able ones like politics. From the sum total of all these influences, we may, with much wisdom, information, and luck, predict how a country's general lines of development will run, and thence what inventions will be fostered and created, if the country be America, or what will be adopted *from* America if the country be like most today, dependent on ours for its inventions, but with the privilege of selecting them. Thus, Mexico adopts our black-and-white "movie" technique entire, but rejects our yachts, church suppers, and chemical laboratories. The task of the social prophet is not easy, but there is no way to simplify it without weakening his veridiction. We may, with great saving of needed labor and knowledge, *restrict* our predictions to the inherent tendencies, the generally likeliest influences from a functional group of inventions; but that will not be the truth of what *will* happen; it may be quite upset by other influences, as many a rosy prediction of growing democracy and liberty has been upset by the two or three successive world wars of the present era. In the same way, economists distinguish the easier, theoretical problem of telling what *tends* to be the effect of any event, such as a big crop or a monopoly, from the harder problem of telling what *will* happen, in view of all other events that will have occurred. Solve this second problem, and you can be a multimillionaire in jig time, through stock market prescience.

Let us reformulate the matter by saying the prophet of invention faces six successive levels of future causality. The first is the prediction of a particular invention, probably already inchoate. The second is the addition of the other, alternative inventions which may serve like purposes. The third is the prediction and measurement of the technical accomplishments that will be attained by any or various of the rivals in that functional group, including alternative means the seer fails to foresee. Fourth come the economic and other social consequences that would tend to flow from the functional group of inventions. Fifth, we may attempt to foretell the social consequences that actually *will* flow directly from this and all other forces and circumstances, including some factors that will counteract and lessen or even reverse the social result expectable from the invention group. Sixth and lastly, we may foresee the secondary or indirect consequences that will follow upon the direct.

The further the stage we press toward, of this six-step predictive series, the greater our possibilities for speaking sooth and prophesying usefully; but the greater also by far will be the difficulties and data and sciences involved. The first two stages—foretold inventions—are of special interest to the inventors and specialized companies involved. It is easy to find fundamental inventions in embryonic state today, dawdling in unpaid obscurity, and to predict a great future for them decades, even a century, before they arrive. But it is hard to foresee how much they will be improved by what date, and whether they, or some functional rivals, will be the chief winners in the race toward perfection and popularity.

The third predictive level—the technical powers to be attained by the functional group of inventions (e.g., the speed at which we shall travel, or the cheapness of a newspaper radio-printed in the home)—is of more concern to the economist, and to the great corporation and government, which can seek this technical goal by various lines of invention and social innovation. This third level of foresight is helped in that technical measures can be expressed numerically (e.g., in miles per hour, dollars, per cent of homes served), and therefore can be graphed and extrapolated into the future; and because the second level involves a larger number of inventions than the first, hence benefiting from the regularity of larger numbers; and because statistics of achievement can often be worked out for centuries back, and even into prehistoric times. Hornell Hart[11] especially has done good work in this line, with measurements of historical speeds of travel, range of missiles, span of bridges, and so forth. I plotted the historigrams of some 30 traits of aviation[12] from their practical beginning to 1945, including speed, safety, costs, number of airports, and the like. The most interesting fact revealed was one not unforeseen—that the two world *wars* made little difference to civil aviation, although one would think the first war quite transformed aviation. Great progress was

[11] Hornell Hart, *Technique of Social Progress* (1931); "Technological Acceleration and the Atomic Age," *American Sociological Review* (June, 1946), pp. 277 ff.; "Technology and the Growth of Political Areas," in *Technology and International Relations*, edited by W. F. Ogburn (1948), pp. 28–57; "Science and the Atomic Crisis," *Journal of Social Issues* (April, 1949).

[12] Unpublished; some others are in Ogburn, *Social Effects of Aviation*. with the assistance of Gilfillan and Adams.

made; but the graphs sweep through the war period as if nothing had happened. The military inventions and construction, while invaluable, did not meet all civil problems; so certain bottlenecks held civil aviation to its steady rate of progress.

However, such statistics, like all others on invention and patents, are much in need of semantic interpretation. Curves may be beautifully regular, yet measure things very different from those they seem to measure, things constantly changing in nature. For instance, in the earliest days of aviation an "airport" could be constituted by driving the cows off a pasture and raising a wind sock on a pole. Today an "airport" like Idlewild may cost $100 million. So what does the historigram of number of "airports" mean? Something, but you have to know what at each year.

Our fourth predictive level might be more fully restated as the economic and other consequences which would tend to flow from the foreseen technical achievement, in the context of everything else we know about the world and science, viewed rather timelessly, as if things in general would remain the same, except for the coming of these new inventions and accomplishments. This is certainly a false assumption, but saves much labor and dispute. It is a field and type of thought that appeals especially to economists of the classical, deductive school, and hardly to other people.

Our fifth and sixth levels, prediction of social effects, situations, and events as affected by invention, are the widest and furthest levels. They are of special concern to the sociologist, publicist, and statesman, involving as they do all the facts and possibilities, inventive and other, that will go to determine the future, and requiring for practical point that someone supply answers to the philosophic question of what sort of future history and civilization we want, anyway, and the social science question of how and how much we *could* remold nearer to what is desired this sorry scheme of things entire. Our fifth and sixth levels differ only in that the fifth flows directly from the use of the inventions (and from other factors), while the sixth flows from these effects (and from other factors). It would be followed by the seventh, the eighth, . . . , etc. derivatives fanning out without limit. But with the effects of the original inventive group continually attenuating in force, immediacy, probability, and verifiability, as endless other causes enter the picture, further prognostications become shortly not worth the making. Professor Ogburn, who has perhaps written best,[13] on the whole subject of predicting inventions and their consequences, uses the example of aviation inventions, which in all their thousands have the direct effect of expanding aviation, and derivative (sixth) effects of cutting down rival transport, building up meteorology, agglomerating nations, etc. This sixth level fills most of his book, *The Social*

---

[13] *The Social Effects of Aviation*, chaps. iii and iv, "On Predicting the Future" and "On Predicting the Social Effects of Invention," pp. 32–80.

Effects of Aviation. We might go on from improved meteorology to better agricultural planning, and control of rainfall, and from those to many further effects, but with ever-fading relation to the aviation inventions from which we started.

In practising prophecy, it is not necessary, however, to take the six levels in the same order as given, although each depends in part on the previous one. For each depends also on other, wider considerations, and insofar as each is true, a fact of the future, it needs no logical base. If truly foretold, we may consider the levels in reversed order, or simultaneously, and start anywhere. One reversal is particularly common and important, namely, when officials of a government or corporation decide first what economic and other social results they seek (levels five and six), then what powers from invention are needed for these (level four), and could be produced by what inventions (three, two). These things determined, they settle on one or two inventions likeliest to attain the goal, and engage inventors to devise or perfect them (level one). Or suppose we conclude from our graphs that by the year 2000, we shall be traveling at 2,000 miles per hour. We may reason backward thence as to what inventions will enable it. No railway could possibly run that fast. An evacuated tube in which cars were supported without touching the walls might, but would be enormously costly. Flight through the stratosphere, propelled by a rocket, or in some way using atomic energy, seems much the most likely.

Whatever the order of procedure, it is evident that the fewer and more adjacent the levels involved, the more accurate as well as easier can be prediction. Thus, in our aviation problem of coping with fog, it was easier to go from step two to step three (the inventive group to the achievement) than from the first level (a particular invention).

The shorter the period of the forecast, also, the easier should be accuracy; and likewise when the inventive development involved is less. So we should be better soothsayers from the first patent or working model, than from the vague ideas or mere hopes which preceded it; and still better as the invention approaches the stage of commercial success, passes it, and marches on to greatness.

But timing, foretelling when an invention will arrive or do what, is always a weak side of the prophetic art, as could be seen from the study of past predictions.

The Basis of Prediction

We have been discussing on six levels the content of the predictions made. Now to consider how, by what sorts of reasoning and information, the forecasts relating to invention are made, how they have been made best, and how best they might be made. We cannot take time here for the detailed evidence, but I shall parallel briefly my chapter on "The Prediction of Inventions" in *Technological Trends and National Policy*,[14]

---
[14] *Ibid.*

and a further elaborated and perfected study I made for Professor Ogburn and the University of Chicago in 1941, which has not been published, but I think should be, and Professor Ogburn's own excellent ideas on the subject, recently published in *Social Effects of Aviation*.[15]

First of all, the foretelling of inventions and their effects should be logical, scientific, and *not* based on the commonest of all foundations, mere optimism, the wish being father to the thought that such and such will happen. Nor should prophecy be based on the dishonest motive that by predicting something, such as the victory of one's own party or sect, as the Communists do, one will encourage people to climb onto the bandwagon. Though intellectually disreputable, these two leads for prophecy —optimism and propaganda—are vastly common, and are taken as human nature and even required for a decent man. If you do not believe, and tell others, that your own country and religion will triumph, and other good things come about, you are eyed askance. Yet the sciences have not been built on optimism nor propaganda, but on the search for truth, welcome or unwelcome.

To be sure, optimism has often in the past produced fairly good predictions, notably from the fathers of the French Revolution. For example, one of them, Mercier,[16] in 1770, was so optimistic (and propagandistic) as to prophesy that in his beautiful future, six centuries thence, hospitals would be resorted to not for free burial, but for cure, that they would have as many beds as patients, and that their wastes would not be dumped into the Seine above the points where most of Paris got its drinking water. The general progress of the last two centuries has tended to validate optimistic vaticinations. And I confess, though it impugn me under my own rule, that I am an optimist, too, and trust—with reason, I hope—that civilization will survive its present deadliest crisis since Hitler or probably since Attila, and continue to cultivate science, invention, and progress.

Optimism does carry at its side two helpful factors which often improve prophecy, though it were better to employ them rationally. One is the fact that whatever the prophet desires, whether stereoscopic color television or a good five-cent cigar, is probably desired also by millions of others; so there is a receptive market, and there will be many inventors to attack the problem if it seems solvable. The other helpful factor in optimism is that it may serve to counteract pessimism in scientific men serving as predictors. Such are apt to be overly careful for their reputations as sober, scientific authorities, speaking only of matters they know and can prove, and duly or unduly respectful of science's proof that certain things cannot be done, notwithstanding that inventors are always circumventing such "laws of nature" in unexpected ways.

---

[15] *Ibid.*

[16] Louis Sébastien Mercier, *L'An 2440*, tr. as *Memories of the Year 2500*.

Another partly illogical source of predictions is fashion, or the imitation of other predictors. Ogburn, who has treated most of these subjects best, cites the case of the helicopter, which around 1940 was a favorite subject for enthusiastic forecasts of prompt and wide use; but then, as dangers and difficulties appeared in the art, the fashion among aviation experts swung to criticism and skepticism. Similarly, private, light-plane aviation enjoyed a strong and continuing rise of faith, flying, and airport building till after World War II, when people began to realize that about all an ordinary man (with plenty of money) can do with an airplane is to fly around near home in daylight and fair weather, and practice enough landings and take-offs to keep up his license.

Yet here, too, in fashion, or the mutual imitation of prophets, there is an element tending to validity. The judgment of many can be more reliable than that of one; and when the fashionable opinion changes, even if excessively, it changes because some truth has been discovered, such as the stubborn shortcomings of the helicopter and light plane.

These side benefits from optimism and fashion, together with all other logical bases for prophecy, can be reduced to two essential principles: the extrapolation of trend, and what we may call the principle of opportunity.

Extrapolation

Extrapolation of trend is so familiar to statisticians that we need say little of it. Let us recall that it requires quantification of the past, and yields a measured trend for the future; so it cannot be used where statistics are lacking, as often in the start of new basic inventions such as the helicopter or color television, nor perhaps to predict a unique future event, such as whether there will arrive control of the sex of human offspring. We may also recall that an extrapolated trend becomes increasingly uncertain the farther we project it into the future, so that it is best represented by a scatter diagram, rapidly widening like the horn of a tuba, measured as, say, one probable error on each side of the line of central trend or most probable prediction. Likewise, this expanding horn of probability will be the longer, narrower, and truer, the longer, fuller, and sounder our past statistics, and the simpler the curve into which the past data appear to fall and the smaller their scatter about it.

Of course, the past data must first be reduced to a smooth curve (or possibly a straight line). I should always draw this curve freehand; some do it by mathematics, but I reject this for three reasons: (1) It assumes the value of time to be zero—the researcher's time. (2) It involves arbitrary, unprovable, unmathematical choices as to what curves to select and where to fit them. (3) It involves assumptions that the forces, their relations, the statistically covered materials, the definitions, the accuracy, and what not, remained the same throughout the covered history; but in our field, this is simply never true.

Another arbitrary choice required, whether in mathematical or free-hand trending, is how large, how smooth a curve one will draw through the past data, as against a more irregular curve that will more closely follow the data from year to year. One criterion for choice will be the reliability of the past data. Another will be our purpose in regard to the future. The shorter the time we wish to look ahead, say only four years, the more closely our curve should follow recent events; but the further our future forecast, the more extensive or generalized should be our sweep over the past. An ideal extrapolation of a trend, therefore, would require several different trend lines for the past, each projected differently into the future, and going further the smoother and longer the past curve. One might say roughly that the *latest section* of a curve, however long or short you choose to cut this, is good for extrapolation into the future for a third as long as long as you have made its past.

The art of extrapolation can be tested experimentally, by using past data whose later developments are first concealed from the extrapolator, then later applied to test his predictive success, after the manner of the experiment I devised and took part in, which Ogburn describes.[17]

We have mentioned for the past the assumption in extrapolation that the forces and their relations held true throughout. Of course, this must be equally assumed for the future covered. So if the future of the United States will be basically different from her past—a nation at war, or heavily under arms and awaiting desperate atomic and germ war at any hour, or a country broken and enslaved under Communism, then of course our best-laid plans, like the fieldmouse's, will all be gone agley.

Principle of Opportunity

We come now to the other basis for prophecy, which might be called the principle of opportunity, or suitability, oftenest used when we say that some invention, say the newspaper printed in the home by radio, will come soon because it is wanted, could pay for itself, inventors with some backing are working on it, and we think no law of nature or of man prevents its attainment. The great use for this formula in economic prediction is with inchoate inventions, already started but requiring 50 years or so to reach importance, as we endeavored to demonstrate by averages. In reasoning from opportunity, the question of time is not dominant; whereas in extrapolation, time is the horizontal parameter. The predictive principle of opportunity sets time aside, and thinks rather of the efforts and forces by which inventions and their consequences are brought about; or takes invention as the accidental product of an ever-turning kaleidoscope of chances. Time enters only in that the longer the wait, the more time there is for the chances and efforts to click into the lucky combination. Hence the principle of opportunity in its pure

---

[17] *Social Effects of Aviation*, pp. 39, 40.

form gives little basis for predicting the date that an invention or its consequence will occur. But mating theory with experience, we find, with our shaky statistics, that great fundamental inventions always require 20 years or more, and an average of 50 or so, to grow to maturity; so this gives us some basis for timing in advance the youth period of a nascent invention, according to its conception date and its apparent degree of maturity, that is, how much developing remains to be done on it. And this is the commonest of all forms of rational prophecy anent inventions.

. . . . . .

QUESTIONS

1. Does the principle of "equivalent invention" hold any significance for top management? For the direction of industrial research and development activities?
2. Could predicting the *effects* of functionally equivalent inventions have usefulness to management?
3. It is technically feasible to record sight and sound received via a TV set, on a permanent, compact, replayable, recording medium that would sell for less than $150 in mass production.
   a) List possible uses of this capability.
   b) Analyze the social effects of such an invention.
   c) Develop the business consequences for appropriate industries.
4. Explain the six levels of causality. How can they be applied to business guidance and planning?
5. Using the utmost technological and economic license, prophesy at least ten technological capabilities that will be in use at the height of your business career—say, in thirty years.
   a) List the capabilities, and identify the types of business consequences.
   b) Choose any firm today, and prescribe an appropriate technological scouting and research effort to be commenced now or at a future time that you would specify, so as to provide suitable business anticipation of one or more of the capabilities that you identified.

Should We Attempt to Forecast Technology?

Effective forecasting of technical progress is a necessary part of today's managerial decisions. The race for progress is one on which bets must be placed, and from which there is no abstaining. Indeed, most managers cannot even control the magnitude of their betting, since it is closely linked to the net worth of the segment of the economy over which the manager exercises control. Since some estimate of future conditions is inherent in each managerial decision, the actual question is whether such an estimate should be made unconsciously as an implicit part of the decision, or whether it should be arrived at deliberately and stated explicitly. The principal reason for an explicit forecast is to place it . . . so that its validity may be tested. The explicit forecast offers the additional advantage of revealing the method, data, and premises used in making the forecast.

RALPH CHARLES LENZ, JR.

FROM: *Technological Forecasting*, Report No. ASD–TDR–62–414, United States Air Force, June, 1962.

ON THE CONCEPT OF TECHNOLOGICAL
FORECASTING

MANKIND HAS long tried to predict the critical events and forces affecting his life. "Rules" for predicting the weather are age-old. Vital statistics on population factors and elementary economic statistics as the basis of forecasting production needs, as well as political implications, can be found as early as the eighteenth century. In our day the idea of forecasting natural phenomena, agricultural output, socioeconomic data, production and marketing needs, and even such mercurial phenomena as voter preferences for candidates are accepted as useful business tools.

Anticipating the shape of things to come is an age-old effort. In explicit or implicit form, it underlies the planning of most industrial, governmental, and institutional actions. Although inaccuracy is common and is expected to some degree, the usefulness of estimates of the future is widely accepted. Since technological progress is one of the most powerful factors in our environment today, should we not give it similar attention? Would it not be useful to try to forecast technological trends and events?

Some arguments against this idea are that technological advances are the result of individual, explicit human decisions; therefore, forecasting is impossible. Others hold that the interrelationships are too complex to be analyzed. Another view is that technological forecasting is merely self-fulfilling prophecy; and another is that we lack the knowledge and the supporting disciplines to forecast in this area. To this last point, we must concede some truth! Nevertheless, the meteorologist, the economist, the sociologist, and the demographer tackle forecasting in areas of great uncertainty with some useful results. Surely it is possible for businessmen and society to do better than simply to ignore the sweep of technology and its implications!

History is filled with thousands of predictions and prophecies about specific inventions and specific capabilities. And many scientists, engineers, inventors, historians, business leaders, and politicians have engaged in serious or speculative reflection about the future.[1]

Science fiction writers also have anticipated many devices, scientific developments, and social consequences of technological change. Neverthe-

---

[1] This has been carefully studied by S. C. Gilfillan. See "The Prediction of Technical Change," in the preceding pages, plus his many references.

less, we sense that there is little more than opinion behind most of these pronouncements. They are not forecasting. Their results are not reproducible according to a disciplined, logical analysis.

In Chapter I is presented a crude step—very crude—toward forecasting. It identifies seven directions of change and four of the factors outside technology that will at times influence technological progress. A study of these directions suggests, in a broad sense, the kinds of effects under way. It is also suggestive of technical parameters to measure, and it points to economic and social phenomena that will result from and influence technological progress. However, this identification is far from a "forecast," for it does not include a time frame or quantitative accomplishment.

What Do We Mean by "Forecasting"?

In a classic paper by Irving Siegel the important types of forecasting are explained.[2] Thoughtful reading makes it clear that these types are quite different and have varying degrees of usefulness to businessmen.

1. *Prediction or Prophecy.* Prediction means the identification of future events without qualification on their occurrence, and with timing specified. It is a precise, definitive, quantified assertion as to what will occur. Although prediction is often considered to be the desired and only useful goal of forecast, this is not so.

2. *Projection.* This useful form of forecasting is a conditional statement about a future event. The forecaster examines the past, sets up a theory of change and appropriate relationships, and from this derives a future relevant state. He does not assert that this state will come to pass. He only claims that given his model and inputs, the future state should occur. Often, he offers alternative inputs and alternative models, each leading to different future states. He usually takes no stand on which assumptions will occur. Obviously, he hopes to bracket the range of likely possibilities.

Projections are frequently misinterpreted and ridiculed as having proved to be poor predictions—an obviously unfair judgment.

3. *Program.* Here the forecaster is a purposeful actor. As corporate officer, a government official, a technical leader, or even a lesser official, he specifies a technological goal (or an economic, political, or social goal that has a train of technical consequences) and then directs the enterprise accordingly. If successfully completed, the program of, say, expanding capacity 200 per cent by using automation, of increasing engine compression ratio to eleven to one, of developing synthetic rubber, or of completing a Mach 2 transport by 1972, is the equivalent to successful prediction.

---

[2] Irving H. Siegel, "Technological Change and Long Run Forecasting," *Journal of Business of the University of Chicago*, Vol. XXVI (July, 1953), pp. 141–56. I am completely indebted to Dr. Seigel for this identification, and trust that this brief abstract has not done error to his more detailed explanations.

Programs and predictions are frequently confused in forecasting. One obvious danger is that the programmer may easily neglect environmental factors outside his control. Another is that his "program" may be technologically overconservative. However, a program can well be a major determinant of technological progress and hence part of a useful forecasting technique. America's "Man on the Moon by 1970" is an example of a program that includes, by definition, numerous technical forecasts.

Propaganda. Here the forecaster is an actor in a limited role. By publicity, exhibits, advertising, and other persuasive devices, he attempts to establish a "trend," or at least to precondition others to accept his trend. He is a programmer who confines means of program accomplishment to one technique. Propaganda has an unsavory connotation which may obscure some possible usefulness.

Poetry. Dr. Siegel applies this term to visions, conjectures, and speculations which are "vague, general and often of obscure time reference" . . . "a vagrant anticipation by a famous man." Science fiction, says Dr. Siegel, belongs in this category. Similarly, the hypotheses and speculations of historians may fall under this heading. But is not this activity useful, in part, to management? Suppose we can identify a technological functional *capability* that is *likely* within a certain five- or ten-year span. Does it not alert us to possibilities and suggest necessary action? See the previous chapter by Gilfillan.

Parrotry. This variety of forecasting consists of repetitions of fashionable comment and imitations of other forecasts, with "oversimplification, or overdramatization of careful or authoritative projections." Economic and labor forecasts are, at times, characterized by parrotry. As horrible examples, review the plethora of comment and statistics by sociologists, labor relations people, labor economists, editors and writers in the popular press, and government and labor officials (and even managers) on automation and unemployment.

Prediction, projection, and programming are the three most useful forms of forecasting. How might they be applied to technology?

Technological Forecasting

Technological forecasting I define as the anticipation of an invention (including machines, materials, and processes as inventions) or of technical characteristics. Unique combinations of these technological elements are subjects for forecasting, and the acquisition of scientific theory and knowledge itself is an element that may be forecast. The probable timing should be included in a forecast, and the method must rest in reproducible, logical derivation. The anticipation of a technical capability without identification of the technical means of achievement is also intended in this forecasting concept (e.g., that "the speed of commercial air transportation will reach 700 miles per hour by 196x. A technical-economic forecast also can be a very useful guide to management—e.g., "a fuel cell cost-performance ratio of $20 per watt of capacity will be achieved by 1970."

The essential value of a forecast lies in identifying a condition or standard to which present conditions can be related. Then appropriate action—be it change of direction, reduction of effort, provision of new resources, activities, or capabilities, or no change at all—can be undertaken with some hope of being in an effective position for the future. If the forecast and subsequent action are recorded and then monitored, a serious deviation from the predicted development becomes a signal that present actions must be re-evaluated. Monitoring a competitor's performance against such a standard is also useful.

Technological forecasts can be criticized on the grounds that they are erroneous, impossible, improbable, too late to be useful, too expensive, or too tenuous to be a basis for investment or major decision. But what are the alternatives? No forecast? Then we must respond to each technological development as it becomes obvious to all. Managers, politicians, and historians should have learned that this approach can be fatal to the life of firms, industries, and nations.

The common alternative to "no forecast" is to assume that current trends and circumstances will continue, or to act as as though they will. Thus the growth of TV screen size from seven inches to 21 inches in 1946–53 suggests that the product of 1956 would have a screen size of, say, 27 inches, with 30 inches indicated for the near time horizon. The increase of automobile horsepower and size from 1946 to 1956 would indicate the continued increase of horsepower (and, by inference, compression ratio) and size through the 1960's. The development of smokeless powder, TNT, and RDX explosives prior to World War II would indicate moderate increases in the intensity of military explosives into the 1940's. Yet each of these trends was wrong in forecasting actual technological developments. Let us gently pass over the consequent errors in managerial and political judgment and leadership.

In his pamphlet, *Technological Forecasting*,[3] Ralph Lenz describes six forecasting methods:

1. *Technological Extrapolation.* This will be discussed later.

2. *Growth Analogies.* Growth analogies assume that technological progress follows exponential trends, in the manner of biological growth. In particular, Raymond Pearl's demonstration that cellular growth, such as the number of fruit flies in a bottle, obeys the formula:

$$Y = \frac{L}{1 + ae^{-bx}}$$

[3] Ralph C. Lenz, *Technological Forecasting*, Report No. ASD–TDR–62–414 (Washington, D.C.: United States Air Force, June, 1962). I am indebted to Mr. Lenz for generous help, and for his kind permission to adapt portions of this pioneering effort to a teaching text.

where Y is the unit of increase; L is the upper limit of that increase; x is a unit of time; and a and b are constants. The weakness of this method lies in choosing L and the constants a and b, and in being sure that this law applies to the phenomenon in question. However, we may surmise that some technological phenomena—perhaps the diffusion of some technological innovations, or the complexity of a machine—may follow this law or a variation.

3. *Trend Correlation.* Here the forecaster assumes that one factor is the primary causal influence in the technological parameter under study. Working with this controlling variable, he predicts the performance of the parameter in question. Thus the invention of the steam engine was a signal that the steam locomotive would follow, and Goddard's rocket flights foreshadowed the ICBM's.

The obvious weakness here is the assumption that there is and will be only one controlling variable. Often, a single technological parameter does control progress initially; but eventually, a social, political, or economic barrier is reached, or another technological parameter becomes the limiting factor. The upper horsepower range of automobiles is limited in the United States by social decisions. In Europe, automobile horsepower is largely limited by the economics: the cost of fuel, and taxes based on horsepower.

Sequential relationships, in which one trend leads another, are frequently used in economic forecasting and also appear in technology. The maximum speed of military aircraft appears to lead the maximum speed of commercial aircraft in a definite manner. Sequential relationship forecasting *without evidence of a causal relationship* is dangerous business.

4. *Interdependent Relationships for Prediction.* Lenz points out that the trend of a technical parameter may be the result of relationship between several other parameters. Then the prediction must be based on establishing a relationship between those primary variables. He gives passenger capacity, load factor, total passenger-miles, and total plane-miles flown for commercial aircraft in domestic trunk-line operations as an example. To predict total plane-miles, the relationship between the other variables must be developed. Lenz shows how a thoughtless extension of any one parameter leads to some economically or socially illogical conclusions. The forecaster, it seems, must make some intelligent assumptions, and even project upon alternate assumptions such as different plane capacities, to arrive at possible total plane-mile figures.

5. *Prediction on the Basis of Trend Characteristics.* The above methods extend a time series to quantify future events. These time series can also foreshadow the future by the characteristics of the curve they form. An example occurs when the extension of a rate of progress, particularly an exponential rate, intercepts a known physical limit. Then, either progress must stop, or the barrier must be broken by a new technology. Either projection may be a useful signal to alert technical management.

6. *Dynamic Forecasting.* If a model could be prepared to describe accurately the relationship of complex technical, economic, social, and political factors, the computer could be applied to determine the results. This is Forrester's "industrial dynamics" concept applied to technology. Lenz suggests that it is applicable to a knowledge-progress system involving education, research, and technological progress.

Technological forecasting is very much an unborn science, but it must be developed as an aid to long-range planning. A few cautions should be emphasized:

1. Prediction, projection, and programming should not be confused with each other. Nor should forecasting be confused with long-range planning.
2. Economic, social, and political factors, which so vitally influence technological progress, should not be introduced so as to inhibit thinking about technological *possibilities*. However, in determining technological *probabilities*, we must remind ourselves that the technological forecast result also depends upon the nontechnological factors which explicitly or implicitly were used.

QUESTIONS

1. Using data from Exhibit 1, prepare, on semilog paper, a time-series graph on the speed trend of U.S. military aircraft through 1943.
   a) Assume it is 1943 and it is well known to aeronautical engineers that the maximum speed feasible for propeller-driven aircraft is something less than the speed of sound in air. What projection would you have made of the speed trend?
   b) Given the wisdom of hindsight, what questions *should* an airframe or engine manufacturer have investigated? What would have been an appropriate research directive in these types of firms at that time?
2. Plot the remaining time series data on the above chart.
   a) What will be the speed of military aircraft in 1960? In 1963? In 1970?
   b) Check the current figures from library sources. What explains the discrepancies, if any?
3. Return to 1943, and assume that you suspect the propeller-drive barrier to speed may be broken pretty much on schedule. What associated technological developments will be necessary in manned fighter aircraft? Business implications?
4. From Exhibit 2, prepare a semilog plot of the time series of wing span to length ratio.
   a) What does this curve suggest?
   b) Bring the curve up to date in the light of known or projected aircraft. What is the suggested significance?
5. Using Exhibit 3 for transport planes and Exhibit 1 for bombers, plot on semilog paper the speed trends for each of these types of planes.
   a) What relationship is suggested?
   b) How would you predict transport plane speeds for 1970?
6. Using data from industrial magazines or technical papers, develop a forecast for some technological concept in 1964. Check your results.
   a) What explains the discrepancy, if any?
   b) How can the forecasting be improved?

7. Prepare a technological forecast for 1970 based upon data you obtain from library or industry sources. Interpret the significance for management in an appropriate firm.
   Suggestions: Technical and technical-economic parameters of (a) foods: shelf life, prepreparation, etc.; (b) power: contrast fuel cells, atomic energy, magnetohydrodynamics, thermoionics, etc.; (c) computers: computation speed, size, cost per manipulation, access time; (d) transportation: technical-economic parameters of water-borne systems.

8. Study NASA planning documents. What type of forecasting is this? Are specific technological and technological-economic events specified? How could we use this program to forecast technological advances?

9. Analyze any portion of the aerospace industries forecast. Relate your conclusions to the R & D planning of a specific firm. The current issue is *Aerospace Technical Forecast, 1962–1972* (available from Aerospace Industries Association of America, 1725 De Sales Street, N.W., Washington, D.C.).

Exhibit 1

SPEED TREND OF U.S. MILITARY AIRCRAFT

Year of First Delivery	Airplane	Maximum Speed (mph)
1909	Wright Bros. B	42
1916	Curtiss JN–4	80
1918	(Nieuport 27 C.1)	110
	(Spad XIII C.1)	135
1921	Boeing MB–3A	141
1924	Curtiss PW–8	161
1925	Curtiss P–1	163
1927	Boeing PW–9C	158
1929	Curtiss P–6	180
1929	Boeing P–12	171
1933	Boeing P–26A	234
1934	Martin B10–B	212
1937	Boeing YB–17	256
	Seversky P–35	281
1938	Curtiss P–36A	300
1939	Curtiss P–40	357
1940	North American B–25	322
	Bell P–39C	379
1941	Martin B–26	315
	Republic P–43	350
1942	Republic P–47D	420
	North American P–51A	390
1943	North American P–51B	436
1945	Lockheed P–80A	578
1946	Republic XP–84A	619
1948	North American F–86A	671
1950	Boeing B–47A	600
1953	Convair F–102A	860
1954	McDonnell F–101C	1200
1956	Convair B–58	1330
1958	Lockheed F–104A	1404

Source: James C. Fahey, *U.S. Army Aircraft 1908–1946* (New York: Ships and Aircraft, 1946). Performance after 1953 from *Aviation Week*, Vol. LXX, No. 10 (March 9, 1959), p. 186.

Exhibit 2

RATIO OF WING SPAN TO LENGTH FOR U.S. COMBAT AIRCRAFT

Year of First Delivery	Airplane	Span (Ft.)	Length (Ft.)
1921	Boeing MB–3A	28.6*	20.0
1922	Curtiss NBS–1	81.5*	42.7
1924	Curtiss PW–8	35.8*	22.5
1925	Curtiss P–1	34.6*	22.9
1927	Boeing PW–9C	35.2*	23.0
1929	Curtiss P–6	34.6*	23.5
	Boeing P–12	33.0*	20.0
1932	Keystone B–4A	82.2*	48.9
1933	Boeing P–26A	28.0	23.9
1934	Martin B–10B	70.5	44.8
1937	Boeing YB–17	103.9	68.3
	Douglas B–18	89.5	56.7
	Seversky P–35	36.0	25.1
1938	Curtiss P–36A	37.4	28.5
1939	Lockheed YP–38	52.0	37.9
	Curtiss P–40	37.4	31.8
1940	North American B–25	67.5	51.1
	Bell P–39C	34.0	30.1
1941	Martin B–26	65.0	56.0
	Convair B–24D	110.0	66.3
	Republic P–43	36.0	28.5
1942	Martin B–26B	71.0	58.3
	Republic P–47D	40.8	36.0
	North American P–51A	37.0	32.3
1943	Bell P–63A	38.3	32.7
1944	Boeing B–29	141.3	99.0
1945	Lockheed P–80A	39.0	34.5
1946	Republic YP–84	36.9	36.5
1947	Convair B–36	230.0	163.0
1948	North American F–86A	37.0	37.0
1949	Boeing B–47A	116.0	107.0
1952	Republic F–84F	33.5	43.4
1953	Convair F–102A	38.0	68.3
1954	Boeing B–52A	185.0	152.8
	McDonnell F–101C	40.0	67.5
1955	North American F–100A	38.0	47.0
1956	Convair B–58	57.0	97.0
1958	Republic F–105B	35.0	64.0
	Lockheed F–104A	22.0	58.8

* Equivalent monoplane span.

Exhibit 3

TRANSPORT AIRCRAFT SPEED

Year of First Air-Line Operation	Airplane	Maximum Speed (mph)	Military Designation
1925	Fokker F–IV	95	T–2
1927	Fokker Trimotor	116	C–2
1928	Ford-Stout 4–AT–B	111	C–3
1931	Ford-Stout 5–AT–B	148	C–4A
1933	Curtiss Condor T–32	161	YC–30
	Boeing 247D	200	C–73
1934	Douglas DC–2	202	C–33
1935	Douglas DC–3	220	C–47
1941	Curtiss-Wright CW–20	264	C–46
1942	Douglas DC–4A	275	C–54
1946	Lockheed 649	329	C–69
1947	Douglas DC–6	370	C–118
1950	Lockheed 1049	370	
1954	Douglas DC–7	409	
1958	Lockheed Electra	450	
1958	Boeing 707	610	
1960	Boeing 720	649	

Source: James C. Fahey, *U.S. Army Aircraft 1908–1946* (New York: Ships and Aircraft, 1946).

Appendixes

Appendix I
QUESTIONS FOR CASE ASSIGNMENTS

Since the instructor may want to use case materials to suit his own purposes, and student analyses may be biased by any guidance given, I have omitted listing questions at the end of each case. For those who wish to consider my teaching approach, the case assignments in the course, *Technological Innovation*, are listed here (in the case sequence in this textbook). All questions have been tested in classroom use.

RIVERLAKE BELT CONVEYOR LINES, INC.

1. Why has this innovation encountered so much resistance?
2. How could Mr. Stewart have handled the introduction of this innovation more effectively?
3. What shall he do now?

PHOTON, INC. (A)

1. What areas should Mr. Garth have explored *before* he signed the contract with the inventors in 1946?
2. What is your decision on the development-v.s.-production issue before the Technical Advisory Board and Lithomat on April 7, 1950?

CLARK EQUIPMENT COMPANY

1. Shall Clark pursue the mechanical fruit harvester program? If so, what steps should be taken now?
2. Analyze the concept, timing and cost of the program exploration to date. Does management now have a sound basis for decision?

PHOTON, INC. (B)

1. Analyze for the new president the significance of Photon's past experience. How does this compare with your response to question 1 in Photon (A)?
2. What can we learn from a critical examination of the Kodak study exhibits?
3. Mr. Hanson desires your specific recommendations on the actions that Photon should take over the next year or so on developing new machines.

HERMAN KURT

1. Reconsider Clark's decision after studying *On the Appraisal of Radical Technological Innovations*, page 435; *On the Appraisal of Risk*, page 460; and your observations and discussions to date.
2. Make a library or field study on the current status of harvesting tree-borne crops. In hindsight, how do you assess Clark's decision?

PHOTON, INC. (C)

1. Which alternative should Photon now pursue? How will you implement your chosen course of action?
2. Contrast Photon's technical and corporate position now with their original concept in 1946–47. What does this experience suggest to finance men? Marketing men? Production men? General management?
3. Review *The Process of Technological Innovation*, page 69. Could it have been a useful guide to Photon's management?

DALLAS CHEMICAL CORPORATION

1. What administrative-human relations problems are revealed in the management of Research and Development?
2. Recommend a program for Dr. Caldwell.

UNION OIL COMPANY OF CALIFORNIA (A)

1. Should the oil shale research appropriation be approved?

PHOTON, INC. (D)

1. What course of action shall Photon take now?

THERMAL DYNAMICS CORPORATION (A)

1. Shall the plasma cutter development be undertaken at this time?

EL PASO ELECTRONICS CORPORATION

1. Contrast the problems facing El Paso with those in Dallas Chemical Corporation.
2. Prepare an appropriate program for Dr. Kane.
3. What seem to be major problems that are *unique* to managing scientific and engineering personnel? How can they be minimized? Use all possible resources in developing your answer.

UNION OIL COMPANY OF CALIFORNIA (B)

1. Shall the research appropriation be granted?

THERMAL DYNAMICS CORPORATION (B)

1. Recommend the best development decision.

PHOTON, INC. (E)

1. Sum up Photon's experience to date. What management lessons are suggested?
2. Define a research–product development strategy for Photon.

THERMAL DYNAMICS CORPORATION (C)

1. What action shall be taken on the issues now facing the company?

THERMAL DYNAMICS CORPORATION (D)

1. What further information would be desirable before reaching a decision on distribution? How could you obtain this information? What time and funds should TDC expend on obtaining additional information?

ELECTRONIC ASSOCIATES, INC.

1. Study the Technical Note on Microelectronics for background:
   a) Develop an appropriate program for EAI on the use and/or manufacture of microelectronic circuits.
   b) Assess the Product Programming Committee as a technological planning and appraisal method.

MARTIN BARRETT

1. a) Apply the product profile chart, with appropriate modification, to Photon A (as a product for Lithomat).
   b) To the ZIP machine in Photon C.
2. Apply the procedure to Clark's tree harvester.
3. What are the strengths and limitations of this approach?

PARSONS AND AKRON

1. Prepare, for Mr. Torn, a critical evaluation of his proposed procedure. Add appropriate improvements.

MODERN PACKAGING MACHINERY CORPORATION

1. Evaluate the concept as proposed by Phillips.
2. What is your recommendation on the two topics prescribed for Burke's meeting?

LOAD GLIDE

1. Examine the literature search as conducted by Clark. What can we learn about sources of technical information? Has any obvious source been neglected?
2. Contrast the explorations of Clark's tree harvester idea and the Aero-lift concept.

3. What "principles" from previous readings and cases can be applied to this decision?
4. In Mr. Spatta's position, what would be your decision?

ADCOLE CORPORATION

1. Assist Dr. Meyer in reaching a decision on the questions expressed at the end of the case.

COLONIAL CABINETS FURNITURE COMPANY (A)

1. What will be the economic justification (for the finishing line conveyor only) at present volume of 250 units per day? At maximum conveyor capacity of 327 units per 8-hour day? At the sales goal of 350 units per day with overtime?
2. Shall the conveyor be installed?

AMPEX CORPORATION

1. Examine the status report in Exhibit 10. What are your conclusions?
2. At 3:00 P.M. January 23, the Vice-President of Manufacturing telephoned Burn and instructed him to bring Anderson to his office at 4:00 P.M. January 24. They were to bring with them a plan which would achieve the scheduled production of acceptable heads. Prepare this plan.

IMPERIAL OIL, LIMITED (A)

1. As Mr. Hamilton's assistant, prepare for him an analysis of the usefulness of the OR study.

   Alternative assignment.

1. A call has just arrived from New York headquarters of Standard Oil of New Jersey indicating that a group purchase of tankers is available at an approximate price of $9,500,000 each (for a 47,000 dwt tanker with 1961 delivery). Using the OR report, determine the desirability of accepting this purchase opportunity.

SAREPTA PAPER COMPANY (A)

1. As Joseph Small, determine the desirability of installing the computer process control system.

COLONIAL CABINETS FURNITURE COMPANY (B)

1. For each of the conditions listed determine immediate, short range action to be taken.
2. Determine the necessary long range action to alleviate each problem.
3. What are the managerial implications of highly mechanized systems, judging from these experiences and your recommended actions?

IMPERIAL OIL, LTD. (B)

1. Examine each of Hamilton's notations. What are your conclusions?
2. Contrast Hamilton's findings and questions to your previous analysis in the (A) case. Conclusions?
3. What action should Hamilton take on this report? With the OR group?
4. What have your learned about the execution of operations research studies? About the written presentation of complex analyses?

SAREPTA PAPER COMPANY (B)

1. Prepare Small's report in accordance with Upton's directions.

Appendix II
BIBLIOGRAPHY

This list provides additional literature to broaden your understanding of technological innovation. We expect the management student to study at least one book in depth, and to sample other items. The list also is useful as a background for major report projects, if one is required. Items have been selected in five areas:

1. Broad perspective on technology and its impact on society.
2. The nature of the processes of invention, discovery, and innovation; special problems in the area, and theories and concepts for dealing with them.
3. Outstanding technological-economic histories of innovation.
4. Natural resources, population, and their interactions with technology.
5. Biographies that stress the role of an individual in relation to technological advances.

The list is a sampling only, and is far from complete. Material bearing on the field can be found in writings on history, sociology, economics, science, engineering, research, organizational behavior, management, biography, industrial and technical history, and even science fiction. Literally thousands of items in periodicals bear on parts of the field. For instance, Dr. Lipitz of Carlisle, Massachusetts has directed a National Science Foundation study that identified over 350 worthwhile "case histories" of technical innovations.

My selection criteria has been to choose items that time and experience have shown to be effective in our Harvard course. Obviously, I may have omitted items of equal or greater merit.

TECHNOLOGY AND SOCIETY

ALLEN, FRANCIS R., and others. *Technology and Social Change*. New York: Appleton-Century Crofts, 1957.
This general textbook describes the process and theories of social change, and the social effects of selected inventions. It presents the hypothesis of cultural lag and problems arising from rapid change. This book develops the complex social implications of technological innovation.

BARBER, B., and HIRSCH, W. *The Sociology of Science*. Glencoe, Ill.: The Free Press of Glencoe, 1962.

GIDEON, SIEGMUND. *Mechanization Takes Command*. New York: Oxford University Press, 1948.
A well-illustrated examination of the influence of mechanization on art, and more particularly on the tools and surroundings of our daily life. Several of the chapters —for example, the one on the assembly line—are outstanding.

MUMFORD, LEWIS. *Technics and Civilization*. London: George Routledge & Sons, 1934.
This semipopular study is a landmark in sociology. Mumford saw civilization as being inundated by "the machine" in three great waves: 10th century, middle 18th

century, and early 20th century. He visualized mankind as engaged in a struggle to direct the "machine" to human purposes, rather then surrendering to a meaningless life created by the world of technics. He analyzes phases of evolution in technics, identifies many events he feels are significant, and offers many conclusions about the destruction of human values in a technological society. Have his conclusions of 1930 been substantiated? The book contains a useful bibliography of literature prior to 1930.

SCHUMPETER, JOSEPH. *Capitalism, Socialism and Democracy*. New York: Harper, 1950.
Contains an interpretation of economic and political evolution with some important ideas on the role of the entrepreneur and technological change.

SURANYI-UNGER, T. "Bibliography on the Economic and Social Implications of Scientific Research and Development," National Science Foundation Publication, No. NSF59–41, 50 pp.
This selected and annotated bibliography is an excellent survey of the field.

THE PROCESSES AND PROBLEMS OF TECHNOLOGICAL INNOVATION

ANTHONY, ROBERT N. *Management Controls in Industrial Research Organizations*. Boston: Harvard Business School, 1952.

BOOKER, P. J. "Principles and Precedents of Engineering Design," *The Engineering Designer*. London, September, 1962.

BRIGHT, J. R. *Automation and Management*. Boston: Harvard Business School, 1958.

BRIGHT, J. R. (ed.). *Technological Planning on the Corporate Level*. Boston: Harvard Business School, 1962.

BURNS, T., and STALKER, G. M. *The Management of Innovation*. London: Tavistock Publications, 1961.

CARTER, C. F., and WILLIAMS, B. R. *Industry and Technical Progress*. London: Oxford University Press, 1957.

The Commercial Utilization of Research Results, Report of the Third Conference of Industrial Research Directors and Managers of the Federated British Industries, 1953.

DEAN, B. V. *Operations Research in Research and Development*. New York: John Wiley, 1963.

GILFILLAN, S. C. "The Prediction of Invention," *Technological Trends and National Policy*, United States National Resources Committee. Washington, D.C.: U.S. Government Printing Office, 1937.

GILFILLAN, S. C. *The Sociology of Invention*. Chicago: Follett Publishing Co., 1935.

HAEFELE, J. W. *Creativity and Innovation*. New York: Reinhold Publishing Corp., 1962.

HANSON, N. R. *Patterns of Discovery*. Cambridge: Cambridge University Press, 1958.
A scientist identifies a logical pattern in the development and use of theories.

HEYEL, C. *Handbook of Industrial Research Management*. New York: Reinhold Publishing Co., 1959.

HINRICHS, J. R. "Creativity in Industrial Scientific Research," American Management Association, Bulletin No. 12, 1961. 35 pp.
A summary of the literature on this subject written from the viewpoint of a nonreformer.

HOWER, R., and ORTH, C. *Managers and Scientists*. Boston: Harvard Business School, 1963.

JEWKES, SAWERS, and STILLERMAN. *Sources of Invention*. London: Macmillan, 1958.
An excellent study of industrial innovation in the 19th and 20th centuries; it examines the way in which the process has changed and considers some critical managerial problems. Some 50 "case studies" are provided. They are interesting, but

often superficial and sometimes erroneous. Many important references are given throughout the book.

KUHN, T. S. *The Structure of Scientific Revolutions.* Chicago: The University of Chicago Press, 1962.

LEVITT, T. "Marketing Myopia," *Harvard Business Review,* July–August, 1960. This is a classic, and deserves study from marketing, research, and business policy viewpoints.

MANSFIELD, E. "The Speed of Response of Firms to New Techniques," *The Quarterly Journal of Economics,* Vol. LXXVII (May, 1963).
Mansfield's many papers in this field are outstanding. His forthcoming book probably will consolidate much of his material.

MANSFIELD, E. "Technical Change and the Rate of Imitation," *Econometrics,* Vol. 29 (October, 1961).

MARPLES, D. L. "The Decisions of Engineering Design," *IRE Transactions on Engineering Management,* Vol. 8 (June, 1961), pp. 55–75.

NELSON, R. R. "The Economics of Invention: A Survey of the Literature," *Journal of Business,* University of Chicago, April 1959, pp. 101–27.
A description of 68 leading books and articles on the economic aspects of research management is available in "Looking Around—Guides to R & D," by Albert H. Rubenstein, reprinted from the *Harvard Business Review,* May–June, 1957. Obviously, this is dated.

PECK, M. J., and SCHERER, F. M. *The Weapons Acquisition Process.* Boston: Harvard Business School, 1962.

QUINN, J. B. *Yardsticks for Industrial Research.* New York: Ronald Press, 1959.

QUINN, J. B. "Transferring Research Results to Operations," *Harvard Business Review,* January–February, 1963.

The Rate and Direction of Inventive Activity. National Bureau Committee for Economic Research. Princeton: Princeton University Press, 1962.
These proceedings of a conference held at Minnesota have many useful papers.

ROBERTS, E. B. *The Dynamics of Research and Development.* New York: Harper & Row, 1964.

ROGERS, E. M. *The Diffusion of Innovations.* New York: Free Press of Glencoe, 1962.

CRITICAL HISTORICAL-ECONOMIC STUDIES OF TECHNOLOGICAL INNOVATION

BAXTER. *An Introduction to the Ironclad Warship.* Cambridge, 1933.

BISHOP, ASMA. *Project Sherwood.* Boston: Addison-Wesley Publishing Co., 1958.

BRIGHT, A. A. *The Development of the Electric Lamp Industry.* New York: Macmillan Co. 1949.

ENOS, J. L. *Petroleum Progress and Profits: A History of Process Innovation.* Cambridge: The M.I.T. Press, 1962.

HABER, L. F. *The Chemical Industry in the 19th Century.* Oxford: Clarendon Press, 1958.

MACLAURIN, W. R. *Invention and Innovation in the Radio Industry.* New York: Macmillan Co., 1949.

PASSER, HAROLD. *The Electrical Manufacturers, 1875–1900.* Cambridge: Harvard University Press, 1953.

SCHLAIFER, ROBERT O., and HERON, M. *Development of Aircraft Engines and Fuels.* Cambridge: Harvard University Press, 1950.

SINGER, C., HOLMYARD, E. J., HALL, A. R., and WILLIAMS, T. I. *A History of Technology.* New York: Oxford University Press, 1957. (5 Vol.)
This monumental study identifies the origin and nature of many developments. Unfortunately, it ignores "how" and "why" and ends in the late 19th century.

NATURAL RESOURCES, POPULATION, AND THEIR INTERACTION WITH TECHNOLOGY

Brown, Harrison S. *The Next Hundred Years*. New York: Viking Press, 1957.
An attempt to project the fundamental requirements of the future based upon an extension of basic requirements to support an estimated population.

Schurr, Sam H., and others. *Energy in the American Economy, 1850–1957*. Baltimore: Johns Hopkins Press, 1960.
A monumental study exemplifying the critical exploration of resource availability. Highly useful for consideration of future energy demands and opportunities for innovation.

Stamp, L. Dudley. *Our Developing World*. London: Faber & Faber, 1960.
A most useful discussion of population versus land and food resources. It includes much basic data on these two topics and is especially useful on clarifying the opportunity for increasing food output in various parts of the world.

Thomas. *Man's Role in Changing the Face of the Earth*. Chicago: University of Chicago Press, 1955.
A series of studies highlighting many aspects of the impact of man upon his physical surroundings, including land, oceans, air, and living species. The section on "Prospects" is most provocative.

TECHNOLOGY AND THE INDIVIDUAL

There are thousands of biographies of inventors and technologically oriented entrepreneurs. The quality and usefulness varies enormously. I list here a few that provide useful understanding to students of management. It is especially significant to note the attitude and personality of men who have tried to introduce changes in the accepted order of things, and the reaction of existing organizations.

Groves, L. R. *Now It Can Be Told*. New York: Harper & Bros., 1962.
A top manager's view of the greatest systems development project in history.

Josephson, Matthew. *Edison*. New York: McGraw-Hill, 1959.
A clear exposure of the process by which Edison created successful innovations. Some light on the problems and personality of an inventor, and the management of one of the earliest industrial laboratories.

Jungk, R. *Brighter Than a Thousand Suns, the Personal History of the Atomic Scientists*. New York: Harcourt, 1958.

Lessing, Lawrence Peter. *Man of High Fidelity: Edwin Howard Armstrong*. Philadelphia: Lippincott, 1956.
Thought-provoking work on the struggle between the innovator and vested interests.

Watson-Watt, Sir Robert. *Three Steps to Victory*. London, 1957.
If this is not available, get *The Pulse of Radar* by the same author (Dial Press, 1959). Contains useful philosophy and procedures of an exceptionally able scientist-manager.

Whittle, Frank. *Jet, the Story of a Pioneer*. London: Muller, 1953.
As with Armstrong, an innovator's struggle (with government and business) is described.

Wright, Orville, and Wright, Wilbur. *Miracle at Kitty Hawk; Letters of the Wright Brothers*. New York: Farrar, Straus, & Young, 1951.
Revealing explanation of the preparation and experimentation underlying this major accomplishment on limited funds.

PERIODICALS

Certain periodicals are worth following and occasionally have an exceptionally useful paper. As a partial listing, I suggest:

Research Management, the Journal of the Industrial Research Institute, New York.

IEEE Transactions on Engineering Management, a publication of the Institute of Electrical and Electronic Engineers. See also its predecessor: *IRE Transactions*.

Publications of the National Science Foundation. These include both statistics and other studies by the NSF staff, and monographs on results of contract research.

Science, the Journal of the American Association for the Advancement of Science, Washington, D.C. Almost every issue contains useful items on scientific research and government relationships.

International Science and Technology. New York, Cowles Publishing Company.

Technology and Culture, The Journal of the Society for the History of Technology. Detroit, Wayne State University Press.

Indexes

INDEX TO CASES

INDEX TO READINGS AND EXCERPTS

This book has been set on the Linotype in 10 on 12 and 9 on 10 Janson. Titles are in 14 point Deepdene italic caps. The size of the type page is 27 by 47 picas.